A Blackfeet camp on Two Medicine Lake in what is now
Glacier National Park, Mont. Late 1800's. From Records
of the National Park Service, Record Group 79.
79-PGN-112

The Reverend Philip B. Gordon, Chippewa, the first
Indian Catholic priest in the United States, shown talking
with Indian soldiers at Camp Grant, Ill. From left to right:
Pvts. George P. DeCota, Roy Deer, Lloyd M. Waukau,
George Peaine, Calvin M. Martin, Anthony T. Schofield,
Mitchell Tepiew, and Ralph C. Mann. From Records of
the Bureau of Indian Affairs, Record Group 75.
75-N- MISC-128

GUIDE TO RECORDS
IN THE
NATIONAL ARCHIVES OF THE UNITED STATES
RELATING TO

AMERICAN INDIANS

COMPILED BY EDWARD E. HILL

NATIONAL ARCHIVES AND RECORDS SERVICE
GENERAL SERVICES ADMINISTRATION
WASHINGTON, D.C.
1981

REPRINTED FOR
THE NATIONAL ARCHIVES AND RECORDS SERVICE
BY THE
NATIONAL ARCHIVES TRUST FUND BOARD

ISBN 0-911333-13-4

Library of Congress Cataloging in Publication Data

Hill, Edward E.
    Guide to records in the National Archives of the
United States relating to American Indians.

    Includes index.
    1. Indians of North America--Government relations--
Sources--Bibliography--Catalogs. 2. Indians of North
America--History--Sources--Bibliography--Catalogs.
3. United States. National Archives--Catalogs.
I. United States. National Archives. II. Title.
Z1209.2.U5H54   [E93]   016.3231'97'073   81-22357
                                                    AACR2

PREFACE

This *Guide to Records in the National Archives of the United States Relating to American Indians* is one of a large number of publications designed to make the records in the National Archives better known and easier to use. Essentially it is a specialized supplement to the general *Guide to the National Archives of the United States* (1974).

From time to time the National Archives and Records Service has published other subject guides to Federal records that have research value to a broad spectrum of scholars. In this category are *Federal Records of World War II* (2 vols., 1951), *Civil War Maps in the National Archives* (1964), *Guide to Federal Records Relating to the Civil War* (1962) and its companion volume *Guide to the Archives of the Government of the Confederate States of America* (1968), *Guide to Cartographic Records in the National Archives* (1971), and *Guide to Materials on Latin America in the National Archives of the United States* (1974). For finding aids and other publications, see the most recent *Select List of Publications of the National Archives and Records Service,* General Information Leaflet No. 3.

It is hoped that the publication of this guide will focus the attention of researchers on the vast research potential of materials relating to American Indians in the National Archives of the United States and aid prospective researchers in the use of this material. If it serves either or both of these purposes, the effort that went into the preparation of the guide will be considered well spent.

ROBERT M. WARNER
Archivist of the United States

CONTENTS

Page

INTRODUCTION

The purposes of this guide are to describe and assist the researcher in locating within the National Archives of the United States materials that are concerned with American Indians and with the relations of the Government and people of the United States with them. Indians who lived along the international boundaries in Canada and Mexico and in former colonies of European nations and who had direct contacts with and were a matter of domestic concern to the United States are within the scope of the guide; Indians in other parts of the Americas with whom the United States may have had more remote concern in the conduct of foreign affairs or who were the subject of a survey or study are not within the scope of the guide.

The National Archives of the United States consist of permanently valuable records of the Federal Government. They are housed in the National Archives Building in Washington, D.C.; in the Washington National Records Center, Suitland, Md.; and in eleven regional Federal archives and records centers. Some of the holdings of the Presidential libraries administered by the National Archives and Records Service also are part of the National Archives of the United States, but the papers of Presidents and many of those of other high officials, including the files of individual Members of Congress, have been regarded as their personal property. About 1,300,000 cubic feet of records are now part of the National Archives. Other noncurrent records created by the Federal Government are in the Federal records centers. Most of them in due course will be destroyed as not worthy of permanent preservation, but some eventually will be made a part of the National Archives.

The basic organizational unit to which all records in the National Archives are assigned is called a record group, which most frequently consists of the records of a single agency, such as the Bureau of Indian Affairs, and its predecessors. The records of the head of an executive department and units with departmentwide responsibility may be assigned to a general record group, such as General Records of the Department of State (Record Group 59) or Records of the Office of the Secretary of the Interior (Record Group 48). Records of a number of agencies are sometimes brought together on the basis of similar function or other relationship. An example of a collective record group is Records of Boundary and Claims Commissions and Arbitrations (Record Group 76). Records collected by an agency, rather

1

than created in the course of business, form another type of record group, such as War Department Collection of Revolutionary War Records (Record Group 93).

The National Archives and Records Service (NARS) endeavors to keep records in the order in which they were maintained by the creating agency, in the belief that this best preserves their integrity and interrelationships. The agency filing systems were designed for administrative purposes and not for the benefit of future researchers. A major reason for the preparation of guides such as this is to assist subject-oriented researchers in understanding the complexities of recordkeeping systems and in locating material of interest among the vast quantities of records irrelevant to their needs.

In this guide the records are described according to the record groups to which they have been allocated. The order of the record groups is intended to reflect a combination of chronology, relationship with the Indians, and Government organization. Pre-Federal records are described first and then general records of the U. S. Government, chiefly treaties negotiated with Indians. Next are the records of the Bureau of Indian Affairs, the agency primarily concerned with Indian affairs. Then follow the records of the Office of the Secretary of the Interior and other agencies of the Department of the Interior, in which the Bureau of Indian Affairs has been since 1849. Until 1849 the War Department supervised the administration of Indian affairs, and from a chronological standpoint it might seem better to describe War Department records concerning this function before the Department of the Interior records. The longer-standing relationship with the Department of the Interior and the difficulty of separating War Department records relating to the administration of Indian affairs from those concerning military activities involving Indians, however, made it seem preferable to describe all of the Department of the Interior records and then all of the War Department records and related Department of the Navy records. The major divisions in the rest of the guide follow the Federal hierarchy fairly closely with records of Congress and legislative agencies; court records; records of Presidential agencies; records of the executive departments, starting with those that have had longstanding relations with Indian matters in such areas as diplomacy and judicial and fiscal matters followed by those with more restricted interests; and finally independent agencies, other governments, and nongovernment sources.

Within record groups, the basic archival unit of control for records is the series, which is a body of records arranged in some serial order or logically grouped together for some other reason. For many record groups, NARS has prepared preliminary inventories or inventories, which describe the records series by series. Typical information in an entry includes series title, covering dates, quantity, types of records, and perhaps some indication of content. In this guide many of the same records are described, but there has been an attempt to present a different viewpoint, with more emphasis on subject matter, specific examples, and practical guidance on using the records. There is more expanded discussion of basic records and more summary treatment of records having less significance. When information about Indians is dispersed among records relating to other subjects, an effort has been made to identify as specifically as possible the Indian-related materials.

For the most part, coverage in this Indian guide has been limited to records that can be identified with existing finding aids. Undoubtedly, some isolated files or documents concerning Indians can be found in the records of many agencies but have not been included in the guide because there is no practical way of identifying them. For example, there probably are records for National Labor Relations Board cases in which Indians were involved. Ordinarily, to learn about the possible existence of such records it is necessary to find a reference in another source (e.g., newspaper, book). However, when experience has demonstrated that some bodies of records contain Indian material of considerable interest, such as Army court-martial records and U.S. district court case files, these records have been described in the guide. Still, it is usually necessary to obtain citations to individual cases, or at least the names of the parties concerned, from sources other than finding aids for the records.

Predominantly, the records described concern Indians in tribes with whom the United States has had a relationship through the Bureau of Indian Affairs or military operations. Some Indian groups, particularly in the Eastern States, have never had such a relationship. In some of these States there were State agencies with specific responsibilities concerning Indians whose records are in State archives.

For individual Indians, the records described relate mainly to persons who maintained some affiliation with a tribe or other Indian group. Many persons of Indian descent have severed all connection with any tribe; for them, researchers should consider the same sources as for anyone else. There has been no attempt to include information about prominent persons who were Indians but had no particular connection with Indian affairs.

Except in direct quotations, currently accepted spellings are used for names of tribes, and, when they could be determined, for names of Indians and other persons, geographical locations, and other proper names.

Citations are given for other published finding aids that are available. Documentary publications and other related publications are noted occasionally, but there has been no attempt at full bibliographic coverage.

Many of the records described have been reproduced as NARS microfilm publications, and citations are given to many of these publications by M or T number. Often for the microfilm publications there are accompanying pamphlets, which may give more detailed information about the records than this guide or the inventories. A Select Catalog of National Archives Microfilm Publications, *The American Indian* (1972), provides general information and the contents of individual rolls for many publications with records concerning Indians. There is also a general *Catalog of National Archives Microfilm Publications,* which is revised periodically.

Two publications of particular interest not cited in this guide in connection with specific records are Carmelita S. Ryan's *Vital Statistics in the National Archives Relating to the American Indian,* Reference Information Paper 61 (1973), and Laura E. Kelsay's *Cartographic Records in the National Archives of the United States Relating to American Indians,* Reference Information Paper 71 (1974). Most of the descriptions of cartographic records in this guide were extracted from the latter publication.

Unless otherwise indicated, the records described are in a depository in the Washington, D.C., metropolitan area. Records in an archives branch of a regional Federal archives and records center are identified by the annotation "FARC" followed by the name of the major city in or near which the center is located.

Most of the records are readily available and researchers are not required to make arrangements in advance to consult them. Some records, however, may be temporarily unavailable (they may be being reproduced for another researcher, for example); there are restrictions on access to some of them, particularly case files of individual Indians among field office records of the Bureau of Indian Affairs. There may be some delay in locating particular records if they are widely dispersed. It is suggested, therefore, that before traveling any extended distance to visit a depository, researchers write and describe as specifically as possible the subject of their interest and the records that they may wish to consult.

Much of this guide was developed from papers prepared for the National Archives Conference on Research in the History of Indian-White Relations, held in the National Archives Building, June 15-16, 1972. National Archives staff members who contributed to these papers included Howard H. Wehmann for records of the Continental and Confederation Congresses; Marie Allen, Robert Gruber, Maida Loescher, Richard Myers, and Geraldine Phillips for military records in the National Archives Building; Richard C. Crawford, Charles E. South, Milton O. Gustafson, and Suzanne Harris for records of civilian agencies in the National Archives Building; Edward E. Hill for records in the General Archives Division; Laura E. Kelsay for cartographic records; Joe Doan Thomas for audiovisual records; and the staffs of the regional archives branches. Edward E. Hill prepared supplementary material, particularly for records of the Bureau of Indian Affairs not described in the conference papers, and revised, updated to June 30, 1976, and organized the guide. It was edited by Jan Shelton Danis. Many other members of the NARS staff contributed by suggesting records to be included and reviewing drafts.

PRE-FEDERAL RECORDS

Administration of Indian affairs in the United States derived from the British system. The royal government and the colonies regulated relations between their subjects and the Indians but did not attempt to control internal relations of the tribes, which were regarded much like foreign governments. After the French and Indian War, two superintendencies of Indian affairs were created, one for the northern and one for the southern colonies. The superintendents were, in effect, ambassadors who observed events, negotiated treaties, and generally sought to keep peace between frontier settlers and Indians. The Continental Congress followed a similar practice, in 1775 establishing three geographical departments with several commissioners for each.

By an ordinance of August 7, 1786, the Confederation Congress established northern and southern Indian departments, divided by the Ohio River; a superintendent, responsible to the Secretary at War, was in charge of each. These positions were continued when the new Government was organized under the Constitution.

Two record groups in the National Archives contain most pre-Federal records—Records of the Continental and Confederation Congresses and the Constitutional Convention, Record Group 360, and War Department Collection of Revolutionary War Records, Record Group 93. Some pre-Federal records, however, are in other record groups and are described in appropriate sections of this guide.

RECORDS OF THE CONTINENTAL AND CONFEDERATION CONGRESSES AND THE CONSTITUTIONAL CONVENTION (RECORD GROUP 360)

The records of the Continental and Confederation Congresses, informally known as the papers of the Continental Congress, are the basic governmental records of the United States before the establishment of the Federal Government in 1789. The First Continental Congress assembled in September and October 1774. The Second Continental Congress first convened May 10, 1775, and assumed direction of the Revolutionary War; standing committees and boards composed of Delegates conducted its affairs. With the adoption of the Articles of Confederation in 1781, Congress established executive offices under the direction of nonmembers. Most of the records of

Congress have been microfilmed as NARS Microfilm Publication M247, *Papers of the Continental Congress, 1774–1789* (204 rolls), and M332, *Miscellaneous Papers of the Continental Congress, 1774–1789* (9 rolls). NARS published a multi-volume, computer-assisted subject and name index to the 200,000 pages of original documents in the papers of the Continental Congress in 1978. A consolidated index to the previously printed *Journals of the Continental Congress, 1774–1789* was published by NARS in 1976.

The journals of Congress (60 volumes), kept mainly by Secretary of Congress Charles Thomson, provide a chronological record of legislative proceedings, including resolutions, orders, vote tabulations, and motions. They are divided into three sets—rough, transcript, and secret. The journals contain references to trade with the Indians, their employment as soldiers, the appointment and issuance of instructions to commissioners for Indian affairs, expeditions against hostile Indians, the appropriation of funds for making treaties with Indians, and the establishment of administrative machinery for supervising relations with them. These journals have been reproduced as rolls 8–22 of M247 and have been published by the Library of Congress as the *Journals of the Continental Congress, 1774–1789* (34 vols.; 1904–37). Related to the journals are four volumes of motions made in Congress by Delegates (M247, rolls 42 and 43), some of which relate to Indian treaties. There is also a volume, once kept in the office of the Secretary of Congress, containing copies of records pertaining to the "Western Territory" of the United States, 1787–88 (M247, roll 194). It includes copies of congressional committee reports, motions, resolutions, and instructions concerning such subjects as negotiations with Indians and the reservation of certain lands for "The Society of the United Brethren for propogating the Gospel among the Heathen" to be used by Christian Indians.

There are two main sets of letter books of outgoing congressional communications—those of the President (7 vols.; M247, rolls 23 and 24) and those of the Secretary (2 vols.; roll 25). Communications received by Congress are divided into many series, chiefly by source but sometimes by type of record or subject.

Memorials (10 vols.; M247, rolls 48–52) and petitions (8 vols.; rolls 53–56) submitted to Congress by individuals and groups relate to such subjects as the protection of peaceful Christian Indians in eastern Ohio, a request from the Stockbridge Indians that new hunting lands be assigned to them to replace lands invaded by whites, the disposal of lands ceded by the Indians in the 1768 Treaty of Fort Stanwix, and the protection of the frontier from Indians. With the memorials is a 47-page extract from the journal of Rev. David Zeisberger, a missionary of the United Brethren (Moravian) Church, describing the removal by the British of the missionaries and Indians from Gnadenhutten on the Muskingum River in eastern Ohio, the trip to Detroit and return, and a massacre by the Americans in 1782. A volume identified as "Memorials of Inhabitants of Illinois, Kaskaskia, and Kentucky, 1780–89" (M247, roll 62) contains memorials from inhabitants of French communities in what became the States of Indiana, Illinois, Kentucky, and Tennessee. The subjects include the formation of a separate State by the people of Kentucky to provide protection against Indians and articles given by French inhabitants of Vincennes to stop an Indian war party.

Reports of several congressional committees contain information about Indians. A volume of reports of committees on Indian affairs and lands in the Western Territory, 1776–88, includes material on the demarcation of boundaries, a council of the Six Nations, and petitions concerning individual Indians (M247, roll 37). Other committees with relevant reports include those on applications of individuals (rolls 26–28), State papers (roll 29), the Army and military affairs (roll 30), and the War Office and the Department of War (roll 34); the Committee of the States, appointed to transact official business during the adjournment of Congress from June 4 to October 31, 1784 (roll 39); and a committee that conferred with George Washington at Valley Forge (roll 40). The reports treat the Christianization of Indians; the education of Indian boys at Princeton; Indian depredations in Georgia; the intrusion of settlers on Indian lands and Indian resistance; depredations committed by settlers, including John Sevier, on Indian lands; the maintenance of frontier posts; supplies for friendly Indians; and the enlistment of Indians in the Continental Army.

From the Board of Treasury there are reports on support and tuition payments for three Indian boys at Princeton College, reports on expenses for the negotiation of treaties and allowances to Indian commissioners, and quarterly accounts for Indian affairs (M247, rolls 147, 152, and 154). There are reports of the Board of War and Ordnance, 1776–81, that relate to the defense of frontier settlements against Indian attacks; the attitude to be taken toward the Indians during a treaty conference at Johnstown, N.Y.; and the issuance of military commissions to Indians (rolls 157–160). Letters to Congress from Secretary at War Henry Knox, 1785–88, transmitted copies of his correspondence with Indian superintendents, military officers, Territorial Governors, and others (rolls 164 and 165). Often enclosed are copies of their correspondence with other persons including chiefs of Indian tribes in the Ohio Valley; copies of speeches of the chiefs; and minutes of conferences held with Indians. There is information about negotiations with Indians, determining boundaries, gathering intelligence about Indians, and presenting plans of Congress to the Indians for the settlement of differences. There are also copies of speeches and reports of Cornplanter and other Indians who supplied information about Ohio Valley Indians; a list of names, numbers of warriors, and locations of tribes near the mouth of the Muskingum River in Ohio; and reports from officers stationed along the Ohio River. There are some papers concerning troubles on the North

Carolina frontier with the Cherokee and border incidents with the Creek Indians. From Arthur St. Clair, Governor of Northwest Territory, are letters concerning dissatisfaction of the Indians with the United States, their growing hostility, and St. Clair's preparations for war. Knox's reports to Congress (roll 165) include his suggestions for treaties with the Indians.

In a volume with letters from John Hancock to Robert Morris are a few letters and reports, 1789, from Col. John Allan concerning the eastern Indians, the encroachment of British settlers on their lands, and the unsettled northeastern boundary between the United States and Canada (M247, roll 71). Another volume contains letters from Joseph Carleton, secretary and paymaster of the Board of War and Ordnance, about stores needed for George Rogers Clark's expedition into the Indian country. The volume also includes letters from Thomas Hutchins, Geographer of the United States, pertaining to the importance of good relations with the Indians and military protection for the survey of the Western Territory. Statements by settlers concerning hostile intentions of and attacks by Indians on frontier settlements (roll 74) are enclosed. There are series of letters and transcripts of letters from various military officers. Those who wrote about Indian affairs include Brig. Gen. James Clinton (roll 180), Maj. Gen. Horatio Gates (rolls 174 and 190), Maj. Gen. Nathanael Greene (rolls 175 and 191), Brig. Gen. Edward Hand (roll 178), Lt. Col. Josiah Harmar (roll 180), Col. George Morgan (roll 180), Maj. Gen. Philip Schuyler (rolls 172, 173, and 189), Brig. Gen. John Stark (roll 179), Maj. Gen. John Sullivan (roll 178), and Gen. George Washington (rolls 166–171 and 186–188). Among the subjects are Indian attacks and protection against them, the organization of expeditions by the Army and by settlers, the destruction of Indian towns, meetings and negotiations with Indians, the purchase of Indian lands, the removal of settlers from western lands, intelligence received from Indians about the British, trade with Indians, aid to friendly tribes, and the policy and conduct of Indian commissioners. Copies of messages from Indians and speeches are included.

Letters from the State Governments ("State Papers") of Georgia (M247, roll 87), Massachusetts (roll 79), New York (roll 81), North and South Carolina (roll 86), Pennsylvania (roll 83), and Virginia (roll 85) have information concerning Indian hostilities and depredations, expeditions against them, the appointment of commissioners, and negotiations. Among the Virginia papers are the "Archives of the Cherokees," captured during an expedition against them. These include transcripts of talks by British officials trying to influence the Indians against the French and Spanish and of talks written for the State by Patrick Henry to counteract British activities. There is also a copy of the treaty concluded at Fort Henry on July 20, 1777, between Virginia and the Overhill Indians, who were part of the Cherokee Nation.

In 24 volumes of miscellaneous letters addressed to Congress (M247, rolls 90–104) are letters, mainly to the President of Congress, on a wide variety of subjects from U.S. and local officials, military and naval personnel, private citizens, and foreigners. There are many communications from Col. John Allan of the Eastern Indian Department, some of which were addressed to the Council of Massachusetts and sent by that body to Congress (roll 90). Allan reported on his work with the Indians, the supplies and actions needed to keep them friendly, and British activities. Letters and reports from other persons concern Indians and troops at Fort Pitt and Detroit, the military service of Indians, a false report that Albert Gallatin had been killed by Indians, the Indian concept of land ownership, and uprisings and treaty negotiations. Included are letters to President George Washington in 1789 warning of the influence of the Creek leader Alexander McGillivray, a copy of a letter from McGillivray, and letters from an Indian being educated at Princeton.

The first 83 pages of a volume of records relating to Indian affairs and the Western Territory, 1765 and 1777–89 (M247, roll 69), are a copy of a journal reporting a conference held with the Six Nations and the Delaware Indians in April and May 1765. Most of the rest of the volume consists of letters, with enclosures, addressed mainly to the President of Congress. They concern such subjects as the appointment of commissioners to negotiate treaties, the progress of messengers sent to invite western Indians to a treaty conference, the friendliness or enmity of particular tribes, the difficulty of establishing peace when settlers occupied Indian lands, the inadequate congressional appropriations for treaty negotiations, the need for troops to protect settlers and to keep settlers out of Indian territory, Indian hostilities, and the role of the British in influencing the Indians against the United States. There are also copies of speeches made by and to Indians, letters concerning the visit to Congress in 1786 of the Seneca chief Cornplanter, and drafts of ordinances concerning the disposal of western lands and the regulation of Indian affairs.

Other records include a volume of proceedings of commissioners appointed by Congress in 1775 to negotiate a treaty with the Six Nations (M247, roll 144); miscellaneous records concerning payments by the Indian Department, local defenses against Indians, and the killing of Moravian Indians on the Muskingum River in 1782 (rolls 72 and 73); "A Short Narration of My Last Journey to the Western Country," ca. 1791 or 1792, which is an account of the experiences of Hendrick Aupamut, an Indian who promoted the cause of the United States in speeches before tribal chiefs and arranged an Indian council on the Miami River (roll 184); a volume with records concerning Gen. John Sullivan's 1779 expedition against Indians who were harassing settlers on the frontier and records concerning negotiations with northern Indians, 1776–79 (roll 183); records of the Quartermaster

General concerning preparations for Sullivan's expedition (rolls 192 and 193); records concerning Indians and British advances in the Mohawk Valley in 1777 (roll 77); and intercepted papers, mainly letters written in Great Britain or British-occupied America, which include letters and reports from Indian agents and commissioners in Florida (roll 65). There are also census returns of inhabitants for Rhode Island (1774 and 1783), Connecticut (1782), and New York (1786), which show the number of Indians and usually give information about age, sex, residence, and status as taxpayers (roll 194); copies of treaties (rolls 144 and 194); copies of broadsides and congressional imprints (M332, roll 9); oaths of allegiance and oaths of office, including some for Indian superintendents (M247, roll 201; an index to the oaths is on roll 196); a volume of letters and miscellaneous papers of the Secretary of Congress, 1781–89, which includes draft forms of commissions for Indian commissioners (roll 63); and a "form book," 1782–88, with copies of commissions to superintendents and to commissioners to negotiate with the Six Nations and the Cherokee Indians (roll 196). Among receipts and related documents are a receipt from a clerk in the War Office, February 14, 1788, for Indian presents transmitted to Congress by General Josiah Harmar and a receipt by Samuel Wharton, Delegate from Delaware, for the journal of the transactions of the Treaty of Fort Stanwix of 1768 (M332, roll 9).

WAR DEPARTMENT COLLECTION OF REVOLUTIONARY WAR RECORDS
(RECORD GROUP 93)

Most of the records of the Continental Army in the custody of the War Department were destroyed by fire on November 8, 1800. The War Department Collection of Revolutionary War Records was begun in 1873, when Secretary of War William Belknap made the first of several purchases of Revolutionary War records for the Department. By acts of July 27, 1892 (27 Stat. 275), and August 18, 1894 (28 Stat. 372, 403), the Congress directed other executive departments of the Federal Government to transfer military records of the Revolutionary War in their possession to the War Department. A final major addition to the collection was made in 1914–15 when photographic copies of records in the possession of individuals and institutions were made by the War Department to supplement the original records. None of the records in the collection contain much information about Indians; there is, however, some relevant information in four major series.

See Mabel E. Deutrich, comp., *Preliminary Inventory of the War Department Collection of Revolutionary War Records,* PI 144, revised by Howard H. Wehmann (1970).

One series consists of approximately 55 feet of originals and copies of muster rolls, payrolls, returns of company and regimental personnel, lists of officers, guard reports, and other records relating to the Revolutionary War. Most of the records pertain to service in the Continental Army, although some State militia records are included. The records are available as M246, *Revolutionary War Rolls, 1775–1783*. Abstracts of these records were transcribed onto cards for each soldier to create the series of Revolutionary War compiled service records. There are a few records of Indians and units involved in Indian campaigns. A "Pay Roll of the Delaware Indians in the service of the United States, commencing June 15, 1780, and ending October 31, 1781" lists 12 Indian names. Other Indian names are scattered among various regiments. The muster rolls for the 8th Massachusetts Regiment, for instance, indicate that Benjamin Waunechnauweet, Daniel Wauwaupequannant, and David Naunechnauweet enlisted for 3 years in that unit and were with Gen. Horatio Gates at White Plains. The names and service of soldiers who fought in Indian campaigns can be found in such records as the lists and returns for Clark's Illinois Regiment, Virginia State Troops, 1781–84, and Willett's New York Regiment, 1781–82. Gen. Edward Hand was sent to Fort Pitt by the Continental Congress to arouse the militia and possibly capture Detroit to neutralize or destroy British influence among the Indians. There are several returns of the garrison at Fort Pitt and the troops under Hand in May and July 1778. Other miscellaneous records pertaining to Indians include an itemized "Account of Col. Timothy Bedel with the United States of America for transporting of Indians from Cambridge to Canada . . ." and a petition to the Council and House of Representatives in New Hampshire, March 10, 1779, for the payment of losses sustained by a company of Colonel Bedel's Regiment in Canada when the British "suffered the savages to rob and plunder us of our packs and baggage, and strip us of our clothes off our backs and left us entirely naked."

Also in the War Department Collection of Revolutionary War Records are about 230 orderly books, letter books, receipt books, journals, ledgers, lists of soldiers, and other bound records, known collectively as numbered record books. Most of these have been reproduced as M853, *Numbered Record Books Concerning Military Operations and Service, Pay and Settlement of Accounts, and Supplies in the War Department Collection of Revolutionary War Records*. Many of the volumes contain information on units involved in Indian campaigns, but four contain more specific information. Volume 88, copies of communications written by Timothy Pickering in connection with quartermaster duties, April 3, 1784–July 9, 1787, includes references to negotiations with Indians and the troops and officers, including Lafayette, who were present at the signing of the 1784 treaty at Fort Stanwix. Volumes 27 and 31 contain some of the orders issued by Gen. John Sullivan in 1779 while he commanded a punitive expedition against the Iroquois, principally in the Wyoming Valley of Pennsylvania. Better sources of information on Indians, however, are the copies of letters sent and a few letters received by Gen. Edward Hand, April 13–August 25, 1778 (vol. 156). Most of Hand's letters were written at Fort Pitt and were directed to George Washington, Patrick Henry, Horatio Gates, George Rogers Clark, and other military officers; Indians, such as Chief White Eyes, and Indian councils; and Spanish officers and military commanders in the West. A few of the letters were written by George Morgan, an agent for Indian affairs for the Continental Congress. Subjects covered in the letters include the activities of the Delaware and Wyandot, depredations by Indians, the raising of regiments to defend the frontier, Indian engagements and campaigns, the discovery of Tory plots and spies, and an expedition down the Ohio and Mississippi Rivers.

About 35,500 miscellaneous numbered documents include originals and copies of records pertaining to Revolutionary War military operations, the service of individuals, the pay and settlement of accounts, and supplies. The series has been reproduced as M859, *Miscellaneous Numbered Records (The Manuscript File) in the War Department Collection of Revolutionary War Records, 1775-1790's.* A large segment of the records were created by the large staff departments of the Continental Army responsible for supplying and paying troops. Some of the records include comments on Indian affairs, such as those from a paymaster at Fort Pitt in 1780 describing conflicts with Indians and the measures taken for defense. There are other miscellaneous items, such as a letter from George Rogers Clark to the military commander at Fort Patrick Henry, November 3, 1779, which describes recent engagements with Delaware, Shawnee, and Wabash Indians.

A fourth series consists of approximately 20 feet of photocopies of documents, the originals of which are in the custody of institutions and individuals in Virginia, North Carolina, and Massachusetts. Photographed in accordance with an act of March 2, 1913 (37 Stat. 723), the records are chiefly letters and reports sent and received by State boards of war, Governors, and Army officers; minutes of boards; rolls and returns; court records; and receipts for money and stores. The Virginia photocopies include a few descriptions and reports of Indian hostilities on the old northwestern frontier, especially rolls and lists relating to the activities of George Rogers Clark. The North Carolina photocopies contain information on the Cherokee Indians. There is, for example, a 40-page report entitled "A Talk with the Cherokee Indians held at Fort Charlotte in South Carolina 1776." Included are copies of speeches delivered by order of John Hancock, President of the Continental Congress, and by the commissioners representing the Congress and a transcript of the statements made by the commissioners and the "Head Men and Warriors of the Valley and Middle Settlements of the Cherokee Nation."

FEDERAL RECORDS

GENERAL RECORDS OF THE UNITED STATES GOVERNMENT (RECORD GROUP 11)

Indian treaties compose one series among the General Records of the U.S. Government. The negotiation of formal treaties with Indians followed the customs established by Great Britain and the colonial governments. Indian treaties were made by the Second Continental Congress and the Congress of the Confederation, and they were continued under the Federal Government.

After 1789, treaties were negotiated by special commissioners acting for the President under the supervision of the Secretary of War. When the Department of the Interior was established in 1849 and the Bureau of Indian Affairs was transferred to it, the supervisory function of negotiating Indian treaties was assigned to the Secretary of the Interior.

The form for Indian treaties and the procedures for putting them into effect were the same as for treaties with foreign nations. The treaties required approval by the Senate and had the same status, force, and dignity as agreements with sovereign nations. The practice of according full treaty status to agreements with Indian tribes was discontinued by an act of March 3, 1871 (16 Stat. 544, 566), which forbade further recognition of the tribes as nations and prohibited further treaty negotiations with them. The act did not, however, abrogate existing treaties. After 1871, agreements were made, often similar in substance to treaties, and these were approved by both Houses of Congress instead of by the Senate alone. There is no segregated series of these agreements.

Treaty provisions relate to many subjects. The most important purpose of many treaties was to extinguish Indian titles to land. Typically, the Indians agreed to reduce their landholdings or to move to an area less desired for white settlement. Often they were compensated for their land and property by lump sum or annuity payments of money or by payments in services or commodities. Sometimes the Indians were guaranteed special rights, such as hunting and fishing privileges in ceded lands. Some treaties provided for the allotment of land to individual Indians and for the dissolution of tribes. Other common subjects of treaty provisions were the cessation of hostilities and maintenance of peace, the status of tribes as dependent nations, criminal and civil jurisdiction, control of tribal affairs, regulation of trade, claims of and against Indians, and rights-of-way across Indian lands.

The originals of Indian treaties, as approved by the Senate, were maintained by the Department of State in chronological order, and each treaty was assigned a number. Treaty 1, between the Five Nations and the Governors of New York, Virginia, and Pennsylvania, had been signed at Fort George, N.Y., on August 14, 1722. The last numbered treaty is 374, with the Nez Percés, signed at Washington on August 13, 1868. This file also includes several unperfected treaties, which did not go into effect. Finding aids include a chronological list of the treaties and indexes by place and by tribe.

A treaty file often consists of an original signed copy of the treaty, the Presidential proclamation of it, the Senate resolution approving ratification, and a printed copy of the treaty. Sometimes there are copies of messages from the President to the Senate, messages or letters of instruction to the treaty commissioners, and other correspondence. In a few cases the original treaty is missing.

The Indian treaties have been reproduced as M668, *Ratified Indian Treaties, 1722–1869*. The texts of the treaties have been published in Charles J. Kappler, ed., *Indian Affairs: Laws and Treaties,* vol. 2, *Treaties* (1904), and in the *Statutes at Large*.

Also in this record group are the original engrossed acts and resolutions of Congress, Presidential proclamations and Executive orders, and rules and regulations of Federal agencies published in the *Federal Register* since 1936. Most of these records, however, are available in published form. Executive orders did not have to be sent to the Department of State until 1905, and many of the earlier orders are with the records of the agency immediately concerned. Among Records of the Bureau of Indian Affairs, Record Group 75, is an Executive order file, 1850–92, that includes many original orders relating to Indian reservations. They and later orders have been published as *Executive Orders Relating to Indian Reservations, 1855 to 1922*, 2 vols. (Washington, 1912, 1922).

See Ralph E. Huss, comp., *United States Government Documents Having General Legal Effect*, PI 159 (1964).

RECORDS OF THE BUREAU OF INDIAN AFFAIRS
(RECORD GROUP 75)

In addition to central and field office records of the Bureau of Indian Affairs, this record group contains records of the Office of the Secretary of War relating to Indian affairs before the establishment of the Bureau in 1824, records of the Office of Indian Trade, and records of the Board of Indian Commissioners.

See Edward E. Hill, comp., *Preliminary Inventory of the Records of the Bureau of Indian Affairs*, PI 163 (2 vols., 1965), and Laura E. Kelsay, comp., *List of Cartographic Records of the Bureau of Indian Affairs*, Special List 13 (rev. 1977).

Records of the Office of the Secretary of War Relating to Indian Affairs

From 1789 until the Bureau of Indian Affairs was established in 1824, Indian affairs were under the direct control of the Secretary of War, except for a Government-operated factory system of trade with the Indians begun in 1795. From 1806 until it was abolished in 1822, the factory system was directed by a Superintendent of Indian Trade, who was responsible to the Secretary of War.

The Federal Government continued the superintendencies provided by the ordinance of August 7, 1786, with a northern and a southern department divided by the Ohio River. In 1789 the Congress appropriated funds for the Governor of the Northwest Territory to discharge the duties of the superintendent of the northern department, and it became a standard practice for the Governor of a Territory to serve ex officio as superintendent of Indian affairs in his area.

Agencies, usually under a superintendency, with immediate responsibility for specified tribes or geographical areas developed gradually. In 1792 the President appointed four special agents, who were charged with special diplomatic missions. In 1793 the Congress authorized the President to appoint temporary agents to reside among the Indians (1 Stat. 331); in time the agents were permanently assigned to particular tribes or areas. By 1818 there were 15 agents and 10 assistants or subagents. In that year the Congress passed a law (3 Stat. 428) providing that agents be appointed by the President with the advice and consent of the Senate, a practice that endured for most of the 19th century.

The fire in the War Department on November 8, 1800, destroyed most of its records; therefore, the records of the Office of the Secretary of War during the period of its direct administration of Indian affairs exist only from that time until 1824. During this period the War Department kept most of its incoming correspondence in one series controlled by registers. Copies of outgoing letters were recorded in several sets of letter books, one of which was for Indian affairs. The six volumes of letters sent (1 ft.) for the years 1800 to 1824 were turned over to the Bureau of Indian Affairs. Other letters relating to Indian affairs had been copied in other volumes, and these remained with the records of the Office of the Secretary of War. Letters received relating to nonmilitary Indian matters were segregated from other letters document by document, but the selection process was imperfect. Only a small part (2 ft.) of the incoming correspondence has survived. The registers of the letters received are in Records of the Office of the Secretary of War, Record Group 107, but a microfilm copy of them (M22) is available for use with the records of the Bureau of Indian Affairs. Some records of the Office of the Secretary of War were incorporated with later records of the Bureau.

The letters received consist of correspondence from Indian superintendents and agents, factors of trading posts, Territorial and State Governors, military commanders, Indians, missionaries, and others. Among them are drafts of letters sent, vouchers, receipts, requisitions, abstracts and financial statements, certificates of deposit, depositions, contracts, and newspapers. The letters sent have a higher proportion of letters to such addressees as the Superintendent of Indian Trade, treaty and other commissioners, Treasury Department officials, and persons having commercial dealings with the War Department. Some of the letters were signed by clerks in the Department or by the President rather than the Secretary of War. Included are copies of speeches to Indians, proceedings of conferences with Indians in Washington, licenses of traders, passports for travel in the Indian country, appointments, and instructions to commissioners, superintendents, agents, and other officials.

During this period the Department was most concerned with the Seneca and other Indians of New York and the Indians in the South, particularly the Cherokee, Chickasaw, Choctaw, and Creek. Also important were the Indians of the Old Northwest, and there was a growing interest in the Indians west of the Mississippi River, especially the Osage and the Caddo and other Indians living in Louisiana.

The correspondence, particularly the letters sent, relates to a broad range of subjects. It was a period of active treaty making, except for the years from 1810 to 1814, when there were wars with the northwestern Indians, led by Tecumseh, and the Creek Indians and the War of 1812. In the correspondence there is much discussion of the establishment and maintenance of peace and friendship with the Indians, but there is more about land matters, particularly cessions. After the War of 1812, the proposed removal of Indians to west of the Mississippi River became a common topic. Other land-related subjects are roads across Indian lands; land reserves for individual Indians, first provided by the treaty of November 16, 1805, with the Choctaw Indians; and boundaries and surveys. There are complaints from Indians about violations of terms of treaties. There is correspondence about the purchase and distribution of annuity goods, including numerous complaints of late deliveries. Even at this early date, there was considerable discussion of educating and "civilizing" Indians, usually in the "useful arts": raising crops and livestock, smithery and carpentry work, and sewing, spinning, and weaving. There are also letters about mission schools and the use of the Civilization Fund, established in 1819, to support such schools, and about missionaries allowed to reside on Indian lands to spread the Christian religion. Other subjects are the Office of Indian Trade and the Government factories; private trade, with frequent mention of the legislation regulating trade and intercourse with the Indians; the sale of liquor to Indians; the issuance of passports; intruders and settlers on Indian lands; houses of entertainment; murders; horse stealing and other depredations committed by and against Indians; stolen children; slaves held by Indians; visits of Indian delegations to Washington and the discouragement of them; disputes between tribes and States; intertribal relations and the refusal of the United States to intervene; the establishment, location, transfer, and discontinuance of superintendencies and agencies and instructions for their operation; the appointment and conduct of officials and complaints and charges against them; agency buildings; the investment of Indian funds; and estimates, allocations of funds, accounts, and other financial matters.

Correspondents, particularly in the letters sent, frequently are identified only by name with no indication of address or position; therefore, even more than with later records, it is necessary to be familiar with the persons involved before attempting to use the records. The letters sent are arranged chronologically and have indexes to recipients. The letters received are arranged by year and thereunder alphabetically by name of writer. The registers of letters received by the Secretary of War can be used to identify specific letters, but when seeking information about a subject area, it usually is easier to go directly to the letters.

The letters received have been microfilmed as M271; letters sent, as M15.

Records of the Office of Indian Trade

From 1795 until 1822 the U.S. Government operated a system of factories or posts to trade with the Indians, one of the earliest ventures of the Federal Government in competition with private enterprise. The Office of Indian Trade was established in 1806 to direct the trade operations. The factories furnished the Indians various kinds of merchandise in exchange for furs, skins, and other commodities. The system was not intended to make a profit; prices were supposed to be high enough only to maintain the original capital and to cover expenses. The main objective was to establish more harmonious relations with the Indians, thus reducing the expenses of defending the frontier. It was hoped also that the Indians would become dependent on the supply of Government goods and more subject to Government control. Private trade was still permitted under the licensing system established by the Congress in 1796 and later modified. Issuing licenses and regulating private trade were responsibilities of the Secretary of War and the superintendents and agents who served under him; the Secretary also had general supervisory control over the factory system.

Two factories were started on an experimental basis in 1795 following an appropriation by the Congress of $50,000 for the purchase of goods to be sold to the Indians under the direction of the President (1 Stat. 443). The following year the Congress raised the capital to $150,000 and specifically provided for the establishment of trading houses and the appointment by the President of the employees needed to operate them (1 Stat. 452). The capital was gradually raised until in 1809 it amounted to $300,000 (2 Stat. 544).

After 1811, the Office of Indian Trade was also responsible for purchasing and transmitting goods for annuity payments and presents to Indians.

For several years no one official had primary responsibility for directing the factories. Originally, the Purveyor of Public Supplies procured goods for the factories and disposed of those received from them. Military agents of the War Department (the predecessors of Quartermaster officers) usually handled the transportation of goods. In November 1796, John Harris, Keeper of Military Stores at Philadelphia, was designated to receive goods and money from the factories and to dispose of them. The Purveyor of Public Supplies continued to purchase goods for the factories. On May 11, 1801, William Irvine, Superintendent of Military Stores, was also appointed Agent for the Indian Factories. He was to receive and dispose of merchandise from the factories and to furnish the Secretary of War with estimates of goods needed for them. Irvine died July 29, 1804, and George Ingels, Military Storekeeper at Philadelphia, temporarily assumed his duties. On March 26, 1805, William Davy was appointed Principal Agent for Indian Factories, purchasing and disposing goods for them—thereby assuming all the duties concerning the factories.

On July 8, 1806, John Shee was appointed Superintendent of Indian Trade under an act of Congress (2 Stat. 402), and he assumed the functions previously exercised by Davy. Shee referred to this post as the "Office of the Superintendent of Indian Trade," and by 1808 the office was called the "Office of Indian Trade" or "Indian Trade Office." Shee maintained his office at Philadelphia, as had his predecessors, but the act provided that it should be moved to the District of Columbia. When Shee decided not to move, Gen. John Mason was appointed Superintendent, and in 1807 he moved the Office of Indian Trade to Georgetown. In 1816 Mason was replaced by Thomas L. McKenney, who remained in office until the closing of the Office of Indian Trade and the factories in 1822 by act of Congress (3 Stat. 679). George Graham, under the direction of the Treasury Department, was in charge of the liquidation.

In immediate charge of the factories were factors or agents. They are called factors in this guide to distinguish them from the regular Indian agents appointed to represent the United States in its relations with the Indian tribes; on occasion, however, factors also served as agents. They sold blankets, clothing, cloth, utensils, weapons, ammunition, and tobacco in exchange for goods, mostly furs and skins, brought in by the Indians. What was received from the Indians was sent to Georgetown and other trade centers, where it was usually sold at public auction. In addition to the factors, the Office of Indian Trade employed purchasing, transportation, and other agents, often on a part-time basis, at such important supply centers and depots as Philadelphia, New York, New Orleans, Savannah, Albany, and St. Louis.

One of the two factories established in 1795 was located at Colerain, Ga., on St. Mary's River, to serve the Creek Indians. The other was located at Tellico, Tenn., for the Cherokee and Choctaw. The Creek factory, usually known by the names of its successive locations or as the Georgia factory, was moved several times but continued in operation until 1820. In practice, the other factory served only the Cherokee. In 1807 it was moved to Hiwassee on the Tennessee River, but it failed to prosper and was closed in 1810.

No new factories were opened until 1802, when they were founded at Fort St. Stephens, in present-day Alabama, for the Choctaw Indians; Chickasaw Bluffs, Tenn.; Fort Wayne, Ind.; and Detroit. The Choctaw factory was moved to Fort Confederation on the Tombigbee River in 1816 and continued to operate until the end of the factory system in 1822. Detroit, Fort Wayne, and Chickasaw Bluffs (which was suspended during the War of 1812) were closed in 1805, 1812, and 1818, respectively.

Four factories were opened in 1805. They were located at Arkansas Post on the Arkansas River, Natchitoches on the Red River, Belle Fontaine near the mouth of the Missouri River, and Chicago. The Arkansas factory was a failure and closed in 1810. The Natchitoches factory was moved to Sulphur Fork in 1818 because of a dispute with the Roman Catholic Church over the land and property, but it continued to operate until the end of the factory system, as did the Chicago factory except during the War of 1812. The Belle Fontaine factory was closed in 1809. The factory opened in 1806 at Sandusky, Ohio, on Lake Erie, was destroyed by the British during the war and never reopened.

In 1808 factories were opened at Mackinac (Michilimackinac), Mich.; Fort Osage on the Missouri River near the site of Sibley, Mo., for the Osage Indians; and Fort Madison on the Mississippi River above the mouth of the Des Moines River. Mackinac was captured by the British during the war and never reopened. Fort Madison was destroyed by the British; the factor established temporary headquarters at St. Louis and at Little Manitou on the Missouri River, but in 1815 the factory was replaced by one at Prairie du Chien. The Osage factory continued to operate until 1822, but from 1813 to 1815 it was located farther east at Arrow Rock. A branch of this factory was opened in 1821 on the Marais de Cygne River.

Four factories, all of which operated until 1822, were established after the war. Two, opened in 1815, were at Green Bay and Prairie du Chien. Another, opened in 1818, was at Fort Edwards near the mouth of the Des Moines River at the site of Warsaw, Ill., until 1822, when it was moved to Fort Armstrong on Rock Island. The fourth factory, opened in 1818 to replace the Chickasaw Bluffs factory, was located temporarily at Illinois Bayou and then at Spadre Bluffs on the Arkansas River in Arkansas.

The following is a list of the factories and their years of operation in the order of their establishment.

Creek
Colerain, 1795–97
Fort Wilkinson, 1797–1806
Ocmulgee Old Fields, 1806–9
Fort Hawkins, 1809–16
Fort Mitchell, 1816–20

Cherokee
Tellico, 1795–1807
Hiwassee, 1807–10

Fort Wayne, 1802–12

Choctaw
Fort St. Stephens, 1802–15
Fort Confederation, 1816–22

Detroit, 1802–5

Chickasaw Bluffs, 1802–18

Arkansas, 1805–10

Chicago, 1805–22

Belle Fontaine, 1805–9

Natchitoches-Sulphur Fork
Natchitoches, 1805–18
Sulphur Fork, 1818–22

Sandusky, 1806–12

Fort Madison, 1808–15

Osage, 1808–22

Mackinac (Michilimackinac), 1808–12

Green Bay, 1815–22

Prairie du Chien, 1815–22

Fort Edwards, 1818–22

Spadre Bluffs (Illinois Bayou), 1818–22

Very little of the incoming correspondence of the Superintendent's Office has survived, only 10 inches for the years 1806 to 1824, which has been reproduced as T58. There are a small volume of letters and instructions sent by the Secretary of War concerning the Indian trade, 1795–1800, and a complete set of six copybooks of letters sent for the years from 1807, when Mason took charge, until the end of the factory system in 1822. A seventh volume, for the letters sent by George Graham, principal agent in charge of liquidation of the factories, contains letters dated as late as 1830. The first six volumes have been reproduced as M16. Some of the correspondence of the Superintendent's Office was conducted by the transportation agent and other assistants. For the years 1816 to 1822, there is a separate copybook for letters sent by Transportation Agent John W. Bronaugh. The correspondence of the Office was conducted with factors, purchasing and transportation agents, the Secretary of War, the Secretary of the Treasury and other Treasury Department officials, the President, Indian agents, merchants, manufacturers, bankers, members of missionary societies, and others. The principal subjects are the purchase and distribution of goods for the factories, the disposal of the furs and other commodities received, and the operation of the factories. After 1811, providing annuity goods and presents for the Indians was important. Financial accounts and appointments to office were always significant. The last Superintendent of Indian Trade, Thomas L. McKenney, who in 1824 became the first head of the Bureau of Indian Affairs, was greatly interested in the education and "civilization" of Indians. As Superintendent, he had no legal responsibility for these matters, but the correspondence for his 6 years in office contains information about them.

Most of the other records of the Superintendent's Office are accounts, the basic ones being the interrelated sets of daybooks, journals, and ledgers. The daybooks, also known as waste books or blotters, are chronological records of financial transactions made at the time of the transactions. Later more finished chronological records, known as journals, were compiled. The ledgers record the same transactions as the journals, but the entries are arranged by account rather than chronologically. Separate accounts were kept for individuals, factories, and firms; separate accounts were also kept for different uses of funds, such as merchandise and salaries. Usually, journals and ledgers cover the same time periods, and the journals give page references to the ledgers. There are waste books or daybooks for the Office of Indian Trade, 1803-6 and 1809-24; four journals, 1805-24; and four ledgers, 1803-6 and 1816-24. Two of the ledgers are indexed, and there is an index for the missing ledger, 1807-16.

Nine indent books, 1804-20, consist of copies of lists of goods ordered or needed by the factories, sometimes with indications of the action taken by the Office of Indian Trade. There are separate volumes for the Arkansas, Cherokee, Chicago, Chickasaw Bluffs, Choctaw, Creek, Fort Wayne, and Natchitoches factories and one volume for the Fort Madison and Fort Edwards factories. There are also a volume of copies of letters from factors and Indian agents to the Superintendent and the Secretary of War, 1811-18, requesting goods for making annuity payments and a volume of copies of orders for goods, 1806-12.

Copies of invoices are divided into those "inward" and those "outward." There are five volumes of invoices inward, 1796-1822, for goods, mostly furs and peltries, received from the factories and for goods received from merchants, and there is a volume of invoices, 1811-19, received from merchants for goods to be used for annuity payments. Five volumes of invoices outward, 1803-24, contain copies of invoices mainly for goods sent to the factories but also for furs and other goods received from the factories and sold by the Office of Indian Trade. One of the volumes is just for invoices of goods sent to the Chicago factory, 1805-12. In the volume later used as a copybook for letters sent by Transportation Agent John W.

Bronaugh (mentioned above as part of the correspondence of the Office) are some copies of invoices, 1803-4, from merchants for goods furnished.

Other records include a memorandum book, 1807-13, with information about prices and quality of goods, transportation costs, sales, the appointment of factors, and other subjects; sales books, 1807-22, recording sales of furs and peltries at Georgetown, Savannah, Philadelphia, New Orleans, and other places; statements of account current, 1805-18; check stubs, 1809-13 and 1821-22; canceled checks, 1808-21; and inventories of goods on hand at the Office of Indian Trade in Georgetown and at the factories at the time they were liquidated. There are also 2 feet of vouchers, receipts, bills of lading, financial statements, abstracts of payments, invoices, inventories, lists, and other records relating to accounts, 1796-1825. These records, some of which were created in the Office and some of which were received from factors and others, are divided into three groups: general accounts, transportation accounts, and annuity accounts.

The records of the individual factories are similar to those of the Superintendent's Office, but there are great variations in what has survived. Each factory was supposed to maintain a daybook, journal, ledger, letter book, cashbook, and invoice book. At the close of each quarter, the factors were to send abstracts of their account books and inventories of stock to the Office of Indian Trade. Over the years, the records of the central office and those of the factories have become intermingled almost indistinguishably, and records relating to a factory that are physically with the records of that factory have been accepted as its records. This includes the quarterly transcripts of accounts. Indians are sometimes named in the accounts, but transactions with them are often indicated only by such terms as "bartered" or "bartered with Indians."

There is a significant amount of correspondence for only three factories. For the Arkansas factory, a volume of copies of incoming and outgoing correspondence, 1805-10, has been reproduced as M142. For the Creek factory, there is 1 foot of correspondence, mostly incoming, 1795-1814, and a volume of copies of letters sent, 1795-1816. The volume is available on microfilm as M4. For the Natchitoches-Sulphur Fork factory, a volume of copies of letters sent, 1809-21, is available as T1029.

For these three factories there also are fairly complete accounting records. For the Arkansas factory there are a daybook, journal, ledger, invoice book, and other records for the entire period of the factory's operation. The records of the Creek factory are the most voluminous, amounting to some 6 feet. They include daybooks, journals, ledgers, vouchers, and miscellaneous accounts. Of particular interest are a journal and a corresponding ledger, 1808-14, which record transactions with Benjamin Hawkins, the U.S. Indian agent for the Creek Indians. For Natchitoches-Sulphur Fork there are daybooks, journals, ledgers, an invoice book, and miscellaneous accounts.

For the Choctaw factory there are 4 feet of records consisting of transcripts of daybooks, 1808–19, and miscellaneous accounts, 1803–25. For the other factories the records are sparse. There are miscellaneous accounts for each of them, ranging from one-half inch for Belle Fontaine, Detroit, and Mackinac to 1 foot for the Prairie du Chien factory. There are incomplete daybooks or other account books for Chicago, Chickasaw Bluffs, Fort Wayne, and Prairie du Chien.

Other records of the Office of Indian Trade, presumably submitted to the auditors of the Treasury Department for settlement, are in Records of the General Accounting Office, Record Group 217. Records of the Office of the Quartermaster General, Record Group 92, includes documents of the offices concerned with the factories before the Office of Indian Trade was established.

The Historical Society of Pennsylvania in Philadelphia has custody of the papers of William Irvine, which contain drafts of his outgoing correspondence while he was serving as Agent for the Indian Factories. Some papers of Thomas L. McKenney, Superintendent of Indian Trade and later first head of the Bureau of Indian Affairs, are at the American Philosophical Society in Philadelphia. The Missouri Historical Society in St. Louis has papers of James Kennerly, agent for the factories at St. Louis, and of George Sibley, factor at the Osage factory. Other papers of Sibley are at Lindenwood College in St. Charles, Mo. An account book of the Fort Wayne factory, consisting mostly of invoices and inventories, has been published in *Indiana Historical Collections* 15(1927):405–663.

Records of the Revenue Office Relating to Procurement for the War Department

By an act of May 8, 1792 (1 Stat. 279), the Congress provided that purchases and supplies for the War Department should be made by or under the supervision of the Treasury Department. On April 4, 1794, Tench Coxe, the Commissioner of Revenue, was designated to supervise purchases for the military, naval, and Indian services. He gave up this responsibility on December 31, 1794, but completed all the unfinished business. The only records of the Revenue Office relating to procurement for the War Department that are known to be in the National Archives are in a volume of letters sent, April 14, 1794–August 26, 1796. Although the letters relate only in part to the purchase of blankets, cloth, clothing, silver ornaments, and other goods for Indians, the volume was placed among the records of the Bureau of Indian Affairs. It has been reproduced as M74, *Letters of Tench Coxe, Commissioner of the Revenue, Relating to the Procurement of Military, Naval, and Indian Supplies, 1794–1796.* The records of the Purveyor of Public Supplies, whose office was established in 1795 with general responsibility for the purchase of Government supplies, are among Records of the Office of the Quartermaster General, Record Group 92.

Records of the Bureau of Indian Affairs

The Bureau of Indian Affairs was established within the War Department on March 11, 1824, by Secretary of War John C. Calhoun. The Bureau operated informally within the Department until 1832, when the Congress authorized the appointment of a Commissioner of Indian Affairs, under the direction of the Secretary of War, to direct and manage all matters arising from relations with the Indians (4 Stat. 564). The Bureau, usually known as the Office of Indian Affairs until 1947, was transferred in 1849 from the War Department to the new Department of the Interior, where it has since remained. The central office of the Bureau in Washington and its field establishment were known collectively as the Indian Service.

The creation of the Bureau was an administrative matter that represented no significant change in policy or field operations. The system of agencies responsible for one or more tribes usually subordinate to a superintendency with general responsibility for Indian affairs in a Territory or other geographical area was continued. (In 1824, however, a comparatively high number of agencies were not assigned to superintendencies.) Territorial Governors continued to serve ex officio as superintendents when appropriate. In 1824 the Federal Government still was primarily concerned with Indians living east of the Mississippi River, particularly the Seneca and other Indians in New York, the Five Civilized Tribes in the South, and the various tribes of the Old Northwest. The St. Louis Superintendency, established in 1822 with William Clark as superintendent, was responsible for most of the Indians and agencies along and west of the Mississippi.

An act of May 28, 1830 (4 Stat. 411), made it the explicit policy of the United States to remove the Indians from the East, and during the 1830's and 1840's, this removal was largely completed. Some Indians remained in or returned to the East, and the Bureau was never able to suspend operations there. Most of the eastern agencies, however, were closed or moved west.

An act of June 30, 1834 (4 Stat. 735), provided for a major reorganization of superintendencies and agencies. The area west of the Mississippi River and east of the Rocky Mountains was divided between the St. Louis Superintendency and the new Western Superintendency. The St. Louis Superintendency was to be responsible for the Indians and Indian country west of the Rocky Mountains. In practice the Western Superintendency became responsible for the Indians in present-day Oklahoma and sometimes for the Osage in southern Kansas. The Upper Missouri Agency of the St. Louis Superintendency had contacts with Indians living as far west as present-day Montana, but farther south the effective jurisdiction of the superintendency did not extend beyond central Kansas until after the establishment of the Upper Platte Agency in 1846.

Wisconsin Territory and the Wisconsin Superintendency were organized in 1836 and originally included present-day Minnesota, Iowa, and parts of the Dakotas. Other changes in jurisdiction in the West were made as new Territories and superintendencies were formed and as Territories became States and superintendencies were discontinued. After the Mexican War and the settlement of the Oregon boundary, there were changes, particularly to conform with an act of February 27, 1851 (9 Stat. 574), that provided for superintendencies and agencies in the Far West, largely for Indians with whom the Federal Government had little previous contact.

With the expansion of the United States to the Pacific Ocean, the Bureau of Indian Affairs became involved with more tribes, but, as the Indians were confined to increasingly smaller reservations, the geographical areas of concern grew smaller. There continued to be some Indians under Federal jurisdiction, however, in all the western States and Territories except Texas. During the 1870's the superintendencies were abolished, and thereafter all agents reported directly to the Bureau of Indian Affairs in Washington. Starting in 1893, the politically appointed agents were gradually replaced by superintendents appointed under civil service regulations.

There were other kinds of field officials, including treaty commissioners, inspectors, and special agents; purchasing and distributing agents concerned with obtaining goods and distributing goods or money; emigration agents, who assisted in the removal of Indians from one area to another; enrolling agents, who prepared tribal rolls for various purposes; and school superintendents.

Starting with the appointment of a Superintendent of Indian Schools in 1883, supervisory positions were established for specialized activities, such as irrigation, forestry, employment of Indians, health, law enforcement, and construction. The incumbents were regarded as field officials, and they developed elaborate organizations that operated outside the agency system.

In 1926 the position of General Superintendent was created with responsibility for field activities relating to agencies and schools, including education, agriculture, and industry. In 1931 directors of both field and central office operations were appointed for specialized activities. By 1937 the Bureau had established uniform districts for the various field services to eliminate the confusion caused when each service set up its own districts. After World War II a system of area offices was established whereby area directors were responsible for supervising all Indian activities within their area, including agencies and other administrative units. Specialists were expected to provide technical supervision but were relieved of executive responsibility.

The organization of the central office of the Bureau was simple for many years. Until 1886 the only positions authorized by statute were those of Commissioner of Indian Affairs and Chief Clerk. In 1886 the latter position was replaced by that of Assistant Commissioner. A new position of Chief

Clerk was established in 1906, called Second Assistant Commissioner from 1910 to 1915, and abolished in 1934. After World War II additional positions of Assistant Commissioner were created and also positions of Deputy Commissioner and Associate Commissioner, ranking above the Assistant Commissioners.

There were no formal subdivisions of the central office until 1846, when four divisions were established—the Land, Civilization, Finance, and Files and Records Divisions. The Files and Records Division had custody of the general records of the Bureau, but the other divisions also kept their own records.

Few changes in the divisional organization of the Bureau were made until 1907. From 1873 to 1881 there was a Medical and Educational Division, which assumed some of the duties of the Civilization Division. The Accounts Division was established in 1876. Most of its functions had formerly been assigned to the Finance Division. In 1884 the Civilization Division became the Education Division. In 1885 the Depredation Division was established to process depredation claims, but in 1893 it was consolidated with the Land Division. The Miscellaneous Division was established in 1889 to take over certain duties of the Office of the Assistant Commissioner, particularly the issuance of traders' licenses.

Between 1907 and 1915 the Bureau's central office was reorganized repeatedly. The Land and Education Divisions survived. The Miscellaneous Division was abolished, and the Files and Records Division was reduced to the Mail and Files Section of the Office of the Chief Clerk. The Finance Division became the Purchase Division, and the Accounts Division became the Finance Division.

There were other units that were short-lived and for which no records are now segregated. Divisions that did survive and for which there are records in the National Archives include the Law (later Probate), Inspection, Irrigation, Forestry, Health, Extension and Industry, and Statistics Divisions. In 1931 the Alaska Division of the Office of Education, in charge of educational and medical work for Alaskan natives, was transferred to the Bureau of Indian Affairs.

The organization of the Bureau became increasingly complicated in the depression years. New divisions were established to expedite emergency programs, including the Civilian Conservation Corps–Indian Division; the Roads Division; the Rehabilitation Division, in charge of Work Projects Administration projects; and the Construction Division, in charge of Public Works Administration projects. The Indian Organization Division was established to supervise the formation of tribal governments under the provisions of the Indian Reorganization Act.

The grouping of divisions under higher level officials started in 1931, when two Assistants to the Commissioner and a Chief Finance Officer each took charge of several divisions. Branches made up of several divisions were established in 1940, but in 1949 the terminology was reversed—the branches became divisions and the divisions became branches. An Assistant Commissioner was placed in charge of each of the two major program divisions, the Division of Community Services and the Division of Resources.

There have been many more recent changes in the branches, but because few of the division and branch records now in the National Archives of the United States date after World War II, the records are organized and identified for the most part according to the pre-1949 division structure. For units with more recent records in the National Archives, information about administrative changes is given in the pertinent sections of this guide.

GENERAL RECORDS, 1824–1907

From 1824 until 1907 the Bureau of Indian Affairs kept its basic records in separate series of incoming and outgoing letters. Most of this correspondence was conducted with field officials: superintendents, agents, subagents, special agents, commissioners, and, later, inspectors and school superintendents. There also was much correspondence with the supervising Cabinet member, the Secretary of War until 1849 and thereafter the Secretary of the Interior. Correspondence from the War Department after 1849 consists chiefly of copies of military reports. There was correspondence with the Commissioner of the General Land Office concerning land surveys, reserves, and the public domain; with the Secretary of the Treasury, Second Auditor, Second Comptroller, and other Treasury Department officials concerning accounts, tribal and individual funds, investments, and other financial matters; with the President, Members of Congress, and other Federal, State, Territorial, and local officials; with attorneys and other persons involved with litigation and other legal matters; with merchants, manufacturers, shippers, bankers, and other persons having commercial relations with the Bureau; and with members of missionary societies, applicants for office, and others. There was comparatively little written communication with Indians, either directly or through superintendents and agents. Members of certain tribes, perhaps most notably the Cherokee, did frequently write letters and petitions, largely about legal matters. In the earlier years, for most tribes proceedings of conferences were the principal written expressions of Indian viewpoints. Toward the end of the 19th century, particularly after the passage of the General Allotment Act, letters from individual Indians, persons who claimed to be Indians, or their representatives became more common, concerning such matters as tribal enrollment, land allotments, and entitlement to monetary benefits.

Often enclosed with the letters received were reports, orders, petitions, financial statements, vouchers, and occasionally newspaper clippings, census rolls, maps, drawings, and other items. Over the years, the correspondence became more voluminous and also more routine. More of the communications received were periodic form reports from agents, and more of the letters sent were acknowledgments.

The subjects of the correspondence reflect the full range of civilian Federal Indian administration and to some extent military matters, although in almost every subject area certain records were separated from the main series of correspondence.

Negotiations with Indian tribes continued to be important. By 1871 the tribes were no longer regarded as independent governments and formal treaty making was discontinued. The negotiation process was continued, however, through the making of agreements that were approved by both houses of Congress. The "enforcement" of treaties was the basis of the Government's relationship with many tribes, although the Bureau could maintain essentially the same relationship with a tribe with or without a treaty.

The names of the three principal divisions established in 1846—Land, Civilization, and Finance—give some indication of the Bureau's conception of its major areas of concern. The principal purpose of most treaties was to extinguish Indian title to land; usually, the Indians agreed to reduce their holdings or to cede all their land and move to another area. Often they were compensated for their land and other property by lump sum or annuity payments or by goods or services, which frequently were intended to assist the Indians to adapt to "civilization."

The Bureau's "land" activities related primarily to ownership, whereas the use of the land was more closely associated with the "civilization" functions. The treaties provided for both tribal and individual reserves, sometimes with persons identified by name. There were surveys to establish locations of reserves and reservations. Conflicting claims and boundary disputes arose; with the individual reserves, there were problems of inheritance and disposition.

An important activity of the Bureau was land allotment. The idea of dividing tribal lands among the members of tribes had been advocated even before the Bureau was established. Some of the treaties by which Indians agreed to move provided reserves for individuals who chose to give up tribal status and remain in the East and sometimes for Indians who were going to move and could sell the land. During the 1850's and later, there was an effort to get tribes, particularly those in Kansas and Nebraska, to move to new reservations in Indian Territory. Many were given the option of accepting a land allotment, giving up tribal status, and living as citizens of the United States. Sometimes there was also the choice of remaining on common land on a diminished reserve. When a tribe agreed to move to a new reservation or to accept a diminished reserve, the surplus land was sold for the benefit of the Indians, and the Secretary of the Interior served as the trustee of the proceeds. Such lands offered for sale were known as trust lands.

With the passage of the General Allotment Act of 1887 (24 Stat. 338), it became the policy to provide every Indian with an allotment, the ultimate objectives being to eliminate tribal lands and to disband the tribes. During a trust period, originally set at 25 years but later modified in many cases, the allottee could sell land only with the permission of the Secretary of the Interior.

Gradually during the latter part of the 19th century, more records about individual Indians were created. In earlier years the Bureau's main interest in individual Indians was to determine their eligibility for benefits, particularly annuity payments. In 1884 the practice of taking annual censuses of Indians on reservations was begun. With the passage of the General Allotment Act, there was increased interest in enrollment or determining the members of the tribes. Records were created about individuals in connection with the making of allotments, determining competency to handle business affairs (which entitled a person to receive a fee patent to land), the sale of land by individuals, leases, and the determination of heirs. Fairly independent of Bureau control for some years, the Five Civilized Tribes came under more direct Federal influence through the Commission to the Five Civilized Tribes.

Other subjects reflected in the correspondence concerning both tribal and individual lands are irrigation, leases, rights-of-way for roads and railroads, mineral and timber rights, and trespasses.

Closely related to land is the subject of emigration or removal, including the selection of the new area, the disposal of land and other Indian property at the old home, transportation, and subsistence during the move and for a period afterwards. A distinct body of records of the Bureau is identified as Indian removal records. Except, however, for the records of the Office of the Commissary General of Subsistence, which from 1830 to 1836 directed the transportation and subsistence of emigrating Indians, they relate primarily to the emigration of the Cherokee, Chickasaw, Choctaw, and Creek Indians to Indian Territory. There are many other records concerning the removal of these and other Indians in the general correspondence of the Bureau, including the successive moves of the Sauk and Fox of the Mississippi to central Iowa, Kansas, and Indian Territory; the removal of most of the Indians from Texas in 1859; the enforced removal of Sioux and Winnebago Indians from Minnesota after the Sioux outbreak in 1862; the removal of the Navajo Indians to Bosque Redondo, New Mexico Territory, after the Navajo war and their return to their old home in 1868; the movement of the Mexican Kickapoo from Mexico to Indian Territory, 1873–75; and the removal of most of the Ute Indians in Colorado to Utah.

"Civilization" essentially meant getting the Indians to adopt white ways of life. The term was used by the Bureau to include the "moral, intellectual, and social improvement of the Indians." In time, the term "civilization" was replaced by "education," but this also was used in a broad sense.

The Civilization Fund established in 1819 was used mainly to support missionary schools. Many treaties provided for the establishment or financing of schools operated by missionary organizations, Indians, or the Government. In 1879 the first of several Government-operated nonreservation schools was opened at Carlisle, Pa. Interest in the education of Indians increased after the passage of the General Allotment Act, when it became the policy to disband the tribes and to seek the "assimilation" of Indians into the general population. This policy included more emphasis on sending Indian children to regular public schools. Many of the periodic reports from schools until 1910 were not preserved, but statistics from them were summarized in volumes among the records of the Education Division.

From an economic standpoint, adopting white ways usually meant farming, and the Bureau sought to train Indians in agricultural and industrial arts. Treaties provided for farmers, blacksmiths, and other skilled workers to train and guide the Indians, and funds were furnished for blacksmith shops, mills, seeds, tools, and other goods and equipment. Much of the correspondence is about such matters, including complaints that the Government failed to fulfill its obligations. Other prominent subjects include progress in agriculture, the success or failure of crops, the condition of livestock, fishing, and timber operations. The employment of Indians both on and off reservations gradually became a common topic. The relief of destitute Indians was a frequent subject of controversy.

Other common subjects of correspondence were the distribution of annuity funds and the purchase, transportation, and distribution of goods and equipment for Indians and the Bureau, including the letting of contracts. Complaints of late arrivals and failures to arrive of funds, goods, and equipment were common. Among other financial matters were budget estimates and the allocation of appropriated funds, accounts of officials, the settlement of claims, and Indian funds.

"Claims" as used by the Bureau usually meant claims for monetary benefits made both by and against Indians. Claims of Indians were for per capita payments under terms of treaties, depredations suffered, losses of land and property through enforced seizures and sales by the Army, and proceeds of land sales. Against the Indians were claims for depredations, for goods furnished, and for legal services. There were also claims for goods and services furnished to the Bureau. Records concerning claims are more likely than most to have been brought together into segregated files.

Proceeds from the sale of land and other tribal funds were often held in trust by the Secretary of War and later the Secretary of the Interior and commonly were invested in Federal and State bonds and other securities. There are records concerning the purchase and sale of securities, the collection of interest and dividends, and the status of trust funds.

The activities of traders and the issuance of licenses to them remained a matter of concern throughout the 19th century and later.

There was also more interest in health, medical care, and sanitation after the Indians were on reservations. Information about customs, religion, missionary activities, social relations, and moral standards is present, although the amount of it depends more on the interests of particular correspondents than is the case for most other subject areas.

Relations between whites and Indians and among various groups of Indians were always a matter of concern. For military operations, the records of the War Department, particularly those of the Adjutant General's Office and Army field commands, are a better source than the Bureau records, although the Adjutant General often sent copies of Army reports to the Bureau. The Bureau correspondence, however, frequently provides information about broader aspects of such matters as bringing [and keeping] Indians on reservations, apprehending Indians who left reservations, raids by and against Indians, depredations, the effects of warfare on Indians who were on reservations, and attacks on agencies. Even when the Indians were not associated with any particular agency, the superintendencies were closely concerned, particularly those in organized Territories.

Army garrisons were often established close to Indian agencies. The respective areas of authority of the agents and the Army commanders often were in dispute, and their viewpoints sometimes conflicted. On a wider scale there were continual controversies over the respective merits of civilian and military control of Indians, particularly during the 1870's, when there was a strong movement to transfer the Bureau back to the War Department.

Well documented are the effects of the Civil War, particularly in Indian Territory, which was taken over by the Confederacy. Indians remaining loyal to the United States were forced to flee to Kansas. The Confederates also seized control and forced the abandonment of some agencies in New Mexico Territory (including present-day Arizona). Following the war, Indian fighting continued in many areas, as attempts were made to force the Indians onto reservations. This warfare included extended conflicts with such Indians as the Sioux of the Upper Plains and the Apache of the Southwest and briefer actions, such as the pursuit of Chief Joseph's band of Nez Percé and the Modoc war of 1872–73.

As the Indians were restricted to reservations, there was a change in emphasis from pacification to law and order. Individual crimes committed by and against Indians were perennial subjects, as were liquor control, guns for Indians, courts and the administration of justice, and Indian police.

There are records concerning Bureau policies and regulations, the organization of the Bureau and its field service, the establishment and discontinuance of superintendencies and agencies, agency sites, buildings, supplies, and equipment.

There are also records concerning the appointment of superintendents, agents, and other officials, particularly the replacement of most civilian agents by Army officers during 1869 and 1870 and the nomination of agents by religious denominations during the 1870's. Beginning in 1893 school superintendents could be assigned duties as agents, and from this evolved the practice of appointing superintendents under civil service regulations to all agencies. The conduct of the officials was also a subject of correspondence, including charges against them made by Indians and others and the investigation of such charges. For applications and recommendations after 1849, the records of the Appointments Division of the Office of the Secretary of the Interior are the basic source (see pages 205 and 206). There are also records concerning employees of agencies and other administrative units, including Indian employees and Indian police.

There is information concerning the relations between superintendents and agents and between field and central office officials. There were controversies, for example, between agents who gave food to hungry Indians and higher officials who maintained this was an unwise policy that would make the Indians unduly dependent upon the Government. The wisdom of permitting Indian delegations to visit the superintendency headquarters or Washington, D.C., was an area of frequent dispute, and communication and transportation problems with remote agencies also provoked comment.

The first Bureau officials in contact with a group of Indians sometimes were among the earliest white persons to visit an area, and sometimes they made detailed reports about the Indians and the country. Some agents, such as the one for the Upper Missouri Agency, did much traveling. Agencies were among the earliest establishments in several now important cities, such as Chicago, Kansas City, and Tucson; occasionally, they were the reason for the origin of a city.

The Bureau of Indian Affairs followed the War Department recordkeeping practice of copying outgoing letters in letter books and of registering and filing incoming letters for each year in alphabetical groups by the initial letter of the surname or other identification of the writer. In 1836 the Bureau modified the controls for incoming letters by assigning them file numbers and jurisdictional headings. About 1910 the Bureau assigned headings to letters for the years 1824 to 1836. For the years 1824 to 1880 the primary arrangement of the incoming letters is by these headings, which makes it comparatively easy to locate letters concerning a particular superintendency, agency, tribe, or geographical location.

The registry system provided a means of controlling each letter that was received. For each letter, a clerk registered the name of the writer, the date it was written, beginning in April 1834 the date it was received, the place it was written, a summary of its contents, the jurisdictional or other heading to which it was assigned, and beginning in July 1836 the file number. Beginning in December 1846, when divisions were formally established in the Bureau, the division to which the letter was referred for action was noted, in later years often by an initial or abbreviation; for example, "F" or "Fin" for Finance. After 1834 there also may be references to related records and an indication of the final action concerning the letter, often the date the letter was answered. There are also cross-references to enclosures, to letters registered under a name different from what might be expected, and to some subjects. The same information entered in the register normally was written on the back of the letter as the endorsement.

Through 1880 each register is divided into alphabetical sections. During 1879 and 1880 two volumes were used simultaneously, one for the first half of the alphabet (A-M) and the other for the second half (N-Z). Letters were entered in order of receipt in the appropriate alphabetical section. For the earlier years, the chronological order is only approximate; apparently, some of the registers were prepared later. The letters "I" and "J" were combined for registering and filing.

Most letters were registered according to the initial letter of the surname of the writer. Correspondence from certain officials, however, was registered under letters indicating their office, such as "W" or "S" for Secretary of War, "I" for Secretary of the Interior, "P" for President, "L" for Commissioner of the General Land Office, "A" for Adjutant General, and "A" or "S" for Second Auditor. (In earlier years, correspondence from such officials often was registered under their surnames.) Correspondence from superintendents and agents was usually registered by the name of the individual rather than the jurisdiction. The major exceptions were the letters from Territorial Governors serving ex officio as superintendents; these were usually registered according to the name of the Territory. Letters from the Governor of Colorado, for example, were registered under "C." For a very brief period, April-December 1877, correspondence from agents and superintendents was registered according to the name of the superintendency or agency. A letter from an agent transmitted by a superintendent may be registered and filed under the agent's name or the superintendent's as an enclosure. Communications from Indian groups usually were registered under the initial letter of the name of the tribe, and letters from representatives of business firms were registered under the name of the company.

When the Bureau began to use file numbers in July 1836, the first letter registered in the A section of the register was designated "A1," the second, "A2," and so on, with no regard for the jurisdictions involved. Letter A1 was filed under "Sac and Fox" and A2 under "Miscellaneous." There was no set interval for starting new series of numbers, and series sometimes were used for several years. In 1859, 1872, and 1873 the numbers were started over in the middle of the year, resulting in two sets of numbers for those years and, in 1873, duplicate numbers. Because letters were registered when they were received, many letters written at the end of one year were registered and filed with the correspondence for the following year.

When a letter was withdrawn from the main series of correspondence and filed with some other series, a practice that increased over the years, a notation was not always made in the register nor was a cross-reference always placed with the correspondence. A few letters were not registered; they are now in the files where they might have been had they been registered.

Many of the letters registered are not among the records of the Bureau of Indian Affairs. Many of them were referred to the Secretary of War, the Secretary of the Interior, the Second Auditor, or some other official outside the Bureau. After April 1834, indications of these referrals were made in the registers. Letters that went back and forth several times between the Bureau and the Office of the Secretary of the Interior are most probably now among the records of the Bureau. They may be filed either in their original place or as an enclosure to a letter from the Secretary.

The 126 volumes of registers, 1824-80, have been reproduced as M18. There is a separate register for letters received, 1836-64, that were omitted from their proper place in the regular register and were registered out of date. There also is a separate register for incoming correspondence relating to the U.S. International Exhibition, or Centennial Exhibition, held at Philadelphia in 1876 to commemorate the 100th anniversary of the independence of the United States. This register has been reproduced as part of roll 53 of M234.

The main series of letters received by the Bureau, 1824-80 (528 linear feet), has been reproduced as M234. The pamphlet accompanying this microfilm includes tribal and jurisdictional indexes. In addition, NARS has prepared historical sketches for each of the jurisdictional and subject headings. These include information concerning dates of establishment and discontinuance of agencies and superintendencies, tribes and geographical areas of responsibility, locations of headquarters, related units, and names and dates of appointment of superintendents and agents. The pamphlet material and the sketches also have been published as Edward E. Hill, *The Office of Indian Affairs, 1824-1880: Historical Sketches* (New York: Clearwater Press, 1974).

The correspondence is arranged alphabetically by name of jurisdiction or other heading. Under each heading, the letters are arranged by year and thereunder alphabetically by initial letter of surname or other identification of writer. Within each alphabetical section, the communications are arranged by date of letter until July 1836 and thereafter by file number that was assigned as it was registered.

The letters filed under the name of a jurisdiction relate to its affairs or to the Indians assigned to it, and they include letters from many persons in addition to the agent or superintendent. A letter received from one agent may be filed under the name of another agency if it is primarily concerned with the affairs of the second agency.

Separate file headings were not established for every agency; in some cases, the letters received were filed under the name of the superintendency, a standard practice for the agencies in the Far West. Separate file headings were established for most of the agencies assigned to the older superintendencies, such as Michigan, St. Louis, Western, Wisconsin, and Iowa. This practice was continued with the Northern, Central, and Southern Superintendencies established by the reorganization of 1851 and with the Dakota Superintendency established in 1861. Theoretically, in these cases letters relating specifically to an agency were filed under the name of that agency, and the superintendency heading was reserved for letters of more general concern. The distinction was not always made in practice, however, and letters concerning an agency may be found in either file.

Even after the discontinuance of the superintendency system during the 1870's, the Bureau continued to use the names of States and Territories as file headings for correspondence relating to the agencies there. In 1876, correspondence concerning some of the agencies in Dakota Territory that previously had their own file headings began to be filed under "Dakota," and a "Nebraska" heading was established, although there had never been a Nebraska Superintendency.

Records were filed under the names of agencies after the agencies had been discontinued and, sometimes, even before they were established. Records relating to Indians who had been moved to the jurisdiction of a new agency often continued to be filed under the name of the former agency, particularly when it was the same as the name of the tribe. Letters received before 1836, when the practice of assigning file headings was started, were assigned file headings about 1910. To some extent, the 1836 headings were used without regard to the field organization of the Bureau at the time the letters were written. Thus records relating to Indians who were later assigned to an agency were filed under that agency's name even though they had been written before it was established and, sometimes, even though another agency then had responsibility for those Indians. The Fort Leavenworth Agency, for example, was established in 1837; but correspondence relating to several predecessor agencies as early as 1824 is filed under its name. In a very few cases the file heading was a tribal designation rather than the name of an agency.

Even after 1836 there continued to be discrepancies between file headings and actual agencies. During 1842, for example, correspondence relating to the subagency for the Winnebago Indians was filed under three different agency headings and a superintendency heading; the heading "St. Peters" continued to be used for some years after the agency had been moved to another location; and the file heading "Red Cloud" continued to be used after the name of the agency was changed to Pine Ridge. To determine the appropriate file headings for information concerning particular Indians and jurisdictions, consult the indexes and historical sketches prepared for use with M234.

Records pertaining to the emigration and land reserves of the Indians of some agencies and superintendencies may be filed separately from the other correspondence relating to the jurisdiction and are designated "Emigration" and "Reserves." These segregated records immediately follow the general records relating to the jurisdiction. Records relating to Winnebago emigration and Winnebago reserves, for example, follow the records relating to the Winnebago Agency. There are, however, many records relating to Indian emigration and land reserves among the general records for the various jurisdictions, including those for which there are segregated records, and also among the Indian removal records and the records of the Land Division of the Bureau.

In addition to the headings for jurisdictions, there are five subject headings: "Annuity Goods," "Centennial," "Schools," "Stocks," and "Miscellaneous." They were intended for correspondence that could not be related to a specific jurisdiction. For some of these subjects, there is much additional information in the correspondence for specific jurisdictions. The correspondence concerning annuity goods relates principally to their purchase and transportation. "Centennial" relates to Indian exhibits at the Centennial Exhibition held at Philadelphia in 1876. The correspondence concerning schools relates to the establishment and operation of missionary, tribal, and Government day and boarding schools for Indians. "Stocks" relates to securities held in trust for Indians. In the Miscellaneous category are letters relating to general policies and to the Indian Service as a whole, the administration of the central office, medals for Indian chiefs, persons captured by Indians, Indians in places where the Bureau had no field representatives or over whom the Federal Government had no jurisdiction, and many matters affecting several jurisdictions.

Whether to consult the registers first or to go directly to the correspondence depends on the subject of the research. If it is a tribe, field jurisdiction, geographical area, or any topic of such a nature that the relevant correspondence is likely to be under one heading or a few headings, it is advisable to consult the correspondence first and to use the registers later to identify items that may have been filed elsewhere. For a subject that cuts across tribal or geographical lines—a study of Indians and the fur trade, for example—it may be better to use the registers first to identify letters of possible interest. If the search is for a particular document, it usually is better to use the register first, even if the likely heading is known. The complete citation for a letter consists of the name of the jurisdiction to which it was assigned, the alphabetical section of the register in which it was entered, the file number, and the year received (for example, Delaware B346-1858). For a letter received before July 1836, when file numbers were not used, the name of the writer and the date of the letter, as well as the name of the jurisdiction, are necessary to identify it.

A list of file headings and years of coverage follows.

Alaska Agency	1873-74	Flandreau Agency	1873-76
Annuity Goods	1856-78	Florida Superintendency	1824-50
Apalachicola Subagency	1826-35	Florida Emigration	1828-53
Apalachicola Reserves	1841-42	Florida Reserves	1839-47
Arizona Superintendency	1863-80	Fort Berthold Agency	1867-80
Arkansas Superintendency	1824-34	Fort Leavenworth Agency	1824-51
Blackfeet Agency	1855-69	Fort Wayne Agency	1824-30
Caddo Agency	1824-42	Grand River Agency	1871-75
California Superintendency	1849-80	Great Nemaha Agency	1837-76
Centennial Exhibition	1875-78	Great Nemaha Emigration	1837-38
Central Superintendency	1851-80	Green Bay Agency	1824-80
Cherokee Agency, East	1824-36	Idaho Superintendency	1863-80
Cherokee Agency, West	1824-36	Indiana Agency	1824-50
Cherokee Agency	1836-80	Indiana Emigration	1833-49
Cherokee Emigration	1828-54	Indiana Reserves	1836-50
Cherokee Reserves	1828-50	Ioway Subagency	1825-37
Cheyenne and Arapahoe Agency	1875-80	Iowa Superintendency	1838-49
Cheyenne River Agency	1871-80	Kansas Agency	1851-76
Chicago Agency	1824-39	Kickapoo Agency	1855-76
Chicago Emigration	1835-47	Kiowa Agency	1864-80
Chickasaw Agency	1824-61	La Pointe Agency	1831-50
	1867-70		1855-80
Chickasaw Emigration	1837-50	Lower Brulé Agency	1875-76
Chickasaw Reserves	1836-50	Mackinac Agency	1828-80
Chippewa Agency	1851-80	Mackinac Emigration	1838-39
Chippewa Emigration	1850-59	Miami Subagency	1824-41
Chippewa Reserves	1853-55		1846-50
Choctaw Agency	1824-76	Miami Emigration	1842-53
Choctaw Agency, West	1825-38	Miami Reserves	1838-50
Choctaw Emigration	1826-59	Michigan Superintendency	1824-51
Choctaw Reserves	1833-60	Michigan Emigration	1830-48
Colorado Superintendency	1861-80	Michigan Reserves	1837-48
Council Bluffs Agency	1836-57	Minnesota Superintendency	1849-56
Creek Agency	1824-76	Miscellaneous	1824-48
Creek Agency, West	1826-36	Miscellaneous Emigration	1824-48
Creek Emigration	1826-49	Montana Superintendency	1864-80
Creek Reserves	1832-50	Nebraska Agencies	1876-80
Crow Creek Agency	1871-76	Neosho Agency	1831-75
Crow Wing Subagency	1835-40	Nevada Superintendency	1861-80
Dakota Superintendency	1861-80	New Mexico Superintendency	1849-80
Delaware Agency	1855-73	New York Agency	1835-80
Devil's Lake Agency	1871-80	New York Emigration	1829-51

Northern Superintendency	1851–76	Seminole Agency	1824–76
Ohio Agency	1831–43	Seminole Emigration	1827–59
Ohio Emigration	1831–39	Seneca Agency in New York	1824–32
Ohio Reserves	1834–43	Shawnee Agency	1855–76
Omaha Agency	1856–76	Sisseton Agency	1867–80
Oregon Superintendency	1842–80	Six Nations Agency	1824–34
Osage Agency	1824–53	Southern Superintendency	1851–71
	1874–80	Spotted Tail Agency	1875–80
Osage River Agency	1824–71	Standing Rock Agency	1875–80
Otoe Agency	1856–76	Stocks	1836–73
Ottawa Agency	1863–73	Texas Agency	1847–59
Pawnee Agency	1859–80	Turkey River Subagency	1842–46
Pima Agency	1859–61	Union Agency	1875–80
Piqua Agency	1824–30	Upper Arkansas Agency	1855–74
Ponca Agency	1859–80	Upper Missouri Agency	1824–74
Potawatomi Agency	1851–80	Upper Missouri Reserves	1837–49
Prairie du Chien Agency	1824–42	Upper Platte Agency	1846–70
Prairie du Chien Emigration	1837–41	Utah Superintendency	1849–80
Quapaw Agency	1871–80	Washington Superintendency	1853–57
Racoon River Agency	1843–45		1861–80
Red Cloud Agency	1871–80		
Red River Agency	1824–30	Western Superintendency	1832–51
Sac and Fox Agency	1824–80	Western Superintendency Emi-	
Sac and Fox Emigration	1845–47	gration	1836–42
Sac and Fox Reserves	1837–50	Whetstone Agency	1871–74
Saginaw Subagency	1824–50	Wichita Agency	1857–78
St. Louis Superintendency	1824–51	Winnebago Agency	1826–76
St. Louis Emigration	1837–51	Winnebago Emigration	1833–52
St. Peters Agency	1824–70	Winnebago Reserves	1836–47
St. Peters Reserves	1839–49	Wisconsin Superintendency	1836–48
Sandy Lake Subagency	1850–51	Wyandot Subagency	1843–51
Santa Fe Agency	1849–51		1870–72
Santee Sioux Agency	1871–76	Wyandot Emigration	1839–51
Sault Ste. Marie Agency	1824–52	Wyandot Reserves	1845–63
Schools	1824–73	Wyoming Superintendency	1869–80
School Reserves	1837–39	Yankton Agency	1859–76

At the beginning of 1881, the Bureau adopted a new system for registering and filing incoming correspondence that was used until 1907. Letters were registered in chronological order as they were received and file numbers, started over each year, were assigned in order of registry without regard to source or content. For each letter the registers give the name and address of the writer, the date of receipt, the date written, an indication of subject matter, and the file number. There is also a notation of the division of the Bureau to which the letter was referred, references to related records, and sometimes an indication of the action taken. There are 144 volumes of these registers. Separate registers were maintained for letters from the Secretary of the Interior, 1905–7; the main series of registers gives only the file numbers assigned to them. There is also a separate register for letters answered by endorsement and referred to offices outside the Bureau, 1883–84.

In 1881, 22,704 letters were registered. In 1906, the last full year in which this filing system was used, 113,838 letters were registered. For the entire period, there are 1,559 linear feet of records. It was necessary for the Bureau to compile elaborate indexes to identify letters relating to particular jurisdictions, tribes, persons, and subjects. These indexes are in 37 volumes (10 linear ft.) and are divided into five chronological periods: 1881-86, 1887-92, 1892-99, 1900-1906, and 1907. Within each period the entries are arranged in rough alphabetical order. Entries for agencies, schools, and some of the other topics are subdivided into subjects and kinds of records in alphabetical order; sometimes there are even further breakdowns. Typical agency and school subheadings include agents' accounts, annual reports, annuity and tribal matters, bills of lading, boards of survey, buildings, census, certificates of deposit, claims, complaints, contracts, councils, delegations, employees, epidemics, estimates, farms and stock, freighting and freighters, goods and supplies, grazing, hunting parties, Indian troubles, Indians off reservation, instructions, intruders, irrigation and water supply, issues, leaves of absence, leases, liquor traffic, lumbering operations, mail and telegraphic services, military, mines and mining, monthly reports, murders, police and scouts, protests and petitions, pupils, receipts, removals, reservation and land matters, sanitary reports, school reports, schools, missions and missionaries, seizures, suits and arrests, special reports, traders, transfer of Indians, urgent needs, and weighers' returns.

Only the years and filing numbers are given in the indexes. For some entries, there may be hundreds of file numbers listed. It is therefore advisable to consult the registers for more detailed information rather than going directly to the letters. The increasing exchange of letters between the Bureau and other offices, particularly the Indian Division and the Indian Territory Division of the Office of the Secretary of the Interior, further complicates research in this time period. Some letters went back and forth several times. Some were finally restored to their original places in the files; others were filed as enclosures to later letters.

The Bureau tried to overcome the dispersion of related records by using special cases and other methods of consolidation. Because the transfer of documents from the main series of letters received to another series often is indicated only by cross-references in the correspondence and not by annotations in the registers, such a removal may add a step to the search for a particular document. The researcher's time is saved, however, if he finds a consolidated file about his subject. Certain types of incoming correspondence, particularly authorities from the Secretary of the Interior and claims and contracts, were registered and maintained separately from the main series of letters received. Also, some records, particularly certain monthly and quarterly reports submitted by agents, were not always preserved. Abstracts of these reports sometimes were maintained by the divisions.

The Bureau continued the War Department practice of copying outgoing letters by hand into letter books. These copies were called fair copies or record copies and the volumes, record books.

Until 1838 all letters were copied in one set of volumes in chronological order. In November of that year, the Bureau began to copy communications to the Secretary of War and certain other officials in separate volumes called report books. The other officials included the President of the United States, chairmen and other members of congressional committees, the Speaker of the House, and the President of the Senate. During the earlier years, the letters to the President and members of congressional committees often were signed by the Secretary of War. In 1849 the Secretary of the Interior replaced the Secretary of War as the principal addressee. The use of the report books to record letters to officials other than the supervising Secretary was gradually discontinued; by 1870 they were being used exclusively for letters to the Secretary of the Interior. Until 1866 the volumes were indexed by name of addressee and to some extent by subject. There are 53 volumes of report books, 1838–85, reproduced as M348.

Most other outgoing letters continued to be copied chronologically in the record books until 1869. Beginning in that year two or more volumes were used simultaneously. Letters relating to certain broad subjects, reflecting the organization of the Bureau, were copied into different books. These subjects were land, civilization, finance, accounts, and miscellaneous. There are 188 volumes of letters sent, 1824–84, and 4 volumes relating only to depredation claims, July 1885–May 1886. The 166 volumes that include letters sent through the end of 1880 have been reproduced as M21.

Most of the volumes are indexed by name of addressee, with some entries for subjects. In most volumes, the index gives only the page number of the first letter to an addressee. A marginal notation beside that letter gives the page number of the next letter. For subsequent letters, except the last one, the marginal notation indicates both the preceding letter and the succeeding letter to that addressee. Beginning in 1868 the surname or initials of the clerk who drafted each letter are given. After 1876 there are references to related incoming correspondence and, in some volumes, the division of the Bureau that handled the letter.

In 1870 the Bureau began to make press copies of outgoing letters. These predecessors of carbon copies were made in a book of tissues by transfer of ink through direct contact with the original, using moisture and pressure in a copy press. At first they were regarded as temporary, to be used until the letters could be copied by hand. During the 1880's, the Bureau began keeping the press copies as the record copies and stopped copying them by hand.

The press copybooks were maintained by the several divisions of the Bureau. Listed below are the number of volumes for each division and the years covered. As many as three letter books may be bound into a single volume.

Division	Vols.	Years
Land	528	1870–1908
Civilization	52	1870–85
(Volumes 31–52 are erroneously labeled "Depredations.")		
Depredation	40	1885–1900
(Included are three volumes of segregated reports to the Secretary of the Interior, 1890–91.)		
Finance	777	1870–1908
(Included are some segregated volumes relating to purchases, remittances, and school expenditures.)		
Accounts	286	1876–1908
Medical and Educational	6	1876–81
Education	352	1885–1908
Miscellaneous	27	1885–1908

There are also 65 volumes of copies of letters sent by the Secretary of the Interior relating chiefly to Indian Territory, 1898–1907.

There are inadequate indexes to the names of the addressees and subjects in the individual volumes of press copies. More useful are the separate indexes and abstracts. In many cases, citations to letters sent can be found in the registers of letters received and in the endorsements of incoming letters. There are 19 volumes of indexes divided into three chronological periods: 1881–90, 1891–99, and 1900–1907. For the final period, letters to the Secretary of the Interior are indexed together in one volume. Entries concerning agencies, schools, and a few other topics are subdivided by subjects in alphabetical order, similar to those used in the indexes to letters received. The index entries give only the year and abstract number of the letter.

There are registers or abstracts of most of the letters sent. For the first five record books, 1824–29, there are registers that give the name of the addressee, a summary of the contents, and volume and page citations (but the volumes are identified by the first five letters of the alphabet rather than by numbers). The entries in each volume are arranged in alphabetical sections by surname or position of addressee. No registers are known to exist for the period July 1829–38. For 1839–1906 abstracts give the name of the addressee, the date, and the subject. From 1847 to 1884 the volume and page number for the handwritten copy in the record or report books are given. Beginning in 1876 the division of the Bureau that handled the letter was indicated. In the earlier abstract volumes, the entries are arranged for the most part by superintendency and thereunder by tribe. This gradually was modified to include agency breakdowns and then to conform with the file headings used for the incoming correspondence. Beginning in 1875 the arrangement within volumes was by these file headings and in the same order as the letters received. When the file headings were discontinued in 1881, the

Bureau began to enter letters in the abstracts in chronological order and number them in order of entry for each year.

Researchers often do not use the abstracts but instead find references to letters sent in the endorsements or in the bodies of incoming letters. When seeking letters to particular persons for the period of handwritten copies, it is usually easier to use the indexes and marginal notations in the individual copybooks than the abstracts. For the years 1881–1906, however, the abstracts should be used in conjunction with the index volumes. First use the indexes to find the abstract numbers of letters of possible interest and then use the abstract to identify specific letters. The locations of letters in the press copybooks can be determined from the dates and the divisions that handled them. For January through August 1907 there are no abstracts, but a register gives the number of the letter book containing each letter. The letters are identified only by number.

Press copies may be considered more accurate copies, but the handwritten ones are more legible and easier to handle. The press copies are flimsy and sometimes faded or blurred, and it is more difficult to find specific letters among them without recourse to the separate indexes and abstracts.

There is a separate volume of letters sent concerning the Centennial Exhibition held at Philadelphia in 1876.

Another series of copybooks complementing the record and report books are nine volumes, 1836–87, identified by the Bureau as miscellaneous records. In them were copied commissions, treaties, congressional bills, regulations, reports, memorandums, circular letters, and public notices; lists of employees, schools, contracts, land locations, patentees, claimants, and population figures; estimates; statements of funds remitted to agents, superintendents, and other persons; other types of financial information; and other types of information kept as memorandums by the Bureau. Most of the information is for the years 1836–51. The eighth volume, 1853–61, contains mostly copies of commissions and statements of funds remitted; the ninth volume was used almost entirely for commissions. For the years before 1866, when the Employees Section began to maintain copies of commissions, the miscellaneous records are often the easiest place to find dates of appointment; even for later years they are useful for special commissions. An item of particular interest is a copy of Revised Regulations, No. 2, April 13, 1837, which provided for the organization of the field service of the Bureau. Each volume contains an index to names of persons and subjects.

Described below are other general records of the Bureau, most of which consist of records withdrawn or kept separately from the general incoming correspondence of the Bureau and in some cases of the Office of the Secretary of War relating to Indian affairs.

The special files, 1807–1904 (38 ft.), consist of correspondence, reports, accounts, affidavits, and other records brought together for easier reference. They relate principally to investigations and claims, including those of traders for goods furnished to the Indians or the Government, of transportation contractors for shipping goods, of attorneys for legal fees, of other persons for services to the Indians or the Government, of Indians and non-Indians for losses from depredations, of Indians for losses resulting from their removal from the East, and of persons for shares in tribal benefits. Many of the claims were submitted under provisions of treaties between Indian tribes and the United States. The investigations, other than those of claims, were conducted principally into the conduct of Bureau employees. A total of 303 special files were established, but the records in some of them are missing. The records within the files are arranged most often either by assigned claim number or in the usual order for incoming correspondence. The special files have been reproduced as M574; the accompanying pamphlet includes an indexed list of the files.

The following special files are representative.

6. John B. Luce, Neosho subagent, claim for expenses incurred in his trial for murder in 1842. 1842–46.

9. James Stryker, subagent, case of, for embezzlement of money belonging to the New York Indians. 1832–51.

10. Lorenzo N. Clarke, claim for subsistence furnished Seminole and Chickasaw emigrants. 1837–50.

19. W. G. & G. W. Ewing, claim under the treaty of 1840 for goods sold to the Miami Indians. 1842.

49. LeRoy Jackson, claim for depredations committed by Winnebago Indians in 1836. 1839–51.

56. James Pool, claim for services as blacksmith for the Delaware, Seneca, and Shawnee Indians in 1823–26 and 1833–38. 1841–58.

70. Charges against the American Fur Company. 1843–44.

79. Money due Winnebago Indians under various treaties. 1850–51.

87. Claims of loyal Seminole for losses suffered during the Civil War. 1867–68.

102. Claims to participate in per capita payments to the Eastern Cherokee. 1849–57.

106. Claims of Delaware Indians for depredations committed by whites. 1862–63.

111. Creek depredation claims against the Osage Indians. 1839.

216. Accounts of Choctaw delegates to Washington in 1866. 1866–69.

218. Cornelius Ferris, claim for transporting supplies to the Red Cloud and Spotted Tail Agencies. 1876–77.

248. Charges against Henry F. Livingston, agent at Crow Creek, and Henry E. Gregory, agent at Lower Brulé. 1870–79.

254. Sale of the agency buildings at Fort Peck and Fort Belknap. 1876–80.

259. Elisha J. Brown, claim to buildings near the Seminole Agency. 1870–73.

261. Nez Percé Indian soldiers, claims for service during the Oregon and Washington war of 1855–56.   1879–83.

283. E. John Ellis, claim for legal services to the Citizen Band of Potawatomi.   1884–89.

The special cases, 1821–1907 (275 ft.), relate predominantly to land disputes. They involve such matters as railroad rights-of-way, wagon roads, the establishment of and changes in reservations, boundaries, trespasses, water and grazing rights, fishing rights, timber contracts, allotments, leases, inheritances, sales, buildings, church and missionary lands, and irrigation. The cases are numbered 1 to 203, but some were canceled; a few are numbered with ½. Individual documents within a case file are usually arranged in the same manner as the main series of letters received at the time. There is a list and an index of the cases.

Many of the cases are identified only by the name of the tribe or the reservation; the following is a list of representative cases with more specific titles.

2. Fort Hall Reserve, intruders and cattle trespassers.

4. Indian Territory, deceased U.S. citizens, estates of.

15. Mescalero Apache Agency buildings.

16. Arizona Central R.R., right-of-way for, through Pima and Maricopa Reservation, and Phoenix and Maricopa R.R. through same.

18. Pyramid Lake, fisherman trespassers.

19. Nez Percé Reservation, mail stations and railroads.

23. Chickasaw Nation, cattle laws of.

51. Boudinot Hotel Case.

61. Devil's Lake Reservation, boundary question.

63. Sioux Reservation, wagon road route no. 3.

75. Seminole and Creek land boundary line.

77. Cherokee, Eastern Band of North Carolina, removal to Indian Territory.

94. San Xavier Mining Co., works on Papago Reservation.

112. Ute Commission.

126. Ottawa University.

142. Concho cattle case (Union Agency).

143. Churches and missions on Indian reservations.

147. Allotments in severalty.

148. Dead and down timber on Indian reservations.

190. Irrigation.

200. Harrison, townsite of on Coeur d'Alène Reservation.

The ratified treaty file, 1801–68 (5 ft.), consists of journals of treaty commissioners, council proceedings, reports, and other records relating to the negotiation of treaties ratified by the Senate. Copies of the treaties sometimes are included, but the originals are in General Records of the U.S. Government, Record Group 11. The records in the file have been reproduced on T494. John H. Martin, comp., *List of Documents Concerning the Negotiation of Ratified Treaties,* Special List 6 (1949), cites documents in various series of records of the Bureau and of the Indian Division of the Office of the Secretary of the Interior.

The unratified treaty file, 1821–69 (2 ft.), includes originals and copies of treaties, journals, council proceedings, reports, correspondence, and other records relating to treaties that were never ratified by the Senate. Some of these treaties were made between Indian tribes without the United States as a signatory. These records also have been reproduced as part of T494.

There are some printed copies of treaties and Executive agreements, 1824–89, and six volumes of journals of commissions to negotiate with the Indians and to implement provisions of treaties, especially those concerning adjudication of claims and making payments to Indians. The journal for one such commission—sent to negotiate with the Indians west of the Mississippi River, 1824–25—also includes a few records of land surveys relating to claims in Arkansas. There are records of commissions sent to implement treaty provisions with the Potawatomi, Menominee, Winnebago, and Miami Indians, 1837–38.

An Executive order file, 1850–92 (2 ft.), consists of correspondence, maps, and other records of Executive orders relating to Indian reservations. In many cases the original Executive order is included. These orders usually either set aside public land for reservations or restored to the public domain lands previously reserved for Indians. The records include the recommendations of superintendents, agents, the Commissioner of Indian Affairs, and the Secretary of the Interior and also reports of surveys and other records relating to the land concerned. Most of these records have been published in *Executive Orders Relating to Indian Reservations, 1855 to 1912* (Washington, 1912).

Authorities, 1880–1907 (89 ft.), are letters from the Secretary of the Interior or his representative that authorized actions, almost all of which involved monetary expenditures. Authorizations were given for making purchases, hiring employees, settling debts, advertising, paying claims, and other actions. Arranged and numbered in order of receipt, the authorities were registered and indexed separately from other incoming correspondence. The request for the authority sent to the Bureau by the agent or other person was referred to the Secretary, often was returned to the Bureau with the authority, and usually was restored to its original place in the main series of letters received. The Commissioner's letter transmitting the request for the authority was returned less frequently, except after April 1907, when the Department began stamping the approval on the Commissioner's letter and returning it rather than writing a separate letter of authority.

There are 6 volumes of indexes and 60 volumes of registers of claims against the Bureau and contracts made by the Bureau with other persons, 1877-1907. Other finding aids and the contracts are among the records of the Finance Division, but the claims for this period were destroyed by authority of the Congress while the records were still at the Bureau. The claims and contracts relate mainly to furnishing supplies, advertising, transportation, salaries, and damages.

Smaller separate items among the general records of the Bureau include a volume of letters sent by the Files Division, 1900-1908, consisting mostly of reports to the Commissioner of Indian Affairs about the Division; a volume of instructions for indexing correspondence, ca. 1900; a data book containing chiefly information about schools supported from the Civilization Fund, ca. 1824-32; a volume containing a record of the distribution of Henry R. Schoolcraft's *Historical and Statistical Information Respecting the History, Condition, and Prospects of the Indian Tribes of the United States . . .,* ca. 1851-60; and a scrapbook containing mainly newspaper clippings, many of them about legal matters, 1885-88.

GENERAL RECORDS, 1907-39

On August 20, 1907, the Bureau stopped maintaining separate series of incoming and outgoing correspondence. Thereafter correspondence was filed according to a decimal-subject classification system. File or registration numbers were still assigned to incoming communications in order of receipt. In addition, the letters were assigned a decimal classification and a jurisdictional or other heading. The jurisdictions were chiefly the field units of the Bureau: agencies, schools, hospitals, sanatoriums, and warehouses. There is also an "Indian Office" designation for records relating to the central office of the Bureau and a "General Service" heading for general administrative records not relating to any particular jurisdiction. There are a few headings for tribes and geographical areas and one for the subject of liquor traffic.

With the first letter received, or base letter, were filed copies of letters sent, later letters received, and any other records relating to the same specific subject; all this material was fastened together to form a dossier, often called by the Bureau a flat file as distinguished from earlier letters received that were folded. In these files were placed reports, memorandums, minutes, petitions, leases, contracts, authorities, affidavits, applications, certificates, licenses, permits, bonds, wills, other legal documents, tables, circulars, accounting records, clippings, photographs, diagrams, blueprints, and other kinds of records, some of which previously had been kept apart from the correspondence. The records are arranged by jurisdiction, thereunder by decimal classification, and thereunder by year and number of base letter.

Within a file the documents usually are arranged chronologically. The complete citation for a file consists of the file or registration number, the year of the base letter, the decimal classification, and the name of the jurisdiction or other heading—for example, 87454-1931-310 Rosebud. Originally the Bureau kept files open indefinitely, but for the files begun after 1932, the Bureau adopted the policy of closing them after 10 years and starting new ones if necessary. The files were culled periodically, and items approved by the Congress for disposal were removed and destroyed. By agreement between the Bureau of Indian Affairs and NARS, the files for certain entire subject classifications also have been destroyed after a specified period. Some examples are the classifications concerning advertising, post offices, fire extinguishers and protection, horses and mules, and institutes and teachers conventions.

Since these records are arranged by subject as well as by jurisdiction, there was less impetus to remove records from the central files to form special files than in earlier periods. Some records, however, filed according to the central filing system, were maintained in the operating divisions rather than in the Mail and Files Section; many classified files are among division records now in the National Archives.

These records, which include files started through 1939 (some individual documents are dated as late as 1949), comprise by far the largest series of records of the Bureau, 8,033 linear feet. A list of the jurisdictions and other headings used and a select list of decimal classifications follow.

LIST OF JURISDICTIONS

Alaska	1908-39	Central Navajo	1934-35
Albuquerque	1907-35	Chamberlain	1907-9
Albuquerque Sanatorium	1932-36	Charles H. Burke	1925-36
Armstrong	1917-20	Chemawa	1936-39
Bay Mills	1907-17	Cherokee Nation	1907-39
Bena	1907-14	Cherokee Orphan Training School	1916-34
Bishop	1908-29	Cherokee School	1907-39
Bismarck	1907-37	Cheyenne and Arapaho	1907-39
Blackfeet	1907-39	Cheyenne River	1907-39
Bloomfield	1917-30	Chicago Warehouse	1907-39
Cahuilla	1907-14	Chickasaw	1907-39
California Special	1907-19	Chilocco	1907-39
Camp Verde	1907-27	Choctaw	1907-39
Campo	1910-20	Choctaw-Chickasaw Sanatorium	1934-38
Canton Asylum	1907-34	Claremore Hospital	1930-38
Cantonment	1907-27	Coeur d'Alène	1907-37
Capitan Grande	1907-14	Collins	1916-19
Carlisle	1907-28	Colorado River	1907-39
Carson	1907-39	Colville	1907-39
Carter	1907-18	Consolidated Chippewa	1922-39
Carter Seminary	1930-37	Consolidated Ute	1922-39
Cass Lake	1907-22	Creek	1907-39

Crow	1907–39	Kiowa	1907–39
Crow Creek	1907–39	Klamath	1907–39
Cushman	1907–29	La Jolla	1908–11
Digger	1907–25	La Pointe	1907–29
Eastern Navajo	1927–35	Lac du Flambeau	1907–36
Euchee	1917–37	Laguna	1924–39
Eufaula	1917–37	Laona	1916–27
Fallon	1908–25	Leech Lake	1907–22
Five Tribes	1907–39	Lemhi	1907–12
Flandreau	1907–39	Leupp	1907–36
Flathead	1907–39	Liquor Traffic	1907–17
Fond du Lac	1907–22	Lovelocks	1910–12
Fort Apache	1907–39	Lower Brulé	1907–25
Fort Belknap	1907–39	Mackinac	1907–27
Fort Berthold	1907–39	Malki	1907–20
Fort Bidwell	1907–31	Martinez	1907–12
Fort Hall	1907–39	Mekusukey	1917–32
Fort Lapwai	1907–37	Menominee	1922–39
Fort Lapwai Sanatorium	1913–37	Mesa Grande	1907–12
Fort Lewis	1907–12	Mescalero	1907–39
Fort McDermitt	1908–22	Mission	1920–39
Fort Mojave	1907–31	Moapa River	1907–26
Fort Peck	1907–39	Moqui	1907–23
Fort Shaw	1907–19	Morris	1907–9
Fort Totten	1907–39	Mount Pleasant	1907–34
Fort Yuma	1907–35	Navajo	1907–39
General Service	1907–39	Navajo Springs	1910–15
Genoa	1907–35	Neah Bay	1907–33
Goshute	1907–24	Nett Lake	1908–20
Grand Junction	1907–12	Nevada	1907–22
Grand Portage	1911–21	New York	1907–39
Grand Rapids	1915–27	New York Warehouse	1907–16
Grand Ronde-Siletz	1907–39	Northern Idaho	1937–39
Great Lakes	1936–39	Northern Navajo	1926–35
Green Bay	1907–9	Northern Pueblo	1920–30
Greenville	1907–23	Nuyaka	1917–26
Hampton Institute	1907–15	Omaha	1907–25
Haskell	1907–39	Omaha Warehouse	1908–15
Havasupai	1907–33	Oneida	1907–21
Hayward	1907–33	Osage	1907–39
Hoopa Valley	1907–39	Otoe	1907–22
Hopi	1907–39	Paiute	1927–39
Hopi-Navajo Sanatorium	1933–34	Pala	1907–20
Indian Office	1907–39	Panguitch	1907–9
Indian Territory	1907–17	Pawnee	1907–39
Jicarilla	1908–39	Pechanga	1909–14
Jones	1917–37	Phoenix	1907–39
Kaibab	1908–27	Phoenix Sanatorium	1907–39
Kaw	1907–20	Pierre	1907–39
Kayenta Sanatorium	1929–35	Pima	1907–39
Keshena	1907–39	Pine Ridge	1907–39
Kickapoo	1907–21	Pipestone	1907–39

Ponca	1907-27	Shoshoni	1907-38
Potawatomi	1907-39	Siletz	1907-25
Potrero	1907-9	Sioux Sanatorium	1938-39
Potter Valley	1909-10	Sisseton	1907-39
Pueblo Bonito	1908-39	Soboba	1907-21
Pueblo Day School	1910-19	Southern Mission	1921-22
Puyallup	1907-17	Southern Navajo	1927-36
Pyramid Lake	1930-33	Southern Pueblo	1919-35
Quapaw	1918-39	Southern Ute	1907-22
Rapid City	1907-33	Spokane	1912-25
Red Cliff	1911-22	Springfield	1907-19
Red Lake	1907-39	Standing Rock	1907-39
Red Moon	1907-17	Tacoma Hospital	1931-39
Reno	1916-25	Taholah	1914-39
Rice Station	1907-18	Theodore Roosevelt School	1923-33
Rincon	1909-12	Tomah	1907-39
Rocky Boy	1917-39	Tongue River	1907-39
Roosevelt	1908-11	Truxton Canon	1907-39
Rosebud	1907-39	Tulalip	1907-39
Roseburg	1909-18	Tule River	1907-23
Round Valley	1907-24	Turtle Mountain	1907-39
Sac and Fox-Iowa	1907-39	Tuskahoma	1907-28
Sac and Fox-Oklahoma	1907-21	Uintah and Ouray	1907-39
Sac and Fox Sanatorium	1922-39	Ukiah	1907-15
Sacramento	1923-39	Umatilla	1907-39
St. Louis Warehouse	1907-35	Union Agency	1907-14
Salem	1907-37	United Pueblos	1934-39
Salt River	1909-24	Upper Lake	1909-11
San Carlos	1907-39	Ute Mountain	1907-22
San Francisco Warehouse	1917-18	Vermillion Lake	1907-21
San Jacinto	1907-9	Volcan	1909-13
San Juan	1907-39	Wahpeton	1907-39
San Xavier	1907-39	Walker River	1907-39
San Xavier Sanatorium	1932	Warm Springs	1907-39
Santa Fe	1907-35	Western Navajo	1907-35
Santee	1907-20	Western Shoshone	1907-39
Scattered Bands in Utah	1913-17	Wheelock	1917-37
Seger	1907-26	White Earth	1907-22
Sells	1918-39	Wind River	1937-39
Seminole	1907-39	Winnebago	1907-39
Seneca	1907-22	Wittenberg	1907-17
Sequoyah Orphan Training School	1924-39	Wyandotte Absentee	1908-20
Shawnee	1907-39	Yakima	1907-39
Shawnee Sanatorium	1934-39	Yankton	1907-34
Sherman Institute	1907-39	Zuni	1907-35
Shivwits	1907-21		

SELECT LIST OF DECIMAL CLASSIFICATIONS

000. GENERAL AND STATISTICAL

010. Legislation

   011. Acts of Congress

   013. Proposed Legislation

   015. Reports—Committees of Congress

020. Department Relations

030. Statistics

   031. Annual Reports

   032. Statistical Records—Weekly or Monthly Reports

   033. Historical Data—Records—Indian Names

   034. Census Matters—Family History

040. Publicity

   042. Relics and Ruins

   044. Monuments and Memorials—Gifts—Presents—Holidays

   047. Fairs and Expositions—Indians for Expositions

   049. Prizes—Bounties—Duties—Rewards

050. Tribal Relations

   051. Negotiations With Indians

   052. Treaties

   053. Enrollment—Citizenship—Degree of Indian Blood

   054. Councils—Acts of Tribal Councils

   055. Elections

   056. Delegations

   057. Business Committee

   058. Adoptions

   059. Petitions

060. Indian Customs

   061. Convocations—Conferences

   062. Feasts—Fiestas—Festivals

   063. Dances

   064. Languages and Dialects

   065. Marriage Customs

   066. Forms of Government—Indian Judges

   067. Charters

   068. Constitutions and Bylaws

100. ADMINISTRATION AND CONTROL

   101. Office Methods—Condition of Work—Instructions

110. Rules and Regulations

   112. Circulars

   113. Permits

     113.1 Permits to Enter Indian Country

174. Attorneys—Powers of Attorney
 174.1 Contract With
 174.2 Admission of
 174.3 Disbarment of
175. Offenses and Crimes
 175.1 Arrests
 175.2 Suits
 175.3 Fines and Penalties
 175.4 Prisons and Prisoners
 175.5 Pardons
 175.6 Statutes of Limitation
177. Business Forms—Bonds, Authority to Sign—Articles of Incorporation
200. FINANCE AND ACCOUNTS
 201. Receipts for Goods
 202. Authorities
210. Annuities
 211. Payments to Indians
 212. Commutation of Annuities
220. Funds
 220.1 Estimate of—Requisition of or for Funds
 223. Division and Transfer of
 224. Trust Funds
 225. Funds From Sales, Rents, Pupil Labor, and Thumbmarks
 226. Funds From Rights-of-Way
 227. Revenue and Toll Matter
 229. Appropriations
240. Property Accounting
 241. Property Auditing and Accounting
 242. Affidavits of Losses
 243. Condemnation of Property, Boards of Survey, and Destruction of Property
 244. Sale and Exchange of Property, Not Reimbursable
 245. Transfer of Property
 246. Issues of Property, Not Reimbursable
 247. Periodic Property Reports
 248. Inventory of Stores and of Personal and Real Property
250. Accounts
 253. Accounts of Traders
 254. Issues and Expenditures to Schools
 255. Issues, Miscellaneous—Reimbursable
 255.1 Retaken Credits, Cancellations, and Loans
 256. Damage by Elements, Fire, Flood, and Pests

313.1 Allotments Under Section 4, Act of February 8, 1887
314. Mortgages
315. Transfer of Military Posts
316. Rifle Ranges and Target Ranges—Drill Grounds
317. Funds for Ex-Soldiers
320. Leasing of Lands
   321. Farming and Grazing—Assignments
   322. Oil and Gas Leases (Originals)—Approval of Only
     322.1 Oil Gauging and Measuring
     322.2 Oil and Gas Leases—Assignments of Only
     322.3 Oil and Gas Leases—Cancellations of Only
     322.4 Casing Head Gas
     322.5 Drilling Contracts—Extension of Drilling Period—Permission to Drill
     322.6 Acreage Limitations
     322.7 Sale of Oil Lands for Oil and Gas Development
   323. Coal and Asphalt-Assignments
   324. Miscellaneous Mineral and Smelting
   325. Oil Tank Sites
330. Resources and Development—Analyses
   331. Prospecting
   332. Mines, Mineral Lands and Mining
   333. Mineral Springs
   334. Quarries
   335. Gravel Pits
   336. Gas Wells
   337. Oil Lands
   338. Fisheries
   339. Forests—Logging and Lumbering Operations—Forest Fires
340. Improvements
   341. Irrigation-Dikes
   342. Fences
   343. Drainage
   344. Emergency Conservation Work (CCC)
   346. CCC Enrollee Program
   347. Telephone Construction
   348. Bridge Construction
   349. Road Construction
     349.1 Trails
350. Estates—Heirship Cases
   351. Wills
   352. Guardians for Minors and Insane Indians
   353. Administrators and Executors

732. Of Persons—Accidents
733. Of Animals
734. Treatment—Dental Work
735. Contracts, Physicians and Surgeons
736. Deaths
737. Medical Examinations
740. Social Relations
   741. Marriage
   742. Intermarriage
   743. Divorce
   744. Polygamy
   745. Support of Family
750. Amusements and Athletics
   751. Music
   752. Dancing
760. Clinical Surveys and Research
770. Reports of Medical Directors
   771. Reports of Supervisory Nurses
780. Social Security
800. EDUCATION
   801. Rules and Regulations
   802. Compulsory Education
   803. Contract and Public Schools
   806. Reservation, Day and Boarding Schools
   808. Summer School
810. Teaching and Training—School Curriculum
   811. Agricultural Training
   812. Domestic Training
   813. Industrial Training
   814. Musical Training
   815. Academic Training
   816. Religious Training
     816.1 Interference
     816.2 Missions, Missionaries, and Churches
   817. Arts and Crafts
   818. Health Education
   819. Adult Education
820. Pupils
   821. Runaway Pupils and Incorrigibles
   822. Morality of
   823. Associations and Clubs
   824. "Outing" Systems
   825. Transfer of

826. Returned Students
827. Monthly and Quarterly Reports of
828. Summer Subsistence
830. Teachers
832. Qualifications of Teachers
833. Examinations for Teachers
850. Educational Aid
851. National Youth Administration
852. Apprenticeships
854. Intelligence Tests
855. Special Aid
900. INDUSTRIES AND EMPLOYMENT
901. Superintendents of
902. Experiment Stations
903. Labor Unions and Troubles
910. Industries
911. Bee Culture
912. Forestry—Nurseries—Fruit Culture—Associations
913. Basket Making
    913.1 Pottery
915. Rug Making
916. Farming and Stock Raising
917. Housekeeping
    917.1 Field Matrons' Work—Home Demonstration
919. Agriculture and Home Extension Work
920. Employment for Indians
921. On Farms
922. On Railroads
923. On Beetfields
924. On Irrigation Projects
925. On Roads
926. Indians in Military Service
927. In Building Trades
928. As Nurses
929. As Musicians
930. Wild Animals—Conservation of Fish and Wildlife
931. Hunting and Fishing
940. Inventions

The change to the decimal classification system did not particularly affect the subject content of the records. The list of decimal classifications gives a good idea of the variety of subjects, but it does not indicate their relative importance. Land-related matters continued to be the most prominent subjects at most agencies. Particular subjects were of more concern at one agency than another. Surveys and appraisements (304) is an unusually large classification for the Flathead Agency, and there is a vast quantity of records concerning the approval of oil and gas leases (322) for the Five Tribes. Frequently, there are many records concerning the transfer of lands (310), leasing (320), irrigation (341), and estates and heirship (350). Other sizable categories include enrollment and citizenship (053), annuity payments to Indians (211), and credit and revolving funds (259). The classifications under health and social relations (700) and education (800), as to be expected, are comparatively large for medical facilities and schools, but the total quantity of records for such units is usually rather small. Agency duties were still sometimes assigned to school superintendents; for some schools, such as the Cherokee School in North Carolina, there are more records concerning agency matters than school activities. Occasionally, a normally small classification contains an unusual accumulation for a particular agency, which is ordinarily the result of a special situation there. In the Indians competent category (127) for Seneca, for example, there is a file of reports on the individual Indians made by a competency commission and two large files concerning the lands and funds of two Quapaw Indians.

Many records under numerous classifications concern individual Indians. Matters relating to lands and finances are most common, but it is possible to find information about almost any subject, such as proposed enrollment in a school or admission to a hospital.

The Indian Reorganization Act of 1934 marked the end of the assimilation movement. This act prohibited further land allotments and suspended sales; indeed, the Government began to buy land for Indians without reservations. The act provided for the organization of tribal governments with written constitutions and for the incorporation of tribes for economic purposes. Many of the records concerning these activities were removed from the central files and are now among the records of the Indian Organization Division.

Many records were created concerning Depression relief and recovery programs for Indians. Particularly important were projects financed by the Public Works Administration, the Work Projects Administration, and the Civilian Conservation Corps, which included irrigation work and construction of roads, homes, farm buildings, and Bureau facilities. The divisions established to handle these programs also maintained large quantities of records apart from the central files, particularly the Construction Division, the Civilian Conservation Corps–Indian Division, and the Rehabilitation Division.

Unlike agencies that regarded their central filing system as self-indexing, the Bureau continued to maintain detailed controls for individual documents by means of three sets of 3- by 5-inch slips, which give the date, writer, and subject of each incoming document. One set is an index to subjects and correspondents; the subjects consist mostly of proper names: persons, agencies, companies, places, and to some extent tribes. These slips give the year and registration number of the specific document but do not always fully cite the file in which it was placed. To establish this, it is necessary to go to the second set of slips, which is a register arranged by year and thereunder by registration number. These second slips indicate where the document was filed by year and the number of base letter, decimal classification, and jurisdiction or other heading. The third and least frequently used set is arranged by jurisdiction and thereunder by decimal classification. The index and register are used principally for finding a particular document or information about a person. For more general subjects, the jurisdictional headings and decimal classifications usually are more useful.

In 1936 the Bureau adopted a different filing system, known as the New System or Shafer System. The following year, however, the decimal system was restored, and most of the 1936 records were converted to the decimal system, although some records later than 1936 were added to New System files. There are 80 feet of records filed according to the New System, but they consist principally of cross-references to decimal files.

The New System was a numerical subject classification scheme. Certain subjects were assigned classification numbers. The subject of reforestation, for example, was assigned classification number 26400. To each classification number was assigned a block of "unit numbers," and 111 field units of the Bureau were assigned unit numbers in alphabetical order. Hoopa Valley, for example, was assigned unit number 42 and Hopi, unit number 43. Eighty-nine unit numbers remained for new jurisdictions that might be established. Thus, correspondence relating to reforestation at Hoopa Valley was designated by the file number 26442. In addition to the file numbers assigned in this manner, there are many special file numbers assigned to correspondence relating to subjects that did not fit into the pattern of classification and unit numbers. Records filed under this system are included in the index and register to the central classified files.

A chronological file of letters sent, 1909–36 (90 ft.), covers only the last 5 working days of March and September of each year, except for the years 1933–34, which are complete. The letters for each day are divided according to the unit of the Bureau handling them or, in some cases, by subject. They have been preserved mainly to indicate the kind and quantity of Bureau correspondence and its distribution within the Bureau organization at different times. Copies of most of the letters are in the central classified files, which should be used for intensive research concerning a particular subject.

Special series A, ca. 1837–1934 (47 ft.), consists of records withdrawn from the letters received by the Bureau, the central classified files, and records of the Land and Inspection Divisions; special reports; materials prepared for congressional hearings; and other records that apparently were segregated to accommodate their unusual size or to bring related records together. They relate to land, heirship cases, claims, personnel, estimates, enrollments, investigations, schools, and many other matters. The following files are representative of the series.

Correspondence concerning improvements for the Alabama and Coushatta (Koasati) Indians, Polk County, Tex.

Blackfeet Indian Agency and School, copies of farming and grazing leases.

Indian Territory, Office of Superintendent of Schools, roll of Indian Students at Bloomfield Seminary.

Digest of reports of various British colonies and protectorates in relation to Indian affairs.

Memorial of the Brotherhood of North American Indians, with petitions from various tribes asking for an account of their money and that their outstanding claims be adjudicated.

Report on policy of Burke Act as compared with that of the Dawes Act.

Correspondence, notes, and related documents, files of John J. Terrell, Inspector and Special Commissioner to the Indians of California.

Settler claims, Camp McDowell Indian Reservation.

Cherokee Nation, reports and documents re oil leases.

Eastern Band of Cherokee, right to dispose of land and timber.

Census of Scattered Bands of Ottawa and Chippewa in Michigan (Durant Roll).

Bounty Land Warrants to Choctaw.

Schedule of appraisement of surplus and unallotted land, Diminished Colville Reservation.

Boundary Disputes, Consolidated Chippewa.

Five Civilized Tribes, reports concerning income taxes.

Haskell Institute, survey of living conditions among Potawatomi, Kickapoo, and Iowa Indians.

Also among the general records of the Bureau are correspondence concerning Christmas gifts for Indian children, 1907; letters received from the Department of Justice concerning the disposition of legal cases, 1925–26; agency 10-year plans, 1940–53; a few organization charts, 1910–11; papers of historian Annie Heloise Abel, ca. 1912–20, which include some personal correspondence but consists mainly of transcripts and copies of Bureau records and notes; and a "Biographical & Historical Index of American Indians and Persons Involved in Indian Affairs," on 3- by 5-inch cards. The index has been published by G. K. Hall in eight volumes and is useful for research in published sources.

ORDERS, CIRCULARS, AND CIRCULAR LETTERS

Orders, circulars, and circular letters were used to issue instructions and to provide and request information. In the earlier years such issuances usually were copied in the letter books of outgoing correspondence. For the years 1854–85 there are three volumes of circulars sent mainly to superintendents and agents and relating primarily to procedural matters, particularly accounts. There are eight volumes of printed, processed, press, and carbon copies of orders, 1884–1925, issued by the President, the Commissioner of Indian Affairs, the Chief Clerk, the Secretary of the Interior, and other officials; these were intended primarily for employees of the central office of the Bureau. In 1916 a new series of orders was started, directed to field officials and relating mainly to financial matters; such directives previously had been issued as circulars or circular letters.

There are Bureau orders, 1916–55; replies to orders, 1916–34; along with numbered circulars to field officials, 1907–50; replies to them, 1907–35; and unnumbered circulars, 1926–50. Some replies are merely acknowledgments, but others furnish requested information. Circular letters are similar to circulars, and there is no clear distinction between them. Circular letters, however, are more likely to give or request information and less likely to deal with procedural matters. There are circular letters and replies, 1915–34; a few separate circulars, 1926–28, issued by the General Superintendent in charge of educational and other activities in the field; and inspection circulars, 1921–22. Other related records include Departmental orders and memorandums, 1927–62, and Indian Service regulations, 1930–47.

CARTOGRAPHIC RECORDS

The central map files of the Bureau of Indian Affairs, 1800–1967, include manuscript, annotated, published, and photoprocessed maps of reconnaissances, explorations, and surveys in the Indian country. The earliest of these are a photoprocessed copy of a map of the Indian country along the Ohio and Muskingum Rivers through which Col. Henry Bouquet marched in 1764; a tracing of the route of Capt. Jonathan Carver's travels in what are now the North Central States, in 1766 and 1767; a blueprint of a map of the northwestern territories showing the route of the expedition under the command of Gov. Lewis Cass through the Chippewa country in 1820; and a manuscript map showing the route of Henry R. Schoolcraft, Indian agent, between Lake Superior and the Mississippi River in the summer of 1831.

The central map files also include published copies of many of the reconnaissance and expedition maps that are in Records of the Office of the Chief of Engineers, Record Group 77. Most of these show Indian tribes, and the Bureau of Indian Affairs added information pertaining to Indians to some. Among them are a map of the Territory of Minnesota, showing the route of the 1849 expedition to the Red River of the North in 1849 by Capt. John Pope; a map of the country between Arkansas and New Mexico explored by Capt. R. B. Marcy, 1849–52; maps of reconnaissances in the Dakota country by Lt. G. K. Warren in 1855; and maps of the Yellowstone and Missouri Rivers and their tributaries explored by Capt. W. F. Raynolds and 1st Lt. H. E. Maynadier, 1859–60, revised to 1876. There also are maps of the Western United States, military departments, States, and Territories that show exploration routes and locations of Indian tribes and reservations. Most of these maps have been annotated in the Bureau of Indian Affairs to show later information about the tribes and reservations.

Concerning settlement on reservations and loss of land, there are numbered manuscript, annotated, published, and photoprocessed maps of the entire United States, the area west of the Mississippi River, Indian tribal lands and land cessions, existing and proposed Indian reservations, and military reservations and forts. There are also maps of separate reservations and boundaries as originally surveyed, maps of diminished reservations and resurveyed boundaries, and maps showing allotments to individual Indians. There are also unnumbered published administrative maps of the United States and the area west of the Mississippi River showing Indian and military reservations, 1878–1941, and published maps of Indian reservations, 1910–21. There are maps of the United States giving population figures for 1878, 1882, and 1883. Other maps, ca. 1824–1921, give Indian population figures for various dates.

Concerning transportation, there are maps submitted by railroad companies showing proposed rights-of-way. They include maps of land required for station grounds, stockyards, spur tracks, terminals, water reservoirs and pipelines, and logging roads, 1872–1956. Unnumbered published maps show the general locations of railroads and roads in relation to Indian reservations. There are also right-of-way maps showing existing and proposed county and State highways across Indian reservations; maps showing proposed and existing roads across Indian allotments within the reservations; and highway maps and roadmaps, 1939–60.

Other maps show agricultural land, grazing and pasture lands, and irrigated and irrigable lands belonging to Indians. Some pertain to farming, stockraising, and subsistence gardening. The maps show, for certain districts, the number of acres that could be cultivated, acreage leased to whites for farming, irrigated land, grazing land, and sometimes population figures and the number of livestock. Many maps relate to forestry and lumbering. A set of 14 State maps was reprinted in 1960 by the Bureau to encourage the tourist industry. A map of the United States, published in 1961, shows Indian reservation areas and gives a brief description of each reservation with principal points of interest to tourists.

Other maps show oil and gas leases, oilfields, producing oil and gas wells, abandoned wells and dry holes, tank farms and tank sites, and pumping station sites. There are also many maps showing rights-of-way of different companies for oil and gas pipelines and refining company telephone and telegraph lines across Indian lands. Most of these maps, dated 1904–59, are of areas in Indian Territory and Oklahoma. A few show reservations in Arizona, Colorado, Montana, New Mexico, and Wyoming. There also are maps of the segregated coal and asphalt lands of the Chickasaw and Choctaw tribes and maps of mineral districts under the Quapaw Agency.

A card index lists the maps three ways: by area or State and thereunder by tribe, Indian reservation, military reservation, or other administrative unit; by subject; and by map number. Four old map registers maintained by the Bureau before 1921 contain much information about individual maps that is not included on the cards. Other cartographic records of the Bureau of Indian Affairs are described with the records of various divisions. See Laura E. Kelsay, comp., *List of Cartographic Records of the Bureau of Indian Affairs,* Special List 13 (rev. 1977).

AUDIOVISUAL RECORDS

A general photographic subject file, 1909–59 (5,700 items), dates chiefly from 1936 to 1951. In addition to photographs of Indians, their activities, and living conditions, there are pictures of superintendents and other Bureau personnel. The arrangement is alphabetical from "Adobe Construction" through "Yakima CCC." Many of the subject headings are the names of reservations, agencies, and schools, but there are also headings for Alaska, Field Personnel, Relocation, Harry S. Truman, and the Washington office. Of the photographs concerning forestry on Indian reservations, 1910–42 (3,700 items), only about 50 show Indians and their homes; the others are related to forestry in general. Among the Alexander Gardner photographs of individual Indian delegates in Washington, D.C., 1872, are photographs of 100 Indian delegates or their wives from the Apache, Sioux, Kiowa, Comanche, Arapaho, Caddo, Wichita, Waco, Kichai, Tawakoni, Delaware, and Ute tribes. Eighteen photographs made by William S. Soule, 1868–74, are of Arapaho, Comanche, and Kiowa Indians and their camps. Three albums of photographs from the Office of the Commissioner of Indian Affairs, 1876–86, show students and their activities and reservation buildings and activities. Among the 37 photographs made by William Dinwiddie, 1895–96, are portraits of individuals and groups from the Piegan, Ojibwa (Chippewa), Sauk and Fox, Shawnee, Kiowa, Teton Sioux, Oto, and Ponca tribes.

Other records are studio portraits and groups of Indians from southeastern Idaho, 1897; photographs of the Indian industrial school at Genoa, Nebr., 1910, showing buildings, drills, and classroom activities; an album of photographs of Seger Colony, Okla., 1886–1913, showing Cheyenne and Arapaho Indians, their homes, and their activities; lantern slides of Seminole Indians in the Florida Everglades, ca. 1913; photographs of Indians suffering from tuberculosis and other diseases and of unhealthy living conditions, ca. 1915; photographs taken at the Sacaton (Pima) Agency, 1918, showing buildings, animals, and improvements; photographs of Indian farms, 1922, mostly in Arizona; panoramic photographs, 1909–30, showing school and reservation buildings and large groups of Indians and Bureau personnel; 13 photograph albums prepared by Indian agencies, 1929–40, illustrating activities at the Carson Indian School and the Crow, Shoshoni, Flathead, Hoopa Valley, Rocky Boy, Standing Rock, Mission, and Ute Mountain Reservations or Agencies, with one album illustrating the 1939 relief and rehabilitation program of the Bureau; a photographic exhibit, "Life in an Indian School," 1925, covering general subjects and items from day and boarding schools; and exhibit photographs, 1904–36, illustrating life at Indian schools and reservations, irrigation, agricultural activities, and works of art done by pupils. There are also 900 nitrate film negatives, 1908–26, some showing Arizona farms in 1922.

Motion pictures include 12 reels of silent films of the Rodman Wanamaker expeditions, made by Joseph K. Dixon in 1908, 1909, 1913, 1915, and 1920, showing Indian customs, dances, and activities; the dedication of the National American Indian Memorial at Fort Wadsworth, N.Y.; and the adoption of Marshal Foch by the Crow Indians. There is also a one-reel silent film, "A Trip to the Arctic with Uncle Sam," 1922, documenting a trip of the revenue cutter *Bear* from the Aleutian Islands to Plover Bay, Siberia, by way of Point Barrow, Alaska, which includes scenes of Eskimo life.

RECORDS OF THE OFFICE OF THE COMMISSIONER OF INDIAN AFFAIRS

The records of the Office of the Commissioner of Indian Affairs are mostly in small, diverse series. They include 13 volumes of press copies of letters sent, 1871, 1873–85, and 1889–1901, relating particularly to personnel matters, especially appointments, and also to charges against the Commissioner and other officials, investigations, procurement of goods for Indians, legislation, relations with religious groups, visitors on reservations, travel plans of the Commissioner, and many other subjects. Many of the letters are marked "informal," "personal," "unofficial," or "confidential," and usually they are not included in the regular outgoing correspondence of the Bureau. For some of the Commissioners there is a considerable amount of nonofficial correspondence. The letters of Acting

Commissioners are usually in the letter books of the Chief Clerk and Assistant Commissioner.

Other records include a ledger with bank records of Commissioner Carey A. Harris, 1837–38, and public and private postage accounts of the Commissioner's office, 1845; a transcript of testimony taken before the House Committee on Indian Affairs concerning the awarding of contracts for annuity goods by Commissioner Lewis V. Bogy, 1866–67 (3 in.); letters received concerning the investigation by a board of inquiry of charges against Chief Clerk Samuel A. Galpin and of alleged irregularities in the Bureau, with a report of the board and printed proceedings, 1866–78 (1 vol. and unbound papers, 4 in.); the report, August 20, 1877, of a board appointed by the Secretary of the Interior to examine the Bureau's methods of transacting business, particularly its accounting and recordkeeping practices; a volume of copies of correspondence concerning Ute lands in Colorado, 1873–79; a volume of copies of correspondence concerning Estelle Reel, Superintendent of Indian Schools, relating particularly to possible violations of civil service regulations, 1902; records relating to the President's Commission on Economy and Efficiency, 1910–12 (3 in.); a scrapbook of newspaper and magazine clippings of Commissioner Cato Sells, 1913–20; a register of Indians visiting the Bureau, 1914–17; and several address and data books.

For more recent years, there are records identified as personal and semi-official files, 1921–32 (2 in.), consisting chiefly of correspondence with and concerning Stella M. (Mrs. H. A.) Atwood, chairman of the Committee on Indian Welfare of the General Federation of Women's Clubs.

The only substantial body of records of any Commissioner is an office file of John Collier, 1933–45 (7 ft.). It relates to many subjects, including alleged Nazi activities in the American Indian Federation, the Court of Claims suit of the California Indians, the Navajo Indians, the Pueblo Indians, peyote, the War Relocation Authority and the internment of Japanese on Indian lands, a study of Indian personality, conferences and other meetings, and trips of the Commissioner. There are a few pre-1933 records, some from the files of the American Indian Defense Association, of which Collier was executive secretary before he became Commissioner of Indian Affairs. A small reference file, 1919–45 (3 in.), includes manuscripts of statements and articles prepared by Collier, printed articles and copies of periodicals, clippings, correspondence, and poems. There is also a chronological file of letters sent, 1943–44.

RECORDS OF THE OFFICES OF THE CHIEF CLERK AND ASSISTANT COMMISSIONERS OF INDIAN AFFAIRS

From 1824 to 1886 the Chief Clerk was the second-ranking official in the Bureau and served as Acting Commissioner during the Commissioner's absences. He was in charge of the Washington office staff, handling office supplies and equipment and other matters that did not seem to belong to one of the divisions, including traders' licenses starting in 1885. In 1886 the Congress established the position of Assistant Commissioner of Indian Affairs. He was to be Acting Commissioner in the absence of the Commissioner and to perform the duties normally assigned to a chief clerk. The Miscellaneous Division, established in 1889, took over traders' licenses and office supplies and later assumed responsibility for other administrative matters that might normally have been assigned to a chief clerk.

There are 11 volumes of press copies of letters sent or prepared by the Chief Clerk, 1871–86 (except there are no letters, Sept. 1, 1875–June 15, 1877), and by the Assistant Commissioner, 1886–93. Many of the letters relate to personnel, office organization, and procedures, but there are also letters concerning such subjects as traders' licenses, transportation for Indian pupils, instructions for field officials, and legislation. For the Assistant Commissioner there is more informal correspondence, sometimes relating to political and personal matters. A separate volume of letters sent, February–June 1880, contains mostly instructions to inspectors and special agents. For the years 1905–8 there is a volume of letters sent by Charles F. Larrabee when he was Acting Commissioner. Other records include some concerning land matters, 1886–94, and a statement with information about Indian agencies, ca. 1881.

In 1906 the position of Chief Clerk was reestablished in addition to that of Assistant Commissioner. From 1910 to 1915 the Chief Clerk was designated as Second Assistant Commissioner. The position was abolished again in 1934. The duties of the office were changed from time to time. Essentially the office was concerned with the administration of the Washington office staff, but during some periods, particularly 1908–9, it had other duties. Six volumes of letters sent, prepared in the office of the Chief Clerk and Second Assistant Commissioner, 1908–12, relate chiefly to Washington office personnel matters. In the first part of the first volume (March 18–May 27, 1908) are included letters relating to traders' licenses, expositions, supplies, and other matters formerly handled by the discontinued Miscellaneous Division.

After he was relieved of the duties of the Chief Clerk, the Assistant Commissioner had no specifically assigned administrative duties other than to act as Commissioner when necessary. In 1944 a second Assistant Commissioner was appointed, and in 1949 each of the Assistant Commissioners was put in charge of an administrative division—the Division of Resources and the Division of Community Services. There are records of three Assistant Commissioners in the National Archives. There is correspondence, 1935–48 (1 ft.), and memorandums, 1944–50 (10 in.), of William Zimmerman, who was Assistant Commissioner from 1933 until 1950. After the reorganization of 1949, he was in charge of the Division of Resources. For Joseph C.

McCaskill, field representative and assistant to the Commissioner before he became Assistant Commissioner in 1944, there is an office file, 1939–46 (3 in.), with records relating to anthropological work, the Indian Rights Association, the internment of Japanese, religious organizations, and the Wardship Committee (Committee on Study of Wardship and Indian Participation in American Life). For John H. Provinse, who was in charge of the Division of Community Services after the reorganization of 1949, an office file, 1946–50 (6 in.), relates mainly to policy and administrative matters, and a reference file, 1932–49 (5 in.), includes reports, pamphlets, maps, and proceedings of departmental hearings concerning the protection of Alaskan fisheries.

RECORDS OF OTHER OFFICIALS

There are a few records, probably a fragment of a once larger series, of Fred H. Daiker, 1929–43, who held a succession of positions in the Bureau. The records relate chiefly to the legal definition of the terms "Indian" and "wardship" and to the American Indian Federation. There is a substantial file for Assistant to the Commissioner John Herrick, 1936–41 (5 ft.), relating to such subject areas as school courses, Bureau divisions, Indian rehabilitation and relief, and various Indian agencies. There are also records concerning legislation, 1933–42, and memorandums, 1937–42 (5 in.), of the Finance Officer until 1940 and thereafter the Chief Administrative Officer.

INDIAN REMOVAL RECORDS

The removal of Indians from the East to west of the Mississippi River was encouraged from the time of the Louisiana Purchase in 1803. An act of May 28, 1830 (4 Stat. 411), specifically authorized the President to exchange land in the unorganized territory west of the Mississippi River for any Indian land in a State or Territory, if the Indians moved. He also could pay for improvements on the abandoned land. There are some records concerning earlier removals, but most of the records relate to removals carried out under the act of 1830. Except for the records of the Office of the Commissary General, they relate almost entirely to four of the Five Civilized Tribes: the Cherokee, Chickasaw, Choctaw, and Creek.

Usually the removals were arranged by negotiating treaties with the tribes. The terms varied, but they all provided some means of compensating the Indians for their land and property in the East and of assisting them during the removal and for 1 year thereafter. Sometimes an individual Indian who wished to stay in the East could accept a reserve of land in fee simple and remain, usually as a citizen of the United States. From 1830 to 1836 the actual removals were conducted by the Office of the Commissary General of Subsistence. Most of the records, however, do not relate to the removals themselves but to the settlement of claims involving the Indians' land and property. They include records of commissions appointed to adjudicate the claims.

RECORDS OF THE OFFICE OF THE COMMISSARY GENERAL OF SUB-
SISTENCE

The Office of the Commissary General of Subsistence, established within
the War Department in 1818 to purchase and issue Army provisions, was
also assigned the task of conducting the removal of the Indians in 1830. The
Office was responsible for their transportation to the West and for their
subsistence for 1 year after they reached their new homes. Gen. George Gibson held the position of Commissary General throughout the period from
1830 to 1836. In November 1836 the Secretary of War transferred the Office's functions and records relating to Indian emigration to the Bureau of
Indian Affairs. The Bureau continued to use a few of the volumes that were
transferred, for a time. Most of the records of the Office are in Records of
the Office of the Commissary General of Subsistence, Record Group 192.

The correspondence is divided into letters received, controlled by registers, and copybooks of letters sent. There are three volumes of registers of
letters received, for 1831–33, 1833–35, and 1836. Entries for individual letters give date of receipt, file number and heading, name and address of
writer, date of letter, and subject matter. Entries in each volume are arranged alphabetically by initial letter of surname of correspondent and
thereunder chronologically by date of receipt. Under each letter of the alphabet entries are numbered consecutively throughout the three volumes.
There is a separate register of letters received by referral from the Secretary
of War, the Commissioner of Indian Affairs, or some other officials, but
the letters entered in this register are also entered in the main series of
registers. Incomplete weekly reports, 1832–35, give summaries of the replies
or reasons for not replying.

The letters received, 1831–36 (7 ft.), are arranged under the following
headings: Cherokee, Chicago, Choctaw, Creek, Florida, Kickapoo, Miscellaneous, Ohio, Ottawa, Potawatomi, Quapaw, St. Louis Superintendency,
Seminole, Western Superintendency, and Winnebago. Within each heading, the letters are arranged for the most part by year and thereunder in
registry order. With the letters are some reports, petitions, muster rolls,
journals of emigrating and exploring parties, estimates, accounts current,
abstracts of disbursements, abstracts of provisions issued, and vouchers.

There are four volumes of letters sent, 1830–36. The letters are arranged
chronologically, and each volume has an alphabetical index to names of addressees and cross-references to the page numbers of other letters to the
same person.

Correspondence was conducted with the Secretary of War, the Commissioner of Indian Affairs, the Second Auditor, superintendents of Indian removal, Army officers in charge of parties of emigrants, disbursing officers,
Indian agents and superintendents, Members of Congress, individual Indians, and others. The letters relate to such subjects as exploring parties,

routes, progress of emigration parties, transportation, health of Indians, purchase and distribution of goods and supplies, disbursement of funds, accounts, and appointments.

There are also drafts of letters sent, 1834–36; a volume of copies of tabular reports and statements, prepared primarily to accompany letters to the Secretary of War and others, 1832–36; a volume of estimates of costs of removal and subsistence, 1832–36; a volume of contracts, 1831–36; a record of the receipt and issue of subsistence goods, 1831–38; a register of requisitions, 1831–36; a volume of requisitions, 1835–36; a journal and a corresponding ledger of financial transactions, 1830–37; two other ledgers; a record of the compensation of agents, 1830–33; and a register of applications for employment, 1831–35.

CHEROKEE REMOVAL RECORDS

The first treaty by which Indians ceded land east of the Mississippi River in exchange for land to the west was that of July 8, 1817, with the Cherokee Nation. Article 8 of this treaty provided that Indian heads of families who wished to remain in the East were entitled to a reservation of 640 acres. A new treaty of February 27, 1819, modified the 1817 treaty but also provided for the 640-acre reservations. The major Cherokee removal, however, did not come until after the treaty of December 29, 1835.

There is a register, 1817–19, of Indians who elected to stay in the East under the terms of the 1817 treaty. It has been reproduced on roll 13 of M208, *Records of the Cherokee Indian Agency in Tennessee, 1801–1835.* There is also a group of applications, with a register, submitted in 1819 by Cherokee Indians who wanted reservations.

Emigration rolls, 1817–38 (1 ft.), include lists of Cherokee Indians who wished to emigrate, rolls of actual emigrants, muster rolls of conducted parties, and lists of Indians able to emigrate unescorted. Some rolls are signed by Indians and constitute relinquishments of lands in the East. Sometimes there is information concerning valuations of property, debts, and other subjects. Usually only heads of families are listed, but often there is some information about other members. Some rolls are indexed.

Census rolls of the Eastern Cherokee, 1835–84 (2 ft.), most of which are indexed, have been maintained among the removal records, although they extend well beyond the removal period. A roll usually is identified by the surname of the person who compiled it. The first, the Henderson Roll, 1835, is the roll customarily made before removal. It lists only heads of families and gives information concerning the family and its property. The other rolls are commonly known as the Mullay Roll, 1848; Siler Roll, 1851; Chapman Roll, 1852; Powell Roll, 1867; Swetland Rolls, 1869; and Hester Roll, 1884. Most were made to determine eligibility for payments due under the 1835 treaty; the Chapman Roll is a receipt roll for payments actually made.

Other general records concerning Cherokee removal include a ledger recording debts of Indians, 1831–36, and 2 feet of miscellaneous records, ca. 1820–54, which include correspondence, property valuations, certificates of valuations, property returns, receipts for payments, petitions, depositions, registers, lists, schedules, notes, opinions, contracts, and powers of attorney.

Records of Boards of Cherokee Commissioners

Article 17 of the treaty of December 29, 1835, provided for the appointment by the President of commissioners to examine and adjudicate claims arising from other articles of the treaty. Four boards of Cherokee commissioners were appointed to settle such claims, most of which were presented by Indians for compensation for abandoned property, spoliations, and lost reservations. There were some claims against the Indians.

The first board was established in 1836. Originally, it consisted of two commissioners, Wilson Lumpkin and John Kennedy. In October 1837 a third commissioner, Thomas Wilson, was added, and in December 1837 Lumpkin was replaced by James Liddell. The board concluded its work in March 1839. Its records include a volume of letters sent; valuations of Indians' land, improvements, and other property and assets in the East (24 vols. and unbound papers); a volume of changes in the assignment of property valuations from one person to another; and returns of property (4 vols.), which are itemized lists of prices of property sold for emigrating Indians. The records concerning individual claims are arranged for the most part by type of claim. For reservation claims there are a docket book, two volumes of decisions, and claim papers (5 in.), consisting of affidavits, depositions, statements, petitions, valuations, copies of land grants, receipts, copies of registrations, copies of decisions, and other records. For spoliation claims there are claim papers (8 in.) and two of three volumes of decisions. There are also papers for claims for debts against Cherokee Indians (1 ft.), a record of judgments in such claims, and decisions on claims of attorneys for payment for services to the Cherokee Nation. Miscellaneous claim papers (2 ft.) are chiefly for rejected spoliation claims and approved claims not included in the main set, but they also include papers for improvement claims, claims for changes in valuations, National Due Bill claims against the Cherokee Nation, debt claims (most of which were rejected), and claims for services to the Cherokee Nation. There are also some stubs for certificates given to Indians for amounts due for the value of improvements and a general abstract (3 vols.) of valuations, spoliation claims allowed, and the balances due at the time the board adjourned. Some records of the board were incorporated with those of the later boards.

The second board of Cherokee commissioners was appointed in November 1842, with John H. Eaton and Edward H. Hubley as commissioners. It adjourned in January 1844 and was replaced in June by the third board, which was appointed for 1 year with George C. Washington and John T. Mason as commissioners. The third board inherited and added to the records of the second board, and thus it is necessary to consider their records together. The second and third boards—in addition to the reservation, spoliation, improvement, and other kinds of claims considered by the first board—considered and rejected a large number of preemption claims based on articles 12 and 13 of the 1835 treaty and the supplementary articles of March 1, 1836. The records consist of a volume of letters sent, proceedings, and a schedule of claims adjudicated by the second board, docket books (4 vols.), claim papers (2 in.), decisions (2 vols.), and registers of payments (5 vols.).

The adjudication of claims was continued by the fourth board, which existed from July 1846 to July 1847, with Benjamin H. Brewster and Edward Harden as commissioners. Its records consist of a volume of letters sent; two volumes of minutes, which include summaries of evidence submitted and decisions rendered; claim papers (3 ft.), many of which were transferred from the records of the earlier boards; and a register of payments.

CHICKASAW REMOVAL RECORDS

The amount of records concerning Chickasaw removal is small, but they include three volumes of letters sent by the Bureau of Indian Affairs, 1832–61, most of which were not copied in the main series of letters sent by the Bureau. There are letters to Chickasaw agents, superintendents, other field officials, the Secretary of War, the Secretary of the Interior, the Commissioner and other officials of the General Land Office, Members of Congress, bankers, members of missionary groups, Indians, and others. They relate to such subjects as removal, land reservations, claims, investment of proceeds of land sales, applications for bounty lands, and education. Other records include a census roll prepared in 1839 by Agent A. M. M. Upshaw, bound with some muster rolls of Indians emigrating in 1837; abstracts of locations of land reserves, 1836–44 (2 vols.); reports of land sales and deeds, 1836–39; a journal of expenditures for implementing the Chickasaw treaties, 1833–36; and financial statements concerning the use of proceeds of land sales, 1849.

CHOCTAW REMOVAL RECORDS

The first treaty providing for the removal of Choctaw Indians to the West was negotiated in 1820, but the major removal was carried out under the provisions of the Treaty of Dancing Rabbit Creek, September 27, 1830. This was the first treaty made and ratified under the Removal Act of 1830. The customary census roll, prepared in 1831, is known as the Armstrong

Roll. For individual Indians owning farms, it shows name, number of acres cultivated, number of persons in the family, number of males over 16, number of children under 10, location of farm, its probable value, and other information. For each Choctaw district, there is a list of Indians entitled to additional land under the provisions of the treaty. An alphabetical list of Choctaw reserves can be used as an index for the census.

In 1856, Agent Douglas Cooper prepared a census of Choctaw Indians still living east of the Mississippi. This roll gives names of heads of families, places of residence, and numbers of men, women, and children in the families. There are also emigration lists, 1831–37, with some schedules of property abandoned and lost (5 vols. and unbound papers). Other records include a register of claims for reservations of Choctaw families who wished to remain in the East and secure title to land, 1834–36; reports, mainly in tabular form, by commissioners certifying contracts for sales of Choctaw reserves, 1836–41; a memorandum book of the commissioners, 1837–39; statements concerning sales of lands of Choctaw orphans, 1838–83 (2 vols.); statements and schedules concerning locations of reservations, claims, issuance of scrip, payments to Indians, use of proceeds from land sales, and other subjects, ca. 1831–1906 (9 in.); and miscellaneous records, ca. 1825–58 (1 ft.).

Records of Claims Commissions

In 1837 the President appointed James Murray, Peter D. Vroom, and Gen. Publius R. Pray (who soon resigned) to adjudicate reservation claims arising under article 14 of the treaty of 1830, which provided for allotments to Indians who chose to stay in the East. The commission sat from June 22, 1837, to May 12, 1838. Its records consist of a journal of proceedings, a docket of claims, depositions of claimants and witnesses, abstracts of claims adjudicated, and a revision of claims decisions made by the Secretary of War in 1846.

In 1842 the President appointed another commission to adjudicate claims under article 14 and also under article 19, which provided for special allotments to certain persons. John Claiborne and Richard Graves were the original commissioners; William Tyler joined them in 1843, and in 1844 George Gaines and Samuel Rush replaced Claiborne and Graves. The commission adjourned in June 1845. The records of this commission consist of a volume of letters sent; eight volumes of proceedings and a separate journal kept by Commissioner Graves, 1842–43, that is more detailed for the claims it covers; claim papers (2 ft.), consisting of application statements, depositions of claimants and witnesses, and other documents; two volumes of judgments; two volumes of abstracts of claims, consisting of schedules submitted by the commissioners and approved by the Secretary of War with some modifications; a revision of claims by the Secretary of War, 1846; and abstracts of claims for land and scrip adjudicated by the Secretaries of War and the Interior, 1846–54, under the provisions of special acts, many of which were rejected September 30, 1854.

Records Relating to Land Scrip

For Choctaw Indians who could not be given the allotments to which they were entitled, an act of August 23, 1842 (5 Stat. 513), provided for the issuance of scrip certificates entitling them to select public lands in Mississippi, Louisiana, Alabama, or Arkansas. Two certificates were prepared for each award, each good for one-half of the land; the second certificate was not to be delivered unless the Indian moved to Indian Territory. An act of March 3, 1845 (5 Stat. 777), provided that instead of delivering the scrip certificates to Indians who had moved, the value of the scrip should be funded and the interest on it paid to the Indians. There are four volumes of scrip and stubs and an accompanying register, 1843–46. For the earlier awards, usually the first of the two certificates has been removed and the second certificate remains; for the later awards, after the funding procedure had been introduced, there are only certificate stubs. There also are some receipts for scrip issued in Mississippi in 1845 and in Indian Territory in 1848 and 1849, and a schedule of annuitants receiving payments under the 1845 law, 1845–49.

Scrip certificates surrendered for land and related records are in Records of the Bureau of Land Management, Record Group 49.

CREEK REMOVAL RECORDS

By the treaty of March 24, 1832, the Creek Indians ceded to the United States all of their land east of the Mississippi River. Heads of families were entitled to tracts of land, which if possible were to include their improvements. The land could either be sold, with the approval of the President, or after 5 years those so wishing could receive patents in fee simple. In 1833 Benjamin S. Parsons and Thomas J. Abbott prepared a census of Creek heads of families, which gives their names and the number of males, females, and slaves in each family. The entries are arranged by town and numbered; these numbers were used for identification in later records. During 1833 and 1834 John J. Abert and James Bright located the reservations to which the heads of families were entitled and prepared land location registers. If the land was sold, the registers give information about the sales; there are notations dated as late as 1886. An index to the Creek reserves can be used for both the census and the land location registers. Other records include land location registers and certifications of contracts prepared by certifying agents Robert McHenry and James F. Sanford, 1834–36; an abstract of Creek land sale contracts, January 22, 1836, which includes judgments on their validity; and a report concerning Creek contracts submitted June 10, 1836, by investigating agents John B. Hogan, James B. Burney, and George D. Anderson. The report gives judgments on the validity of certain contracts for the sale of Creek reserves that were certified by Leonard Tarrant.

As a result of reports of frauds in the sale of Creek lands and of Creek hostilities, the President in 1836 appointed Thomas Hartley Crawford and Alfred Balch as commissioners to conduct an investigation. The records of the commissioners include a journal of proceedings, five docket books, and reports summarizing fraud cases and decisions of the commissioners, 1836–38. There is also a volume of schedules of revisions by the Secretary of War, approved by the President, 1839.

Other Creek removal records include abstracts of approved contracts for sales of reservations, 1839–42; five reports concerning the land of deceased reservees, 1841; a report of special commissioner John W. Edmonds on the validity of contracts made with J. C. Watson and Company, February 22, 1841; emigration lists, 1836–38 (8 vols. and unbound papers); and miscellaneous records, ca. 1827–59 (2 ft.). For case files concerning alleged fraud in the sale of Creek land in the east, see the records of the Land Division relating to land claims (page 92).

OTHER REMOVAL RECORDS

There are also a few muster rolls of Apalachicola and Seminole Indians of Florida, Kickapoo, New York, Ottawa, Potawatomi, Quapaw, and Wyandot Indians, 1832–46.

RECORDS OF THE LAND DIVISION

The Land Division was established in 1846 when divisions were first organized within the Bureau of Indian Affairs. It was at first known as the Land Statistics, Reservations, and Grants Division, and until 1907 it was sometimes called the Land and Law Division. The regulations adopted in 1846 provided that the Land Division would "embrace all business connected with the location and survey of lands set apart for the various tribes; the examinations of claims arising out of Reservations and grants to individual Indians; the assignment or conveyance thereof; and the correspondence which appropriately relates thereto." These duties remained major areas of concern, but they were soon expanded to include other activities.

Major activities for which there are records are the surveying and allotting of land and the sale and leasing of it. When the Indian Reorganization Act of 1934 prohibited further allotments and suspended land sales, efforts were made to acquire land for Indians rather than to dispose of it. Two other major subject areas of the records are claims and the enrollment of Indians, a process that entitled them to land.

In 1940 the Land Division became part of the Indian Resources Branch. In 1949 the terminology was reversed, and it became the Branch of Land, later the Branch of Realty.

GENERAL RECORDS

Most of the correspondence handled by the Land Division is now among the general correspondence of the Bureau, but there are a number of finding aids among the Division's records. There are nine registers of letters received, 1855–80, in which the entries are arranged chronologically rather than alphabetically by section as are the main series of registers of the Bureau for those years. The Division's registers for letters received after 1880, when the Bureau changed to chronological registers, were destroyed. There are 16 volumes of indexes to letters received, 1891–96; 5 volumes of digests of letters sent, 1870–86; and 2 volumes of abstracts of important correspondence and other sources of information, 1870–ca. 1905. Docket books, 1897–1910 (41 vols.), for correspondence concerning land matters and the enrollment of the Five Civilized Tribes include volumes for subject areas and volumes for the Commission to the Five Civilized Tribes and the Inspector for Indian Territory. There are also lists of authorities concerning land matters, 1896–1907, and records concerning Choctaw and Chickasaw Indians, ca. 1882.

The irregularly shaped papers, 1849–1907 (17 ft.), are particularly interesting. They consist of bulky and odd-sized documents, chiefly correspondence and enclosures that were separated from the general correspondence of the Bureau and the special cases. They include reports, proceedings, transcripts of testimony, journals, census rolls, schedules, plats, field notes of surveys, patent applications, financial records, and newspaper clippings. They relate to such subjects as appraisals and allotments of land, boundaries, leases, railroad rights-of-way, enrollment of Indians, special commissions, timber operations, and irrigation projects. There is a list of the bundles in which the records are arranged. Representative examples of specific subjects are listed below.

Investigation of La Pointe timber contracts, 1888.

Oto and Missouri land sales in Kansas and Nebraska, 1889.

Disapproved deeds for Creek lands, 1903.

Report and proceedings of the Sioux Commission, 1890.

Removal of the Southern Ute, 1890.

Appraisement of unimproved lots, Wagoner, Creek Nation, Indian Territory.

Southwestern Coal & Improvement Co. leases, 1902.

Answers to the Board of Indian Commissioners' circular letter relating to allotments, 1902.

Proceedings of the investigation of charges against Agent David W. Day, Southern Ute Agency, 1895.

Winnebago homestead entries, 1881–95.

Settlement with guardians of Shawnee and Wyandot orphans and incompetents, 1871.

Chippewa census rolls, 1889–91.

Petition of Nellie Lydick for an allotment on the Chippewa Reservation, 1903.

Stockbridge and Munsee selections and allotments, 1905-7.

Reports on Fort Hall irrigation, 1907.

Archerd V. McGahey, a Chickasaw allotment contest, 1905.

SURVEYING RECORDS

Most of the surveys of Indian lands and reservations were cadastral, by which land boundaries were established and identified by monuments or marks. The actual work was usually done under the supervision of the General Land Office. The basic records created were field notes and plats. Most of the plats are with the cartographic records maintained apart from the textual records and are described on page 98. The main series of field notes, for 1832-1919, are bound in 287 volumes arranged roughly in alphabetical order by name of State or Territory. There are lists to identify specific survey volumes. Field notes from early surveys and some later ones not voluminous enough for a separate volume, at one time bound as four volumes in the main series, were unbound and are now identified as "Field Notes of Ancient and Miscellaneous Surveys," 1797-1887. There are also unbound field notes, 1910-40 (7 ft.), which, despite the overlapping dates, are essentially a continuation of the bound volumes.

Other records concerning surveying include 29 volumes of field notes of surveys and resurveys of the Bad River Reservation in Wisconsin (Chippewa Indians), with partial indexes, 1915-17; photographs and field notes of surveys of the Navajo Reservation relating to proposed irrigation work along the San Juan River, 1903; field notes of a survey of the Thurston Lake Storage Reservoir on the Wind River Reservation in Wyoming (Shoshoni and Arapaho Indians), 1900; a surveyor's report concerning Wyandot lands in Kansas, 1858; a few maps showing Indian cessions and reservations; an undated reference book for Indian reservations in eight States of the Far West, which contains maps, historical sketches, and abstracts of correspondence; drawings of agency grounds and buildings, ca. 1868-70; descriptions of agencies and schools, 1904-6; and a list of pastures on the Osage and Kaw Reservations in Oklahoma, 1900.

RECORDS CONCERNING ALLOTMENTS

The records concerning allotments of land to individual Indians include some letters received, mostly transmitting receipts for certificates of allotment and often including the receipts, 1871-87; letters received, 1878-80, concerning a controversy over the occupation of an area along the James River in Dakota Territory by members of a band of Yanktonai Sioux led by Magaboda or Drifting Goose and their eventual settlement on allotments on the Crow Creek Reservation; an index to letters received relating to allotments, 1907-9; a volume of instructions to allotting agents, 1892-1909; a record of applications for allotments, 1908-18; applications of Mohave Indians in Arizona and California who did not have a reservation for allotments from public lands, 1908-10; records concerning Chemehuevi nonreservation allotments in California, 1910; eight registers of correspondence relating chiefly to individual allotments and heirship cases, 1915-22; and letters sent relating to allotments, 1920-26 (2 ft.).

The principal kinds of records concerning allotments, however, are plats, tractbooks, and allotment schedules. Most of the plats are with the separately maintained cartographic records described on page 98, but among the textual records of the Land Division are 23 platbooks and unbound papers, 1858-1923, mainly concerning reservations and usually showing individual allotments; 14 volumes of printed plats of the land of the Five Civilized Tribes, compiled by the Geological Survey, 1897-1900 (not showing individual tracts); and 4 binders of plats concerning allotments to nonreservation Indians as provided by section 4 of the General Allotment Act of 1887. Other plats are with the allotment schedules and other records.

Tractbooks are records of the status of land and land transactions, arranged geographically by subdivisions, usually in terms of range, township, section, and fraction of section. There are about 55 tractbooks for allotments on reservations, ca. 1857-1912. They give some information, at least the location, for each subdivision. Given for allotted tracts are the English or Indian name of the allottee, information concerning the approval and issuance of the patent, and sometimes the valuation of the land. Records concerning allotted lands are included in some of the tractbooks for sales of trust lands described below.

Allotment schedules chiefly record allotments to individual Indians, but sometimes they include schedules for lands set aside for special purposes, such as schools, missions, agency buildings, and cemeteries. Sometimes plats, census rolls, or appraisements are bound with allotment schedules, and sometimes affidavits and correspondence accompany the schedules. Information about individual allotments includes name of allottee, some personal information (such as age, sex, and position in family), and location and acreage of land. Sometimes there is information about the issuance of the patent and the sale of the allotment. Rather than being arranged geographically as are the tractbooks, the entries in individual schedules usually are arranged by allotment number. The numbers sometimes were assigned in alphabetical order by name of allottee or in chronological order, but often there is no discernible pattern to their sequence. Some are indexed. There are 73 volumes and unbound papers, 1856-1935. Some were prepared for timber allotments, nonreservation allotments, and changes in allotments; some were not approved.

A schedule for the Agua Caliente (Palm Springs) Reservation in California, identified as an index to Indian land records, is an example of a more recent record control for the status of land. It is arranged geographically by subdivision like a tractbook. The information given includes location of the allotment or tract, type of instrument (for example, trust patent or right-of-way), name of grantor (often the United States), name of grantee (usually an individual Indian or the tribe), and date approved. The schedule is undated, but there are records of transactions from 1911 to 1959.

There are also schedules relating to homestead entries by Winnebago Indians of Wisconsin, 1873–95; schedules of nonreservation Indian homesteads on which the trust period was due to expire, ca. 1915–17; financial records concerning surveying and allotting; and reference materials. One unusual item is a volume of proceedings of the Wyandot Executive Council, 1855–62, which relates in large part to questions of tribal membership; it probably was used to help determine eligibility for allotments.

Some treaties and acts of Congress provided for the issuance of scrip certificates that could be exchanged for allotments. There are several sets of stubs for such certificates and some unissued certificates and relinquished certificates of persons who had died or abandoned their allotment. The stubs typically give the certificate number, name of allottee, location and amount of land, date of issue, and information concerning delivery of the certificate. There are such records for the Kansa (unissued), 1862; Omaha in Nebraska, 1871; Pawnee in Indian Territory, 1882–83; Potawatomi in Kansas, 1866 and 1868 (the latter set unissued); Citizen Potawatomi in Kansas (lists), 1868–71, and in Indian Territory, 1877–95; Sauk and Fox of the Mississippi in Kansas (unissued), 1862; Santee Sioux in Nebraska (including relinquished certificates), 1872, 1875, and 1885; Sisseton and Wahpeton Sioux in Dakota (including relinquished certificates), 1876 and 1884–88; Skokomish in Washington Territory, 1881; and Stockbridge Indians in Wisconsin, 1876. Tractbooks and allotment schedules complementing some of these records are with the main series of such records and sometimes with the records concerning sales of trust lands.

Issuances for which there are also other kinds of records are described below.

Chippewa

The treaty of September 30, 1854, with the Chippewa Indians provided for the issuance of scrip to mixed-blood Chippewa, which entitled the holder to select 80 acres of ceded Chippewa lands. Most certificates issued were good only for land ceded by the Chippewa of Lake Superior, but a few were issued for land ceded by the Chippewa of the Mississippi and the Red Lake and Pembina Chippewa. The records include a register and several lists of persons to whom scrip was issued, 1856–69; some applications for allotments submitted in 1871; two volumes of stubs for scrip issued, 1868–69 and 1873; and schedules accompanying a report of a special commission to investigate the issuance of the scrip, 1871, which include abstracts of the evidence taken by the commission and its recommendations. The commission report was published in the *Annual Report of the Commissioner of Indian Affairs* for 1871. There are also stubs for allotment certificates issued to the Chippewa of the Mississippi, 1876–86, under provisions of the treaty of March 19, 1867.

Between 1867 and 1882, under the provisions of treaties of October 3, 1863, and April 12, 1864, Red Lake and Pembina Chippewa Half-Breed scrip was issued to mixed-bloods, who could exchange it for 160 acres selected from lands ceded by the Red Lake and Pembina Chippewa. The records include applications, 1865 and 1868–71; a register of persons to whom scrip was issued, 1872–82; two volumes of certificate stubs, 1867–82; an index to names of applicants and other persons; and some letters received, 1877–83. In 1880 Special Agent C. W. McIntyre investigated for the General Land Office alleged frauds in the issuance of the scrip. His report of August 20, 1880, is accompanied by an index, lists of cases investigated, findings on individual cases, and forms completed by successful applicants indicating they wished to receive scrip rather than allotments.

Lake Pepin Half-Breed Sioux

The records consist of a roll prepared in 1856 of persons claiming an interest in the Lake Pepin Reserve in Minnesota as provided by article 9 of the Treaty of Prairie du Chien of 1830; 19 volumes of stubs of land certificates issued to Lake Pepin Half-Breed Sioux, entitling them to select allotments on the reserve in return for relinquishing their rights to it, 1856–1915 (most of those issued after 1860 were exchanges or reissues of lost certificates); receipts for certificates, 1857; and relinquishments signed by individuals, entitling them to receive certificates, 1857–60.

Indians in Michigan

Under the provisions of treaties of 1855 and 1864 with the Chippewa of Saginaw, Swan Creek, and Black River and the Ottawa and Chippewa Indians of Michigan, individual Indians could select allotments from specified lands and receive certificates as proof of their holdings. After a 10-year trust period, the certificates were to be replaced by regular fee patents. There are tractbooks and allotment schedules for these allotments among the main series of these records. Other records include lists and schedules of land selections, most of which were compiled by the Mackinac agent, and related correspondence, 1857–75; completed forms by which Chippewa Indians of Saginaw, Swan Creek, and Black River and Chippewa of Lake

Superior applied for specific allotments, 1878; stubs for allotment certificates, unissued certificates, and certificates presumably surrendered for patents, 1857–65; undated plats; and receipts for patents, 1871. Most records for allotments to the Chippewa of Lake Superior are mixed with those for the Chippewa of Lake Superior living in other areas.

Nemaha Half-Breed Reserve

Article 10 of the Treaty of Prairie du Chien, July 15, 1830, provided for a reserve for mixed-bloods on the west bank of the Missouri River between the Great and Little Nemaha Rivers. There are records relating to Oto, Yankton and Santee Sioux, Omaha, and Iowa mixed-bloods, including rolls of claimants, 1857–59; abstracts of claims with summaries of evidence and notations of decisions, 1857–59; allotment certificates and stubs, 1857–59; undated lists of allotted and unallotted mixed-bloods; and a schedule, 1863–69, of persons eligible to participate in the distribution of proceeds from the sale of a tract excluded from the reserve by a survey of 1837–38. Field notes of the survey are among those for "Ancient and Miscellaneous Surveys," and an allotment schedule is with the main series of those records.

Records Concerning Patents and Deeds to Indians

A patent is the document by which the United States transfers title to land to another party. Usually the original patent is sent to the new owner, and the General Land Office (now the Bureau of Land Management) keeps a record copy. Deeds document subsequent transfers of title. Among the records of the Land Division of the Bureau of Indian Affairs are some patents for individual Indians and bands, 1855–1915 (1 ft.), but most of them are designated as being canceled. There are Seminole homestead deeds, called deeds rather than patents, because they were to be issued by the Seminole Nation rather than the United States. One set, 1907, are stamped void; a second set, 1909, were unissued; deeds in a third set, prepared in 1912, were the ones finally distributed. Other records concerning patents and deeds include schedules of unpatented Creek lands, 1878; lists of Choctaw and Chickasaw homestead patents, 1906; receipts for patents issued to Indians of the Pine Ridge, Turtle Mountain, and Standing Rock Agencies, 1911–28; an index to nonreservation land deeds and deeds to the United States in trust, 1933–48; and a record of fee patents, 1943–52.

Records concerning deeds transferring title to land from Indians to other parties are described on page 86.

Records Concerning the Purchase of Land for Indian Use

These few records include an abstract of title to land purchased for the Haskell Institute, Lawrence, Kans., prepared in 1887; an abstract of title prepared in 1900 for property in Riverside, Calif., acquired by the United States for the Sherman Institute; a record of land purchased for schools and for resale to Choctaw Indians in Mississippi, 1920–25; maps and plats, ca. 1934–38, prepared in connection with a program to acquire submarginal land for development as demonstration projects; records, chiefly on cards, concerning land needs and purchases following the Indian Reorganization Act of 1934; records of purchases of land with tribal and individual funds, 1939–45; and records of tax exemption certificates issued for homesteads purchased from trust funds or restricted funds, 1938–51.

RECORDS CONCERNING LAND SALES AND LEASES

Records Relating to Appraisements

Customarily, before Indian land was sold, it was appraised, usually by commissions established for that purpose. Appraisement records consist of schedules of valuations, which give the location, area (usually in acres), and appraised value of tracts or lots of reservation lands, trust lands, townsites, and other lands. There also may be a classification of the land by character (such as agricultural or grazing) or quality, the names of settlers, appraisals of improvements, and other information. Included with some of the appraisements are plats, reports, letters, and other records. There is a general series of appraisements, 1844–1922 (19 vols. and unbound papers, 3 ft.).

Other appraisement records include an appraisement of land and timber on surplus lands of the Yakima Reservation, 1910 (4 vols.). In a single volume are bound a registry of Delaware Indians, patent lists, an appraisement, and a schedule of payments for improvements, 1867–74, created in connection with the enforcement of the treaty of July 4, 1866, which gave the Indians the choice of selling their lands in Kansas and moving to Indian Territory or renouncing their tribal status and remaining in Kansas as U.S. citizens. Also bound in a single volume are appraisements, 1883 and 1885, of parts of the Omaha Reservation in Nebraska; census rolls, 1887, of the Cayuse, Wallawalla, and Umatilla Indians on the Umatilla Reservation, Oreg.; an appraisement, 1883, of Pendleton, Oreg., townsite; and a classification and appraisement, 1891, of surplus land of the Umatilla Reservation not included in the reservation as defined by the Secretary of the Interior in 1888.

An act of March 3, 1893 (27 Stat. 612, 640), provided for the appraisement of improvements made by persons, including freedmen, regarded by the Cherokee Indians in Indian Territory as intruders on their land. A board appointed for the purpose made its final report in 1895. As enclosures to this report are narrative reports of findings in specific cases, with transcripts of testimony (2 ft.). There are also a letter of comments from the Secretary of the Interior and rolls of intruders submitted to the board by the principal chief of the Cherokee Nation.

Other records concerning appraisements include three volumes of schedules of appraisements of damages and improvements to Indian lands resulting from the construction of railroads, 1899–1908, prepared under provisions of an act of March 2, 1899 (30 Stat. 990), and a land classification schedule for the Tongue River Reservation, Mont., prepared in 1929 and revised in 1930.

Other appraisements are with records relating to sales of lands of particular tribes.

Records Relating to Certificates of Indebtedness

Certificates of indebtedness were issued to persons with claims against tribes. Usually, the certificates could be either used to pay for reservation land that was being sold or surrendered for money raised from the sale.

There are letters received, 1861–85 (8 in.), withdrawn from the general incoming correspondence of the Bureau, concerning Kansa certificates of indebtedness ("Kaw Scrip") issued under provisions of treaties of October 5, 1859 (proclaimed Nov. 17, 1860), and March 13, 1862; stubs for the certificates, 1862–67; and a ledger of accounts for certificates and land sales of Kansa and Sauk and Fox of the Mississippi, 1863–67. There are Sauk and Fox stubs and unissued and canceled certificates, 1865 and 1869, intended as refunds to persons who had surrendered certificates issued in 1861 in payment for trust lands and who had paid less than the amount of the certificate; stubs for Osage certificates of indebtedness issued to James N. Coffey and A. B. Canville, July 17, 1867, as provided by the treaty of September 29, 1865; stubs, 1862–65, for Winnebago certificates issued under provisions of the treaty of April 15, 1859 (ratified Mar. 16, 1861); a ledger of accounts for Winnebago certificates surrendered for trust lands and cash, and for cash paid for trust lands, 1863–65; and an account book for certificates of indebtedness and sales of Indian trust lands, 1865–73.

Records Relating to Indian Trust Lands

Many treaties provided for the sale of tribal lands, with the proceeds to be used for the benefit of the Indians. The sales usually were made by the sealed-bid method, but sometimes special sales were arranged. Some of the same kinds of records, particularly tractbooks, were created for both allotments and land sales; sometimes the same tractbook was used for both.

Cherokee Neutral Lands

The most extensive records relating to the sale of land of a particular tribe are those concerning the disposal of the Cherokee Neutral Lands in southeastern Kansas. Article 17 of the treaty of July 19, 1866, modified by the treaty of April 27, 1868, provided for the cession of these lands in trust to the United States to be sold for the benefit of the Cherokee Nation. Persons who had settled on the land were granted preemption rights to a maximum of 160 acres at the appraised value. Article 19 of the treaty provided that Indians living on the land could receive a patent for 320 acres but stipulated that they would no longer be members of the Cherokee Nation. The remaining land could be sold by sealed bids in tracts of not more than 160 acres or it could be sold in its entirety for a minimum of $1 an acre.The second method was chosen, and most of the land was sold to James F. Joy. About 5,000 acres awarded to settlers who had then defaulted were sold in 1871 by sealed bids.

Article 17 provided for the appraisal of the land by a commission of two persons, one to be designated by the Secretary of the Interior and the other by the Cherokee National Council. John T. Cox was appointed as the Government representative, and William A. Phillips was the representative of the Cherokee. This commission, in addition to appraising the land, received the preemption and Indian applications and recommended the actions to be taken by the Secretary of the Interior.

Many of the records described below were created or accumulated by the commissioners and sent by them to Washington.

The records include correspondence, 1866–72 (5 in.), withdrawn from the general incoming correspondence of the Bureau; a docket book of the commissioners for preemption and Indian claims, 1867–68; appraisal reports of the commissioners, 1867–68 (2 ft.), usually consisting of a detailed description of each township, a tabular statement of values, a recapitulation, abstracts of claim dockets, an index to names of claimants, a general description of the land, and a certificate of correctness; tabular schedules of land and improvements compiled by the commissioners, 1867–68 (2 vols.), showing for each tract that was claimed for preemption or by an Indian the name of claimant, value of improvements, docket number, type of claim, applicable treaty article, and the decision of the commissioners; affidavits of preemption claimants and witnesses, each endorsed by the commissioners with a statement concerning the credibility of the witness and their decision on the claim, 1867–68 (10 in.); affidavits of additional witnesses, 1868, and a few of Indian claimants and witnesses, 1867–68; testimony concerning disputed claims, 1867–69; various form letters used by the Bureau to notify preemption claimants of the approval of their claims by the Secretary of the Interior and to process payments and patents, 1869–72; a volume of schedules of land recommended for patent, 1869–71; bids submitted for the purchase of defaulted preemption claims that were sold in 1871; and three tractbooks, 1868–71.

Kansas Trust Lands and Diminished Reserve

By the treaty of October 5, 1859, the Kansa (Kansas or Kaw) Indians agreed to accept a diminished reserve with allotments to individual Indians. The remaining land was to be sold as trust lands, with settlers already there having preemption rights. Settlers on the diminished reserve were to be removed but compensated for their improvements. Subsequently, the Congress provided for the removal of the Indians to Indian Territory and the sale of the diminished reserve. The records of the sales include an 1862 census roll indicating the allotment of each Indian and an appraisement of the value of improvements of white settlers on the diminished reserve; bids submitted, 1862–73; affidavits of bidders, 1871, testifying to improvements or other evidence of permanent settlement; a register of rejected bids and two volumes of notifications of rejections, 1871; notices to settlers on the trust lands of the acceptance of their applications to purchase tracts at the appraised value and giving them instructions for making payments, 1873 (2 vols.); a few similar notices to bidders on diminished reserve tracts, July 17, 1873; three tractbooks recording trust land sales, 1863–67, including a section for Sauk and Fox of the Missouri lands; and a tractbook for the diminished reserve, 1873–74.

Other Tribes

For most other tribes there are comparatively few records. For Chippewa and Munsee lands in Kansas there is only one volume relating to sales of trust lands in 1866 and 1871 and allotments on the diminished reserve in 1860 and 1871; it contains tractbooks for the trust lands and the diminished reserve, census rolls compiled in 1859, a map, and a schedule of allotments. There are two tractbooks, 1857, for the sale of Kaskaskia, Peoria, Piankashaw, Wea, and Iowa trust lands in Kansas; a tractbook, 1871, for Kickapoo lands in Kansas sold, allotted, and held in common and stubs for land certificates issued to the Atchison and Pike's Peak Railroad Co., the only purchaser, January 2, 1866; a tractbook for sales and allotments of Miami lands in Kansas, ca. 1863–74, and notices to settlers of approved awards, December 4, 1873; a tractbook, 1871–83, for Omaha lands in Nebraska allotted, sold (including some to the Winnebago Indians), and set aside for railroads; an undated schedule of purchasers of Osage lands in Kansas; a tractbook, journal of sales, certificates of ownership, and receipts for payments and patents for sales of Ottawa trust lands in Kansas, 1864–77 and 1887; two undated tractbooks, one including appraised value of tracts, for Pawnee trust lands in Nebraska; two tractbooks, 1866–73, for Potawatomi lands in Kansas sold, allotted, and held in common; the canceled general certificate for Potawatomi land purchased by the Atchison, Topeka, and Santa Fe Railroad Co., October 17, 1868, and stubs for certificates for quarter sections issued February 25, 1869, to replace it; bids and two tractbooks for Sauk and Fox of the Mississippi trust lands in Kansas, 1862–71; bids and two tractbooks for Sauk and Fox of the Missouri trust lands in Kansas and Nebraska, 1864–72 and 1877; and bids, notices, two tractbooks, and schedules for Winnebago trust lands in Minnesota, 1863–75.

Records Relating to Sales of Allotments on the Puyallup Reservation in Washington

These records consist of a single volume each of schedules of consents to sales, 1895–1902; schedules of blocks sold and added to the city of Tacoma, Wash., 1895–1912; and records of ownership of allotments, 1895–1907, and of financial settlements, 1896–1915, concerning the sales of allotments of individual Indians. Lands not purchased at the first appraised price could be reappraised at a lower price and again offered for sale.

Records Relating to Choctaw and Chickasaw Segregated Coal and Asphalt Lands

The Choctaw and Chickasaw tribes, by an agreement in 1902 (32 Stat. 641, 654), consented to the sale by public auction of unleased lands in Indian Territory reserved from allotment because of coal or asphalt deposits. Further leasing was prohibited. An act of April 21, 1904 (33 Stat. 189, 209), changed the method of sale to sealed bids and withheld from sale all leased lands. All the bids submitted were rejected. An act of April 26, 1906 (34 Stat. 137, 142), suspended sales, and an act of February 19, 1912 (37 Stat. 67), provided for the sale by public auction of the surface of the coal and asphalt lands but reserved the subsurface rights. A board appraised the land and improvements, 1913–14, before the sale. The records consist of a tract-book, 1904–5, for land offered for sale under the 1904 act, and schedules for the appraisement, 1913–14, with different forms for townsite lots and for other tracts (8 in.).

Records Concerning Removals of Restrictions on Land Sales and Certificates of Competency

The General Allotment Act of 1887 required a trust period of 25 years before an Indian could sell his allotment without the permission of the Secretary of the Interior. Subsequent acts for particular tribes and a general act of June 25, 1910 (36 Stat. 855), however, permitted the issuance of certificates of competency to Indians considered capable of handling their own affairs. These certificates removed the restrictions on land sales, although some of the specific acts exempted the homestead or land on which the Indian was living. The certificates were issued on the recommendations of special boards, Indian agents, and the Commissioner to the Five Civilized Tribes. Other records concerning removals of restrictions are in the 306 classifications of the central files of the Bureau and among the records of the Finance Division.

For the Cherokee Indians there are records relating to applications for removal of restrictions on allotments, 1906–8 (11 in.); the Secretary of the Interior did not act on these in 1906 in the mistaken belief that the allotments were located on oil- and gas-bearing land nor in 1908 because most of the restrictions were due to expire soon. There is a five-volume journal with a record of the proceedings and findings of a board that in 1917 attempted to ascertain the ability of individual Cheyenne and Arapaho Indians to manage their own affairs. There are stubs for certificates of competency issued to Osage Indians, 1909–22 (7 vols.); and stubs and duplicates of certificates issued to the Kansa Indians, 1906–28 (2 vols.). There are also three binders with copies of certificates issued to members of various tribes pursuant to the 1910 act, 1911–54.

Records Concerning Deeds

Most of these records concerning deeds relate to the conveyance of title to land from individual Indians to other parties. The records concerning deeds transferring land titles to Indians are described on page 80.

There are several sets of copies and sometimes abstracts of deeds, 1824–1967, and a consolidated card index to most of them. One general set, 1824–1956 (22 vols. and 2 ft. of unbound records), includes many deeds and accompanying papers for those sales of reserves of individual Indians that required the approval of the Secretary of the Interior. Another set, identified as miscellaneous deeds, 1880–1932 (9 vols.), includes deeds for railroad rights-of-way and terminals, mortgages of railroad companies, deeds to the United States for official purposes, tribal and individual contracts with attorneys and agents, logging contracts, leases, and various other kinds of deeds and related documents. Another set, 1903–67 (51 vols. and 3 ft. of unbound records), is for sales of inherited allotments and allotments of noncompetents. For these there are an index and a register for the years 1903 to 1909 in addition to the card index. There are other sets for lands of individual or groups of tribes and bands, including the Miami, Kaskaskia, Peoria, Piankashaw, Wea, Citizen Potawatomi, Absentee Shawnee, Shawnee, Osage, and Chippewa of L'Anse. There are deeds connected with the termination of Federal responsibility for tribes and reservations following World War II. There are also deeds from the Eastern Band of Cherokee of North Carolina conveying all their land in trust to the United States: the deed of September 24, 1924, was not approved; the deed of July 21, 1925, was approved. Both were prepared in connection with the intended dissolution of the band and the allotment of land to individual Indians.

Other records concerning deeds include a volume of letters sent, 1862–67, chiefly returning, unapproved or for correction, deeds from Shawnee and other Indians in Kansas; two registers of deeds received for approval, 1865–97; affidavits submitted by persons claiming entitlement to patents for Ottawa lands in Kansas, often with a receipt for the patent on the same paper, 1870–75; form letters for the processing of Shawnee deeds, 1869–80; and docket books, 1896–1907.

Other Records Concerning Disposal of Indian Lands

Records concerning the sale and leasing of the Cherokee Outlet, a strip of land west of the 96th meridian in what is now northern Oklahoma, 1889 (2 in.), consist chiefly of a letter from the Secretary of the Interior to the President and several enclosures, including proceedings and correspondence of a commission appointed to negotiate for the cession of the Outlet. These records relate mainly to the legal right of the Cherokee to sell or lease the lands.

Records of the Warm Springs and Colville Commission, 1891 (4 in.), consist of reports, affidavits, transcripts of testimony, an agreement with the Colville Indians, and other records. The commission was appointed to determine the north boundary of the Warm Springs Reservation in Oregon and to negotiate with the Indians of the Colville Reservation in Washington for the cession and opening to white settlement of some of their lands.

Letters received concerning the Muskogee Townsite, Creek Nation, 1900–1902 and 1905–7 (10 in.), relate to the appraisal of lots, patents, the disposal of Indian homesteads that were to be added to the townsite, individual claims, investigations of fraud, and other subjects. Many certificates of payment for lots and owners' certificates of identification are enclosed.

There are also a few records concerning the opening to white settlement of parts of the Lake Traverse Reservation of the Sisseton and Wahpeton Sioux in North and South Dakota, 1892; rules and regulations concerning land use, sales, and leases in Indian Territory, 1891–1905; a volume of schedules of the acreage of ceded lands, ca. 1875–92; and a register of sales of Indian land, 1910.

Records Relating to Leases

Records concerning leases include an account of leases for the Allegany Reservation, N.Y., 1874; five volumes of timber contracts between individual Chippewa Indians of the La Pointe Agency and contractors, with copies of the contractors' bonds, 1883–89, and a volume of renewals of contracts, 1888–89; indexes and registers of leases by members of the Five Civilized Tribes, 1903–9 (8 vols.); a record of Winnebago leases, 1907–8; powers of attorney signed by Indian allottees or heirs authorizing agency superintendents to enter into agreements for grazing leases, 1931–35 (8 ft.); lists of Spokan tribal mining leases and sureties on bonds, 1916–17; and a corporation reference book, 1907–12, mostly concerning leases by Indians to oil companies.

RECORDS RELATING TO CLAIMS

Records Concerning Indian Land Reserves

Various treaties and acts of Congress provided for allotting land reserves to individual Indians from lands that the tribes ceded. Sometimes those entitled to reserves were identified by name in the treaty; other reserves were allocated to persons who met certain requirements. (Reserves on lands that the tribes ceded are not the same as allotments to members of tribes made by dividing tribal reservations.) There are four series concerning individual reserve claims identified as reserve files A–D and records identified as miscellaneous reserve papers. They relate to the establishment and location of claims and to later problems arising from transfers, inheritance, and disposal. There is a general index to reserve files A–D and registers of cases in each file; two registers are electrostatic copies of the originals still held by the Bureau of Indian Affairs. The files, mostly withdrawn from the general incoming correspondence of the Bureau, include letters, reports, legal documents, maps, plats, and other records.

Reserve file A, ca. 1825–1907 (9 ft.), is for land reserved under provisions of treaties negotiated between 1805 and 1830 and includes records transferred from the General Land Office in 1837. Until the establishment of the position of Commissioner of Indian Affairs in 1832, the General Land Office was responsible for the supervision of Indian reserves. The Choctaw treaty of 1830 was the last treaty whose reserve provisions were originally administered by the General Land Office.

Reserve file B, 1832–1907 (2 ft.), relates to reserves under terms of treaties negotiated between 1831 and 1860. Reserve file C, 1831–89 (2 ft.), is for land reserved under article 19 of the 1830 Choctaw treaty. Reserve file D, 1845–1907 (8 in.), concerns reserves under terms of treaties negotiated between 1825 and 1869 and certain acts of Congress.

The miscellaneous reserve papers, 1825–1907 (32 ft.), consist of records relating both to reserves of individuals and groups of Indians and to Indian reserves in general; they are arranged for the most part alphabetically by name or geographical location of tribe. Beginning about 1851 some of the records are continuations of "reserve" subheadings of the letters received, 1824–80.

Records Relating to the Choctaw Net Proceeds Case

The Choctaw Net Proceeds Case derived from claims of individual Choctaw Indians arising from their removal to Indian Territory under the provisions of the 1830 Treaty of Dancing Rabbit Creek. The term "net proceeds" refers to money remaining from the sale of the ceded land in the East after necessary expenses had been deducted. In addition to claims for the value of their land, the Choctaw made claims for the value of improvements, emigration expenses, and other losses. For many years the United States made no payment to the Choctaw for these claims. The treaty of June 22, 1855, provided for the Senate to arbitrate the general claim for net proceeds and to determine a gross sum for all claims of the Choctaw Nation and of individual Choctaw against the United States. The Choctaw Government was to handle the adjudication of individual claims. In 1859 the Senate made a general award of $2,981,247.30 based on the net proceeds alone. The only payment actually made by the United States at that time, however, was one of $250,000 in 1861.

In 1875, although the Congress still had not appropriated the money, the Choctaw Government began proceedings to adjudicate individual claims. By this time most of the original claimants were dead and the proceedings concerned their heirs. During 1875 and 1876 courts of claims in each of the three Choctaw judicial districts received claims and rendered decisions, which were reviewed by a board composed of the chief commissioner of each of the district courts. In 1881 the U.S. Court of Claims awarded the Choctaw $408,120.32 for the net proceeds and for other claims against the United States. The Supreme Court reversed this judgment and confirmed the larger Senate award made in 1859. In 1888 the Congress appropriated $2,731,247.30, the amount of the Senate award less the $250,000 paid in 1861. The Choctaw Council created the Net Proceed Commission with responsibility for issuing certificates to claimants on the basis of the findings of the courts of claims and the board of chief commissioners in 1875 and 1876. Payments were made to settle individual claims in 1889, but much of the money was used for attorneys' fees and other expenses. In 1897–98 another commission, appointed by the Choctaw Council, undertook the settlement of the remaining unpaid claims. The records described below consist mainly of those accumulated by the courts and commissions of 1875–76, 1889, and 1897–98 that were transmitted to the Bureau in Washington. Related records are in Court of Claims General Jurisdiction Case File 12742 in Records of the U.S. Court of Claims, Record Group 123.

Evidence and other records concerning individual claims, 1875–89 (3 ft.), include applications, affidavits, testimony, contracts, powers of attorney, and receipts. Some documents are written in the Choctaw language. The powers of attorney and contracts relate chiefly to the distribution of awards in 1889 rather than to the adjudication of the claims. The records concerning each claim are in envelopes with endorsements that indicate the findings of the courts of claims and the board of chief commissioners in 1875–76.

For the proceedings of the courts of claims, 1875–76, there are two docket books and a journal for the First (Moshulatubbee) District, a docket book for the Second (Apukshunnubbee) District, and an incomplete register of claimants of the Third (Pushmataha) District.

There are also minutes of the board of chief commissioners and three registers of claims awarded by district courts and confirmed by the board, 1876–77; a journal, proceedings, and two docket books of the Net Proceed Commission, 1889; certificates of payment, issued in 1889 in settlement of claims by the fiscal agent of the Choctaw Nation and countersigned by the commissioners, and receipts; and a volume of lists of unpaid and unsettled claims and claims that were to be checked to determine if payment had been made, 1897–98.

Records Concerning Military Bounty Lands

An act of March 3, 1855 (10 Stat. 701), specifically extended the military bounty land laws to Indians. Under these laws, military veterans from the time of the Revolution, or their heirs, were entitled to warrants that could be exchanged for public lands. The records include a two-volume abstract of Indian applicants, 1855–82, with a separate index, 1855–75; schedules of warrants sent to agents and superintendents, usually for a particular group of Indians, 1856–62; and letters received from the Pension Office concerning claims, mostly of Creek Indians, June–September 1870.

Applications for military bounty land warrants are in Records of the Veterans Administration, Record Group 15; warrants surrendered for land are in Records of the Bureau of Land Management, Record Group 49.

Records Relating to Claims Arising From Military Service of Indians During the Civil War

Indian veterans of the Civil War and their heirs made claims for bounties, arrears of pay, and pensions. Records about these claims include a list of claimants, 1865–72; a register of admitted pension claims by heirs of Indians killed in service and by invalid Indians, 1866–69; a register of pension claims based on death or injury, 1873–75; a register of claims for bounties and backpay, 1869–90; and a ledger of accounts of E. B. Stover, a legal guardian for several minor heirs of deceased members of the 9th Kansas Cavalry, 1869–70. There are also correspondence, reports, legal documents, and other records, 1865–75 (1 ft.), concerning John W. Wright and Indian Home Guard claims; these were accumulated during an investigation of charges against Wright, who was an attorney and agent for Indians in presenting claims and also a special agent for the Department of the Interior in making payments to successful claimants.

Applications for pensions are in Record Group 15. Claims for bounties and backpay that were settled by the Second Auditor of the Treasury Department are in Records of the U.S. General Accounting Office, Record Group 217.

Records Relating to Claims of White Settlers Evicted From the Crow Creek and Winnebago Reservations

By an Executive order of February 27, 1885, parts of the Crow Creek (Sioux) and old Winnebago Reservations in South Dakota were opened for public entry. On April 17, 1885, the order was revoked, and the settlers who had moved in were evicted. The evicted settlers then filed claims against the United States for their losses. In 1890 special agent Henry R. Pease began an investigation of the claims as provided by an act of October 1, 1890 (26 Stat. 659). He made his final report on December 15, 1892. Most of the records were created or gathered as a result of his work, but there are some records relating to claims filed under an act of March 2, 1895 (28 Stat. 876, 899). Most of the claims had been settled by 1900. The records include two schedules of claims investigated by Pease, ca. 1894–1900; Pease's report, accompanied by evidence for individual claims (3 ft.); and a schedule of claimants and some affidavits submitted under the 1895 act.

Records Relating to Sioux Property and Allotment Claims

In 1891 Congress appropriated $200,000 to settle at the rate of $40 per pony claims by Sioux Indians for ponies seized by the Army at the Cheyenne River and Standing Rock Agencies (26 Stat. 720) and $100,000 for claims of friendly Sioux Indians and legal residents within the limits of Sioux agencies for damages suffered from depredations by hostile Indians during the winter of 1890–91, the period of the battle of Wounded Knee (26 Stat. 1002). In 1891–92 special agent E. B. Reynolds investigated the pony claims and special agent James A. Cooper, the property claims.

There is a roll of pony claimants, 1892, prepared in the Bureau from information furnished by Reynolds, and affidavits of claimants and witnesses and other records submitted as enclosures to his report of August 24, 1891 (letter received No. 31497–1891). Many were returned to Reynolds for revision, and he submitted them again with a letter of August 4, 1892 (28740–1892). For the property claims there are four feet of records, including depositions, transcripts of testimony, and recommendations of the agent, submitted by Cooper with his report of February 25, 1892 (7805–1892). Claims were received from the Pine Ridge, Cheyenne River, Rosebud, Standing Rock, and Tongue River Agencies.

An act of May 3, 1928 (45 Stat. 484), provided for the investigation under the supervision of the Secretary of the Interior of allotment and property claims of Sioux Indians. An allotment claim was for a lost or short allotment resulting from the failure of the United States to provide the correct allotment to which an Indian was entitled. The property claims were for losses of personal property and improvements, 1874–1901, including claims for seizures of ponies, losses of improvements due to removals, losses through military actions, and property destroyed during a smallpox epidemic. Most claims were submitted by heirs of the original claimants. They were first investigated by the regular agency superintendents and then by a special field agent, Herbert H. Fiske. The Congress later appropriated funds to pay the claims that were allowed, but most of them were rejected. The records relating to these claims, 1928–ca. 1938 (22 ft.), consist chiefly of application forms. There are also affidavits of witnesses, correspondence, reports, memorandums, lists, indexes, and other kinds of records. They are arranged by agency and thereunder by type of claim. There is a separate consolidated card index to names of original and later claimants, but it is incomplete. Other records concerning the claims are with the central classified files of the Bureau (4994-1926-260 General Service and 7113-1939-260 General Service).

Other Records Concerning Claims and Legal Disputes

There are case files concerning charges of fraud in the sale of land of Creek Indians in the East; a few records, 1836-57, concerning a legal dispute between Sally Ladiga, a Creek Indian, and Richard D. Rowland and their heirs for possession of a tract of land in Alabama; two reports by Caius E. Triplett concerning his 1916 investigation of land claims of individual Indians in North Carolina against the Eastern Band of Cherokee Indians; some records concerning a Potawatomi Indian claim to the Chicago lakefront area, 1919; a few letters relating to intruders on the land of the Me-Shin-Go-Me-Sia band of Miami Indians of Indiana, 1871-72; and a report of May 21, 1919, with exhibits (2 ft.) submitted by William L. Bowie in connection with a suit of the Papago Indians of the Pueblo of Santa Rosa against the Secretary of the Interior and the Commissioner of the General Land Office, concerning the Papago title to lands in southern Arizona.

ENROLLMENT RECORDS

Records Relating to Enrollment of California Indians

An act of May 18, 1928 (45 Stat. 602), authorized the attorney general of California to bring suit in the U.S. Court of Claims on behalf of the Indians of that State for compensation for lands taken by the United States. For this purpose the Indians of California were defined as those living in the State on June 1, 1852, and their descendants living in the State on May 18, 1928. The Secretary of the Interior was directed to have compiled a roll of Indians who qualified and a roll of other Indians living in California. Applications for enrollment were to be accepted for 2 years from the date of the act, and the Secretary of the Interior was allowed an additional year to alter or revise the rolls. These limits were later extended 2 years. Charles L. Ellis, superintendent of the Mission Agency, was put in general charge of the enrollment. Several examiners of inheritance and special allotting agents were detailed to the work, but examiner Fred A. Baker finally assumed most of the responsibility and actually prepared the rolls, which are among the annuity payrolls. Applications, 1928-32 (20 ft.), consist of forms completed by the applicants for themselves and minor children, accompanied by affidavits signed by two witnesses. Shown is the name of each person, position in family, age, sex, birth date, and degree of Indian blood claimed. There is also information concerning residence, marital status, land allotments, ancestry, and other subjects, along with an indication of the action taken on the application. There are some group applications for the Indians of a particular agency. The applications are arranged by application number. There is a numerical list of applications, but the alphabetically arranged, completed rolls are more useful as finding aids. Related records are in Court of Claims General Jurisdiction Case File K–344 in Record Group 123.

Records Relating to Cherokee Citizenship

Following the Civil War, many former slaves of the Cherokee Indians in Indian Territory and some Shawnee and Delaware Indians who had settled in the Cherokee Nation claimed Cherokee citizenship. Such citizenship was important to establish their right to remain on Cherokee land and to share in annuity and other payments, including a special $75,000 award voted by the Congress in 1888. The Cherokee disputed many of these citizenship claims and regarded the claimants as intruders; a series of investigations was conducted to compile rolls. There are letters received, 1875–89 (1 ft.), withdrawn from the general incoming correspondence of the Bureau relating to individual claims and more general matters.

Commissioner John Wallace conducted the first investigation in 1889–90. There are affidavits (3 ft.) submitted by applicants and witnesses, with some supporting evidence. Shawnee chiefs often made recommendations on the affidavits of Shawnee applicants. The affidavits were submitted as exhibits to Wallace's report, which is among the letters received by the Bureau (No. 21833–1890). They are divided into the following groups: Admitted Shawnee, Rejected Shawnee, Deceased Shawnee, Admitted Delaware, Rejected Delaware, Free Negroes, Admitted Cherokee Freedmen, Authenticated Cherokee Freedmen, and Rejected Cherokee Freedmen. Authenticated freedmen were those previously recognized as Cherokee citizens; most of their affidavits were submitted to secure the enrollment of small children or to establish their identity as recognized citizens.

Some affidavits from applicants whose citizenship was doubted were given to Leo E. Bennett, the agent of the Union Agency, for further investigation, and he added more evidence for some of the claims. His report is with the letters received (No. 14704–1891). Also submitted to Bennett were affidavits of persons who were rejected by Wallace or who did not apply to him. More affidavits were submitted in 1893 to special commissioner Marcus D. Shelby by applicants for enrollment as freedmen. For his report see letter received 26695–1893.

There are also rolls prepared by the investigating officials, including those prepared by Wallace in 1890; supplements prepared by Bennett, 1891–92; revisions, with indexes, prepared in the Bureau of some of the Wallace rolls (none for rejected applicants); a roll of Shawnee Cherokee prepared by special agent James G. Dickson in 1896, accompanied by a roll of Shawnee admitted to Cherokee citizenship before June 10, 1871, as certified by the assistant executive secretary of the Cherokee Nation in 1889; and a roll of Cherokee freedmen compiled by commissioners William Clifton, William Thompson, and Robert H. Kern, 1896–97.

Records Relating to Enrollment of Eastern Cherokee

In 1905 the U.S. Court of Claims decided in favor of the Eastern Cherokee in certain claims against the United States for moneys due under treaty stipulations. The following year the Congress appropriated funds for the payment, which was to be made to the individual Indians in line with the expected disbanding of the tribe. Those eligible were persons who were Eastern Cherokee at the time of the treaties of 1835–36 and 1846 or their descendants, as opposed to the Old Settler or Western Cherokee who had settled in Indian Territory earlier. They did not have to be members of the Eastern Band of Cherokee of North Carolina who still lived in the East. Guion Miller, first as a special agent of the Department of the Interior and later as a special commissioner of the Court of Claims, undertook the preparation of a roll of persons eligible to participate in the fund.

The records of Miller's work include a copy of his report of May 28, 1909, with exhibits; and a supplementary report of January 5, 1910, concerning exceptions to his findings. The exhibits include 10 volumes of findings on individual applications, a 2-volume alphabetical index to names of applicants, and 10 volumes of transcripts of testimony. The decisions on individual applications are particularly interesting, because they give the reasons for accepting or rejecting the claim. Many people were rejected because they were Creek rather than Cherokee. Other records include a printed copy of the completed roll with two 1910 supplements and copies of older rolls used by Miller. The records have been reproduced as M685. Additional records are in the central classified files of the Bureau (33931–1911–053 Cherokee Nation), and other records, including the applications, are in Records of the U.S. Court of Claims, Record Group 123.

While Miller prepared his roll, inspector Frank C. Churchill, under instructions from the Secretary of the Interior, prepared a roll of just the Eastern Band of Cherokee of North Carolina. Objections were made to the roll he submitted in 1908. Further investigations were made by special agent Charles L. Davis in 1910–11 and by an enrollment committee headed by special agent Orlando M. McPherson in 1913–14. There are correspondence, reports, transcripts of testimony, council proceedings, and other records, 1907–16 (3 ft.), relating to the three investigations. Present also are two somewhat different copies of the Council Roll of the Eastern Band of Cherokee, which is a list of persons recommended for enrollment furnished to Churchill by the tribal council in 1907; two versions of the roll prepared by Churchill in 1908 and approved with revisions by the Commissioner of Indian Affairs and Assistant Secretary of the Interior (one version includes only those accepted and the other lists rejected applicants); and a volume of copies of letters and reports by special agent Davis, depositions, and other records, 1910–11.

An act of June 4, 1924 (43 Stat. 376), providing for the final disposition of the affairs of the Eastern Band of Cherokee of North Carolina required the compilation of another roll. This work was assigned to an enrolling commission consisting of special agent A. W. Symington and the superintendent of the Cherokee Agency, James E. Henderson. In 1926, examiner of inheritance Fred A. Baker replaced Symington, and in 1928 he assumed full responsibility for the work. Baker submitted his final report and roll on December 1, 1928; the roll was approved by the Secretary of the Interior in 1931. Among the records concerning the commission are applications and related records, 1925-28 (15 ft.), including affidavits of witnesses, notices of decisions, appeals, and correspondence concerning individual claims. There are also other correspondence, 1925-28 (1 ft.); transcripts of testimony, 1927-28 (5 vols.), with a separate index; five volumes of decisions, 1926-28 (two other volumes are missing); the roll of the band with a list of deceased annuitants whose enrollment was contested; and a report of the Commissioner of Indian Affairs to the Secretary of the Interior on the findings of the commission, November 20, 1930.

Other Records Relating to Enrollment of the Five Civilized Tribes

There are some letters, 1878-84, with the file designation "Freedmen in Indian Territory," segregated from the general incoming correspondence of the Bureau; these relate principally to the citizenship status and land rights of former slaves of the Choctaw. There is also a volume of rolls of Choctaw freedmen submitted by the national secretary of the Choctaw Nation in 1885.

The records relating to applications for identification as Mississippi Choctaw, 1901-7 (17 ft.), consist principally of documents received by the Bureau from the Commission to the Five Civilized Tribes (Dawes Commission). The enclosures consist of applications, petitions, affidavits and other evidence, transcripts of testimony, correspondence of the Commission, including notifications of decisions, and other records. They relate to applications filed pursuant to an act of June 28, 1898 (30 Stat. 495, 503), which provided that the Commission should determine the identity of Choctaw Indians who, under article 14 of the Treaty of Dancing Rabbit Creek of 1830, claimed rights to Choctaw lands in Indian Territory. Almost all of the original applications and requests for review of claims were rejected.

Other records, 1910-15 (1 ft.), relating to applications for enrollment as members of the Five Civilized Tribes consist of transcripts of testimony, affidavits, memorandums, correspondence of the Bureau and field officials, and other records accumulated for the most part by W. C. Pollock, Assistant Attorney for the Department of the Interior, as part of his investigation of enrollments, made between 1910 and 1912, when he submitted his final report (17711-1912-053 Five Tribes; see also 90635-1913-053 Five Tribes).

Additional records concerning enrollments of the Five Civilized Tribes are among general records of the Bureau, the records of the Indian Territory Division of the Office of the Secretary of the Interior in Record Group 48, and the records of the Commission to the Five Civilized Tribes in FARC Fort Worth. The applications submitted to the Commission are in the custody of the Muskogee Area Office of the Bureau of Indian Affairs.

Records Relating to Flathead Enrollment

In 1905 special agent Thomas Downs compiled a new roll of the Indians of the Flathead Agency in Montana (Flathead, Kutenai, Pend d'Oreille, Kalispel, and Spokan Indians). The records of this enrollment, 1903–8 (8 in.), consist of letters received, with applications, affidavits, and other evidence submitted by applicants; copies of a 1903 roll and supplement; the roll prepared by Downs in 1905; and 1908 supplements.

Records Relating to Osage Enrollment

These records, 1827–1910 (2 ft.), consist of correspondence, reports, affidavits, briefs, transcripts of testimony, copies of annuity payment rolls, maps, and other records concerning contested enrollments in the Osage Nation. Most of the records were withdrawn from the general incoming correspondence of the Bureau in connection with the work of the Osage allotting commission in settling disputed enrollment cases and in making land allotments, 1906–7.

Records Relating to Enrollment of Washington Indians

In 1916 special agent Charles E. Roblin was instructed to investigate adoptions of persons by Indians of the Quinaielt Reservation in Washington. Such adoptions would entitle them to land allotments on the reservation. Roblin was also to prepare a roll of those Indians in western Washington who were not attached to any agency and who had no allotment. His final reports of January 31, 1919, and other records are in the central classified files of the Bureau (11697–1919–053 Taholah). Separate records among those of the Land Division include applications for enrollment and allotment, 1911–19 (2 ft.), many of which are on forms transmitted by Thomas G. Bishop, president of the Northwestern Federation of American Indians; the forms also granted Bishop power of attorney. There are also Roblin's reports of findings, with supporting papers, including correspondence, application forms, affidavits, and powers of attorney, 1910–19 (2 ft.); these records relate to 82 cases in which adoption had been approved by the tribal council in 1912 but had never been acted upon by the Bureau of Indian Affairs and to later applications submitted to the tribal council in 1918. Applications of persons claiming common ancestry were consolidated to form cases.

In 1928 and 1929 special agent F. A. Gross and examiner of inheritance

Mike Lynch prepared an enrollment of the Puyallup Indians in connection with an intended distribution of tribal funds. The reports (2 ft.) concerning their findings on individual applications are accompanied by applications, decisions of the tribal committee, notices to applicants, affidavits, briefs, and correspondence. Other reports and the roll are in the central classified files of the Bureau (79470-1925-210 Tulalip).

Records Relating to Registrations Under the Indian Reorganization Act of 1934

Section 19 of the Indian Reorganization Act permitted the registration as Indians of persons who were at least one-half Indian and not enrolled as members of any tribe. This made them eligible for education loans and for preference in employment with the Indian Service. Funds were also made available to purchase lands for groups or individuals. The records, 1935-42 (5 ft.), include application forms, affidavits, memorandums, reports, correspondence, photographs, lists, and rolls. Most of them relate to Indian groups in California, Montana, Nevada, North Carolina, and North Dakota and concern both individual applications and programs in the States. For North Carolina there is an extensive report by Carl C. Seltzer, who attempted to use anthropological methods to ascertain the degree of Indian blood in a large family group.

Other Enrollment Records

Other records concerning the enrollment of Indians include 11 indexed volumes of registers of Indian families compiled by allotting agents for the Turtle Mountain, Colville, Klamath, Makah, Nez Percé, Coeur d'Alène, Wittenburg, Omaha, and Winnebago Agencies or Reservations, 1884-1909; rolls compiled to establish permanent family names for Indians of the Cheyenne River, Devil's Lake, Lower Brulé, Fort Peck, Pine Ridge, Rosebud, Sisseton, and Standing Rock Agencies, 1903-10 (7 vols. and unbound papers); a 1932 schedule of enrollment of Blackfeet children born since December 30, 1919; a census roll and list of allotments of the Ottawa Indians of Kansas, 1863-64; and a census roll of the Stockbridge and Munsee Indians of Wisconsin, 1894.

OTHER RECORDS

Other records of the Land Division include registers and correspondence concerning the rights of certain attorneys to represent claimants before the Department of the Interior and its bureaus, 1875-1907; records concerning bonds and banks, 1904-24; dockets and account books concerning various subjects; schedules concerning per capita payments to removed Cherokee Indians, 1871-73; printed matter concerning attorneys' claims against the Old Settler Cherokee, 1888-95; records concerning a land dispute on the Klamath Reservation in Oregon, 1926-27; letters received from the Geological Survey, 1911–14, chiefly in response to requests for information concerning the mineral character, power site, and reservoir possibilities of Indian reservations; copies of treaties and Executive orders; and a personal scrapbook of Charles C. Royce of the Bureau of Ethnology, 1888–1900.

CARTOGRAPHIC RECORDS

Cartographic records of the Land Division include 78 volumes of plats of townships in Indian reservations or former reservations. Most of the maps are lithograph copies from the General Land Office and date from about 1850 to 1920. The volumes also include some manuscript and annotated maps and plats of special surveys. Many of the plats and some of the maps are annotated to show allotments, withdrawals, and disposition of lands. There is also a series of unbound plats of townships on Indian reservations, 1852–1935. There are two index volumes to the bound volumes of plats. One is arranged alphabetically by name of Indian reservation and the other by State and thereunder by Indian reservation.

Another series of Land Division records consists largely of unnumbered published and photoprocessed maps annotated in the Division; it includes several large-scale manuscript maps received from field offices. These maps of Indian lands and reservations relate to surveys and allotments, land claims, cessions, acquisitions, sales, leases, and land status and classification, 1911–40. They include many maps that pertain to land acquisitions after the passage of the Indian Reorganization Act of 1934. A few maps prepared during the 1940's are included. The maps are arranged by State and thereunder by Indian reservation.

RECORDS OF THE LAW AND PROBATE DIVISIONS

The Law and Probate Divisions evolved from the Land Division, which handled legal matters until a separate Law Office was established in 1907. By 1911 this office was usually called the Law Division. An act of June 25, 1910 (36 Stat. 855), authorized the Secretary of the Interior to determine the heirs of deceased Indian trust allottees. Both the Land Division and the Law Division handled work resulting from this legislation. In 1913 an Heirship Section was established in the Land Division; but it was soon transferred to the Law Division, which thereafter was chiefly concerned with probate work. By 1917 the Division was usually called the Probate Division.

The records of this succession of units include a volume of communications sent by the law clerk, 1907–13, chiefly containing monthly reports on the status of work and legal opinions in the form of memorandums. For the period May 1, 1907, to April 1, 1908, the volume was used by the law clerk in his capacity as chief of a short-lived Indian Territory Division. There are also eight volumes of copies of Indian wills, 1911–21, that, pursuant to the act of 1910 and an act of February 13, 1913 (37 Stat. 678), were referred to the Bureau and the Office of the Secretary of the Interior for approval. The recommendation of an Assistant Commissioner and the decision of an Assistant Secretary are with each will, and, sometimes, there are other accompanying documents. There are also monthly reports of examiners of inheritance, 1919–23 (5 in.), concerning the accomplishments and status of field work; a volume of statistical tables showing the progress of probate work in Oklahoma, 1920–21, and notes concerning cases, attorneys, guardians, and other matters; a volume of opinions of the Attorney General, 1848–66, relating to interpretations of laws and treaties, land ownership, claims of Indians and others, determination of tribal membership, and disputed jurisdictions of officials; copies of court decisions relating to heirship, enrollment, and other disputes concerning members of the Five Civilized Tribes, 1904–12 (1 in.); decisions and opinions, 1911–23 (4 ft.), of the Comptroller of the Treasury (1911–21), Comptroller General (1921–23), Solicitor of the Department of the Interior, Attorney General, and Secretary of the Treasury relating mainly to the legality of expenditures and the interpretation of appropriation acts; printed copies of acts of Congress relating to Indian administration, 1867–1917 (2 ft.); and printed copies of congressional hearings and other reference material concerning appropriations, 1911–23 (2 ft.).

Many other records concerning legal and probate work are among the general records of the Bureau; many original wills and related records are in the central classified files.

RECORDS OF THE IRRIGATION DIVISION

The Irrigation Division was formally established in 1924, but its records include those of predecessor units dated as early as 1891. Irrigation officers in the field were appointed before 1900 and an Inspector of Irrigation (later Chief Engineer) was appointed in 1898. Irrigation districts were gradually established with superintendents of irrigation in charge. In 1918 permanent districts under supervising engineers were established. Project engineers were in charge of individual projects, and other employees had more specific duties. The irrigation force as a whole was known as the Indian Irrigation Service, and it was concerned with all phases of irrigation activity—planning, construction, and often operation and maintenance. In 1931 the Chief Engineer was replaced by a Director of Irrigation, who was in charge of central office and field operations.

The combined correspondence of the Office of the Chief Engineer and the Irrigation Division, 1901–31 (33 ft.), consists chiefly of letters received and sent, but includes reports, memorandums, photographs, maps, blueprints, clippings, and other kinds of records. It is divided into general correspondence, arranged alphabetically by State or subject, and correspondence relating to each district, arranged alphabetically by name of jurisdiction, reservation, or project.

There are several series of periodic narrative and statistical reports concerning the progress and cost of irrigation work. The reports are illustrated with maps, photographs, charts, and tables. There are annual reports of the Chief Engineer, 1908–24, and of the Director of Irrigation, 1932 (3 ft.); annual district and project reports, 1908–40 (19 ft.); and monthly progress reports, 1907–34 (34 ft.). There is also a series of nonperiodic reports, 1891–46 (36 ft.), by Bureau officials and by other agencies, particularly the Bureau of Reclamation, the Geological Survey, and the War Department. They relate to such matters as water supply, land classifications, feasibility of projects, plans and estimates for construction, power possibilities, progress on projects, special phases of project work, testing of equipment, irrigation conditions, silt accumulation, investigations, histories of projects, and histories of irrigation in certain geographical areas. A list of these reports is available.

Other records include summary irrigation data sheets, 1910–29 (2 ft.), chiefly forms submitted semiannually by irrigation officers giving information on the location of projects, climatic conditions, water supply, costs, and other aspects of irrigation projects (other data sheets are with the annual reports of the Chief Engineer); weekly and biweekly activity reports, 1934–36 (1 ft.), relating chiefly to Public Works Administration projects; photographs; an atlas of reservation and project maps, 1908–32; and some monthly financial statements for Bureau of Reclamation projects on Indian lands, 1918–24.

Many other records concerning irrigation up to 1907 have been brought together as case 190 in the special cases of the Bureau. Records from 1907 are in the 341 classifications of the central classified files of the Bureau.

Cartographic records maintained apart from the textual records include manuscript, annotated, published, and photoprocessed maps of Indian reservations, 1872–1948. Included are general topographic and outline maps and maps showing allotments, irrigable and nonirrigable lands, locations of proposed and existing irrigation projects, cultivated areas, lands cultivated by Indians, canals and ditches, pumping stations, wells, dams, and the classification of land according to potential use. A few maps of the United States show projects supervised by the Bureau of Indian Affairs. Other records include plans of canals, dams, reservoirs, and various irrigation facilities located on the reservations. For a detailed list of the maps of the Irrigation Division, see Laura E. Kelsay, comp., *List of Cartographic Records of the Bureau of Indian Affairs,* Special List 13 (rev. 1977).

See also Records of the Bureau of Reclamation, Record Group 115.

RECORDS OF THE FORESTRY DIVISION

The Forestry (later Forestry and Grazing) Division was not formally established until 1924, but there are records of predecessor units dated as early as 1907. Most records concerning forestry activities are among the general records of the Bureau, particularly in the 339 classifications of the central classified files. There are separate records of the Forestry Division concerning the sale of Choctaw timberlands, 1910–14; 24 volumes of reports of inspection and appraisal of timberlands on the Flathead Reservation, 1908–9, prepared in connection with the work of the Flathead appraising commission; 17 field notebooks, 1909–10, used by topographers and timber cruisers during an examination of the Red Lake Reservation in Minnesota by the Forest Service in cooperation with the Bureau of Indian Affairs; schedules of timber appraisements on the Colville Reservation, 1914 (1 ft.), completed under the supervision of the Colville appraising commission; maps and plats for the Flathead, Klamath, Menominee, and Spokane Reservations, showing timberlands, 1910 and 1914–26 (13 vols. and unbound papers, 1 ft.); and Menominee Agency reports, 1907–44.

Cartographic records maintained apart from the textual records include manuscript and annotated maps of Indian lands and reserves, ca. 1908–45, which show forest and timberland reserves, types of timber, estimated board feet per acre, tracts on which timber was offered for sale, allotments on which contracts were approved for sale of timber, logging units, timber sale units, the status of timber cutting and logging, cutover lands, and locations of sawmills. Some maps show types of roads, telephone lines, grazing units and reserves, livestock capacity, and stock driveways. There are also published maps of Indian reservations, ca. 1920–46, which show roads, railroads, trails, telephone lines, forest ranger lookout stations, sawmills, reservation boundary lines, parts of adjoining national forests, stock driveways, reservoirs, and water facilities for livestock. Included are fire control maps for several reservations.

RECORDS OF THE CIVILIZATION DIVISION

The Civilization Division, known at first as the Civilization and General Statistics Division, was one of the original divisions of the Bureau, established in 1846. It had charge of such matters as education, emigration, agriculture, mechanical pursuits, trade and intercourse with the Indians (including traders' licenses), and the maintenance of information on a variety of subjects. Later it was given additional responsibilities, including depredation claims, conduct of Indians, liquor control, and intrusions on Indian lands. There was a separate Medical and Educational Division from 1873 to 1881, after which educational matters were assigned to the Civilization Division and medical matters were the responsibility of the Accounts Division. By 1884 the Civilization Division usually was called the Civilization and Education Division. In September 1885 it was assigned responsibility for educational matters only, and it became the Education Division. Its other duties were divided among other units of the Bureau, and most of the Division records were transferred with the functions. Other records, such as farming reports, were destroyed by the authority of the Congress. Comparatively few records identified as those of the Civilization Division remain, but they include some of particular interest.

They include a volume of Indian population figures, 1800–53; census rolls, 1835–69 (5 in.); a volume of abstracts of farming reports, 1863–65; memorials of the New Mexico Legislature, 1863, concerning Indian depredations, the establishment of reservations, and the release of Indian captives; certificates, 1872–73, by which the United States recognized certain Sioux Indians as chiefs of bands and acknowledged that the bands were at peace with the United States; schedules of Indians, soldiers, and citizens killed, 1873–75; a volume of copies of correspondence concerning the White River Agency, 1877–79, probably prepared for the investigation of the destruction of the agency and the killing of agent Nathan C. Meeker and other employees by the Indians in 1879; and correspondence relating to the Ute Commission, 1881–82 (2 in.), appointed by the President chiefly to supervise the removal of the Ute Indians in Colorado to a new reservation (see also Special Case 112).

There are records (1 ft.) concerning the investigation of one of the better known incidents in the history of the West, the killing by Sioux Indians of an entire detachment of troops from Fort Phil Kearny, led by Capt. William Fetterman on December 21, 1866. President Andrew Johnson appointed a special commission to investigate this incident, known as the Fort Phil Kearny or Fetterman massacre. The records include a volume of the proceedings of the commission, March 4–June 12, 1867; a volume of the proceedings of a detachment of the commission that visited the upper Missouri River area, May 21–July 31, 1867; the testimony of the commander of the troops, Col. Henry B. Carrington, with exhibits, and the testimony of other witnesses; reports of commissioners; and minutes, reports, and letters received by the commissioners and other records transmitted by them to the Bureau of Indian Affairs. These records have been reproduced as M740. Some have been published in *Information Touching the Origin and Progress of Indian Hostilities on the Frontier*, Senate Executive Document 13, 40th Congress, 1st session.

Other records relate to claims of Indians, chiefly in Indian Territory, who remained loyal to the United States during the Civil War and, as a consequence, were driven from their homes or suffered property damage when the Confederates occupied the area. Several treaties negotiated after the war provided for the determination of these losses and compensation for the Indians. There are petitions, affidavits, lists of damages claimed, findings of commissioners appointed to adjudicate the claims, and other records, 1866 (4 in.), concerning claims of individual Indians against the Choctaw and Chickasaw Nations as provided by article 49 of the treaty of April 28,

1866. There is also a receipt book, ca. 1868, for payments made.

Under article 4 of the treaty of June 14, 1866, claims of loyal Creek Indians and freedmen were investigated by the agent of the Creek Agency and the superintendent of the Southern Superintendency. The records, 1869-70 (1 ft.), consist of affidavits by claimants and witnesses, joint findings of the two officials, and an abstract of claims. Later records concerning loyal Creek claims are in special series A, described on pages 59 and 60.

Article 12 of the treaty of February 23, 1867, provided for the appointment of commissioners to investigate claims of Seneca, Mixed Seneca and Shawnee, and Quapaw Indians. The records, 1869-70 (4 in.), consist of claims, affidavits, testimony, and findings of the commissioners.

For the Shawnee Indians in Kansas, there are claims, evidence (including a volume of depositions taken by their agent, James B. Abbott), powers of attorney, correspondence, and other records concerning claims for property losses suffered during and after the war, 1861-68 (3 in.).

RECORDS OF THE DEPREDATION DIVISION

The Depredation Division (also known as the Depredation Claims Division) was established in October 1885 to carry out provisions of an act of March 3, 1885 (23 Stat. 376), which required the Secretary of the Interior to investigate depredation claims against Indians that had been approved but never paid and those that were pending but not yet examined. The Division was made responsible for conducting investigations and making reports to the Secretary, who in turn was to report to the Congress on each claim. By an act of March 3, 1891 (26 Stat. 851), the investigation and determination of Indian depredation claims were transferred to the U.S. Court of Claims. The Depredation Division continued to operate until 1893, mainly to maintain records and answer inquiries. The records described below include some inherited from the Land and Civilization Divisions and a few records dated after 1893, when the Land Division handled the remaining work concerning the claims. Many records concerning depredation claims were transferred to the Court of Claims and are now in Records of the U.S. Court of Claims, Record Group 123, the principal source for information concerning these claims.

There are some finding aids for correspondence, including two registers of letters received, 1889-98; an index to letters sent, 1889-90; and an index to reports, 1890-91. The letters sent, reports, and many of the letters received are among the general correspondence of the Bureau. There are also indexed registers of depredation claims submitted, ca. 1835-91 (9 vols.), and four docket books for individual claims considered by the Depredation Division, 1885-91. The registers are somewhat confusing because a claim may have been registered either when first submitted or when it was reconsidered. Some of the older claims seem to have been registered for reference only.

The main series of records of the Division consists of evidence concerning claims, ca. 1835–96 (22 ft.). It includes affidavits of claimants and witnesses, reports of agents and other field officials, reports of the Commissioner of Indian Affairs to the Secretary of the Interior, and correspondence concerning individual claims by whites and Indians for depredations committed by Indians and a few Indian claims against whites. For many cases there are only endorsement sheets or jackets because the records were transferred to the Court of Claims. The case files are arranged by claim number assigned in order of registration.

There are separate records relating to claims for depredations committed by Sioux Indians in Minnesota during the outbreak of 1862. An act of February 16, 1863 (12 Stat. 652), authorized the President to appoint commissioners to investigate these claims and make awards. The commission consisted of Albert S. White, Eli R. Chase, and Cyrus Aldrich. There are affidavits, petitions, powers of attorney, and other records submitted to the commissioners and certificates of their findings, 1862–63 (2 ft.), and a few general records, 1862–69. Records concerning payments made by the commission are among the records of the Finance Division.

Other records of the Depredation Division include schedules and abstracts, 1835–78 and 1891 (8 in.); a volume with schedules of claims against the Sioux and Chippewa of the Mississippi, 1857–62; and lists of claims.

RECORDS OF THE EDUCATION DIVISION

The Education Division was established in September 1885, but its records include some of predecessor units—the Civilization Division, 1846–85, and the Medical and Educational Division, 1873–81. The term "education" was used in a broad sense to encompass the physical, mental, moral, industrial, and social advancement of Indians. The Division had charge of school administration, including plans and specifications for buildings, personnel, and the purchase of supplies. It supervised agricultural and mechanical training, and for many years it handled matters concerning law and order (including liquor suppression) and health and sanitation. At times it had charge of marriage, divorce, morals, industries, Indian employment, traders' licenses, roads, construction, and exhibits. Most of the records now identified as those of the Division, however, relate to schools.

On June 1, 1926, the Education Division was renamed the Administrative Division, and on August 15, 1930, the Schools Section of the Administrative Division became the Education Division.

In 1931 the Alaska Division of the Office of Education, which had charge of education and medical relief for the natives of Alaska, was transferred to the Bureau of Indian Affairs. Its work was gradually merged with that of the Education Division, but separate records of the Alaska Division continued to be maintained. In 1949 the Education Division became the Branch of Education.

For the field the position of Superintendent of Indian Schools was established in 1883; the title was changed to Chief Supervisor of Education in 1910. Similar positions were established for the supervision of medical work, Indian employment, law enforcement, and construction. Considerable confusion developed over the authority of the Education Division, the field supervisors, and the regular agency and school officials. In 1926 the position of General Superintendent was established with overall responsibility for school, agricultural, and industrial matters. In 1931 directors in charge of field and central office activities were appointed for the various services. A Director of Education was put in charge of educational matters.

GENERAL RECORDS

Most of the correspondence of the Division is now with the general correspondence of the Bureau, but there are some finding aids, including a register of letters received by the Medical and Educational Division, 1878-81; 13 volumes of indexes to letters received by the Education Division, 1895-1907; four registers of letters received by the Education Division, 1906-8; and five indexes to letters received by the Superintendent of Indian Schools, 1895-1907. Other records include a volume which contains weekly summaries of work completed, 1887-88; weekly reports of uncompleted work, March-May 1890; and some documents concerning the Bureau of Catholic Indian Missions, mission schools, and the teaching of English rather than Indian languages in Indian schools. There are also three volumes of memorandums and others records on various subjects, 1905-15; a volume of circulars issued by the Education Division, 1897-1909, relating primarily to the operation of schools; and one volume of circulars issued by the Superintendent of Indian Schools, 1899-1908, relating to meetings and institutes; three volumes of copies of authorities from the Secretary of the Interior or his representative; and a volume of letters sent concerning textbooks, 1907-9, including many to publishers who had submitted books for examination.

There are office files of four officials. For Hervey B. Peairs, Chief Supervisor of Education and General Superintendent, there are correspondence, programs, copies of speeches, clippings, statistical reports, outlines, and other records, 1910-27 (3 in.), relating to such subjects as examination papers, courses of study, textbooks, and conferences. The file of W. Carson Ryan, Director of Education, 1931-35 (2 ft.), includes correspondence, reports, memorandums, copies of speeches, historical sketches, notes, clippings, congressional bills, maps, bulletins, copies of pamphlets, and other printed and processed reference materials relating to Federal-State relations, program planning, field trips, conferences, mission schools, histories of schools and reservations, and other subjects. The records of Mary Stewart, Assistant Director of Education, 1929–36 (3 ft.), include correspondence, memorandums, reports, survey forms, worksheets, historical sketches, printed reference materials, copies of addresses, photographs, and tables. Most of them relate to a survey of school enrollment and vocational opportunities for Indians in Oregon, Washington, Idaho, Montana, and northern California. The survey was conducted at the Salem School in Chemawa, Oreg. There are an office file, 1929–32 (6 in.), and a reference file, ca. 1921–32, of Carrie A. Lyford, Demonstration Teacher of Home Economics and later Associate Supervisor of Home Economics, who spent much of her time visiting schools.

There are many records that abstract information from correspondence, reports, and other records, most of which were then destroyed (although copies sometimes are with field office records). There are eight reference books, which consist chiefly of abstracts from letters and reports relating to the physical condition of schools and general conditions in them, 1882–1909. Two volumes of briefs of investigations, 1899–1911, consist chiefly of abstracts of records relating to charges, evidence, and recommendations of inspecting officers concerning Bureau employees. There is also a volume of statistics taken from monthly sanitary reports from agencies, 1880–81, which give the number of cases of different diseases and the number of births, deaths, and vaccinations. Two volumes of abstracts of letters relate to epidemics, 1901–8.

Most periodic reports on education and schools during the latter part of the 19th century and up to 1910 were not preserved, but information was abstracted from them. The Division customarily identified this information as statistics, but it includes other kinds of data. There are two volumes of statistics and other information taken from reports submitted by Indian agents, 1859–69. The information given includes the location of schools, number of pupils and teachers, religious denominations operating schools, financial support, wealth of tribes in individual property, and number of missionaries. For the years 1874 to 1884 there are four volumes of employee rosters and information concerning the attendance and progress of children taken from reports submitted by agents and school superintendents. The largest series consists of 22 volumes of information taken from monthly and quarterly reports of agents and superintendents, 1882–1909. An entry usually gives salaries of teachers and other employees, capacity of schools, number of daily sessions, enrollment, attendance, and different kinds of expenditures. For the years 1890 to 1908 two volumes consisting chiefly of tables prepared quarterly compare enrollment and attendance at different types of schools with the same quarters of the previous year. A volume of figures for school capacity, enrollment, and attendance was taken from semimonthly reports of school superintendents, 1893–95, and a volume of figures for enrollment and attendance was taken from monthly reports, January–October 1895. For July 1895 to June 1896, a volume of figures taken from the monthly reports concerning capacity, enrollment, attendance, and status of pupils is considerably more detailed than the two earlier volumes. Three other volumes of information from monthly reports, 1904–10, concern pupils, including the number who had run away, returned, been expelled, or died. A volume for Choctaw neighborhood schools in Indian Territory in fiscal years 1901 and 1907 (mostly just the first half of each year) and Chickasaw schools in fiscal year 1907 gives names of teachers, number of days in session, and information concerning enrollment and attendance of Indian, white, and black children. A similar volume for Cherokee day schools intended for fiscal year 1907 contains mainly figures for September 1906.

Two volumes, 1887–1911, give information concerning contracts negotiated with public school systems and private groups, mainly missionary societies, for the education of Indian children. In the first volume there is also information concerning authorities for transportation of pupils. Entries for individual contracts give name of school and contractor, number of pupils, rate charged for each pupil, total amount of contract, and, for the later years, information concerning approval by the Secretary of the Interior and financial settlement. A register of public school contracts, 1923–24, gives contract number, name of school, district, number of pupils, daily rate for each pupil, total amount of contract, and information concerning administrative handling of it.

Other records relate primarily to school physical plants. A volume for 1895 gives information taken from reports of agents and superintendents including name of school, location, date of organization, capacity, brief description of buildings, and data concerning water supply, drainage, sewerage, ventilation, and facilities for industrial education. Five volumes of abstracts of reports from various field officials, 1898–1905, concern school locations, buildings, lighting, electrical systems, water supply, sewerage, and heating, sometimes with recommendations.

The only periodic school reports earlier than 1910 among the records of the Education Division are monthly reports from the Tulalip Agency, Wash., 1874–85 (2 in.), and quarterly reports from the Puyallup and Tulalip Agencies, Wash., 1886–1910 (3 in.). The main series of reports after 1909 usually are on standard forms and are arranged by fiscal year, thereunder alphabetically by name of agency or other jurisdiction, and thereunder by school. Quarterly reports, 1910–39 (58 ft.), were submitted for both Government and private contract schools. For most of the years there is information about individual pupils as well as summary information. This includes name, age, tribe and degree of Indian blood, date of enrollment, grade, type of training, number of days in attendance, and distance of home from a public school. Beginning in 1936 the information concerning individual pupils, except those who were dropped from the school rolls, was gradually eliminated. During the years 1925–36 semiannual reports were in general use, and there are few quarterly reports. The semiannual reports, 1925–37 (18 ft.), give substantially the same information as the earlier quarterly reports. There are also annual reports, 1924–37 (4 ft.), that give much the same information as the quarterly and semiannual reports; often they were submitted on forms intended for the more frequent reports. They were not, however, submitted as systematically.

There are also annual school census reports, 1912–39 (32 ft.). These are actually census rolls of children of school age both in and out of school. Entries for individual children give name, sex, age, tribe and degree of Indian blood, distance of home from a public school, and name of parent or guardian. Included for children attending school are the school, grade, length of term, and number of grades. The reason for nonattendance is given for children not in school.

There are a few public school monthly attendance reports submitted by public schools in Nebraska and South Dakota, 1913–14, and a large number of public school quarterly attendance reports, 1913–15 and 1922–37 (7 ft.). The forms vary for different periods, but they all give general information concerning the schools and attendance.

There are also samples of statistical reports concerning examinations and promotions, 1924–25 and 1930–34; examples of examination papers of pupils at the Green Bay Agency, 1888, the Grand Junction School, 1899, and the Haskell Institute, 1915; and examples of school calendars, 1930–34.

Other records include completed forms, 1929–32 (1 ft.), for an educational survey conducted to determine which children should attend public schools and which children should be given Federal aid. These give information about individual families, including members, homelife, and distance of home from a public school. There are forms for the Chemawa (Salem) School; for the Cheyenne and Arapaho, Cheyenne River, Consolidated Chippewa, Crow Creek, and Kiowa Agencies; and for the Creek Nation. There are also monthly reports of school social workers and some of home economics teachers, 1932–36; case records, 1935, concerning a traveling mental health clinic organized as part of a school social work program to study Indian problem children in Oklahoma; information files, including correspondence about Carlisle School, 1910–66; and a few maps.

RECORDS OF THE INDUSTRIES SECTION

The Industries Section was in charge of such matters as agriculture, Indian employment, traders' licenses, roads, and exhibits. The only separate records of the section, however, are some reports and other records relating to graduates of Indian schools and their subsequent careers, 1910–25 (5 in.), and reports with many photographs of industrial surveys, 1922–29 (22 ft.), submitted by agency superintendents and consisting chiefly of descriptions of home and farm conditions of individual Indian families. See also the records of the Division of Extension and Industry on pages 111 and 112.

RECORDS OF THE LAW AND ORDER SECTION

The records of this section consist of two volumes of records of arrests, 1909–10, chiefly for liquor violations; some correspondence of the Chief Special Officer (who was in charge of field operations) relating to peyote, 1908–11, and 1915–18 (4 in.); weekly narrative reports of special officers and deputies, relating mainly to liquor control activities, 1915–17 (2 ft.); reports of liquor seizures on reservations, mainly in Minnesota, 1915–17 (5 in.); case reports, 1923–33 (4 ft.), prepared by special officers and relating chiefly to liquor law violations; general correspondence of the Chief Special Officer, 1933–47 (7 ft.), relating to law enforcement (including individual cases), the jurisdiction of tribal and Federal courts, the appointment of deputy special officers, administrative matters, and other subjects; correspondence of the Chief Special Officer with special officers, 1933–47 (3 ft.), relating to case activities and administration; and some personnel and financial records.

RECORDS OF THE HEALTH DIVISION

The Health Division, known as the Medical Division until 1931, was established in 1924; previously, health activities had been assigned to the Education Division. The objectives of the Indian health program were the prevention and cure of illnesses—particularly tuberculosis, trachoma, venereal diseases, and diseases of infancy and childhood. Medical and dental services were provided to Indians in hospitals, sanatoriums, and dispensaries and by traveling health officials.

The medical service of the Bureau was reorganized in 1926 in cooperation with the Public Health Service, which detailed a physician to serve as Chief Medical Director. Four districts were established, each under a district medical director. In 1931 the designation Chief Medical Director was changed to Director of Health.

Physicians and nurses were assigned to agency and school hospitals, and additional physicians were employed by contract. There were traveling eye, ear, nose, and throat specialists, who concerned themselves particularly with trachoma, and traveling field dentists and nurses. Field matrons were employed to teach hygiene, housekeeping, and child care to Indian women.

In 1949 the Health Division became the Branch of Health. On July 1, 1955, responsibility for Indian health activities was transferred to the Public Health Service.

The records of the Health Division consist chiefly of different kinds of reports. Correspondence concerning health activities is filed under appropriate headings in the central classified files of the Bureau and in the inspection reports and special agent files of the Inspection Division. (Access to records less than 75 years old containing information about the physical or mental health or care and treatment of individuals is subject to the current regulations of the creating agency, its successor, or, if there are no applicable regulations, the Public Health Service.)

The largest series of records of the Division consists of hospital reports, 1923–38 (33 ft.). These are several kinds of statistical reports, chiefly on standard forms. Most are weekly and monthly reports but there are some annual and semiannual summary reports. Few reports are dated before 1926. Through 1930 the two main kinds of reports are hospital reports, usually submitted monthly, of the number of patients and medical and surgical services furnished, and weekly reports of bed occupancy and the number of patients and employees. Included are some copies of the health sections from the annual statistical reports of Indian agencies and schools and monthly trachoma reports for fiscal years 1929 and 1930. In 1931 the several kinds of reports were replaced by weekly reports of health activities, which in turn were replaced in July 1932 by two kinds of reports: weekly reports of in-patient and dispensary patients and weekly reports of domiciliary patients and out-patients. There are no reports for the period July 1933 through June 1936. For fiscal years 1937 and 1938 there are monthly reports of in-patients and dispensary patients. With these there are often individual cards for patients suffering from more than one ailment. The domiciliary and out-patient reports for these two fiscal years are filed separately. The reports are arranged alphabetically by name of jurisdiction (school, agency, or hospital) and thereunder in rough chronological order.

Other series of reports include some physicians' annual and semiannual statistical reports, 1925–30 (3 in.); physicians' annual, semiannual, and monthly statistical reports on patients and out-patients, 1936–38 (2 ft.), relating to medical work done outside of hospital buildings or attached dispensaries; trachoma reports, January 1926–June 1928 and July–December 1930 (1 ft.); statistical and narrative reports of special physicians, 1925–32 (8 in.), also relating in large part to trachoma cases; statistical reports of field dentists, 1926–32 (6 in.); statistical and narrative reports, chiefly monthly, of field nurses, 1931–43 (14 ft.); and weekly reports of field matrons, 1933–38 (2 in.).

There are also records concerning four surveys, including a narrative report with accompanying statistical tables, photographs, and other materials, concerning a general health survey of the Eastern Band of Cherokee Indians in North Carolina, June 5–17, 1933 (1 in.); completed forms for a sanitation survey of the Fort Totten Agency, N. Dak., August 26, 1929 (3 in.), giving information on housing, water supply, sanitary facilities, farming, and health of families and individuals; similar but more detailed forms for a health survey of the Potawatomi Indians in Kansas, ca. 1928 (2 in.); and clinical record forms completed for a health survey of persons living on the Zuni Reservation, N. Mex., 1934 (1 ft.), giving personal and family medical histories and the results of physical and medical examinations. The report on the findings of the Zuñi survey and related correspondence are in the central files of the Bureau (49558-1934-737 Zuni).

RECORDS OF THE DIVISION OF EXTENSION AND INDUSTRY

The Division of Extension and Industry was established December 5, 1930, as the successor to the Industries Section of the Administrative Division, formerly the Education Division. At first it was known as the Division of Agricultural Extension and Industry, and it was often called simply the Extension Division. In 1941 the Rehabilitation Division, which was in charge of WPA projects for Indians, was merged with the Extension Division. Beginning about 1948 there was a series of name changes, and in 1955 the Division's activities were made part of those of the Branch of Land Operations.

The Division was organized to assist Indians in solving home and economic problems. It gave instruction and guidance by means of classes, demonstrations, visits, and work supervision. The Division promoted 4-H Club activities for young people, cooperated in experimental work, and had charge of the extension of credit to Indians.

The Division worked to improve crops and livestock, soil conditions, weed control, farm management, and marketing methods. During World War II its major concern was to increase food production. In home extension, the Division was concerned mainly with food conservation, nutrition, clothing, sanitation, and household budgets.

A Director of Extension and Industry was in charge of the Division, and agricultural extension agents or regular agency superintendents were in charge of extension work at the individual agencies. In addition, there were home extension agents, farm agents, farmers, stockmen, dairymen, and other field employees.

The records of the Division include eight volumes of annual reports of the Director, 1932-39, containing narrative statements, tables, and photographs; reports and related correspondence, 1930-43 (17 ft.), including annual and, until 1934, monthly and weekly narrative and statistical reports from field officials, illustrated with many photographs; some work programs, chiefly for 1935; weekly narrative and statistical reports of home extension agents, March 1937-January 1938 (4 in.); monthly reports of extension workers, 1938 (2 ft.); and a few records concerning the Alaska Reindeer Service, 1939-42 and 1950-53 (2 in.).

There are also records concerning five surveys. For a social and economic survey, there are records, 1933–34 (2 ft.), including final survey reports submitted by agency superintendents, weekly progress reports, reports on Indians owning no land, and correspondence. The purpose of the survey, which was conducted with Civil Works Administration funds, was to collect information concerning population, education, employment, relief assistance, family income, housing facilities, food and clothing, land, agricultural produce, livestock, farming equipment, and other social and economic aspects of Indian life.

The records of a land use survey conducted by the Indian Land Unit of the Natural Resources Board contain reports, completed forms, correspondence, and other records, 1934–35 (1 ft.). The survey was conducted to assist in planning a land acquisition program for Indians. The records give information on population, income needed for an adequate standard of living, wages earned by Indians, potential annual production of reservations, current land use, unclaimed surplus lands, estimated costs of land systems, and other matters.

There are also forms completed by agency officials for surveys of the kinds and amounts of noxious weeds on Indian reservations, 1932 (1 in.) and 1941 (2 in.), and a narrative report, illustrated with photographs, maps, tables, and other materials, of a general survey of the Jicarilla Apache Reservation, N. Mex., 1939 (1 in.).

Other records concerning extension activities are among the central classified files of the Bureau, the records of the Rehabilitation Division, and the Records of the Federal Extension Service, Record Group 33.

RECORDS OF THE ALASKA DIVISION

The Alaska Division of the Office of Education was established in 1885 pursuant to an act of May 17, 1884 (23 Stat. 24), which directed the Secretary of the Interior to provide education for children in Alaska. On April 11, 1885, the Commissioner of Education appointed Sheldon Jackson of the Presbyterian Board of Home Missions as general agent for education in Alaska. The Division consisted of a section in the central office in Washington, D.C., and a field office in Seattle, Wash.; Jackson divided his time between the two. Six school districts were established; at first, existing buildings were used, but later combined schools and teachers' dwellings were constructed.

Medical relief work among Alaskan natives began about 1915, and by the early 1920's, there were five hospitals. The medical service was carried out with the advice and assistance of the Public Health Service. At first the service was operated by the Seattle field office, but on July 1, 1930, the educational and medical relief functions were transferred from Seattle to Juneau and placed under a director of education and a director of the Alaska Medical Service. Thereafter, the Seattle office performed largely routine administrative functions.

By March 14, 1931, when the Secretary of the Interior transferred the Alaska Division from the Office of Education to the Bureau of Indian Affairs, the Division's activities had expanded beyond education and medical care into economic assistance, necessitated by the depletion of the seal herds and whale fisheries. In 1891 Sheldon Jackson led an expedition to Siberia to import the first Siberian reindeer into Alaska to provide food, clothing, and a source of income from the sale of hides and meat. Responsibility for the reindeer herds shifted several times; in 1937 it was returned to the Alaska Division, and an Alaska Reindeer Service was established. Other economic and social programs included the Alaska Trust Fund, which provided banking services for Alaskan natives and Federal employees; loans for vocational education; and assistance for the incorporation of towns to engage in business.

Some of the series of records of the Alaska Division were continued for a time after the Division was transferred to the Bureau of Indian Affairs, but gradually more and more records were filed in the Bureau's central classified files rather than the older series. See also Records of the Office of Education, Record Group 12, on page 388.

Until 1908 the general records were divided for the most part into copybooks of letters sent, mostly by the general agent but also by the Commissioner of Education (including a main series of 63 volumes, 1887–1908, and several smaller series), and unbound letters received, 1883–1907 (26 ft.), arranged chronologically.

In 1908 the Division started a general correspondence file used until 1935 (96 ft.). It is arranged for the most part by fiscal year and thereunder by main and subsidiary headings, which varied somewhat from year to year. Typical headings are legislation, department relations (with folders for individual departments and bureaus), Executive orders, natives, land, reindeer, outside relations, monthly office reports, Alaska Trust Fund, contracts, leases, estimates, circular letters, new schools and hospitals, inspection, officers and employees, appointments, supplies, financial matters, buildings, U.S.S. *Boxer*, Seattle office, names of individual districts, and in the earlier years individual schools in alphabetical order. There is a card index for the years 1910 to 1930.

There is a separate series of correspondence, reports, and other records, 1897–1931 (4 ft.), concerning the Metlakahtla controversy, which involved William Duncan and the colony he dominated on Annette Island. There are also some copies of telegrams and letters sent by the Chief of the Alaska Section of the Bureau of Indian Affairs, 1935–37.

Budget and accounting records include estimates, 1934–36; appropriation and other ledgers, 1907–22; a journal and contracts concerning reindeer,

1891–1905; and contract papers concerning construction of Federal buildings, 1930–32. Other records include annual reports concerning reindeer, 1912–17; annual school reports, 1933–37, and quarterly reports, 1937–40; community activity reports, 1939; a reference file of William Hamilton, Assistant Chief of the Division, 1888–1926; two scrapbooks of newspaper clippings, 1897–1908; copies of Executive orders; and a file of Sheldon Jackson on Alaskan school matters, 1886–89.

RECORDS OF THE FINANCE DIVISION

The records described in this section were actually created by several units concerned with financial matters, but for most purposes, it is more useful to consider the records as an entity rather than to attempt to divide them according to the changing administrative organization of the Bureau. The designation "Finance Division" was the most enduring.

The Finance Division was one of the original divisions established in 1846. It was responsible for administrative examinations of accounts, appropriations, remittances, stock investments, claim settlements, and generally for all matters involving the expenditure of money for or on account of Indians.

An Accounts Division was established in 1876 to examine the cash and property accounts of agents and other disbursing officers. The Finance Division retained responsibility for appropriation ledgers, contracts, purchases, transportation of supplies and persons, remittances of funds, settlement of claims, and trust funds. By this time, however, most of the work concerning trust funds was handled in the Office of the Secretary of the Interior. The Accounts Division assumed a number of duties not directly relating to accounts, particularly those relating to agency personnel, but there are almost no nonfinancial records in the records of the Accounts Division now with the records of the Finance Division.

From 1908 to 1914 there was a series of changes by which the Accounts Division took over most of the duties of the Finance Division and was renamed the Finance Division. The former Finance Division became the Purchase Division, with sections for contracts, supplies, and transportation. This organization endured until 1931, when a position of Chief Finance Officer (later Finance Officer) was established with general responsibility for fiscal and financial matters. The Finance Division became first the Division of Accounting and Bookkeeping and then the Fiscal Division. The Purchase Division was abolished in 1932 when purchasing activities for the Bureau were transferred to a new Purchasing Office in the Office of the Secretary of the Interior. There were further changes starting in 1940, when the Finance Officer was replaced by a Chief Administrative Officer, but, except for the annuity payment rolls, there are few financial records of the Bureau dated that recently.

The small amount of correspondence and related records includes a register of letters received by the Secretary of War concerning Indian finances, 1834–38; a few letters received by Samuel Humes Porter, disbursing agent for the central office of the Bureau, 1844–46; a volume of instructions to new agents and their predecessors, relating chiefly to the submission of bonds, transfer of cash and property, and rendering of accounts, 1881–84; a volume of abstracts of reports chiefly to the Secretary of the Interior, 1870–75 and 1891–99; and a press copybook of Samuel E. Slater, Chief of the Finance Division until 1908 and then of the Purchase Division, consisting of reports to the Commissioner of Indian Affairs, letters sent, and memorandums, 1900–1909. There are also copies of records concerning policies and procedures, 1906–8, in a reference book; circulars, 1890–1918; and various procedural materials, 1950–67.

Records concerning investigations of accounts of field officials, operation of agencies, and other matters, ca. 1857–82, include materials about the New Mexico and Utah Superintendencies, Southwestern Nevada Special Agency, and the Whetstone, Red Cloud, and Pine Ridge Agencies. There are also records, 1895–1914 (2 ft.), relating to charges of fraud in the sale of Mexican Kickapoo allotments in Oklahoma and the distribution of funds to individual Indians (many of the documents have been published in *Hearings on Affairs of Mexican Kickapoo Indians*, Senate Document 215, 60th Cong., 1st sess.) and records relating to accounts, 1897–1902, of Martin J. Bentley, a special agent assigned to the Mexican Kickapoo and later implicated.

One of the principal duties of the Finance Division was to keep a record of appropriated funds. The Division maintained ledgers, journals, and other records to account for the receipt and use of funds, primarily by individual items in congressional appropriations. The basic records are appropriation ledgers, 1837–1921 (96 vols.). From 1837 until 1856 each volume contains the accounts for several fiscal years and is arranged either by fiscal year and thereunder by account or by account and thereunder chronologically. Beginning in 1856 more than one volume was used at the same time. Gradually, different volumes were set up for different classes of appropriation items: treaties and supports, schools and school buildings, Indian moneys-proceeds of labor, trust and interest funds, reimbursable appropriations, and miscellaneous. Accounts in the individual volumes are arranged for the most part alphabetically by tribe or jurisdiction, and thereunder the individual accounts are arranged chronologically. Later appropriation ledgers are among the Records of the U.S. General Accounting Office, Record Group 217.

Other journals and ledgers include a journal, 1827–31, recording transactions under the headings of appropriations and sundries; ledgers, 1833–53 (7 vols.), with accounts of appropriation items, accounts with banks, and some other accounts; general appropriation ledgers, 1869-94 (8 vols.), which balance Bureau receipts and disbursements but without breakdowns as in the appropriation ledgers; a summary ledger for reimbursable appropriations, 1866–1930, relating in large part to irrigation work and surveying and allotting; two appropriation ledgers for expenditures for field work, such as irrigation, surveying and allotting, determining heirs, support of schools, support of Indians, and proceeds of labor, 1917–24; apportionment ledgers, 1911–18 (4 vols.), which record the status of appropriation accounts by type of item, alphabetically by title of item, or alphabetically by State; a general appropriation liability ledger, 1909–11, recording credits and debits to general accounts; liability registers, 1909–16 (39 vols., other volumes are missing), which record individual authorizations for disbursements and are arranged for the most part by fiscal year and thereunder alphabetically by name of agency or other jurisdiction; an income and expense ledger, 1919–22, which balances for jurisdictions different kinds of expenditures against receipts, showing gains or losses; and cost ledgers, 1921–36 (16 vols. and unbound papers), used to account for the apportionment of individual disbursements and of disbursements over periods of time (chiefly months and quarters) by jurisdiction according to the purpose of the expenditure, such as salaries, transportation, buildings, purchases, annuity payments, and trust fund payments.

Summary records of expenditures include annual statements with analyses of appropriations, statements of expenditures, and summaries of expenditures, 1917–31, using the same headings as the cost ledgers, and annual statements of expenditures arranged by State, 1920–25.

There are some unbound statements of funds remitted to field officials for the years 1837–45, 1855–56, 1858–60, and 1877. For the years 1870 to 1908 they were systematically copied in volumes and usually indexed. Similarly, there are a few appropriation warrants, which were notices from the Secretary of the Treasury to the appropriate official in the Treasury Department requesting that action be taken to credit congressional appropriations for the Indian Service, 1843–63, and a bound set of warrants (13 vols.) for the years 1861–1934.

Other records relating mainly to central office activities include a record of requisitions, 1817–19; requests for requisitions, 1832–35; payrolls, 1834–52; accounts of disbursing agents, 1847–54; canceled checks, 1832, 1836–42, and 1850–53; and check stubs, 1838–41 and 1845–47.

Estimates for the most part have not been preserved, but there are estimates of funds needed, 1836–56 (3 vols.); abstracts of estimates of goods needed at agencies, 1879–80; and abstracts of estimates of goods needed for Pacific Coast agencies, 1882–83.

Records concerning accounts of superintendents, agents, and other field officials include schedules taken from accounts concerning the use of funds, 1833; a register of accounts and claims received, 1838–46; abstracts of accounts of superintendents and agents, 1847–69 with gaps (5 vols.); schedules of receipts and disbursements at certain agencies, 1869–81 (2 vols.); a record of referral of accounts to the Board of Indian Commissioners, 1871–75; statements of public funds, which were forms submitted periodically by superintendents and agents to show the amount of funds on deposit and on hand, 1873–78; a schedule of unsettled accounts, 1877–83; registers of accounts received from disbursing officers, 1878–1902 (3 vols.); a ledger for remittances and accounts rendered, 1869–76, in which receipts of disbursing officers are balanced against their accounts for expenditures; and statements of accounts of disbursing officers, 1900–1908 (5 vols., other volumes are missing), that balance receipts and disbursements under appropriation item headings. Only a small proportion of the actual accounts submitted are among the records of the Finance Division, 1827–82 (7 ft.). Other accounts are among the general records of the Bureau and field office records; the best source is Records of the U.S. General Accounting Office, Record Group 217.

Concerning goods and supplies, there are a property book, 1840–46, compiled from property returns submitted by field officials, that gives information concerning receipts and issuances of different kinds of goods; letters sent from warehouses in San Francisco, 1879, 1881–84, and 1897, and in New York and Chicago, 1898–99, concerning bids, contracts, open market purchases, the inspection and shipping of goods, and other subjects; a schedule of supplies contracted for during fiscal year 1882; lists of prices of supplies, 1898–1901; and a record of public property purchased for agencies, 1906–8 (18 vols.).

For the years 1836 to 1877 there are contracts with persons supplying goods and services (including certain employees) and bonds of contractors, agents, other officials, and, for 1865–72, traders (14 vols.). For later traders' bonds and employees' bonds beginning in 1867, see the records of the Miscellaneous Division and the Employees Section. For 1875 to 1911 there are contracts and bonds for goods and services on standard forms (139 vols.), with indexed stub books or registers, 1876–1926. The contracts and bonds are divided into the following types: goods and supplies, miscellaneous, transportation, beef cattle, buildings and plants, etc. (construction and leases), and schools (operation rather than construction). After 1911 there are no copies of the contracts and bonds among the central office records of the Bureau. There are also registers of open market purchases, 1891–1908 (37 vols.), and records of special accounts, 1876–1920 (250 vols.), which concern the settlement of accounts for individual transactions.

RECORDS RELATING TO CLAIMS

Records concerning claims, 1921–35 (162 ft.), include letters, applications, vouchers, disbursement schedules, affidavits, and other records concerning individual claims for compensation for such items as goods furnished, salaries, expenses, transportation, advertising, other services rendered, annuity payments, and shares in funds. Records concerning claims, 1877–1921, were destroyed by authority of the Congress while they were still in the Bureau, but there are indexes and registers for the 1877–1907 claims among the general records of the Bureau. Entries for the claims since 1907 are in the indexes to the central classified files of the Bureau.

Records concerning traders' claims, ca. 1819–64 (66 vols. and unbound papers), include ledgers, daybooks, and other accounts of traders; transcripts of testimony; reports and decisions of commissioners; and schedules concerning claims of traders against Indians, usually submitted under provisions of treaties. There are records for claims against Chippewa and Ottawa, Eastern Cherokee, Kansa, Miami, Potawatomi, Sauk and Fox, Winnebago, and some unidentified Indians. There are also schedules, 1911, of claims of traders against individual Indians (not including members of the Five Civilized Tribes in Oklahoma) before December 17, 1909. Other records concerning claims of traders are among the special files and in special series A.

There are records concerning claims made against the Old Settler Cherokee for services rendered, goods furnished, and damages suffered, 1842–53 (including claims for compiling the Drennen Roll for a per capita payment to the Indians in 1851); records concerning War Department claims, chiefly for the subsistence of Indian prisoners, 1877–83 (2 ft.); abstracts of disbursements by Sioux depredation claims commissioners and receipts for payments, 1863; and copies of accounts of the law firm of Mansfield, McMurray, and Cornish for legal services furnished the Choctaw and Chickasaw Nations, 1918.

Relating more directly to Indians than many of the records of the Finance Division are those concerning claims of New York Indians to participate in an award made by the Court of Claims in 1898 for the proceeds of the sale of lands in Kansas allocated to the New York Indians by the Treaty of Buffalo Creek, January 15, 1838, but never occupied. The Congress appropriated the necessary funds in 1900. Investigation of the claims was begun by the regular agent of the New York Agency, but during 1903 and 1904, special agent Guion Miller examined all the claims and compiled rolls of the persons he considered eligible. Revisions were made in Miller's rolls under orders of the Court of Claims in 1905 and 1906. The records include indexes to names of claimants; letters received, 1901–7; applications of individual Indians with related papers, 1901–4; and Miller's reports, 1903–5, with exhibits, including rolls, reports on individual claims, a copy of an 1859 report by special agent A. S. Stevens, and copies of earlier rolls used by Miller. Rolls of persons actually paid are among the annuity payment rolls. See also general jurisdiction case 17861, in Records of the U.S. Court of Claims, Record Group 123.

RECORDS CONCERNING TRIBAL AND INDIVIDUAL INDIAN MONEYS AND PAYMENTS TO INDIANS

Among the most heavily used records of the Bureau are the annuity payment rolls, 1841–1949, with a few as late as 1961 (959 vols. and unbound papers, 140 ft.). They consist chiefly of receipt rolls for periodic annuity payments to individual Indians. Also included are rolls for equalization payments (money instead of land allotments); the distribution of proceeds of sales of townsites, timber, and mineral rights; compensation for improvements on ceded land; payments for expenses of removal; and other payments. Some of the rolls are for single payments provided by awards of courts or acts of Congress. Sometimes payments were made in goods instead of money. It cannot always be established from the rolls that the persons listed were actually paid; they may be only those who were entitled to be paid. Vouchers accompany some of the rolls. The rolls sometimes give personal information about an Indian, such as age, sex, degree of Indian blood, and relationship to head of family. They are arranged for the most part alphabetically by name of tribe or band and thereunder chronologically. The individual rolls are usually arranged by family groups, sometimes alphabetically by surname but usually in no discernible order. A list of most of the rolls can be used in the National Archives Building. There also are annuity payment rolls in Records of the U.S. General Accounting Office, Record Group 217. Particularly for the period before 1884, when annual census rolls began to be made, the annuity payment rolls are often the best means of determining the members of a tribe or band at any given time.

There are also receipts of Delaware Indians for money received from the proceeds of the sale of land to the Missouri Pacific Railroad Company, 1867–69; affidavits, 1897 (9 vols.), submitted by persons claiming a share in payments to Cherokee freedmen and rolls of persons paid; a census roll of persons eligible to participate in a payment to the Cherokee Old Settlers in Indian Territory, 1895; rolls, 1900 and 1902, for payments of principal and interest to holders of Cherokee warrants; a census of Creek orphans and their heirs who were entitled to the benefits of the treaty of 1832 and a list of payments to be made on the basis of the census, 1870; a roll, 1904, of Creek Indians and their heirs who were eligible to participate in a payment to Creeks who had emigrated west of the Mississippi and supported themselves for 1 year in accordance with article 12 of the treaty of March 24, 1832; records concerning payments to various bands of Potawatomi; and a list of Sioux who served as scouts and soldiers during the Civil War and the 1862 Sioux uprising in Minnesota, with the names and relationships of heirs eligible to participate in a payment, 1892.

Other records concerning tribal and individual Indian moneys include recapitulations of accounts of individual Indians, 1930–32; a record of collections of moneys due the Five Civilized Tribes, 1898–1906; a ledger for tribal moneys, 1909–10; land sale orders for the Five Civilized Tribes, 1908–13 (3 ft.), directing sales of lands of individual members and providing for the use of the proceeds; and two ledgers for depositories of funds of the Five Civilized Tribes, 1911–18.

RECORDS CONCERNING INDIAN TRUST FUNDS

Trust funds for Indians came largely from the proceeds from sales of land. The Secretary of War was the trustee for such funds until 1849, when the Secretary of the Interior took over this responsibility. In 1876 physical custody of certificates of stocks and bonds owned by Indians was transferred to the Treasurer of the United States. Both the Office of the Secretary of the Interior and the Bureau of Indian Affairs maintained records about trust funds.

Among the records of the Finance Division are letters sent, 1843–57 and 1861–74 (5 vols.), relating to investments, interest, deposits, and other subjects. During other periods, such letters were copied in the main series of letters sent and the report books among the general records of the Bureau. By 1874 most of the correspondence concerning trust funds was handled in the Office of the Secretary of the Interior. There are also corresponding chronological journals and ledgers with accounts for States, banks, and disbursing officers, 1837–65. There is a separate ledger for trust funds of Chickasaw incompetents and minors, 1837–43. Other records include a register of stockholdings, 1869–73; statements concerning interest payments, 1869–74, and trust funds, 1867–84; and ledgers, 1903–9, for accounts of individual Indians (mainly minors) participating in trust funds and general accounts of the funds themselves for the Kansa, Iowa, Oto and Missouri, Tonkawa, Sauk and Fox of the Missouri, Grand Ronde, Flandreau Sioux, Omaha, Devil's Lake Sioux, Red Lake Chippewa, Rosebud Sioux, Sisseton and Wahpeton Sioux, and Santee Sioux.

OTHER RECORDS

Other records include a ledger for the participation of the Bureau in the Centennial Exhibition at Philadelphia, 1875–76; bills of lading and invoices for goods purchased by traders in Indian Territory, 1877–78; a journal of the Ute Commission, 1894–96; records concerning the fulfillment of treaties with Sioux Indians, ca. 1897–1903; and copies of constitutions and bylaws of tribes.

RECORDS OF THE MISCELLANEOUS DIVISION CONCERNING TRADERS' LICENSES

The Miscellaneous Division existed from 1889 to 1908 and was charged with various responsibilities, largely administrative, that did not seem appropriate for any of the other divisions. The only records of the Division, however, other than a set of press copies of letters sent now with the general records of the Bureau, relate to traders' licenses. They include records inherited from other divisions of the Bureau, especially the Civilization Division, which was responsible for Indian trade throughout its existence, 1846-85.

The first Indian Intercourse Act, that of July 22, 1790 (1 Stat. 137), required the licensing of persons who wished to trade with Indians in Indian country. Until 1876 superintendents and agents issued the licenses, which after 1834 were subject to the approval of the Commissioner of Indian Affairs. By an act of August 15, 1876, the Commissioner of Indian Affairs was given sole authority to license traders and to make rules and regulations concerning them.

The records include letters, chiefly from Indian agents and applicants for licenses, 1878-80 and 1889-1905 (4 ft.), withdrawn from the general incoming correspondence of the Bureau; application forms with bonds, recommendations, transmittal letters, and other documents concerning approved applications for licenses, 1892-99 (5 ft.); a register of licenses issued by superintendents and agents and approved by the Bureau, 1847-73; a register of licenses issued by the Commissioner of Indian Affairs, 1876-82; 15 volumes of copies of licenses, 1865-98, and of bonds, 1872-90; and two rosters of licensed traders, 1885-1909.

RECORDS OF THE INSPECTION DIVISION

Inspectors for the Indian Service were first appointed on July 1, 1873, as provided by an act of February 14, 1873 (17 Stat. 473). Records for earlier inspections and investigations conducted by special agents, superintendents, commissioners, and other officials are with the general correspondence of the Bureau or in such segregated series as special files and special cases. The administrative position of inspectors was confused. From 1873 to March 25, 1880, they were responsible to the Commissioner of Indian Affairs. Thereafter, they were under the direct supervision of the Secretary of the Interior. An inspection unit was established in the Bureau in 1908 without inspectors. Special agents and various other officials not assigned to a particular agency or school were considered to be inspecting officers. From 1915 to 1924 inspectors were again assigned to the Bureau, but afterwards they returned to the Office of the Secretary. There continued to be an Inspection Division in the Bureau until 1931, although it had only one employee.

For the period from 1873 to 1880, when the inspectors were in the Bureau, there are reports (3 ft.) and a volume of abstracts of them. Included are reports of general inspections and special reports on such matters as charges against agents, claims, and changes in personnel at agencies. There is also a volume of press copies of letters sent by Inspector William J.

McConnell in 1899 chiefly to the Secretary of the Interior.

The principal records of the Division, however, consist of two series, one identified as special agent files, 1907–48 (102 ft.), and the other as inspection reports, 1908–40 (42 ft.).

The special agent files consist of letters received and sent, statistical and narrative reports, memorandums, financial records, photographs, mimeographed procedural materials, and other kinds of records. They relate to the activities of field officials not assigned to a particular agency or school. In addition to special agents, these officials included inspectors, field representatives, school supervisors, construction supervisors, irrigation engineers, special officers (liquor control), examiners of inheritance, traveling auditors, clerks and special disbursing agents for irrigation districts, medical supervisors, special physicians, and field dentists. Some records concern tours of the Commissioner of Indian Affairs. The records relate largely to administrative matters, such as travel itineraries, work assignments, supplies, accounts, and the submission of reports, but there are some reports and other records concerning operations in the areas of irrigation, education, and health. For the years after 1932 there are only a few files, which are for irrigation officers started in 1936 and 1939, but these include records dated as late as 1948. Within three time periods, 1907–21, 1922–32, and 1936–48, the files are arranged alphabetically by name of officer.

Inspectors, special agents, school supervisors, medical supervisors, special physicians, construction supervisors, district superintendents, field representatives, members of the Board of Indian Commissioners, and other officials made inspection reports about agencies, schools, hospitals, and other Bureau facilities. They relate to general conditions at agencies and schools, health conditions and facilities, construction projects, irrigation projects, timber and mill operations, grazing, audits of accounts, investigations of charges against employees and others, employee efficiency ratings, disputes over land ownership, tribal enrollment, and many other subjects. Most of the reports are narrative, but often enclosed are transcripts of testimony, copies of correspondence, forms, and photographs. The reports are arranged in several overlapping time periods and thereunder for the most part alphabetically by name of jurisdiction. Later reports are almost entirely those of special agents of the Department of the Interior and relate chiefly to audits of accounts.

Other records include a small office file of Chief Supervisor Ernest P. Holcombe, 1909–10, relating largely to attempts to prevent the sale of liquor, particularly in Minnesota; files, 1908–10, for district agents in Oklahoma, who were appointed to help with the affairs of minors and restricted allottees; some abstracts of recommendations made and actions taken for reports submitted by Inspector Wade H. Gibbs, 1916; and transcripts of proceedings of a conference of supervisors in Washington, D.C., February 16–24, 1914.

RECORDS OF THE STATISTICS DIVISION

There was a Statistics Section, subordinate to various units, from 1909 until 1939, when it became the Statistics Division. The Division was abolished in 1947, and the statistician in charge was assigned to the Tribal Relations Division. The Statistics Division processed census rolls, reports of births and deaths, health reports, extension reports, annual narrative and statistical reports submitted by field officials, and other kinds of reports and statistical data. It also compiled information for the *Annual Report of the Commissioner of Indian Affairs.* Many of the records it once held are now with records of other divisions, particularly the Health and Education Divisions, but some of the most significant and popular records of the Bureau are still among the records of the Statistics Division.

The superintendents' annual narrative and statistical reports, 1910–38 (116 ft.), are the best source for summary information about a field jurisdiction during any given year, and they are essential for jurisdictional and tribal histories. Until 1906 annual reports of field officials regularly were published as part of the *Annual Report of the Commissioner of Indian Affairs,* but later reports were usually not available in published form. For the complete period there are narrative reports, sometimes illustrated with photographs, from agencies, schools, hospitals, and other field jurisdictions. They relate to law and order, education, health, population, land ownership, agriculture and land use, industry, forestry, welfare, social conditions, tribal organization, and other subjects. For the years 1920 to 1935 there are also statistical reports prepared on standard forms. Individual sections relate to population, school enrollment, health, industries, agriculture and livestock, forestry, irrigation, land ownership, employment, Government property, and other subjects. The reports are arranged alphabetically by name of jurisdiction and thereunder chronologically. Some narrative and statistical reports for the years 1907–9 are among the central classified files of the Bureau. Narrative reports, 1907–38, and statistical reports, 1907–35, have been reproduced as M1011.

For the years 1933 to 1948, there are additional reports and other records (40 ft.) that include later narrative and statistical reports and reports on extension activities, land tenure, income of individual Indians, acreage verification, Federal real estate, population and vital statistics, law and order, surveys conducted by Technical Cooperation-Bureau of Indian Affairs of the Soil Conservation Service, verification of spellings of place names, and other subjects. They also are arranged alphabetically by jurisdiction.

The other major series of records of the Statistics Division consists of census rolls and supplements, 1885–1940 (420 ft.). An act of July 4, 1884 (23 Stat. 76, 98), required agents and superintendents to submit an annual census of the Indians in their charge. In practice, many were unable to comply every year, and some (for example, the Navajo agents and superintendents) were unable to comply for many years. The information given for an individual varies but usually includes English or Indian name, roll number, age or date of birth, sex, and relationship to head of family. Beginning in 1930 the rolls also give the degree of Indian blood, marital status, ward status, residence, and sometimes other information. During the 1930's complete new rolls were not prepared every year. For certain years, 1935, 1936, 1938, and 1939 for most jurisdictions, there are only supplemental rolls of additions and deductions, usually lists of births and deaths. For 1931 or 1932 there are often recapitulations of births and deaths since 1924. There are a few rolls dated later than 1940, but they were not required after that year. Most of the 1940 rolls are still held by the Bureau of Indian Affairs. The census rolls are arranged alphabetically by name of agency or school and thereunder by year. For jurisdictions with more than one tribe or band, there may be several rolls for each year. On the earlier rolls often there is no discernible order to the listing of families, but the later rolls are arranged alphabetically by surname of head of family. These census rolls have been reproduced as M595, and the accompanying descriptive pamphlet includes a tribal index.

There are also some office records of statisticians, correspondence, and other records chiefly concerning the submission and correction of reports, census rolls, and other statistical information. Among the cartographic records are a few maps showing Indian population in the United States and Alaska at various times, 1930–43.

RECORDS OF THE EMPLOYEES SECTION

The Employees Section operated from 1909 until 1939 and inherited records from units previously concerned with personnel. The earliest records of the section are registers of applications and recommendations for appointments, 1833–49 and 1866–68. Most records concerning applications and recommendations after 1849 are among those of the Appointments Division in Records of the Office of the Secretary of the Interior, Record Group 48.

A set of copies of commissions, 1866–1909 (4 vols.), is often the easiest place to find the dates of appointment for persons appointed by the President and the Secretary of the Interior, particularly superintendents and agents. There are also bonds for field employees, 1867–1935 (27 vols.); form letters sent to agents and superintendents approving the appointment of persons recommended for positions by the field official; and registers of personnel actions in the school service, 1894–1909 (11 vols.).

Most of the other records of the Section are rosters of officials and employees, including Indian employees. They are usually indexed. There are rosters of field employees, 1848–50; superintendents and agents, 1853–63; field officials, 1849–1911 (8 vols.); agency employees, 1853–1909 (38 vols.); school employees, 1884–1909 (22 vols.); school employees in Indian Territory, 1899–1909 (4 vols.); Indian police, 1878–1906 (16 vols.); employees of the Commission to the Five Civilized Tribes, 1899–1909 (2 vols.); and irrigation and allotment employees, 1908–9. The information given concerning individuals varies but may include name, position, salary, name of tribe to which appointed, former occupation, dates of service, age, sex, race, marital status, birthplace, and legal residence or State from which appointed. For the Indian police, tribal affiliation, degree of Indian blood, and physical measurements usually are given.

There are also school personnel rating books, 1889–95, and school employee efficiency ratings, 1895–1906. For more recent years, there are personnel organization (salary) lists, 1912–40 (11 ft.), which do not usually give the names of incumbents, and correspondence concerning field personnel, 1930–36 and 1939 (8 ft.), arranged by jurisdiction.

RECORDS OF THE LIBRARY SECTION

The records of this section consist chiefly of newspaper clippings on various subjects, congressional reports and documents, and copies of publications.

RECORDS OF THE CONSTRUCTION DIVISION

The Construction Division was established in 1939 to replace the Construction Section, which had existed since 1908. The Division was in charge of the construction and repair of various kinds of buildings and other structures. The only records of the Division now in the National Archives relate to construction projects financed by the Public Works Administration (PWA). They include correspondence, memorandums, narrative and statistical reports, completed forms, estimates, specifications, court records, blueprints, schedules, tables, graphs, photographs, clippings, catalogs, and samples of materials. They relate chiefly to projects for the construction and repair of school buildings, hospitals, housing facilities for employees, sewerage and water systems, heating and power plants, and other structures. Many of the projects were started by the Bureau before the PWA was established. There are few records concerning irrigation or road and bridge projects, which usually were handled by the Irrigation and Road Divisions. Subjects include surveys, plans, estimates, bids, equipment and materials, construction progress, inspections, legal questions, and employees. The records are arranged by PWA project number, with many gaps for irrigation and road projects. An index by agency or other jurisdiction is available.

See also Records of the Public Works Administration, Record Group 135.

RECORDS OF THE CIVILIAN CONSERVATION CORPS-INDIAN DIVISION

The Emergency Conservation Work (later Civilian Conservation Corps) program was established in 1933, and work on Indian reservations was included from the beginning. The Indian Emergency Conservation Work Division was established in 1933 and renamed the Civilian Conservation Corps-Indian Division in 1937. The Bureau of Indian Affairs had full responsibility for the selection and training of enrollees and for the management and operation of CCC work on Indian lands, but the Director of the CCC approved the allotment of funds. The objectives of the CCC-ID program were to provide employment for Indians and to accomplish useful conservation work. The projects included fire prevention work, road and trail construction, weed and pest control, construction of telephone lines, fence construction, erosion and flood control work, water supply projects, and tree planting and forest improvement work. An Enrollee Program provided for the training, recreation, and welfare of the Indians. The CCC-ID program was ended in the field on July 10, 1942, but the Washington office force continued for some time afterwards.

General records, 1933-44 (87 ft.), include correspondence, reports, memorandums, photographs, plans, maps, specifications, tables, schedules, lists, forms, applications, agreements, minutes, circulars and other procedural materials, financial records, clippings, and catalogs. They relate to project proposals, surveys, work programs, work progress, training, enrollee programs, allotment of funds, accounts, equipment, materials, camps, buildings, water supply, investigations, and many other subjects. They are arranged in the same way as the central files of the Bureau, with general service records and records concerning individual jurisdictions each arranged by the decimal classification system.

Separate records concerning the Enrollee Program, 1937-42 (8 ft.), include correspondence, reports, memorandums, photographs, clippings, tables, lists, circulars and other procedural materials, requisitions, and camp menus. They relate to such subjects as training and education, recreation, vocational guidance and job placement, former enrollees, camp facilities, health, and food. Nearly all the records are designated as parts of the 346 classification (CCC Enrollee Program) of the central classified files of the Bureau, but most records with this classification are in this series rather than the central files or the general records of the Division. There are general service records and records concerning individual jurisdictions.

Other records of the Division include correspondence with the Director of Emergency Conservation Work, 1933-37; special files relating to beetle control, blister rust control, leader camps, health, and forestry, 1933-36; narrative and pictorial reports, 1937-42; records relating to *Indians at Work,* a magazine published by the Bureau; and a few maps showing the construction of truck trails, telephone lines, ranger stations, guard stations, lookout towers, and reservoirs.

There are records concerning CCC activities among the general records of the Bureau, field office records, and Records of the Civilian Conservation Corps, Record Group 35.

RECORDS OF THE REHABILITATION DIVISION

The Rehabilitation Division was formally established in 1936 to carry out the Indian Relief and Rehabilitation Program, but persons had been assigned to work on the program development the previous year. Early in 1936, about $2 million appropriated under the Emergency Relief Appropriation Act of 1935 was allotted to the Indian Service. Additional funds were provided by subsequent acts of 1937, 1938, 1939, and 1941. Most of the funds were provided through the Work Projects Administration (WPA), but the Resettlement Administration and its successor, the Farm Security Administration, also contributed.

Major emphasis was on the "rehabilitation" part of the program. This consisted of work projects serving the dual purposes of providing employment for Indians and of accomplishing needed work. There were projects for the construction and repair of homes, barns, and other structures; for water development and distribution; for the clearing of land for gardens and small farms; and for other improvements on Indian land holdings. There were also "self help projects," which included canning, sewing, handicrafts, the operation of mills and dipping vats, and other community projects. The "relief" part of the program consisted of direct relief through the distribution of commodities and cash. In 1941 the Rehabilitation Division was consolidated with the Extension Division, but separate records were maintained for the Rehabilitation Division until 1944. By that time available funds had been exhausted. The WPA was abolished in 1943.

General records, 1935-44 (2 ft.), concern legislation, budgets and allotments, program proposals, surveys, accomplishments, relations with other divisions and agencies, regulations, organization, office procedures, personnel, and many other subjects designated by the New System file classification 76039—Rehabilitation-General Correspondence. Most of the records (22 ft.), however, relate to projects at individual schools and agencies. They consist of correspondence, reports, memorandums, lists, forms, resolutions, legal papers, minutes, financial records, clippings, photographs, maps, plats, and other kinds of records concerning project proposals, surveys, work progress, accomplishments, distribution of goods, allotment of funds, accounts, legal matters, personnel, and many other subjects. Most of the records are designated as parts of the 76000 series (Rehabilitation) of the New System. Numbers from 76001 to 76110 were assigned to the records for the individual agencies in alphabetical order.

Thereunder, the records are arranged by subject headings assigned alpha-betical-numerical symbols. Most frequently used are P-1-a—Current Program, P-1-b—Data for Later Program, P-2—General Correspondence, and P-13—General Correspondence—Relief. Other records of the Division include program proposals, analyses, and pictorial reports.

There are related records in the central classified files of the Bureau and the New System files, in Records of the Work Projects Administration, Record Group 69, and in Records of the Farmers Home Administration, Record Group 96.

RECORDS OF THE BRANCH OF ROADS

Some of the records of the Branch of Roads, earlier the Roads Division, relate to the termination of road systems at the Klamath Agency, 1938–61, and the Menominee Agency, 1942–61. There are also annotated, photo-processed, and manuscript maps of Indian reservations showing different types of roads, proposed road construction, and the status of work in the 1930's and early 1940's.

RECORDS OF THE INDIAN ORGANIZATION DIVISION

The Indian Organization Division (or Organization Division) was established in 1934 to supervise the organization of Indian tribes as provided by the Indian Reorganization Act of 1934 (48 Stat. 984). This authorized the organization of tribal governments for political purposes and the incorporation of tribes for economic enterprises. In 1943 the Division became the Division of Tribal Relations, and later it was known successively as the Branch of Tribal Affairs and the Branch of Tribal Programs. Almost all of the records described, however, are for the period before 1943.

One series, 1933–37 (4 ft.), relates principally to reactions to the Reorganization Act, chiefly before but also after its passage by the Congress. The records include correspondence, reports, memorandums, minutes of tribal meetings, petitions, resolutions, completed questionnaires, mimeographed statements, and clippings. They relate to official and unofficial tribal actions and opinions expressed by individual Indians and whites and by newspapers. There are also records concerning a survey taken among anthropologists.

The records of actual operations under the act, ca. 1934–56 (16 ft.), consist of correspondence; memorandums; reports; copies of proposed and approved constitutions, bylaws, and charters; petitions; resolutions; census rolls; voting lists; completed questionnaires; clippings; and other kinds of records. They relate to preliminary surveys; the preparation of constitutions, bylaws, and charters and their submission for approval; the determination of tribal membership; elections; the opposition to organization;

and other subjects. The records are in files, most of which were part of the central classified files of the Bureau until 1938, and are arranged by jurisdiction, mainly agency.

There are also correspondence with field and central office officials of the Bureau and the Department of the Interior, 1934–46; questionnaires completed by field officials in Alaska, 1934–35, concerning tribal organization in Alaska; and Menominee tribal minutes, 1953–61.

FIELD OFFICE RECORDS

The records described in this section were created by field offices of the Bureau of Indian Affairs, chiefly superintendencies, agencies, schools, and area offices. The records in National Archives depositories in the Washington, D.C., area are mainly those of discontinued offices that transferred their records to the Bureau in Washington, particularly the 19th-century superintendencies. They include few records dated later than 1900, except for those of some nonreservation schools, the New York Agency, and several agencies for Chippewa Indians in Minnesota. Most of the records of field offices that are part of the National Archives of the United States are in the archives branches of Federal archives and records centers. The records of the 19th-century superintendencies are described in alphabetical order in one section of this guide and the records of the other field offices are described in alphabetical order in another section. It proved impractical to divide these other offices according to type, primarily because of the practice of assigning agency duties to school superintendents and the intermingling of records of different offices. Sometimes a school did not actually exist, and the superintendent had only agency duties. Field office records typically were kept in a less orderly manner than central office records. There are great variations in what has survived and how it is arranged. Usually area office records include some but not all of the records of subordinate agencies and predecessors. Agency records often include records of predecessors and of reservation schools and other units.

The kinds of records maintained at any given time did not vary much from one jurisdiction to another of the same type. Most of the correspondence of superintendents and independent agents was conducted with the central office of the Bureau, but there was also much correspondence between superintendents and agents within the superintendency. Superintendents and agents also corresponded with other field officials and employees, Army officers, Indians, businessmen, and others. During the 19th century and the early part of the 20th century, outgoing letters usually were copied into letter books. Often filed with the incoming correspondence, particularly of superintendencies, were various kinds of reports, accounts, and other records, in many cases copies of documents submitted to the central office. In more recent years many field offices have used an adaptation of the Bureau's decimal filing system. These files may include records concerning land transactions, forestry, grazing, irrigation, education, health, heirship and probate matters, vital statistics, and special programs, such as those of the Civilian Conservation Corps.

If the records of an agency are reasonably complete, they relate to almost every aspect of its work and to the same subjects as those of the central office records. There are, however, differences in areas of concern resulting from local conditions. In Minnesota, for example, forestry was important and irrigation was not, but the reverse was true in Arizona. Field office records also tend to contain more specific information about individuals than central office records, particularly in such areas as land ownership, inheritance, education, health, and financial affairs.

The records of most field offices are described comparatively briefly in this guide. This is partly to avoid the repetitiveness in kinds of records and content, but it is also because many of these records are not yet under sufficient archival control to make accurate detailed descriptions possible. The more detailed descriptions given for some of the offices serve as examples of what one may expect to find in records of other offices.

Some records that might be regarded as those of field offices have been incorporated with those of central office units, including those of many of the special commissions. Records of field supervisors, such as the Chief Supervisor of Education or the Chief Engineer (in charge of irrigation) have been incorporated into the records of the appropriate divisions of the Bureau.

RECORDS OF SUPERINTENDENCIES

Arizona Superintendency

The Arizona Superintendency was established in 1863 at the same time as Arizona Territory, which previously had been part of New Mexico Territory. Although it was customary for the Territorial Governor to serve ex officio as superintendent for several years after a territory was established, in Arizona Territory there was always a separate superintendent.

In the next 2 years the superintendent established a number of temporary agencies. The following permanent agencies were established: Colorado River in 1864 for Yavapai, Walapai, Mohave, Yuma, scattered Apache bands, and other small tribes; Gila River in 1864 (known as the Papago Agency, 1864–65, and as the Pima, Papago, and Maricopa Agency, 1865–69) for the Pima, Papago, Maricopa, and "Tame" Apache; Moqui Pueblo in 1869 for the Hopi Indians; and Papago (separated from Gila River) in 1871 for the Papago Indians. During 1871 and 1872, the Camp Apache, Chiricahua, Camp Grant, Rio Verde, and San Carlos Agencies were established for several different groups of Apache Indians. By 1876 these agencies were consolidated into the San Carlos Agency. The Navajo Agency, although located most of the time at Fort Defiance, Ariz., was assigned to the New Mexico Superintendency. The Arizona Superintendency was abolished in 1873, and thereafter the agents reported directly to the Bureau of Indian Affairs in Washington, D.C. The records of the superintendency, 1863-73 (4 ft.), include two registers of letters received, 1868-72; a main series of letters received, copies of letters sent, accounts, rosters of employees, and other records, 1863-73 (3 ft.); a letter book of Charles D. Poston, the first superintendent, 1863-64; and five volumes of copies of letters sent, 1865-66 and 1868-73. These records have been reproduced as M734.

Central Superintendency

The Central Superintendency was established in 1851 as the successor to the St. Louis Superintendency, which had replaced the Missouri Superintendency in 1822. The records of the Central Superintendency include some inherited from its predecessors.

Originally the Central Superintendency was responsible mainly for the agencies and Indians (except the Osage) in the present States of Kansas and Nebraska. The upper regions of the Missouri, Platte, and Arkansas Rivers, extending into the Dakotas, Wyoming, and Colorado, also were within the jurisdiction of the superintendency. With the establishment of the Colorado and Dakota Superintendencies in 1861 and the reorganization of the Northern Superintendency in 1865, the Central Superintendency was restricted to Kansas. Soon, however, the superintendency expanded into Indian Territory. By 1869 the Osage Indians of southern Kansas and all of the Indians in Indian Territory except the Five Civilized Tribes were assigned to the Central Superintendency. After the Southern Superintendency was abolished in 1870, its four remaining agencies (Creek, Choctaw and Chickasaw, Cherokee, and Seminole) reported directly to the Bureau of Indian Affairs, except that the Central Superintendency was responsible for handling matters that by treaty required the services of a superintendent.

The Indians and agencies of the Central Superintendency continued to change as Indians were moved from Kansas and Nebraska to Indian Territory. By 1874 the Potawatomi Agency for Potawatomi and Kickapoo Indians was the only agency still in Kansas.

Indians at some time within the Central Superintendency included Delaware, Shawnee, Wyandot, Munsee, Potawatomi, Kansa, Sauk and Fox of the Mississippi and the Missouri, Chippewa, Ottawa, Iowa, Kickapoo, Miami, Peoria, Wea, Kaskaskia, Piankashaw, Oto, Missouri, Omaha, Pawnee, Kiowa, Comanche, Kiowa-Apache, Cheyenne, Arapaho, Blackfeet, Sioux, Osage, Quapaw, Seneca, and Wichita and affiliated Indians. They were attached to the following agencies: Kansas (there were two agencies with this name), Potawatomi, Sac and Fox, Great Nemaha, Osage River, Council Bluffs, Upper Platte, Upper Missouri, Delaware, Shawnee, Kickapoo, Upper Arkansas, Blackfeet, Omaha, Otoe, Pawnee, Ponca, Yankton, Ottawa, Neosho, Osage, Kiowa, Wichita, Quapaw, and Cheyenne and Arapaho.

In October 1877 the agents were instructed to report directly to the Bureau of Indian Affairs rather than to the superintendent. In 1878 the Central Superintendency was abolished.

The records of the Central Superintendency, 1813–78, are the most voluminous of any of the 19th-century superintendencies (43 ft.). The largest series (37 ft.) includes letters received and some copies of letters sent, statements of letters received, Treasury Department notices, estimates, bids, contracts, vouchers, receipts, invoices, abstracts of disbursements, statements of public money, statements of funds remitted and received, returns of provisions, journals, printed copies of treaties, annual reports of agents, reports of employees, school reports, medical reports, reports of changes in employees, supply reports, and other records. They are arranged by year and thereunder by kind of record. The letters received, which constitute the larger part of the records, are arranged by source. For most years, there are separate folders for letters received from the Commissioner of Indian Affairs and from each of the agencies in the superintendency. Frequently there is a folder for letters from the Army Department of the Missouri, and there are other special folders, some of which contain letters relating to a particular subject, such as land surveys or a council, rather than from a particular person or office.

There are handwritten copies of letters sent grouped by addressee: Commissioner of Indian Affairs, 1855–76; agents, 1858–71; and other persons, 1853–71. There are press copies for the same three groups covering, respectively, 1875–78, 1873 and 1875–78, and 1876–78.

Finding aids include registers of incoming and outgoing correspondence with the Commissioner of Indian Affairs, 1847–66; registers of letters received from the Commissioner of Indian Affairs, 1866–78; registers of letters and endorsements sent to the Commissioner of Indian Affairs, 1866–78; and registers of letters sent to agents, 1876–78.

The other records of the superintendency relate to finances and accounts. There are statements of funds received and other statements, 1868–77; tabular statements of funds remitted, 1876–77; statements of receipts and disbursements, 1872–78; a ledger for receipts and disbursements, 1874–78; abstracts of disbursements, 1849–76; statements of account current, 1849–67; statements of account current and property returns, 1853–65; property returns, 1865–76; and letters sent by the disbursing agent at St. Louis, 1834–40. There are from one to three volumes for each of these series.

The records of the Central Superintendency have been reproduced as M856. There are also records of the Central Superintendency and its predecessors in the possession of the Kansas State Historical Society at Topeka. The National Archives has microfilm copies of these records in the National Archives Gift Collection, Record Group 200.

Dakota Superintendency

The Dakota Superintendency was established in 1861 with the organization of Dakota Territory. The original area of the Territory extended from the 43d parallel to Canada and from Minnesota to the Continental Divide. Before 1861 the Indians in this region had been assigned to the Central Superintendency. In 1863 that part of Dakota west of the present States of North and South Dakota was made part of Idaho Territory. With the organization of Montana Territory in 1864, most of the present State of Wyoming was attached to Dakota Territory, where it remained until Wyoming Territory was established in 1868. Thereafter, Dakota Territory included only the present States of North and South Dakota. The Dakota Superintendency, however, at times supervised some agencies actually located in Nebraska and Wyoming.

The Territorial Governor at Yankton served ex officio as superintendent from the creation of the superintendency until it was abolished in 1870. The superintendency was reactivated in 1877 with headquarters at Yankton and a fulltime superintendent in charge, but it was again abolished in 1878. Thereafter the agents reported directly to the Bureau of Indian Affairs in Washington.

Most of the Indians in Dakota belonged to various bands of Sioux, including Hunkpapa, Oglala, Yankton, Blackfeet (Sihasapa), Brulé, Sisseton, Wahpeton, Yanktonai, Sans Arcs, Miniconjou, Two Kettle (Oohenonpa), Cut Head (Pabaksa), and Santee. There were also Blackfeet (Siksika), Cheyenne, Arapaho, Arikara (Arickaree), Mandan, Ponca, and Crow Indians.

The Blackfeet, Ponca, Upper Missouri, and Yankton Agencies were operating in Dakota when the Dakota Superintendency was organized. In 1863 the Blackfeet Agency was transferred to the Idaho Superintendency and, in the following year, to the Montana Superintendency. The Ponca Agency was moved to Indian Territory in 1877. The Upper Missouri Agency was renamed the Crow Creek Agency in 1874. Between 1863 and 1866, the Indians of the Winnebago and St. Peters (Santee) Agencies were living at Crow Creek. The Fort Berthold Agency was established in 1864, but it was not included in the revived Dakota Superintendency in 1877. The Grand River (Standing Rock), Whetstone (Spotted Tail), and Cheyenne River Agencies all were established in 1869, the Red Cloud Agency in 1871, the Flandreau Agency in 1873, and the Lower Brulé Agency in 1875. The

Sisseton and Devil's Lake Agencies, established in 1867 and 1871, were located in Dakota Territory, but they were never under the supervision of the Dakota Superintendency.

The records of the superintendency, 1860–78 (5 ft.), include the typical major series (4 ft.), consisting largely of letters received but also including copies of letters sent, vouchers, receipts, payrolls, statements of funds remitted, abstracts of disbursements, statements of account current, Treasury Department notices, statements of letters received, reports on farming and education, reports on employees, inventories, and other records. They are arranged by year, and thereunder the correspondence is usually separated from the accounts and statistical reports. The correspondence for each year is usually grouped by correspondent: the Commissioner of Indian Affairs, agents in the superintendency, and other persons. There are records for the years 1873–76 concerning agencies in Dakota even though the superintendency was not in operation during this period. There are a volume of letters sent, 1865–69, and one volume each, 1869–70, for letters sent to the Grand River, Ponca, Upper Missouri and Fort Berthold, Whetstone, and Yankton Agencies. There are two volumes of letters sent for the revived superintendency, 1877–78, one of which is made up almost entirely of letters to the Commissioner of Indian Affairs and the other of letters to other persons. The records of the Dakota Superintendency have been reproduced as M1016.

Idaho Superintendency

The Idaho Superintendency was established in 1863, at the same time as Idaho Territory. From 1848 until 1853 the present State of Idaho was part of Oregon Territory; part of it was transferred to Washington Territory in 1853 and the rest in 1859. From 1863 until Montana Territory was organized in 1864, Idaho included Montana and part of Wyoming. Thereafter Idaho had its present boundaries. Until 1869 the Territorial Governor served ex officio as superintendent; thereafter an Army officer was detailed to the position.

After 1864 the principal Indian tribes under the supervision of the Idaho Superintendency were the Nez Percé, Shoshoni, and Bannock, but Coeur d'Alène, Kutenai, Pend d'Oreille, and Spokan Indians also lived or roamed there. The Coeur d'Alène and Spokan, however, were more closely associated with the Washington Superintendency, and the Kutenai and Pend d'Oreille with the Flathead Agency of the Montana Superintendency.

The Nez Percé, Flathead, and Blackfeet Agencies were assigned to the Idaho Superintendency in 1863, but in 1864 the Blackfeet and Flathead Agencies were transferred to the new Montana Superintendency. The Flathead Agency was again assigned to the Idaho Superintendency from September 1865 until February 1866. In 1867 a special agent was assigned to the

Boise and Bruneau bands of Shoshoni. In 1869 these Indians and some Western Shoshoni and Bannock were moved to the Fort Hall Reservation in southeastern Idaho, and the agency thereafter was called the Fort Hall Agency. The Idaho Superintendency was discontinued in 1870. Thereafter the agents in Idaho reported directly to the Bureau of Indian Affairs.

The comparatively few records of the superintendency, 1863–70 (1 ft.), consist of a register of letters received, 1867–70; letters received with accounts and reports from the Commissioner of Indian Affairs, the Nez Percé and Fort Hall Agencies, special agents, and other sources; letters sent, 1863–70; and miscellaneous records, 1863 and 1866–70. They have been reproduced as M832.

Michigan Superintendency and Mackinac Agency

The Michigan Superintendency was established in 1805 with the organization of Michigan Territory. Until 1836 the Territorial Governor at Detroit served ex officio as superintendent. The Michigan Territory originally consisted of only the Lower Peninsula and the eastern tip of the Upper Peninsula. In 1818 its boundaries were extended to include the present States of Wisconsin and Minnesota east of the Mississippi River. The jurisdiction of the Michigan Superintendency, however, did not always coincide with the territorial boundaries. The principal tribes under the supervision of the Michigan Superintendency were Chippewa, Ottawa, Potawatomi, Menominee, Winnebago, Wyandot, Seneca, Shawnee, Delaware, Miami, Oneida, Stockbridge, and Munsee.

Until after the War of 1812 there were no permanent agencies in Michigan, and the superintendent had immediate charge of Indian affairs. When agencies were established, they were organized more on a geographical than a tribal basis. They included the Mackinac, Chicago, and Green Bay Agencies, established in 1815; the Fort Wayne (later Indiana) and Piqua (later Ohio) Agencies, assigned to the Michigan Superintendency in 1817; the Sault Ste. Marie Agency, established in 1822 and consolidated with the Mackinac Agency in 1832; and a number of subagencies, including the New York Subagency from 1832 to 1834.

Although Michigan Territory was expanded from the Mississippi to the Missouri River in 1834, the jurisdiction of the Michigan Superintendency was reduced to the Mackinac and Sault Ste. Marie Agency, the Green Bay Agency, the Fort Winnebago Subagency, the Maumee Subagency in Ohio (abolished in 1836), and a subagency at Detroit for the lower part of Michigan. In 1836 Michigan lost the Green Bay Agency and the Fort Winnebago Subagency to the new Wisconsin Superintendency. This left the Michigan Superintendency with primary responsibility for only Chippewa, Ottawa, and some Potawatomi Indians.

In July 1836, in anticipation of Michigan's admission to statehood, the

Mackinac agent was designated to act as superintendent instead of the Territorial Governor. Under the regulations adopted in 1837, the Michigan Superintendency was made responsible for the Indians in Michigan and the Ottawa Indians at Maumee. Under the superintendency were the Mackinac Agency for the northern part of the Lower Peninsula, the Sault Ste. Marie Subagency for the Upper Peninsula, and the Saginaw Subagency, which replaced the Detroit Subagency for the southern part of the Lower Peninsula. The Saginaw Subagency was abolished in 1846, and its duties were assigned to the Mackinac Agency.

The Michigan Superintendency was abolished in 1851. The new Northern Superintendency was given nominal authority over Indian affairs in Michigan, but this was ended in 1853. The Sault Ste. Marie Subagency was abolished in 1852. Thereafter the Mackinac Agency (sometimes called the Michigan Agency) had charge of all the Indians in Michigan. From 1853 to 1858 it also had some responsibility for the Chippewa Indians living along Lake Superior in Minnesota and Wisconsin. The Mackinac Agency was abolished in 1889. There was a later Mackinac Agency, records of which are described on pages 165 and 166 in this guide.

The records described below, 1814–85 (20 ft.), were created in four different field offices: the Michigan Superintendency, the Mackinac Agency, the Sault Ste. Marie Agency, and the Sault Ste. Marie Subagency. The earlier records consist chiefly of those maintained by the Territorial Governors in their capacities as superintendent and by Henry R. Schoolcraft in his successive posts as agent at Sault Ste. Marie, 1822–33; agent at Mackinac, 1833–36; and agent at Mackinac and acting superintendent, 1836–41. He maintained continuous sets of volumes of letters received and letters sent throughout the period 1822–41, and these sets were continued by his successors.

For the Michigan Superintendency during the period when the Territorial Governor was ex officio superintendent, the earliest records are in two volumes of copies of letters received and letters sent, 1814–18. Beginning in 1819 letters received were no longer copied, but the original letters were bound; there are 31 volumes, 1819–35. There are two volumes of letters sent, 1818–23, and unbound letters sent, 1823, 1826, and 1831–33. There is also a small amount of unbound correspondence and accounts, 1815–24.

Schoolcraft also followed the practice of copying letters sent into volumes and binding original letters received. For his years at Sault Ste. Marie, 1822–33, there are three volumes of letters received and a volume of letters sent. There also is a ledger kept by his mother-in-law, Susan Johnston, who was an Indian trader in the Sault Ste. Marie area; this ledger has accounts for individual Indians.

For the Mackinac Agency there are a volume of letters received, 1816–31, and two volumes of letters received and a volume of letters sent for the years

1833 to 1836, when Schoolcraft was agent. For the years of the combined superintendency and agency and of the agency alone, there are 42 volumes of letters received, 1836–70, and unbound letters, 1849–82 (2 ft.). The volumes are the principal series for the overlapping period. There are also letters sent, 1836–59, 1865–68, and 1877–85 (16 vols.). Other records include financial and statistical records, 1845–82; school reports, 1855–61, 1864, and 1871–82; ledgers, 1841–45 and 1849–51; letters sent by the principal disbursing officer at Detroit, 1838–39; and correspondence and accounts of the Sault Ste. Marie Subagency, 1837–52.

The bound volumes of correspondence until the end of the superintendency in 1851 have been reproduced as M1.

Minnesota Superintendency

The Minnesota Superintendency was established in 1849 with the organization of Minnesota Territory, which included the eastern part of what later became North and South Dakota. The Territorial Governor at St. Paul served ex officio as superintendent throughout the existence of the superintendency. The Indians living in Minnesota were mainly Sioux, Chippewa, and Winnebago. There also were some Assiniboin and Mandan, but they had few contacts with the superintendent.

When the superintendency was established, the Winnebago (Winnebago and Chippewa Indians) and the St. Peters (Sioux Indians) Agencies were transferred to it from the St. Louis Superintendency. In 1850 the La Pointe Subagency, which had been moved from Wisconsin to Minnesota and renamed the Sandy Lake Subagency, was placed under the Minnesota Superintendency. The following year it became the Chippewa Agency and was made responsible for the Chippewa of the Mississippi, previously assigned to the Winnebago Agency, and for the Chippewa of Lake Superior living in Minnesota and Wisconsin. After 1853, however, the Mackinac Agency handled the affairs of the Lake Superior Chippewa. The Minnesota Superintendency was abolished in 1856, and its three agencies were transferred to the Northern Superintendency.

The records of the superintendency, 1849–56 (4 ft.), include the usual series of letters received, petitions, affidavits, subpenas, muster rolls, contracts, bonds, accounts, and other records (3 ft.) and four volumes of copies of letters sent. Some of the records relate to territorial matters other than Indian affairs. These records have been reproduced as M842.

Montana Superintendency

The Montana Superintendency was established in 1864 with the organization of Montana Territory. Montana had been part of Idaho Territory since 1863; before that it had been divided between Washington and Dakota Territories. The Territorial Governor served ex officio as superintendent until 1869; thereafter, a separate superintendent was appointed.

The principal tribes in Montana were Blackfeet (Siksika), Piegan, Blood (Kainah), Grosventre, Flathead, Kutenai, Pend d'Oreille, Crow, Assiniboin, and several bands of Sioux. The Blackfeet and Flathead Agencies were the original agencies in the superintendency, and both remained there throughout its existence, except when the Flathead Agency was assigned to the Idaho Superintendency, September 1865–February 1866. Established later were the Crow Agency in 1869, the Milk River Agency in 1870 (moved in 1873 and renamed the Fort Peck Agency in 1874), and the Fort Belknap Agency in 1873 for the Indians still living along the Milk River. The Montana Superintendency was abolished in 1873, and thereafter the agents reported directly to the Bureau of Indian Affairs in Washington.

The records of the superintendency, 1867–73 (2 ft.), consist of an incomplete series of letters received from the Commissioner of Indian Affairs, agents, and other sources; letters sent, 1867, 1869–70, and 1873; and miscellaneous records, including contracts, bonds, licenses, affidavits, financial records, and statistical reports. They have been reproduced as M833.

Nevada Superintendency

The Nevada Superintendency was established in 1861 and operated until 1870. There are records, however, only for the incumbency of the last superintendent, Maj. Henry Douglas, 1869–70. The principal tribes living in Nevada were Paiute, Washo, and Shoshoni. During 1869 and 1870 there were two agencies in Nevada: the South East Nevada Agency (or Pi-Ute Agency), responsible for the Paiute Indians living in southeastern Nevada and adjacent parts of Utah and Arizona, and the Nevada Agency, responsible for the other Indians in Nevada. The records (6 in.) include letters received, two volumes of letters sent, and statistical and financial records, including a ledger of receipts and disbursements. They have been reproduced as M837.

New Mexico Superintendency

The New Mexico Superintendency was established at Santa Fe in 1850, with the organization of New Mexico Territory, to replace the Santa Fe Agency, which had been established March 28, 1849. New Mexico originally included Arizona and parts of Colorado and Nevada. When Colorado and Arizona Territories were established in 1861 and 1863, respectively, New Mexico was reduced to its present boundaries. Until 1857 the Territorial Governor served ex officio as superintendent; thereafter, a separate official was appointed.

The principal Indians in New Mexico were Ute, Apache, Navajo, Pueblo, Pima, Papago, and Maricopa.

In 1851, the Congress authorized the appointment of four agents to serve under the superintendent. At first these agents did not have specific assignments but were sent wherever the superintendent decided they were needed.

Regular agencies gradually were established for the different tribes. The first permanent agencies were the Navajo, 1852; Southern Apache, 1852, for Mimbreño, Mogollon, Coyotero, and, for a time, the Mescalero Apache Indians; Utah, 1853, for various bands of Ute and, at times, the Jicarilla Apache Indians; Abiquiu, 1854, for Capote Ute and Jicarilla Apache Indians until 1862 and thereafter for Capote and Wiminuche Ute Indians; and Pueblo, 1854. The Tucson Agency was established in 1857 for the Pima, Papago, Maricopa, and "Tame" Apache Indians, who lived mainly on the land acquired by the Gadsden Purchase. The agency was abandoned in 1861, when Confederate troops occupied the area, and control was not reestablished until after Arizona had been made a separate superintendency. The Conejos Agency for the Tabaquache Ute was established in 1860 and transferred to the Colorado Superintendency in 1861. The Mescalero Agency was established in 1861. In 1862 the Cimarron Agency for the Jicarilla Apache and Moache Ute replaced the Utah Agency. The Navajo Agency, although located in Arizona after 1868, remained in the New Mexico Superintendency. The New Mexico Superintendency was abolished in 1874; thereafter, the agents in New Mexico reported directly to the Bureau of Indian Affairs in Washington.

Among the superintendency records, 1849-74 (8 ft.), the major series, 1850-74 (6 ft.), includes letters received, with some copies and drafts of letters sent, circulars, vouchers, invoices, financial statements, licenses, contracts, proposals, estimates, and printed Army orders. They are arranged by year and thereunder for the most part by kind of record. The letters received are usually grouped by source: the Commissioner of Indian Affairs, agents in the superintendency, and others.

Some of the Indian agents and other persons wrote in Spanish, and for the years 1852 to 1859 some of their letters have been separated from the other correspondence. There also are some segregated letters, 1854-60, from Christopher (Kit) Carson, written while he was agent at the Utah Agency.

The letters sent, 1851-73, are in nine letter books. There is also a journal, 1852-53 and September-November 1863, which consists of a daily record of events and transactions, such as visits of Indians, arrivals and departures of agents, and issuances of license to traders. The financial records include a cashbook, journal, and several ledgers, including one kept by the Southern Apache Agency, 1870-74.

With the superintendency records are a volume of letters sent by the Cimarron Agency, July-October 1870, and some records, 1849-50, of Henry Dodge, the Army subsistence agent at Cibolletta, later Navajo agent.

Most of the superintendency records have been reproduced as T21.

Northern Superintendency

The Northern Superintendency was established in 1851 as part of the general reorganization of the field service in that year. The superintendent was informed that he would be in charge of the Indians living in Wisconsin and Michigan, that is, the Indians of the Mackinac Agency and Sault Ste. Marie Subagency in Michigan (Chippewa, Ottawa, and Potawatomi Indians) and the Indians of the Green Bay Subagency in Wisconsin (Menominee, Oneida, and Stockbridge Indians). There also were some Potawatomi and other Indians in Wisconsin. Actually, the superintendent had little contact with Indian affairs in Michigan, and in 1853 he was informed that only the three tribes of the Green Bay Subagency (made a full agency in 1855) were under his authority.

When the Minnesota Superintendency was discontinued in 1856, the St. Peters (Sioux of the Mississippi), Winnebago, and Chippewa (Chippewa of the Mississippi) Agencies were assigned to the Northern Superintendency. In 1857 the Green Bay Agency was made independent. In 1858 the La Pointe Agency was established under the Northern Superintendency for the Chippewa of Lake Superior in Minnesota and Wisconsin. In 1863 many of the Winnebago and Sioux Indians and the Winnebago Agency were moved to Dakota, but they remained under the Northern Superintendency.

In 1865 the Northern Superintendency was completely reorganized. Its office was moved from St. Paul, Minn., to Omaha, Nebr., and it was made responsible for the Omaha, Pawnee, Otoe (Oto and Missouri Indians), Great Nemaha (Iowa Indians and Sauk and Fox of the Missouri), and Winnebago Agencies in Nebraska and the Upper Platte Agency (Cheyenne, Arapaho, and Sioux Indians), then located at Fort Laramie but later moved to Nebraska. All except the Winnebago Agency were transferred from the Central Superintendency. The St. Peters Agency, which had been moved to Dakota Territory, was moved again in 1866 to Nebraska and was once more within the limits of the Northern Superintendency, where it became known as the Santee Sioux Agency. The Upper Platte Agency was moved to Dakota in 1868 and in 1869 was transferred to the Dakota Superintendency and renamed the Whetstone Agency. In 1875 the Pawnee Indians moved to Indian Territory, and the following year the Pawnee Agency was transferred to the Central Superintendency.

The Northern Superintendency was discontinued June 30, 1876, and the Otoe, Omaha, Great Nemaha, Winnebago, and Santee Sioux agents thereafter reported directly to the Bureau of Indian Affairs in Washington.

The superintendency records, 1851–76 (14 ft.), include the usual series of correspondence, vouchers, receipts, invoices, bills of lading, estimates, bids, contracts, financial statements, property returns, affidavits, licenses, annual reports, school and other reports, and applications of Indians for credit from traders, and other records, arranged by year and thereunder for the most part by kind of record (6 ft.). The letters received during each year are usually divided according to source, particularly the Commissioner of

Indian Affairs and each of the agencies in the superintendency. For the years 1865 to 1876, however, most of the original letters received were bound in volumes or fastened together. There are also three copybooks for letters sent and received, 1851–56, and one just for letters sent, 1857–61. For the years 1865 to 1876 there are several sets of letters sent, with registers, 1869–75. There are also two account books of the superintendency and a volume of letters sent and financial statements of the Winnebago Agency, 1846–73, with gaps.

Oregon Superintendency

The Oregon Superintendency was established in 1848 with the organization of Oregon Territory. It originally had jurisdiction over the area west of the Rocky Mountains and north of the 42d parallel, but when Washington Territory was established in 1853, the region north of the Columbia River and the 46th parallel came under the Washington Superintendency. Oregon was reduced to its present boundaries when it became a State in 1859. Between 1857 and 1861 the Oregon and Washington Superintendencies were combined. For this period the records relating to the superintendency in general and to Indian matters in Oregon are usually to be found with the records of the Oregon Superintendency; records relating only to Washington are usually with the records of the Washington Superintendency. The Territorial Governor served ex officio as superintendent until 1850, when a separate official was appointed.

There were many bands of Indians in Oregon, including the Umpqua, Umatilla, Cayuse, Wallawalla, Wasco, "Snake," Kalapuya, Clackamas, Rogue River, Warm Springs, Shasta, Klamath, Modoc, Paiute, Tenino, Nez Percé, Molala, Yamel, Joshua, Sixes (Kwatami), Chastacosta, and Chetco.

The agency structure in Oregon was unusually complicated, in large part as a result of the removal of Indians from their old homes and the concentration of them on reservations. There were many subagencies, special agencies, and local agencies. The first regular agents were appointed in 1850 and usually were assigned on a geographical basis rather than to particular tribes. There was a Rogue River Agency from 1850 to 1856 for the Rogue River and Umpqua Indians. The agency established in 1851 for Indians living east of the Cascade Mountains, after several changes, became the Warm Springs Agency. The Puget Sound Agency was established in 1851 and transferred to the Washington Superintendency in 1853. The Port Orford and Southeastern District Agencies were shortlived, 1854–56. The Grand Ronde Agency was established in 1856 for remnants of bands mainly from the Willamette and Rogue River Valleys then living in the eastern part of the Coast Reservation. The Siletz Agency was established on the Coast Reservation in 1856 for Indians who had been removed from along the coast, the

Rogue River area, and other parts of Oregon. The Umatilla Agency was transferred from Washington in 1862. The Klamath Agency was established as a full agency in 1872 although it had been in operation since 1861. The Oregon Superintendency was abolished in 1873, and thereafter the agents of the Warm Springs, Grand Ronde, Siletz, Umatilla, and Klamath Agencies reported directly to the Bureau of Indian Affairs in Washington.

The superintendency records, 1848–73 with a few as late as 1878 (10 ft.), include registers of letters received, letters received, and letters sent; a volume of reports and instructions, 1850–55; two volumes of records concerning the negotiations of treaties, 1851–55 (chiefly council proceedings and copies of treaties); a record book concerning the Rogue River Commission, established to decide on claims for property destroyed by Indians during the Rogue River war and to assess the value of permanent improvements on land set aside as a reservation for the Indians, 1854–55; and unbound accounts and several account books. There also are some letters received by the agent at Grand Ronde, 1861–64, and by other persons, chiefly agents, 1850–73. A ledger from the Warm Springs Reservation, 1861–63, probably was maintained by a trader. The records for the period after the discontinuance of the Oregon Superintendency relate chiefly to the Klamath and Siletz Agencies.

Many of the records of the Oregon Superintendency have been reproduced as M2.

Southern Superintendency

The Southern Superintendency was not established until 1851, but its records include those of its predecessor, the Western Superintendency, established in 1834. There are a few earlier records that are actually records of the Choctaw Agency, West. The area of jurisdiction of the Western Superintendency extended west of the Mississippi River from Arkansas to the Rocky Mountains and south of the limits of the St. Louis Superintendency, which was the northern boundary of the land of the Osage Indians. The principal tribes originally within the superintendency were Choctaw, Cherokee, Creek, Osage, Seneca, and the Mixed Band of Seneca and Shawnee. Quapaw, Seminole, and Chickasaw Indians moved into the area of the superintendency within a few years, and on occasion the superintendency had some responsibilities relating to Caddo, Comanche, Kiowa, and other Indians.

The agency structure of the superintendency changed several times, but throughout its existence there was an agency or subagency with primary responsibility for the Choctaw Indians, one for the Creek, and one for the Cherokee. There was also a subagency for the Osage Indians, but it alternated between the Western and St. Louis Superintendencies. In 1837 the Neosho Subagency was established for the Quapaw, Seneca, and the Mixed

Band of Seneca and Shawnee, who previously had been divided between the Osage and Cherokee Subagencies. The Seminole Indians were attached to the Creek Agency until a separate subagency was established for them in 1842. In 1839 the Chickasaw Agency was established for the Chickasaw Indians who by then had moved west onto Choctaw land.

In 1851 the Western Superintendency was replaced by the Southern Superintendency as part of a general reorganization of the field service of the Bureau. The agencies and tribes were unchanged except that the superintendency was in charge of a new Neosho Agency, formed by a consolidation of the Neosho and Osage Subagencies. In 1855 the Chickasaw Agency was consolidated with the Choctaw Agency and the Seminole Subagency was made a full agency. In 1857 the Wichita Agency, for the Wichita and Kichai Indians, was established. In 1859 Caddo, Anadarko, Waco, Tonkawa, Hanai, Kichai, Tawakoni, Delaware, Shawnee, and Comanche Indians were moved from Texas to the Wichita Agency in Indian Territory. In 1869 the Wichita Agency was consolidated with the Kiowa Agency of the Central Superintendency, successor to the St. Louis Superintendency. It was reestablished as a separate agency the following year, but remained in the Central Superintendency. The Neosho Agency had been transferred in 1867 to the Central Superintendency. By 1870 the Southern Superintendency was responsible for the Cherokee, Creek, Choctaw and Chickasaw, and Seminole Agencies.

At the beginning of the Civil War, Indian Territory was occupied by Confederate troops. The superintendent and some of the agents of the Southern Superintendency accepted equivalent positions under the Confederacy. Indians remaining loyal to the United States took refuge in Kansas, and temporary headquarters for the superintendency and the various agencies were established in that State. The Indians began to return to Indian Territory in 1864 and the superintendency was returned to its former location at Fort Smith, Ark., in 1866. There are few records of the superintendency after 1861, however. The Southern Superintendency was closed in 1869, but an Army officer was detailed to act as superintendent in connection with treaty provisions that stipulated the services of a superintendent for certain matters, such as the investigation of some claims. The following year the superintendent of the Central Superintendency took over these duties.

The records of the superintendency, 1832–70 (7 ft.), include a substantial series of letters received, vouchers, estimates, contracts, financial statements, and other records, 1832–61 (6 ft.), arranged by year and thereunder for the most part by source, particularly the Commissioner of Indian Affairs and the agents. There are also letters sent, 1853–61 (4 vols. and unbound papers); a volume of copies of correspondence, 1869–70, when an Army officer was detailed to act as superintendent; some correspondence of the Wichita Agency, 1860–61; correspondence and other records of the Cherokee Agency, 1866–67; and correspondence, 1868–70, of Richard Fields, a special agent appointed by the Cherokee Nation to examine its accounts with the United States.

The only records of field offices of the Confederate Bureau of Indian Affairs known to be in the National Archives are with the records of the Southern Superintendency. They consist of some correspondence of the Arkansas Superintendency, the Confederate equivalent of the Southern Superintendency, 1861–62; correspondence of the Wichita Agency, 1861–62; and some accounts, licenses to trade, and other records of the Arkansas Superintendency and its agencies, particularly the Creek Agency, 1861–62.

The records of the Southern Superintendency have been reproduced as M640.

Utah Superintendency

The Utah Superintendency was established in 1850 with the organization of Utah Territory. Since 1849 the Salt Lake Agency had been in charge of the Ute, Paiute, Shoshoni, Bannock, Pahvant, and other Indians who lived in the Great Basin area between the Rocky Mountains and the Sierra Nevada. Utah Territory originally included most of the present State of Nevada, the western part of Colorado, and a corner of Wyoming as well as the present State of Utah. It was reduced to its present boundaries by the creation of the Territories of Nevada and Colorado in 1861 and Wyoming in 1868. The Territorial Governor, Brigham Young, served ex officio as superintendent until 1857, when a full-time superintendent was appointed.

There were three agencies in Utah during the existence of the superintendency. The first regular agency was established at Salt Lake City in 1851, moved to the Spanish Fork Reservation for Ute Indians in 1859, and moved in 1865 to the Uintah Valley, where it became known as the Uintah Valley Agency. A second agency was established at Provo in 1855. It was moved to Fort Bridger in 1861 and given responsibility for the Shoshoni and Bannock Indians. In 1869 the Fort Bridger Agency was transferred to the Wyoming Superintendency. The Carson Valley Agency was established in 1858 for the Paiute and Washo Indians in the western part of the Territory. It was transferred to the Nevada Superintendency in 1861. The Utah Superintendency was abolished in 1870. Thereafter the Uintah Valley agent reported directly to the Bureau of Indian Affairs in Washington.

The records of the superintendency (10 in.) consist of letters received, 1858–70; letters sent, 1857, 1859–64, and 1866–67; and miscellaneous records, 1853 and 1855–70, which include statistical reports, affidavits, and financial records. They have been reproduced as M834.

Washington Superintendency

The Washington Superintendency was established in 1853 with the organization of Washington Territory. The Indians in Washington previously had been assigned to the Oregon Superintendency. Washington originally included the area north of the Columbia River and the 46th parallel and west of the Continental Divide. When Oregon became a State in 1859, the eastern part of the former Oregon Territory was transferred to Washington, which then included all of the present State of Idaho and parts of Montana and Wyoming. With the organization of Idaho Territory in 1863, Washington was reduced to its present boundaries. Between 1857 and 1861 the Oregon and Washington Superintendencies were combined. For this period most of the records relating to the superintendency in general and to Oregon in particular are with the records of the Oregon Superintendency. Records relating specifically to Washington are usually with the records of the Washington Superintendency. The Governor of the Territory of Washington served ex officio as superintendent until the merger of 1857. After a separate Washington Superintendency was reestablished in 1861, a full-time superintendent was appointed.

There were many groups of Indians in Washington, including the Makah, Skokomish, Sklallam, Yakima, Colville, Puyallup, Tulalip, Nisqualli, Nez Percé, Flathead, Spokan, Pend d'Oreille, Kutenai, Cayuse, Paloos, Wallawalla, Quinaielt, Blackfeet, Chehalis, Chilkat, Chinook, Clackamas, Clallam, Lake, Klikitat, Coeur d'Alène, Cowlitz, Dwamish, Lummi, Muckleshoot, Quileute, Quaitso (Queet), Squaxon, and Swinomish.

The first agents in Washington usually were assigned on a geographical basis. After a series of treaties were negotiated between 1854 and 1856, the Indians who had agreed to a particular treaty generally were assigned to one agency. In addition to the regular agencies, there were many special agencies, subagencies, and local agencies.

The Puget Sound District Agency, established under the Oregon Superintendency in 1851, was transferred to the Washington Superintendency in 1853. During 1861 and 1862 the Puyallup, Tulalip, Neah Bay, Skokomish, and Quinaielt Agencies were established in the Puget Sound area, some originally as subagencies, and the Puget Sound District Agency was discontinued. The Puyallup Agency was the outgrowth of a special agency begun in 1856 for the Indians who had agreed to the Treaty of Medicine Creek. During the years 1865 to 1869 the Puyallup and Tulalip Agencies were consolidated.

The Columbia River, or Southern District, Agency was established in 1854 for the Indians who lived north of the Columbia River and south of the Skookumchuck and Chehalis Rivers. In 1859 it was moved to the Yakima Reservation and thereafter was known as the Yakima Agency. There were also agencies, established in 1854 and 1857, that developed into the Flathead and Nez Percé Agencies. Both were transferred to the Idaho Superintendency in 1863. The Colville Agency was established as a special agency in 1872 and became a regular agency in 1875. The Washington Superintendency was abolished in 1874. Thereafter the agents in Washington reported directly to the Bureau of Indian Affairs.

The records of the Washington Superintendency, 1853–74 (8 ft.), include letters received from the Commissioner of Indian Affairs, local jurisdictions, and other sources, including Indians; letters sent; records concerning the negotiation of treaties, including a journal, 1854–55, of Governor Isaac I. Stevens in his capacity as treaty commissioner; and accounts, contracts, periodical reports, and other records. Most of the superintendency records have been reproduced as M5.

Wisconsin Superintendency

The Wisconsin Superintendency was established in 1836 with the creation of Wisconsin Territory from the western part of Michigan Territory. Wisconsin originally included the present States of Iowa and Minnesota and much of the Dakotas. With the creation of Iowa Territory in 1838, Wisconsin was reduced to the boundaries of the present State and that part of Minnesota east of the Mississippi River. The Territorial Governor served ex officio as superintendent throughout the existence of the superintendency.

Sauk and Fox, Sioux, Winnebago, Chippewa, Menominee, Oneida, Stockbridge, Munsee, Iowa, and other Indians lived in Wisconsin Territory. The Prairie du Chien Agency (Winnebago and Sauk and Fox Indians), St. Peters Agency (Sioux of the Mississippi), and Green Bay Agency (Menominee and other Indians) and the Sioux, Ioway, Fort Winnebago, and Crow Wing (Chippewa of the Mississippi) Subagencies were originally assigned to the Wisconsin Superintendency. The La Pointe Subagency for the Chippewa of Lake Superior in Wisconsin was soon added. From 1836 to 1841 there were many changes in agencies and subagencies, as the result of reorganizations, the establishment of Iowa Territory, and the removal of Indians. By 1841 the Wisconsin Superintendency was left with the Green Bay Subagency for the Menominee, Oneida, Stockbridge, and Munsee Indians and the La Pointe Subagency for the Chippewa Indians in Wisconsin, including those formerly assigned to the Crow Wing Subagency, which had been abolished in 1839. The Wisconsin Superintendency was abolished in 1848. Thereafter the two subagents reported directly to the Bureau of Indian Affairs in Washington.

The records of the superintendency, 1836–48 (2 ft.), include letters received; a volume of copies of reports of agents; a volume of letters sent to the Commissioner of Indian Affairs and other officials in Washington; a volume of letters sent to agents and other persons; a volume of copies of council proceedings, particularly of the speeches made by Indians, and letters, petitions, memorials, and other documents received from Indians; and estimates and contracts. These records have been reproduced as M951, which also includes some records of the Green Bay Subagency, 1850. See also the records of Menominee Agencies in Wisconsin on page 166.

Wyoming Superintendency

The Wyoming Superintendency was established in 1868 with the organization of Wyoming Territory. Territorial officials, however, were not appointed until April 1869. The Territorial Governor served ex officio as superintendent. During the period of the Wyoming Superintendency, there was only one agency in Wyoming, the Shoshone and Bannock Agency. The successor of the Fort Bridger Agency, which had been assigned to the Utah Superintendency, it was responsible for the Eastern bands of Shoshoni and Bannock Indians. There were also Cheyenne, Arapaho, and Sioux Indians in Wyoming. The Wyoming Superintendency was discontinued in 1870, and thereafter the agent reported directly to the Bureau of Indian Affairs in Washington. The only records of the superintendency are a volume of letters sent, July–November 1870, and a volume of copies of endorsements on letters received by the superintendent and referred to other officials, usually the Commissioner of Indian Affairs, August–October 1870. They have been reproduced as part of M1016.

RECORDS OF AGENCIES, SCHOOLS, AND OTHER FIELD OFFICES

Aberdeen Area Office

The Aberdeen Area Office was created in 1949 and given jurisdiction over the Cheyenne River, Crow Creek, Fort Berthold, Pine Ridge, Rosebud, Yankton, Sisseton, Standing Rock, Turtle Mountain, Fort Totten, and Winnebago Agencies and Subagencies and the Flandreau and Wahpeton Schools.

The records, incorporating those of some subordinate units, 1934–52 (31 ft. in FARC Kansas City), include general correspondence and a decimal file; range, wildlife, fire, and forestry reports; and records concerning irrigation, soil conservation, and subsistence gardens.

Abiquiu and Cimarron Agencies

The Abiquiu Agency was established in 1854 for the Capote Ute and Jicarilla Apache in the northwestern part of present New Mexico. After the Cimarron Agency was established in 1862, the Abiquiu Agency had charge of the Capote and Wiminuche Ute. The new agency, which replaced the Utah Agency for various bands of Ute in New Mexico, was responsible for the Jicarilla Apache and Moache Ute. No agent was assigned to the Cimarron Agency from April 1872 until July 1874. The Cimarron and Abiquiu Agencies were consolidated with the Pueblo Agency in 1876 and 1878, respectively. The Ute Indians moved to the Southern Ute Agency in

Colorado in 1878, and the Jicarilla Apache moved from Cimarron to the Abiquiu Agency area. Cimarron was discontinued, but a farmer in charge was assigned to the Abiquiu Agency, which was renamed the Jicarilla Agency in 1881. In 1882 supervision of the Jicarilla Agency was transferred from the Pueblo Agency to the Mescalero Agency, and the following year the Jicarilla Apache moved to the Mescalero Reservation in southern New Mexico.

The records, 1869–82 (5 ft. in FARC Denver), are mostly from the Abiquiu Agency. They include a volume of letters sent, 1875–80, and correspondence, circulars, accounts, and other records, 1869–82. See also the records of the New Mexico Superintendency on pages 138 and 139.

Albuquerque Indian School

This boarding school was established in 1881 at Duranes, New Mexico Territory, and moved to its present site the following year. The Presbyterian Home Mission Board operated the school under contract until 1886, when the Bureau of Indian Affairs assumed control. From 1901 to 1911 the Albuquerque Indian School had jurisdiction over the day schools and agency duties for the pueblos in the vicinity. In 1935 the school was placed under the jurisdiction of the United Pueblos Agency.

The records of the school, 1886–1951 (16 ft. in FARC Denver), include folders for nongraduated students (surnames beginning A through C only), 1886–1951, and a decimal file, 1917–36.

Anadarko Area Office

The Anadarko Area Office, established in 1948, is essentially a continuation of the Kiowa Agency, created in 1864 and permanently located in Indian Territory in 1869. After the Wichita Agency was merged with it in 1878, the Kiowa Agency, for some years usually called the Kiowa, Comanche, and Wichita Agency, was responsible for Kiowa, Comanche, Kiowa-Apache, Delaware, Caddo, Wichita and affiliated Indians, and, later, Fort Sill Apache. In more recent years the agency had some responsibilities for the Alabama-Coushatti Indians of Texas.

The records, 1881–1952 (1,523 ft. in FARC Fort Worth), include general correspondence and correspondence concerning lands, heirship, townsites, and schools; accounts and case files for individual Indians; land transaction files; annuity payrolls; annual reports; student records; and records of employees.

Billings Area Office

The Billings Area Office was established in 1946. It has jurisdiction over Indian agencies in Montana and Wyoming, and its records incorporate many of earlier jurisdictions in those States.

The records, 1912–52 (340 ft. in FARC Seattle), relate predominantly to

Indian lands and resources. They include general decimal files, grazing leases, and records concerning education, health, tribal enactments, irrigation, land transactions, forestry, soil conservation, agricultural extension, and road construction.

Bismarck Indian School

The Bismarck Indian School, Bismarck, N. Dak., originally to be known as the Mandan Indian School, was authorized in 1901 but not opened until 1908. It was closed for several months in 1918. In 1922 it was changed from a coeducational to a girls' nonreservation boarding school, and it was closed permanently in 1937. The school records, 1904–38 (4 ft. in FARC Kansas City), include general correspondence (some arranged by the decimal system), money receipts of individual Indians, and student enrollment applications.

Blackfeet Agency

The Blackfeet Agency was established in 1855 for the three bands of Siksika Indians living in present Montana known collectively as Blackfeet and, for a number of years, some Grosventre Indians.

The agency records, 1875–1952 (230 ft. in FARC Seattle), include general correspondence, grazing permits, oil and gas production reports, census records, birth and health records, ledgers and abstracts of accounts of individual Indians, tribal council records, and records concerning education, road, forestry, irrigation, credit, welfare, and rehabilitation programs.

Carlisle Indian Industrial School

The Carlisle Indian Industrial School at Carlisle, Pa., was established in 1879 and closed in 1918. It was the first Government-operated nonreservation boarding school for Indians. A feature of the school was the outing system, under which students could live and work outside the school and attend public school while still enrolled at Carlisle.

Among the school records, 1879–1918 (91 ft.), the only general correspondence is two volumes of letters sent, August–October 1900 and January–May 1901. Most of the records relate to students. There are registers of pupils, 1890–1906, and a consecutive record of pupils enrolled, 1905–18. The largest series, student records, 1879–1918 (53 ft.), consists of correspondence, cards designated as "Descriptive and Historical Record of Student," promotion certificates (including ratings in subjects), records of outings, medical and dental records, form reports concerning post-school careers, records from other schools, information forms concerning eligibility for Federal aid, clippings, photographs, and other records. They relate to enrollment, transportation, progress at school, outings, health, financial affairs, withdrawals from school, careers after leaving school, special problems, and other subjects. The folders for individual students are arranged numerically. Other "Descriptive and Historical Record of Student" cards are separate, as are enrollment cards, and cards concerning students' potential and actual employment after leaving Carlisle; most of these are for students for whom there are no folders. There are three sets of index slips to the folders and cards, arranged, respectively, by folder number, alphabetically by surname of student, and alphabetically by tribe and thereunder alphabetically by surname of student.

Student information cards, 1879–1918 (10 ft.), may give name, tribe, agency, age, degree of Indian blood, name of father, date of arrival at Carlisle, date of and reason for departure, time spent on outings, trade, name of spouse, character rating, religion, date of death, and other information. Other records include enrollment cards, ca. 1897–1913; two attendance books labeled "morning reports," 1884–91; an enrollment status book, 1898–1902; a volume with information concerning former students, ca. 1898; a register of applications for student workers, 1885–90; and four registers of outings, 1881–97 and 1912–18. There are also 10 ledgers for student savings accounts, 1890–1918; a journal for payments to boys, 1908–12; a journal for the YMCA account, 1910–14; minutes of the Invincible Debating Society, which was composed of boys in the school; an address book for letters written by students; a register of visitors; time books for employees; financial records; and records concerning goods and supplies.

Carson School and Agency

The Carson or Stewart Indian School was established near Carson City, Nev., in 1890 as a nonreservation boarding school. During the years 1897 to 1908 the school supervised the Walker River Reservation for Paiute Indians. It also had agency duties for other Indian groups and for different periods of time supervised several day schools in Nevada and California. With the establishment of the Reno Agency in 1912, the school lost its remaining outside responsibilities. In 1925 the Reno Agency was consolidated with the school to form the Carson Agency. The agency supervised the Pyramid Lake, Fort McDermitt, and Summit Lake Reservations and various other Indian groups in northern Nevada. Pyramid Lake was reestablished as an independent jurisdiction from 1930 to 1933. In 1935 the Walker River Agency was merged with Carson, giving it responsibility for most of the Indians in Nevada and some in California, chiefly Paiute, Shoshoni, and Washo.

The school and agency records, ca. 1890–1955 (101 ft. in FARC San Francisco), include correspondence, administrative files, a register of pupils, pupil record books, individual Indian pupil records, and records of goods issued to Indians. See also the records of the Walker River Agency on page 189.

Carter and Laona Agencies

The Carter Agency was established at Carter, Wisc., in 1911. In 1916 it was moved to Laona, Wisc., and renamed the Laona Agency. It was responsible for several bands of Potawatomi Indians in Wisconsin and, later, in Michigan. It also had duties concerning the Rice Lake Band of Chippewa Indians, who lived mainly in Forest and Langlade Counties, Wisc. The Laona Agency was consolidated with the Lac du Flambeau Agency in 1927, but a subagency was maintained at Laona for some years thereafter. The records of the Laona Agency, 1911–27 (14 ft. in FARC Chicago), consist chiefly of correspondence. There are also some fiscal records and records concerning efforts to enroll nonreservation Chippewa in 1920.

Chamberlain Indian School

This nonreservation boarding school at Chamberlain, S. Dak., was established in 1898 and closed in 1909. Its records, 1897–1909 (1 ft.), consist of a blotter, 1907–9, which contains notations concerning arrivals and departures of students and employees, progress on work projects, purchases, disbursements, visits, weather conditions, and other matters; two registers of pupils, 1901–6; rosters of employees; and several account books.

Chemawa Indian School

A nonreservation boarding school was opened at Forest Grove, Oreg., in 1880. In 1885 it was moved to a site north of Salem that became known as Chemawa. The school has been called both Chemawa and Salem. From 1925 to 1938 the school had agency duties for the Indians of the Grand Ronde and Siletz Reservations and nonreservation Indians, but most of its records relate to school activities.

The school records, 1880–1952 (210 ft. in FARC Seattle), include general correspondence and decimal files, descriptive statements about children, applications for admission, attendance records, student health records, student and graduate student case files, ledgers for accounts of individual Indians, fiscal records concerning maintenance of the school, and records concerning Civilian Conservation Corps work and irrigation projects. See also the records of the Grand Ronde-Siletz Agency on page 161.

Cherokee Agency, East

An agent was appointed for the Cherokee Indians living east of the Mississippi River, mainly in Tennessee and Georgia, as early as 1792. There is very little information concerning the agent and his immediate successors; but by 1801 the Cherokee Agency was permanently established at South West Point, now Kingston, Tenn. Between 1807 and 1820 the agency was at or near Hiwassee Garrison at the mouth of the Hiwassee River. After 1820 the agency was located farther up the Hiwassee River, opposite Calhoun, Tenn. On December 31, 1834, the Cherokee Agency in the East was discontinued as a regular agency, and the superintendent of emigration for the Cherokee was designated to perform the duties of the agent. By 1839 the Bureau considered the removal of the Cherokee Indians to Indian Territory complete. The position of superintendent of emigration and the Cherokee Agency in Tennessee were discontinued January 26, 1839. Actually, however, many Cherokee Indians still lived in the East.

For many years the Cherokee agent also served as agent of the War Department in Tennessee. In this capacity he handled such matters as payments to troops, procurement of supplies, and accounts of military officers and other Indian agents.

Among the records of the agency, 1798–1839 (10 ft.), the largest series consists of correspondence, vouchers, receipts, financial statements, abstracts, Treasury Department notices, minutes, journals, rolls, lists, affidavits, petitions, addresses, passports, and other records, 1798–1838 (6 ft.), arranged in rough chronological order. Copies of correspondence for the years 1822 to 1827 and 1832 to 1835 have been bound in two letter books, and there are seven letter books for copies of correspondence of the superintendency of emigration, 1831–34, and the combined superintendency and agency, 1835–39. There are several account books, including daybooks, journals, ledgers, and receipt books, covering various periods. There are also unbound accounts, 1801–20, including some records in the agent's capacity as agent of the War Department. One journal, 1825–28, is a record of disbursements to help Indians in suits to recover lost reservations and in other legal cases. There is correspondence of the agent of the War Department in Tennessee, 1800–15, and some correspondence of Governor Joseph McMinn of Tennessee relating particularly to the enforcement of the treaty of July 8, 1817, and the removal of Cherokee Indians to Arkansas, 1817–21. (McMinn later was Cherokee agent.)

Many of the records of the Cherokee Agency, East, have been reproduced as M208.

Cherokee Agency, North Carolina

Many Cherokee Indians continued to live in the region of the Great Smoky Mountains after the removal of most of the tribe and the discontinuance of the Cherokee Agency in the East in 1839. Although there was no regular agent assigned to them for several decades, from time to time the Bureau did appoint special agents and commissioners to perform various duties relating to them. In 1882 a regular agency was established. Since 1893 it has been at Cherokee, N.C. For many years the superintendent of the Cherokee School also served as agency superintendent.

The agency records, 1886–1952 (158 ft. in FARC Atlanta), include general files, student folders and other school records, training case files for veterans after World War II, census records, tribal financial records, annuity payment records, files for accounts of individual Indians, timber sales and cutting permits, Civilian Conservation Corps project files, and law and order reports.

Cherokee Agency, West

The only known records of the Cherokee Agency in the West in the National Archives consist of correspondence, transcripts of speeches, vouchers, and receipts, 1816–19, when the Western Cherokee were living between the Arkansas and White Rivers in the present State of Arkansas.

Cheyenne River Agency

The Cheyenne River Agency, S. Dak., was established in 1869 for several bands of Sioux Indians. It was known as the Forest City Agency from 1892 to 1894. The agency records, 1869–1955 (310 ft. in FARC Kansas City), include several series of general correspondence; school, range and forestry, census, birth and death, heirship and probate, allotment, and annuity records; folders and money accounts for individual Indians; and tribal court records.

Chickasaw Agency, East

The Chickasaw Agency in the East was established in 1800 for the Chickasaw Indians, who then lived mainly in the present State of Mississippi but also in adjacent parts of Alabama and Tennessee. The agency remained in operation until 1839, but there are only a few records, chiefly letters received and sent, 1812–16, and an estimate of expenses for 1806.

Chilocco Indian School

This school was opened in Indian Territory in 1884 as a nonreservation industrial and agricultural training school for Indians. The records, 1890–1952 (346 ft. in FARC Fort Worth), include correspondence with the Commissioner of Indian Affairs, decimal files, accounts of individual Indians, student files, attendance records, employee records, records concerning the Civilian Conservation Corps program and national defense during World War II, and a collection of photographs of individuals and campus scenes.

Choctaw Agency, East

There was an agency for the Choctaw Indians living east of the Mississippi River, mainly in the present State of Mississippi, from before 1800 until 1832. The only records, however, are some correspondence, vouchers, and a list of employees, 1817–21. These have not been positively identified as records of the agency, but there are no other records with which they seem more likely to belong.

Colorado River Agency

The Colorado River Agency was established in 1864 for the Indians living in the Colorado River area, chiefly in Arizona but also in California and Nevada. The tribes included Mohave, Chemehuevi, Walapai, Havasupai, Cocopa, and Yavapai, but the agency came to be concerned primarily with the Mohave and Chemehuevi Indians, at first those living on and near the Colorado River Reservation and later over a wider area. New agencies were created for the other tribes. The Fort Mojave School, established in 1890, had agency duties for the Mohave and Chemehuevi Indians living near it until it was consolidated with the Colorado River Agency in 1915. Fort Mojave was an independent jurisdiction again from 1917 until the school was closed in 1931, but it did not have any agency responsibilities. In 1935 the Fort Yuma Agency for Yuma and Cocopa Indians was merged with the Colorado River Agency.

The agency records, 1867–1952 (322 ft. in FARC Los Angeles), include administrative, hospital, and fiscal records and records concerning irrigation, property reports, contracts, leases, field notes of land surveys, and registers of Indian families.

Colville Agency

The Colville Agency was established in 1872 for the Indians of the Colville Reservation and later the Spokane and Coeur d'Alène Reservations in Washington and Idaho and nonreservation Indians in the area. They included the Colville, Spokan, Coeur d'Alène, Lake, Nespelim, Okinagan, Kalispel, Sanpoil, Methow, Joseph's Band of Nez Percé, Moses Band of Columbia, and Wenatchi Indians. In time the tribal distinctions were dropped, and the Indians were identified by the reservation on which they lived. A separate Coeur d'Alène Agency was established in 1905 and a Spokane Agency in 1912. The Spokane Agency was consolidated with the Colville Agency in 1925.

The records of the Colville Agency, 1865–1952 (222 ft. in FARC Seattle), include general correspondence, day school correspondence, census and annuity payment rolls, tribal council minutes, maps, and records concerning grazing and forestry, irrigation, accounts of individual Indians, land sales, vital statistics, and judicial and legal services. See also the records of the Spokane Agency on page 185.

Concho Agency

The Concho Agency, formerly the Cheyenne and Arapaho Agency, is responsible for the Southern Cheyenne and Arapaho of Oklahoma. The Cheyenne and Arapaho Agency was established in 1874 as the successor to the Upper Arkansas Agency. In 1902 the agency was divided into the Cheyenne and Arapaho, Seger, and Cantonment Agencies, and from 1908 to

1917 a fourth agency, Red Moon, was separated from Seger. The Cheyenne and Arapaho Agency was reunited in 1927, and its name was changed to Concho in 1963.

The agency records, 1891–1952 (457 ft. in FARC Fort Worth), include general correspondence and decimal files, census records, accounts of individual Indians, land transaction files, maps, plats, tractbooks, registers of Indian families and children, records of marriage licenses, records of births and deaths at Red Moon, and heirship and school records.

Consolidated Chippewa Agency

The Consolidated Chippewa Agency was established in 1922 for Chippewa Indians living on various reservations in northern Minnesota previously assigned to the White Earth, Leech Lake, and Red Lake Agencies. The White Earth and Leech Lake Agencies were abolished. The Red Lake Agency continued to be responsible for the Red Lake Chippewa but not the Indians of the Nett Lake (Bois Fort Chippewa), Grand Portage, and Fond du Lac Reservations, who had been assigned to the Red Lake Agency only since 1920. (These three reservations had been consolidated under the Fond du Lac Agency in 1919; an agency for each had been broken off from the La Pointe Agency during the years 1906 to 1911.) In December 1954 the Consolidated Chippewa Agency and the Red Lake Agency were merged to form the Minnesota Agency. Red Lake was reestablished as an independent unit in 1964, and the name Minnesota Agency was retained for the former Consolidated Chippewa Agency.

The records of the Consolidated Chippewa Agency, 1889–1954 (186 ft. in FARC Kansas City and 4 ft. in Washington, D.C.), include many inherited from predecessors. The agency records include general correspondence, ledgers and accounts for individual Indians, census data, council proceedings of negotiations between Chippewa Indians and the United States in 1889, and records concerning births and deaths, heirship, tribal enrollment, unpaid annuities, tribal delegations, forestry, grazing, and land.

Identified as records from Leech Lake, 1915–31, are general correspondence, including letters received by the farmer in charge at Leech Lake, 1922–30 (in Washington), and accounts of individual Indians, a reservation census, land allotment files, timber sales records, a register of employees, and Leech Lake Hospital and Sanatorium correspondence.

Identified as records from White Earth, 1892–1931, are general correspondence, including correspondence of the forest guard who was the agency field representative at Beaulieu, 1922–26, and at White Earth, 1926–29, and of the field clerks at White Earth and Mahnomen, 1930–35 (in Washington). There are also school correspondence, records of accounts of individual Indians, stubs of certificates for land allotments, equity files for land claims, records of timber sales, and census, allotment, and annuity rolls.

For the Grand Portage School there are some records, 1913–31 (in Washington), relating to activites of the teacher, who also had general charge of the Grand Portage Reservation and for a time served as deputy special officer for liquor control.

See also the records of the Leech Lake, Nett Lake, and White Earth Agencies on pages 165, 170, and 190 and 191, respectively.

Creek Agency, East

An agent was appointed for the Creek Indians living east of the Mississippi River, chiefly in Georgia and Alabama, as early as 1792. The agency continued in operation until 1836. The few records of the agency, 1794–1818, include correspondence, licenses to trade, and vouchers.

Crow Agency

The Crow Agency was established in 1869 for the Mountain Crow Indians of Montana. Gradually, the other main group of Crows, the River 'Crows, also came under the control of the Crow Agency.

The agency records, 1877–1952 (162 ft. in FARC Seattle), include general correspondence and decimal files, student case files, school censuses, tractbooks, maps of the Crow Reservations, grazing leases, building plans, annuity payrolls, ledgers for accounts of individual Indians, records of goods issued to Indians, census rolls, Indian court dockets, and records concerning irrigation, forestry, Civilian Conservation Corps, and road programs.

Crow Creek Agency

The Crow Creek Agency was formally established in 1874 as the successor of the Upper Missouri Agency, although the predecessor agency had been commonly known as Crow Creek as early as 1866, when a new location for the agency office was selected near Crow Creek below the Great Bend of the Missouri River in Dakota Territory. The jurisdiction of the Upper Missouri Agency had been gradually reduced by the establishment of new agencies; by 1871 it was responsible only for the Lower Yanktonai and Lower Brulé Sioux. In 1875 a separate agency was established for the Lower Brulé. From 1882 to 1896 the Crow Creek and Lower Brulé Agencies were consolidated as the Crow Creek and Lower Brulé Agency. They were again separate until 1924 when Lower Brulé was made a subagency of Crow Creek. In 1954 Crow Creek and its subagency were merged with the Pierre School to form the Pierre Agency.

The records of the Crow Creek Agency, 1861–1955 (196 ft. in FARC Kansas City), include general correspondence, tribal correspondence for the Yanktonai and Brulé, census rolls, birth and death registers, case files for accounts of individual Indians and special deposits and disbursements, land transaction and heirship records, annuity payrolls, school records, lease accounting records, tribal court records, and records of an economic and social survey at Lower Brulé, 1938.

Digger Agency

There had been a farmer in charge assigned to the Digger Reservation near Jackson, Calif., as early as 1899, but the few records of the agency are only for the years 1915 to 1920. During this period the farmer in charge was also responsible for the Indians of the Tuolumne Reservation. The agency was discontinued in 1921, and its duties were assigned to the Reno Agency. The records (in FARC San Francisco) consist of general correspondence, pupils' applications to enter schools with related correspondence, and tribal and school census records.

Fallon School and Agency

The Fallon Day School was established in 1908 near Fallon, Nev. The superintendent also had agency duties for a reservation established for a colony of Paiute Indians. In 1912 the Lovelocks School was subordinated to the Fallon School; Fallon was ended as an independent jurisdiction in 1925 and put under the Walker River Agency. The only separate records of the school are some administrative files, 1909-25 (1 ft. in FARC San Francisco).

Flandreau School and Agency

The Flandreau Agency was established in 1873 for the Santee Sioux living at Flandreau, Dakota Territory. From 1879 until 1902 the Flandreau Agency was consolidated with the Santee Agency. The Flandreau Indian School, now known as Flandreau Indian Vocational High School, was opened as a nonreservation boarding school in 1893. From 1901 until 1906 it was called Riggs Institute. In 1902 the school superintendent was assigned the duties of agent for the Flandreau Agency. During 1948 and 1949 the Pipestone Indian School was under Flandreau.

The school and agency records, 1880-1954 (113 ft. in FARC Kansas City), include general correspondence, individual student folders, census rolls, records of accounts of individual Indians and special deposits, a marriage register for 1900, and records concerning annuity payments, money allotments, and Civilian Conservation Corps and Work Projects Administration projects.

Flathead Agency

The Flathead Agency, Mont., was established in 1854 principally for the Flathead, Upper Pend d'Oreille, and Kutenai Indians. Lower Kalispel Indians moved onto the Flathead Reservation in 1887 and Spokan Indians in 1894. In time the tribal distinctions were ignored, and the Indians became known collectively as Flatheads.

The records of the agency, 1875–1952 (540 ft. in FARC Seattle), include general correspondence and decimal files; correspondence, reports, and censuses concerning schools; grazing permits, leases, records concerning allotments and land transactions, and other records concerning land; records concerning irrigation, Civilian Conservation Corps, engineering, road, and forestry programs; ledgers for accounts of individual Indians; and census reports, records concerning relief and welfare projects and cases, Indian police and court records, credit program files, tribal accounts, and annuity payrolls.

There are separate records, 1906–52 (540 ft. in FARC Seattle), of the Flathead Irrigation Project, started by the Bureau of Reclamation in 1908 and turned over to the Bureau of Indian Affairs in 1924. The records include general subject files, water delivery records, level books, transit books, canal cross section books, diaries, engineering and operation and maintenance files, reports and studies, maps, photographs, records concerning power and electrical services, contract files, and fiscal records.

Fort Apache Agency

The White Mountain Reservation for Apache Indians in Arizona was established in 1872 with two divisions, the northern one under the Camp Apache Agency and the southern one under the San Carlos Agency. In 1875 the San Carlos Agency assumed control of both divisions, and by 1876 it was in charge of all the Apache Indians in Arizona. In 1897 the reservation was divided, and the Fort Apache Agency was established for the White Mountain Apache in the northern part, now called the Fort Apache Reservation.

The agency records, 1875–1952 (229 ft. in FARC Los Angeles), include correspondence, annual narrative and statistical reports, census records, Indian police dockets and court records, records concerning asbestos mining claims, many fiscal records, and some maps, charts, and drawings. Some records of the Army command at Fort Apache, 1890–1912, are with the agency records.

Fort Belknap Agency

The Fort Belknap Agency was established in 1873 for the Grosventre and Assiniboin Indians living along the Milk River in northern Montana. It was combined with the Fort Peck Agency in 1876 but reestablished as a separate agency in 1878.

The agency records, 1878–1952 (285 ft. in FARC Seattle), include general correspondence and decimal files, correspondence concerning education and school reports and applications, grazing permits, leases, ledgers for accounts of individual Indians, correspondence and reports about health and welfare, census rolls, family history cards, traders' licenses, police and court records, and records concerning roads, land sales, Civilian Conservation Corps work, and financial matters.

Fort Berthold Agency

The Fort Berthold Agency, N. Dak., was established in 1864 when the Upper Missouri Agency was divided. A new agent was assigned to the Arikara, Grosventre, Mandan, Assiniboin, and Crow Indians living along the Missouri River near Fort Berthold. During 1869 and 1870 the Assiniboin, Crow, and some of the Grosventres were assigned to other agencies. The Fort Berthold Reservation was established in 1870, and an agent was first specifically assigned to the Fort Berthold Agency in 1871.

The records of the agency, 1877–1955 (340 ft. in FARC Kansas City), include general correspondence; ledgers for accounts of individual Indians and special deposits; land sale, lease, and allotment records; timber records; grazing permit files; heirship records; census and birth and death records; school records; records concerning Civilian Conservation Corps work; and tribal council and business committee minutes.

Fort Bidwell School and Agency

The Fort Bidwell School was opened in 1898, and within a few years it had agency duties for the Indians, chiefly Pit River and Paiute, of Modoc County, Calif. The school was closed in 1930, and the following year the agency duties were transferred to the Sacramento Agency. Some records through 1936, maintained at Fort Bidwell, are included with the agency records.

The records, 1898–1936 (9 ft. in FARC San Francisco), include administrative files, farming and grazing leases, school reports, individual Indian pupil records, a pupil register, and school census records.

Fort Hall Agency

In 1867 a special agent was assigned to the Boise and Bruneau bands of Shoshoni Indians. In 1869 these Indians and some Western Shoshoni and Bannock were moved to the Fort Hall Reservation in southeastern Idaho. In 1872 the Bannock previously assigned to the Shoshone and Bannock Agency in Wyoming also moved to Fort Hall. The Lemhi Agency was consolidated with the Fort Hall Agency from January 1879 until February 1880. The Indians moved from Lemhi to Fort Hall, and the Lemhi Agency was closed in 1907.

The records of the Fort Hall Agency, 1889–1952 (70 ft. in FARC Seattle), include school surveys and censuses, mining permits, grazing leases, ledgers and cards for accounts of individual Indians, and records concerning owners of ceded land, irrigation, forestry, loans, and law suits.

Fort Peck Agency

The Fort Peck Agency, Mont., replaced the Milk River Agency in 1874. It was responsible primarily for Assiniboin and Sioux, principally Yanktonai, Indians.

The agency records, 1877–1952 (248 ft. in FARC Seattle), include general correspondence and decimal files, school reports, records of 4-H activities, grazing permits, mining leases, ledgers for accounts of individual Indians, credit rehabilitation ledgers, industrial status reports, census records, medical reports, registers of Indians and of births and deaths, welfare relief case files, tribal council records, and records concerning land allotments and sales, forestry and range management, irrigation, and road construction.

Fort Shaw Indian School

This nonreservation boarding school at Fort Shaw, Mont., was established in 1892 and closed in 1910. Its records, 1892–1910 (1 ft.), consist of letters received, 1897–98; three registers of pupils, 1892–1910; sanitary reports, 1894–99; rosters of employees; and cashbooks.

Fort Totten Agency

The Devil's Lake Agency, N. Dak., was established in 1881 for the Sisseton, Wahpeton, and Cut Head (Pabaksa) Sioux living on the Devil's Lake Reservation. Beginning in 1884 it also had charge of the Turtle Mountain Chippewa. In 1903 the agency was merged with the Fort Totten School, which had been established in 1890. In 1910 a separate agency was established for the Turtle Mountain Chippewa. From 1947 to 1949 Fort Totten was part of the Turtle Mountain Consolidated Agency; thereafter, it was again independent.

Records of the Fort Totten Agency, 1890–1950 (89 ft. in FARC Kansas City), include general correspondence, census rolls, vital statistics, probate and heirship files, records of accounts of individual Indians, land records, records concerning Civilian Conservation Corps work, tribal court records, and individual student folders.

Fort Yuma Subagency

The Fort Yuma Reservation in southeastern California and a reservation boarding school were established in 1884 for the Yuma Indians. The reservation was supervised first by the Colorado River and then the Mission Tule River Agency. In 1900 the Fort Yuma School was given agency status. In 1935 it was placed under the Colorado River Agency and reduced to a subagency.

The records, 1907–52 (43 ft. in FARC Los Angeles), include correspondence and school, court, election, and financial records, including accounts of individual Indians.

Grand Rapids Agency

The Grand Rapids Agency was established in 1916 for the Winnebago Indians of Wisconsin, who previously had been assigned to the Tomah School. It was consolidated with the Laona Agency for several months during 1917 and 1918. The name of the community of Grand Rapids was changed to Wisconsin Rapids in 1920, but the agency kept its original name. In 1921 responsibility for the Arpin Band of Potawatomi Indians was transferred from the Laona Agency to the Grand Rapids Agency. In 1927 the Grand Rapids Agency was discontinued, and its duties were returned to the Tomah Indian School, which again was given agency status. Most of the records of the Grand Rapids Agency, 1900–26 (6 ft. in FARC Chicago), relate to individual estates and land allotments under the General Allotment Act of 1887. Other records include annuity rolls, some correspondence, justifications for withdrawals of minors' funds, and a list of married Indian couples in Thurston, Nebr., in 1921.

Grand Ronde–Siletz Agency

The Grand Ronde and Siletz Agencies were established in 1856 for Indians living on the Coast Reservation who had been moved from other parts of Oregon. The Indians were usually identified by reservation rather than original tribe or band. In 1909 and 1925 the Grand Ronde and Siletz Agencies, respectively, were consolidated with the Salem (Chemawa) School. When the Roseburg Agency was abolished in 1918, some of the nonreservation Indians in Oregon had been assigned to Siletz, and they were also transferred to Salem. The Grand Ronde-Siletz Agency was established in 1938, relieving the Salem School of its agency duties. The consolidated agency was terminated in 1956. Most of the agency records appear to be with those of the Grand Ronde-Siletz Agency rather than those of the school.

The records, 1863–1952 (70 ft. in FARC Seattle), include general correspondence and decimal files, school records, heirship cards, maps, annuity payrolls, ledgers for accounts of individual Indians, vital statistics and census rolls, health reports, social service case files, court records, tribal constitutions, and records concerning land allotments and sales, forestry, Civilian Conservation Corps work, and relief and rehabilitation.

Great Lakes Consolidated Agency

The Great Lakes Agency was established in 1936 as the successor to the Lac du Flambeau Agency for various bands of Chippewa and Potawatomi Indians in Wisconsin and Michigan. In 1949 the agency absorbed the Tomah Agency and was renamed the Great Lakes Consolidated Agency. Previously assigned to the Tomah Agency were the Winnebago Indians in Wisconsin, Minnesota, and Iowa; Stockbridge and Oneida Indians in Wisconsin; Ottawa and Potawatomi Indians in Michigan; and Saginaw, Swan Creek, and Black River Bands of Chippewa Indians in Michigan. The Great Lakes Consolidated Agency was made an area field office of the Minneapolis Area Office in 1952 but returned to agency status in 1956.

The agency records, 1875–1952 (approximately 350 ft. in FARC Chicago), include materials inherited from jurisdictions that came under its control, including Lac du Flambeau, Tomah, Mount Pleasant, Hayward, and La Pointe. Other records of these jurisdictions have been kept apart from those of the consolidated agency.

There are general records and records concerning health and medical care, social relations, censuses and tribal enrollment, heirship, payments to Indians, schools and students, employment, timber and forestry, Civilian Conservation Corps work, relief and rehabilitation, accounts of individual Indians, other financial matters, liquor and drug traffic, law and order, and Selective Service during World War II.

Greenville School and Agency

The Greenville School, which earlier had been a contract school, was converted to a Government nonreservation boarding school in 1895. For a number of years it had agency duties for the Indians of Butte, Plumas, Sierra, and Yuba Counties in California. In 1918 all but Plumas County were transferred to the Reno Agency, and Indians of the discontinued Roseburg Agency living south of the Umpqua Valley in Oregon and California were transferred to Greenville. In 1923 Greenville was made a subagency of the new Sacramento Agency.

Records of the agency and school, 1897–1923 (22 ft. in FARC San Francisco), include letters sent, administrative files, correspondence concerning schools, annual reports, census rolls, plats, and records concerning Indian pupils. See also the records of the Roseburg Agency on pages 180 and 181.

Haskell Institute

Haskell Institute, a nonreservation boarding school, was opened in Lawrence, Kans., in 1884 and is still operating as Haskell Junior College. From 1927 until 1935 the Potawatomi Agency was a subagency of the Haskell Institute. The records, 1884–1954 (243 ft. in FARC Kansas City), include general correspondence, individual student folders, other student records, records of accounts of individual Indians, claims files, and minutes of Haskell Club meetings.

Hayward Indian School

The Hayward Indian School, Hayward, Wisc., was opened in 1901 as a boarding school for the Chippewa of the Lac Courte Oreille Reservation. It was subordinate to the La Pointe Agency until 1904. About 1911 it was given agency duties for the reservation. The school was closed in 1933, and its duties were transferred to the Lac du Flambeau Agency. The school records, 1908-28 (8 ft. in FARC Chicago), consist chiefly of correspondence, but there are also some school attendance reports, records of land transactions, records concerning timber and lumbering, and financial and personnel records.

Hoopa Valley Agency

The Hoopa Valley Agency was established in 1864. It was responsible primarily for the Hupa Indians living on the Hoopa Valley Reservation in California along the Trinity River near its junction with the Klamath River; the Klamath Indians nearby; and, after 1869, the Indians who moved from the Smith River Reservation.

The agency records, 1875-1952 (67 ft. in FARC San Francisco), include general correspondence, administrative files, correspondence concerning land and land allotment records, reports, an agency diary for 1919, Indian wills, Indian court records, and vital statistics, medical, school, and Civilian Conservation Corps work records. See also the records of the Sacramento Area Office on pages 181 and 182.

Hopi Agency

The Moqui Agency was separated from the Navajo Agency in 1899 and renamed the Hopi Agency in 1923. Until 1937 there were Navajo as well as Hopi Indians in its charge. It now administers the Hopi and Kaibab Reservations. The agency records (7 ft. in FARC Los Angeles), consist of circular letters from the Commissioner of Indian Affairs, 1907-20, and a decimal file, 1935-56. See also the records of the earlier Moqui Pueblo Agency on page 168.

Jicarilla Agency

The Jicarilla Agency for the Jicarilla Apache of northern New Mexico was established in 1901, but its records include some from predecessors. The Jicarilla Apache were assigned to the Southern Ute Agency from 1887 to 1891 and to the Pueblo and Jicarilla Agency from 1891 to 1901. The records, 1890-1952 (57 ft. in FARC Denver), include decimal files of the agency and of the Jicarilla Boarding School, land allotment records, supply reports and records of livestock issued to Indians, and school reports and censuses, including some reports prepared by the Jicarilla Southern Mountain Sanatorium.

Juneau Area Office

The Juneau Area Office inherited records from predecessor units of the Alaska Division of the Office of Education (until 1931) and the Bureau of Indian Affairs. The Division directed education, medical care, and economic assistance activities for Alaskan natives.

The records, 1905-52 (135 ft. in FARC Seattle), include a decimal file, student case files, reindeer herd reports, welfare case files, and education program, individual account, loan, allotment, medical, and Indian industry ledgers.

Klamath Agency

A special agent was appointed for the Indians of the Klamath Lake area in southern Oregon in 1861, and a subagent was appointed the following year. In 1867 the subagency was moved to the Klamath Reservation, and in 1872 it was made a full agency. Klamath, Modoc, "Snake," Pit River, and other Indians lived on the reservation, which was terminated in 1961.

The agency records, 1867-1952 (520 ft. in FARC Seattle), include general subject files, tribal election ballots, business committee and general council minutes, Klamath Loan Board files, and records concerning irrigation, allotments and other land transactions, forestry, grazing, agricultural extension, accounts of individual Indians, law and order, annuities, and medical care.

Lac du Flambeau Agency and School

The Lac du Flambeau Boarding School for the Chippewa Indians living on the Lac du Flambeau Reservation in Wisconsin was opened in 1895 under the direction of the La Pointe Agency. In 1907 it was made independent and given agency status. A major reorganization in 1927 consolidated the La Pointe, Laona, Red Cliff, and Mackinac Agencies with the Lac du Flambeau Agency, and in 1933 the Hayward School was added. The consolidated agency was responsible for Chippewa and Potawatomi Indians living in Wisconsin and Michigan. In 1936 the Lac du Flambeau Agency was superseded by the Great Lakes Agency.

The records of the Lac du Flambeau Agency and School, 1896-1932 (39 ft. in FARC Chicago), include general correspondence; letters received by the Government farmer; administrative and fiscal records, including some for the accounts of individual Indians; family and personal histories of students; other school records; records of an industrial survey, with photographs and personal and economic information about Indian households, 1922; timber contracts; and heirship case files.

Laguna Sanatorium

The Laguna Sanatorium was established in 1911 at Laguna, N. Mex., to care for Indians with tuberculosis, although until July 1929 it also treated general patients. Between 1911 and 1924 the sanatorium was successively under the jurisdiction of the Pueblo Day Schools at Albuquerque, the Pueblo Agency, and the Southern Pueblos Agency. It was independent from 1924 until it was closed in 1933. The records of the sanatorium, 1926-33 (15 ft. in FARC Denver), consist of a decimal file and three registers of patients treated, giving age, degree of Indian blood, occupation, and other information.

Leech Lake Agency

The Leech Lake Agency was established in 1899 for the Leech Lake Pillager, Cass and Winnibigoshish Pillager, White Oak Point, and Red Lake bands of Chippewa Indians living on reservations in Minnesota. These Indians formerly had been under the White Earth Agency, although there had been a Leech Lake Agency from 1874 to 1879. In 1906 a separate Red Lake Agency was established. The Leech Lake Agency was abolished in 1922, and the Indians were assigned to the new Consolidated Chippewa Agency. The sale of timber was particularly important at the Leech Lake Agency.

Agency records, 1899-1922 (43 ft.), include a large series of correspondence, with some petitions, affidavits, reports, contracts, schedules, school calendars, and other records (23 ft.); general letters sent to the Commissioner of Indian Affairs; letters sent concerning logging, timber, and allotments; other letters sent; annuity applications, payment certificates, and rolls; applications and schedules for allotments and applications for sale of inherited land; timber contracts; industrial survey reports; a census, World War I draft registration cards, birth certificates, death certificates, and marriage licenses and certificates; medical reports; records concerning licenses to trade; financial records; and school reports, applications for enrollment in nonreservation schools, "descriptive statements of children," school census reports, and school attendance records. For the Leech Lake Boarding School there are letters sent, attendance and enrollment books, programs, examination papers, and other records. See also the records of the Consolidated Chippewa Agency on pages 155 and 156.

Lower Brulé Agency

The Lower Brulé Agency, S. Dak., for the Lower Brulé Band of Sioux Indians, was established in 1875 as the White River Agency and renamed the following year. From 1882 to 1896 it was combined with the Crow Creek Agency as the Crow Creek and Lower Brulé Agency. The two were combined again in 1924 with Lower Brulé becoming a subagency of the Crow Creek Agency and then consolidated with the Pierre School in 1954 to form the Pierre Agency.

The records of the agency, 1915-55 (7 ft. in FARC Kansas City), consist chiefly of correspondence files, 1915-23. Other records include land transaction files, tribal correspondence, and records of an economic and social survey in 1938.

Mackinac Agency

The Mackinac Agency for the Chippewa of Lake Superior living on the L'Anse and Ontonagon Reservations in Michigan was established in 1899.

In 1927 it was consolidated with the Lac du Flambeau Agency. The agency records, 1903–27 (14 ft. in FARC Chicago), include several series of correspondence; fiscal records, including statements of accounts of individual Indians; and records concerning land and timber.

Records of an earlier Mackinac Agency are described with those of the Michigan Superintendency on pages 135–137.

Malheur Agency

The Malheur Agency was established in 1873 for bands of Shoshoni, Bannock, and Paiute Indians living on the Malheur Reservation in eastern Oregon. The Indians left the reservation in 1878, and most of them eventually were settled on the Yakima Reservation. In 1880 the agent was demoted to the position of farmer in charge, and the agency was abolished in 1882.

The records of the agency, 1875–82 (1 ft.), include letters received and reports, two volumes of letters sent, a cashbook, and account books for Indian labor and goods paid to Indians.

Menominee Agencies in Wisconsin

The Green Bay Agency was established in 1815 and continued to operate as an agency or subagency until 1909, when it was renamed the Keshena Agency. During most of its years, it was responsible for the Menominee, Oneida, and Stockbridge and Munsee Indians of Wisconsin. There was a separate Oneida Agency from 1900 to 1919. The Keshena Agency came to have few duties except those concerning the Menominee. The Oneida were transferred to the Tomah School in 1932 and the Stockbridge and Munsee in 1935.

The Menominee Indian Mills were established in 1908 for the production of lumber. In 1927 they were made a separate jurisdiction independent of the Keshena Agency. About 1943 the mills and the Keshena Agency were merged to form the Menominee Agency, which operated until 1961, when the Bureau of Indian Affairs terminated its relationship with the Menominee Indians.

The records of the agencies, 1850 (less than 1 in. in Washington, D.C.) and 1865–1959 (approximately 100 ft. in FARC Chicago), include several series of correspondence, tribal resolutions and minutes, census rolls, records concerning logging and mill operations, ledgers and other records concerning accounts of individual Indians, records concerning Menominee fairs, and records of the Neopit Day School. The small amount of correspondence of the Green Bay Subagency, 1850, has been reproduced with the records of the Wisconsin Superintendency on M951.

Mescalero Agency

An agent was sent to Fort Stanton, New Mexico Territory, in 1861 to assume control of the Mescalero Apache. Fort Stanton soon fell to Confederate troops and the Mescalero Agency, although nominally in existence, did not operate until 1871. In 1875 the agency was moved to South Fork on the Mescalero Apache Reservation. The Mescalero and Jicarilla Agencies were consolidated in 1882, and from 1883 until 1887 the Jicarilla Apache lived on the Mescalero Reservation. In 1887 they moved to a new reservation in northern New Mexico and were assigned to the Southern Ute Agency.

The agency records, 1874–1942 (36 ft. in FARC Denver), include copies of letters sent, 1882–1914; letters received from the Commissioner of Indian Affairs, 1902–9; accounts, correspondence, and other records, 1874–1942; birth and death rolls, 1925–34; a register of vital statistics, 1910–16; and vouchers for rations issued to heads of Indian households, 1879–81.

Miami Agency

The Miami Agency, formerly the Quapaw Agency, was established in 1871 for the several bands of Indians living on reserves east of the Neosho River in what is now the northeastern corner of Oklahoma. Previously they had been assigned to the Neosho Agency. The Indians originally under the Quapaw Agency were Seneca, Eastern Shawnee, Quapaw, Ottawa, Confederated Peoria and Miami, Wyandot, and a few members of other tribes. In 1873, following the Modoc War, members of Captain Jack's band of Modoc were moved onto a section of the Shawnee Reserve. During 1878 and 1879 Chief Joseph's band of Nez Percé Indians was attached to the Quapaw Agency before they moved to the Ponca Agency. In 1879 most of the Quapaw Indians joined the Osage Indians. In 1900 the Quapaw Agency was placed under the Seneca School, but it was still usually called by its original name. Business concerning the Modoc Indians gradually declined, and, after the termination of the trust periods on their allotments, the agency had little to do with the Peoria and Miami. A separate agency was established for the Quapaw Indians in 1920, but in 1922 the Quapaw Agency was reunited with the Seneca School as the Quapaw Agency. The name was changed to the Miami Agency in 1947.

The records of the agency, 1870–1952 (324 ft. in FARC Fort Worth), include general correspondence, accounts of individual Indians, enrollment cards, a register of Indian families and other family history records, census records, student records, medical files, records of Indian courts, fiscal records, maps, and records concerning land transactions, Civilian Conservation Corps work, heirship, and annuities.

Minneapolis Area Office

The Minneapolis Area Office was established in 1949 to exercise jurisdiction over the Consolidated Chippewa, Red Lake, and Great Lakes Agencies and the Sac and Fox Area Office.

The records, which incorporate some from subordinate units and predecessors, 1909–52 (60 ft. in FARC Kansas City), include correspondence, administrative records, minutes of tribal meetings, individual Indian case files, vital statistics, and records concerning heirship, land allotments, sales and leases, annuities, social and economic surveys, welfare, and Civilian Conservation Corps work.

Minnesota Agency

The Minnesota Agency was established under the Minneapolis Area Office in 1954 by the merger of the Consolidated Chippewa and Red Lake Agencies for the various bands of Chippewa Indians in Minnesota. The Red Lake Agency was reestablished in 1964.

The records of the Minnesota Agency, 1955–69 (10 ft. in FARC Kansas City), include general correspondence, timber cutting permits, ledgers for accounts of individual Indians, records concerning court disposition cases and law and order, and narrative reports.

Moqui Pueblo Agency

The agency for the Moqui Pueblo (Hopi Indians) was established in 1869. From October 1876 until December 1877, when there was no agent assigned to the Moqui Pueblo Agency, its business was assigned to the Navajo agent, and in 1883 it was consolidated with the Navajo Agency. The records of the Moqui Pueblo Agency, 1875–83 (1 ft.), consist of a series of correspondence, accounts, and other records, 1875–83; a volume of letters sent, 1882–83; a diary kept by the agent, 1880–82; and an account book, 1878–83. See also the records of the Hopi Agency on page 163.

Mount Pleasant Indian School

Mount Pleasant was opened as a nonreservation boarding school in 1892 and operated until 1932. It performed some agency duties for Indians in the Lower Peninsula of Michigan, particularly the Chippewa of Saginaw, Swan Creek, and Black River on the Isabella Reservation. These duties were taken over by the Tomah School.

The records of the Mount Pleasant School, 1904–26 (7 ft. in FARC Chicago), consist chiefly of several series of correspondence.

Muskogee Area Office

The Muskogee Area Office was established in 1948 to administer the Bureau's business concerning the Cherokee (including Delaware and Shawnee), Chickasaw, Choctaw, Creek, and Seminole Indians of Oklahoma. Until 1874 there had been agencies for the individual tribes, except the agency for the Choctaw and Chickasaw was consolidated. The Union Agency was established in 1874 for all five tribes. Until 1898 the tribes largely governed themselves. In 1893 the Commission to the Five Civilized Tribes

(Dawes Commission) was established to negotiate agreements with the Indians to exchange tribal lands for individual allotments. The Curtis Act of 1898 (30 Stat. 495) provided for the preparation of tribal rolls and the making of allotments by the Commission, leasing of mineral lands, creation of townsites, and increased jurisdiction of Federal courts. The act also created positions of Inspector for Indian Territory and superintendent of schools. In general the Commission handled tribal matters, such as enrollment, allotments, and collection of tribal revenues, and the agency handled matters concerning individual Indians: education, health, leasing of land, removals of restrictions, land sales, leasing, and collecting and investing money. In 1905 the Commission was reduced to a single Commissioner, and in 1907 the position of Inspector was combined with that of Commissioner. The Union Agency and the Commission were combined in 1914 to form the Five Civilized Tribes Agency, which was absorbed by the Muskogee Area Office in 1948.

The records, 1835-1952 (7,855 ft. in FARC Fort Worth, with exceptions as noted), include a volume of letters sent by the Choctaw and Chickasaw Agency, 1867 and 1870-73 (in Washington, D.C.); account books of the Union Agency, 1876-78, Choctaw National Treasurer, 1868-77, and Creek Nation, 1905-11 (in Washington, D.C.); journals (minutes) of the House of Kings, Creek Nation, 1895-97 and 1899 (in Washington, D.C.); general records of the Union Agency and Five Civilized Tribes Agency; records of the Commission to the Five Civilized Tribes concerning citizenship, enrollment, and allotments; other records concerning tribal enrollments; census rolls dating from 1852; and case files for individual Indians. There are records of allotments and other land transactions, plats, appraisals, right-of-way files for pipelines, mining applications, records concerning oil and gas, and records concerning removal of restrictions on land sales. Fiscal records include money files for individual Indians, accounts current and other accounts, applications for per capita payments, and annuity and other payrolls. Other records include correspondence concerning lawsuits, probate case files and related records, records concerning Civilian Conservation Corps activities, and records concerning schools, including the Mekasukey Academy (Seminole), the Armstrong and Wheeler Academies (Choctaw), and the Euchee Boarding School (Creek).

There are separate records for some of the district offices established in 1908 to investigate the conduct of guardians in charge of the estates of minors and to advise allottees having restricted lands of their legal rights. There are district office records, 1907-53, that have not been interfiled with other records of the Muskogee Area Office and its predecessors from Ardmore, Durant, Hugo, and McAlester for the Choctaw and Chickasaw; Okmulgee for the Creek; Vinita for the Cherokee; and Wewoka for the Seminole. For all of the offices there are case files for individual Indians; for some there is also general correspondence, and for Hugo there are school census rolls.

There are also separate records, 1901-52, not interfiled with other records of the area office, for some of the schools, including the Sequoyah Boarding School (Cherokee), Eufaula Boarding School (Creek), Jones Academy (Choctaw), and Carter Boarding (Chickasaw). Usually there are general correspondence and individual student records, and sometimes there are also school census rolls, employee records, and accounts.

Navajo Agencies and Window Rock Area Office

After 1901 jurisdiction over the Navajo Indians in Arizona, New Mexico, and Utah, for whom the Navajo Agency had been established in 1852, was gradually divided among several independent agencies. These were consolidated in 1935 to form one agency called the Navajo Service, with headquarters at Window Rock, Ariz. When the Window Rock Area Office was established in 1949, a separate Navajo Agency was created under its jurisdiction. Some of the former agencies were reduced to subagency status.

Records of the Navajo Agency, Window Rock Area Office, and other units, 1880-1955 (60 ft. in FARC Denver and 568 ft. in FARC Los Angeles), include general correspondence and decimal files (Denver and Los Angeles), tribal census rolls, accounts of individual Indians, trading post records, administrative and reference files, and records concerning rehabilitation and schools (Los Angeles); decimal files of the Northern Navajo Agency, 1923-34, Shiprock Boarding School, 1944-51, and Charles H. Burke School, 1926-39 (Denver); letters sent by the farmer in charge of the Navajo Extension Agency, 1903-6, and the superintendent of the Leupp Training School, 1909 (Denver); correspondence of the Chinle Subagency, 1938-55 (Los Angeles); correspondence, census records, and drawings of the Fort Defiance Subagency, 1880-1939 (Los Angeles); correspondence of the Shiprock Subagency, 1936-55 (Los Angeles); correspondence and other records of the Tuba City Subagency, 1922-54 (Los Angeles); and aerial photographs of the Navajo and Zuni Reservations (Los Angeles).

Nett Lake Agency

The Nett Lake Agency was established in 1908 for the Bois Fort Band of Chippewa. Previously these Indians had been under the La Pointe Agency and the Vermilion Lake School. In 1919 the Nett Lake Agency was consolidated with the Fond du Lac Agency, which in turn was merged with the Red Lake Agency in 1920. In 1922 the Bois Fort Chippewa were assigned to the new Consolidated Chippewa Agency.

The only separate records of the Nett Lake Agency are two data books, 1908-14, which include a diary of events, a transcript of council proceedings, abstracts and lists concerning allotments, and digests of court findings; and a record of receipts and disbursements, 1914-17.

Nevada Agency

The Nevada Agency, a continuation of the Carson Valley Agency established in 1858, existed until 1921. The only separate records of the agency, however, are in a volume of letters sent by the agent, 1869–71 (in FARC San Francisco). During this period, the agent was concerned principally with the Paiute Indians of the Pyramid Lake and Walker River Reservations in Nevada.

New York Agency

The New York Agency, originally known as the Six Nations Agency, was established in 1792. It remained in operation, either as an agency or a subagency, until 1949. There are, however, records of the agency in the National Archives only for the years 1938–49. The Indians living in New York at this time were Alleghany and Cattaraugus Seneca, Tonawanda Seneca, Tuscarora, Onondaga, Cayuga, Oneida, and St. Regis.

The records (4 ft.) include letters received, copies of letters sent, reports, copies of tribal acts and resolutions, certificates of election, contracts, leases, affidavits, briefs, questionnaire forms, rosters, schedules, maps, plats, and clippings. Most of them relate to tribal relations and tribal governments or land matters, particularly leases. They are arranged by a modification of the decimal classification system used by the central office of the Bureau.

Northern Cheyenne Agency

The Tongue River, now known as Northern Cheyenne, Agency was established in 1886 for the Northern Cheyenne Indians living on the reservation established for them in 1884 in southeastern Montana.

The agency records, 1884–1952 (136 ft. in FARC Seattle), include general correspondence, school reports and censuses, student case files, leases, census rolls, hospital and public health reports, Indian court and police proceedings, and records concerning forestry, Civilian Conservation Corps and Work Projects Administration programs, accounts of individual Indians, credit, industrial surveys, births and deaths, and tribal relations.

Northern Idaho Agency

The Northern Idaho Agency is the successor of the Coeur d'Alène Agency and the Fort Lapwai or Nez Percé Agency. The Nez Percé Agency was a continuation of an agency for "Washington East of the Cascades" established in 1857 for the Nez Percé and other Indians. After 1861 it was called the Nez Percé Agency and was responsible only for the Nez Percé Indians living on their reservation in the western part of present Idaho. After the superintendent of the Fort Lapwai School was assigned the duties of agent in 1902, the agency usually was called Fort Lapwai.

The Coeur d'Alène Agency was established in 1905 for the Coeur d'Alène and Spokan Indians living on the Coeur d'Alène Reservation in Idaho. Previously they had been assigned to the Colville Agency. Within a few years the Spokan Indians were no longer distinguished from the Coeur d'Alène. In 1912 the agency was made responsible for Kutenai and Kalispel Indians who had reservations in Idaho and Washington, respectively. In 1933 the Fort Lapwai Agency was combined with the Coeur d'Alène Agency, and in 1937 the name was changed to Northern Idaho Agency.

The agency records, 1875–1952 (160 ft. in FARC Seattle), include general correspondence and a decimal file, historical files, correspondence concerning Kutenai educational contracts, grazing and timber leases, ledgers for accounts of individual Indians, annuity payrolls, vital statistics and census records, Nez Percé tribal minutes, and records concerning forestry, roads, and economic and social surveys.

Northern Pueblos Agency

In 1919 the Pueblo Agency was divided into a Northern and a Southern Pueblos Agency. The Northern Pueblos Agency was responsible for the Indians in the northern pueblos of New Mexico. In 1930 it was consolidated with the Santa Fe Indian School, and in 1935 the agency duties and control of the school were assigned to the new United Pueblos Agency.

The agency records, 1904–36 (45 ft. in FARC Denver), include correspondence and other records, 1919–35, and a decimal file, 1904–36, which includes records created by jurisdictions previously responsible for Pueblo Indians and day schools.

Oneida School and Agency

A boarding school was established on the Oneida Reservation, Wisc., in 1892 under the jurisdiction of the Green Bay Agency. The school was made independent in 1895 and given agency status in 1900. The agency and school were closed in 1919 and the Oneida Indians were assigned to the Keshena Agency, successor to the Green Bay Agency, until 1932, when they were transferred to the Tomah School.

The records of the school and agency, 1897–1923 (2 ft. in FARC Chicago), consist chiefly of correspondence and financial records.

Osage Agency

The Osage Agency was established in 1824, and generally headquarters were along the Neosho River in southeastern Kansas. In 1834 it was reduced to a subagency, and in 1851 it was consolidated with the Neosho Subagency for Quapaw and other Indians living in northeastern Indian Territory to form the Neosho Agency. In 1871 the Indians other than the Osage were assigned to the new Quapaw Agency. In 1874 the Neosho Agency was renamed the Osage Agency. By then the Indians and the agency had moved to the new Osage Reservation in northern Indian Territory. Until 1904 the agency also was responsible for the Kansa (Kaw) Indians living in the northwestern corner of the Osage Reservation, and for a number of years after 1879 some Quapaw Indians also lived on the reservation.

The records of the Osage Agency, 1858-1952 (2,156 ft. in FARC Fort Worth), include correspondence and accounts dating from 1858, including more than 1,000 volumes of press copies of letters sent, 1876-1933; traders' licenses and related records; case files, plats and maps, and other records concerning land transactions; records concerning mineral and oil lands; records concerning money and accounts of individual Indians; and proceedings of the Osage Council, census rolls, student records, medical records, vital statistics records, annuity payment rolls and records of goods issued to families, guardianship files, probate records, and records concerning Civilian Conservation Corps work, sanitation and social services, and the agency buildings.

Pala Subagency

The Pala Agency was established in 1903 when the Mission Tule River Agency was divided. It was responsible for several of the reservations for Mission Indians in California; the specific assignments were changed several times. In 1913 it was merged with the Pechanga Agency, but the following year the agency was moved to Pala. In 1920 a consolidated Mission Agency was established; it was divided into a Northern and a Southern Mission Agency in 1921 but recombined the following year. Pala operated as a subagency of the Mission Agency until it was made part of the California Agency in 1948.

The subagency records, 1880-1948 (128 ft. in FARC Los Angeles), include correspondence, fiscal records, census and vital statistics records, and records concerning farming, grazing, and irrigation activities.

Palm Springs Agency

The Palm Springs Agency administers the reservation for the Agua Caliente Band of Mission Indians in California.

The agency records, 1935-56 (48 ft. in FARC Los Angeles), include correspondence, administrative records, fiscal records, accounts for individual Indians, permits and contracts for housing and land, census rolls, and photographs and drawings.

Papago Agency

The Papago Agency was established about 1948 by the renaming of the Sells Agency, which was one of a succession of agencies for the Papago Indians of Arizona. An agency for them was established in 1864, but the following year it was expanded into an agency for Pima, Maricopa, and Apache Indians. There was a separate agency for the Papago from 1871 to

1876, after which they were again assigned to an agency also responsible for the Pima and Maricopa and usually known as the Pima Agency. In 1902 the farmer in charge of the San Xavier Reservation, on which some of the Papago lived, was made independent of the Pima Agency. An enlarged reservation was established for the Papago in 1917, and in 1919 the superintendent at San Xavier moved to Indian Oasis, which was renamed Sells. Some Papago remained under the Pima Agency until 1934.

The records of the Papago Agency and its predecessors, 1870–1953 (321 ft. in FARC Los Angeles), include correspondence, administrative files, census records, personal histories, medical records, Civilian Conservation Corps program records, records concerning livestock, and fiscal records.

Pawnee Agency

The Pawnee Agency was established in Nebraska in 1859. During 1875 and 1876 the Pawnee Indians and Agency moved to Indian Territory. The Ponca Agency, established in 1859, and the Otoe Agency for Oto and Missouri Indians, established in 1856, moved from Nebraska to Indian Territory in 1877 and 1881, respectively. In 1882 these three agencies were merged to form the Ponca, Pawnee, and Otoe Agency. Chief Joseph's band of Nez Percé Indians lived near the Ponca at a place known as the Oakland Agency from 1879 to 1885. When they left, a group of Tonkawa Indians moved in, and thereafter the agency was called the Ponca, Pawnee, Otoe, and Oakland Agency. From 1901 to 1904 separate Pawnee, Otoe, and Oakland Agencies were reestablished. The Kaw Agency, established for the Kansa Indians in 1904, was merged with the Ponca Agency in 1912. In 1919 the Otoe and Ponca Agencies were merged with the Pawnee Agency, but in 1921 the Ponca Agency was reestablished for the Ponca, Tonkawa, and Oto and Missouri Indians. The Kansa stayed with the Pawnee Agency. The Ponca Agency was permanently merged with the Pawnee Agency in 1927.

The records of the Pawnee and affiliated agencies, 1870–1952 (690 ft. in FARC Fort Worth), include general correspondence, annuity payrolls, census rolls, case files and accounts for individual Indians, correspondence and minutes of tribal committees, maps, plats, records, accounts, and records concerning the Kaw Indian Claims Commission, Civilian Conservation Corps work, heirship, medical care, and education.

Phoenix Area Office

The Phoenix Regional Office was organized about 1946 and made an area office about 1950. Between 1946 and 1965 it was given jurisdiction over all the Indian agencies in Arizona except the Navajo Agency, the Sherman Institute (formerly under the Sacramento Area Office), the Uintah and Ouray Agency in Utah, and the Carson and Western Shoshone Agencies in Nevada.

The records of the office, 1891–1954 (614 ft. in FARC Los Angeles), incorporate records of subordinate and predecessor units. Included are records concerning land, extension, forestry and grazing operations, irrigation, soil and moisture programs, health, education, loan agreements, fiscal matters, and credit. There are records of the Phoenix Indian School, 1891–1950, and of the Phoenix Indian Hospital, 1948–49.

Pierre Agency

The Pierre Agency was created in 1954 by the merger of the Crow Creek Agency and Pierre Indian School. It operated until 1972. The agency records, 1918–67 (42 ft. in FARC Kansas City), with some inherited from the Crow Creek and Lower Brulé Agencies, include decimal files, records of individual Indian accounts and special deposits, reports, law and order records, and forestry and grazing reports.

Pierre Indian School

The Pierre Indian School, Pierre, S. Dak., was authorized in 1888 and opened in 1891 as a nonreservation boarding school. In 1954 it was consolidated with the Crow Creek Agency to become the Pierre Agency.

Records of the school, 1911–51 (47 ft. in FARC Kansas City), include general correspondence files, records concerning Civilian Conservation Corps work, ledgers of accounts of individual Indians and special deposits, statements of receipts and disbursements, and appropriation ledgers.

Pima Agency

The Pima Agency evolved from an agency established in 1864 for the Papago Indians and known successively as the Pima, Papago, and Maricopa; Gila River; and Pima Agency. By the time of the earliest records, 1888, it was responsible for the Pima, Papago, and Maricopa Indians of Arizona. In 1902 a separate jurisdiction was established for the Papago of the San Xavier Reservation and vicinity, and, with the establishment of an enlarged reservation for the Papago in 1917, the Pima Agency lost more of them. The Salt River Reservation (Pima Indians) was transferred to the Camp McDowell Agency in 1910. In 1934 the Salt River and Camp McDowell (Mohave-Apache Indians) Reservations, then under the Phoenix School, were transferred to the Pima Agency and the remaining separate groups of Papago Indians were transferred to the Papago Agency.

The agency records, 1888–1947 (389 ft. in FARC Los Angeles), include correspondence, diaries of employees, hospital and school records, census records, history cards for individual Indians, and fiscal records.

Pine Ridge Agency

The Red Cloud Agency was established in 1871 and renamed the Pine Ridge Agency in 1878. It was primarily responsible for the Oglala Sioux, but at times it had charge of Cheyenne Indians and members of other bands of Sioux.

Agency records, 1874–1965 (547 ft. in FARC Kansas City), include general correspondence, records concerning Civilian Conservation Corps work, land allotment records, annuity payrolls, records concerning individual Indian accounts, Sioux benefits records, heirship files, census rolls, and student folders.

Pipestone Indian School

The Pipestone Indian School, Minn., was opened as a nonreservation boarding school in 1893. It supervised the Birch Cooley (Coulee) Day School from about 1899 until the day school was closed in 1920. Beginning about 1914 the Pipestone Indian School had agency duties for Indians, mostly Mdewakanton Sioux, living in various parts of southern Minnesota. The school acquired records from the Canton Asylum for Insane Indians when the asylum closed in 1934. During 1948 and 1949, the Flandreau School controlled Pipestone, which was closed in 1953.

The school records, 1895–1952, (71 ft. in FARC Kansas City), include general correspondence, individual student records, individual Indian folders, correspondence of the principal of Birch Cooley School, and records of the Canton Asylum.

Portland Area Office

The Portland Area Office was established in 1950. It has jurisdiction over agencies in Idaho, Oregon, and Washington, and its records incorporate many acquired from district offices and agencies.

The records, 1902–52 (305 ft. in FARC Seattle), include decimal files of the Area Director's Office, program planning records, minutes of the Columbia Basin Inter-Agency Committee, correspondence and reports concerning schools, grazing permits, welfare case files, tribal constitutions, legal case files, allotment ledgers, and records concerning land allotments and sales, land classification, heirship, forestry, irrigation, road construction, tribal welfare, and health.

Potawatomi Agency

The Potawatomi Agency was established in 1851 for the Potawatomi and, until 1855, the Kansa Indians of Kansas. By 1871 the only Potawatomi remaining in Kansas were members of the Prairie Band. In 1874 the Kickapoo Agency was consolidated with the Potawatomi Agency, making it the only agency in Kansas; it was sometimes called the Kansas Agency. By 1876 the Chippewa and Munsee, who for some years had not had an agency, were assigned to the Potawatomi Agency. In 1882 the Potawatomi Agency and the Great Nemaha Agency for the Sauk and Fox of the Missouri and Iowa Indians of Nebraska were merged to form the Potawatomi and Great Nemaha Agency. In 1903 the agency was divided into a Potawatomi Agency for the Potawatomi Indians and the Kickapoo Agency for the Kickapoo,

Sauk and Fox, and Iowa. They were combined again as the Kickapoo Agency in 1919, but in 1921 the name was changed to Potawatomi. From 1927 until 1935 the Potawatomi Agency was consolidated with the Haskell Institute. In 1950 the agency's name was changed to Potawatomi Area Field Office and in 1964 to Horton Agency.

The agency records, 1851–1963 (59 ft. in FARC Kansas City), include general correspondence and decimal files, individual Indian files, census rolls, probate case files, a marriage license register, farming and grazing permits, and records concerning accounts of individual Indians, annuities, Civilian Conservation Corps work, land allotments and sales, leases, and births and deaths.

Pueblo and Pueblo and Jicarilla Agencies

The Pueblo Agency was established at Santa Fe in 1854 with jurisdiction over 19 Pueblo villages in New Mexico Territory. In 1876 and 1878, the Cimarron and Abiquiu Agencies, respectively, were placed under the supervision of the Pueblo Agency. The Ute Indians previously assigned to these agencies were transferred to the Southern Ute Agency in Colorado. The Jicarilla Apache moved from the Cimarron to the Abiquiu Agency, and the Cimarron Agency was discontinued in 1878. A farmer in charge was assigned to the Abiquiu Agency, which was renamed the Jicarilla Agency in 1881. In 1882 supervision of the Jicarilla Agency was transferred from the Pueblo to the Mescalero Agency. The Jicarilla Apache moved to the Mescalero Reservation in 1883 but returned to a new reservation near their old home in northern New Mexico in 1887. From 1887 to 1891 they were assigned to the Southern Ute Agency. In 1891 they were transferred to the Pueblo Agency, which then became the Pueblo and Jicarilla Agency. In 1901 the agency was abolished. Jurisdiction over the pueblos was divided between the superintendents of Albuquerque and Santa Fe Schools, and a separate Jicarilla Agency was established.

Agency records, 1874–1900 (24 ft. in FARC Denver), include miscellaneous letters sent (36 vols.; those for 1874–91 have been reproduced as M941); letters sent concerning Pueblo censuses, 1880–81; letters sent concerning the Cimarron and Abiquiu Agencies, 1876–80, and the Jicarilla Reservation, 1882–83; letters sent to Pueblo day schools, 1898–1900 (8 vols.); and letters received from the Commissioner of Indian Affairs, 1885–1900.

Pueblo Day Schools at Albuquerque

In 1911 responsibility for the southern district Pueblo Indians and day schools was transferred from the superintendent of the Albuquerque Indian School to the superintendent of the Pueblo Day Schools at Albuquerque. He also was responsible for the Laguna Sanatorium and the Navajo Indians in the communities of Canoncito and Alamo. The Pueblo Day Schools at Albuquerque jurisdiction was abolished in 1914, and its responsibilities were transferred to the Pueblo Indian Agency and Pueblo Day Schools.

Records of the jurisdiction (in FARC Denver) consist of a volume of letters sent to the Commissioner of Indian Affairs, 1911, and a volume of miscellaneous letters sent, 1911-13.

Pueblo Day Schools at Santa Fe

In 1911 responsibility for the northern group of Pueblo Indians and day schools was transferred from the superintendent of the Santa Fe Indian School to the superintendent of the Pueblo Day Schools at Santa Fe. This jurisdiction was abolished in 1912, however, and its duties were returned to the superintendent of the Santa Fe Indian School.

The records (in FARC Denver) include a volume of copies of letters sent to the Commissioner of Indian Affairs, 1911-12, and a property roll of Pueblo day schools, 1907-12, which includes entries made when the schools were under the jurisdiction of the Santa Fe Indian School.

Pueblo Indian Agency and Pueblo Day Schools

This jurisdiction was created at Albuquerque in 1914 to administer the affairs of those Pueblo Indians and day schools formerly under the Santa Fe and Albuquerque Indian Schools as well as the Laguna Sanatorium and the Navajo communities at Canoncito and Puertocito. In 1919 it was replaced by the newly created Northern and Southern Pueblos Agencies. The only separate records of this jurisdiction are four volumes of miscellaneous letters sent, 1918-19, which include copies of letters sent to the Commissioner of Indian Affairs (in FARC Denver).

Puyallup Agency and Cushman School

The Puyallup Consolidated Agency was established in 1888 by a merger of the Nisqually and Skokomish Agency and the Quinaielt Agency. It was responsible for Quinaielt, Puyallup, Chehalis, Nisqualli, Squaxin Island, Clallam or Sklallam, and other Indians. There had been many previous agencies for these and other Indians of the Puget Sound area of Washington, including a Puyallup Agency first established in 1861. In 1895 the superintendent of the Puyallup School in Tacoma was assigned the duties of the agent. When the name of the school was changed to Cushman in 1910, this was adopted as the name of the jurisdiction. By then there were few agency duties concerning the Puyallup Indians, most of whom had sold their land after the restrictions on sales had been removed in 1903. The Taholah Agency was established for the Quinaielt Indians in 1914. Cushman was abolished in 1920, when the Muckleshoot and Clallam Indians were transferred to Tulalip and the other tribes to Taholah.

The records, 1880-1928 (27 ft. in FARC Seattle), include general correspondence with the Commissioner of Indian Affairs, school correspondence and student records, census rolls, and records concerning land allotments and sales, including correspondence of the Puyallup Land Commission.

Rapid City Indian School

This nonreservation boarding school was opened at Rapid City, S. Dak., in 1898. For the school year 1929-30 it was converted to a sanatorium school for children with tuberculosis. It was reconverted to a regular boarding school in 1930 but closed in 1934. Its records, 1909-33 (39 ft. in FARC Kansas City), include correspondence, individual student folders, annual reports, and ledgers for individual accounts and special deposits and related records.

Red Cliff School and Agency

The long established school for the Chippewa Indians on the Red Cliff Reservation, Wisc., was under the La Pointe Agency until it was given agency status in 1912. The jurisdiction was closed in 1922, and the Indians were reassigned to the La Pointe Agency. The school was closed the following year.

The records of the school and agency, 1901-22 (7 ft. in FARC Chicago), include correspondence, much of it relating to service by Indians during World War I and in the Wisconsin Defense League; administrative records; case files for individual Indians; and records concerning lumber operations and other economic activities and land sales.

Red Lake Agency

The Red Lake Agency for the Red Lake and Pembina Chippewa of the Red Lake Reservation in Minnesota was separated from the Leech Lake Agency in 1906. (There had been an earlier Red Lake Agency from 1873 to 1879.) From 1920 to 1922 the Red Lake Agency also was in charge of the Chippewa Indians of the Fond du Lac, Nett Lake, and Grand Portage Reservations, who previously had been attached to the Fond du Lac Agency. In 1922 they were transferred to the new Consolidated Chippewa Agency. The Red Lake Agency and the Consolidated Chippewa Agency were merged as the Minnesota Agency in 1954, but Red Lake was separated again in 1964.

The agency records, 1894-1965 (58 ft. in FARC Kansas City), include general correspondence, welfare assistance reports, financial reports of fisheries, forestry receipts and log scale book, a timber journal, and records concerning allotments, accounts of individual Indians, tribal court cases, and Civilian Conservation Corps work.

Reno Agency

The Reno Agency was established in 1912 for numerous small groups of Indians scattered over Nevada and much of California. Between 1918 and 1921 Indians formerly assigned to the Greenville, Fort McDermitt, and

Nevada Agencies were transferred to the Reno Agency. In 1923 the California Indians were transferred to the Sacramento Agency, and in 1925 the Reno Agency was consolidated with the Carson School.

The agency records, 1920–25 (12 ft. in FARC San Francisco), include administrative files, correspondence concerning land allotments, individual history cards and marriage cards for Washo Indians, and school records.

Riverside Area Field Office

The Riverside Area Field Office was established in 1955 as a subordinate unit of the Sacramento Area Office. It was a successor to the Mission Agency, originally established in 1865 for the various bands of Mission Indians of California. In 1948 the Mission Agency was consolidated with the Sacramento and Hoopa Valley Agencies to form the California Agency. The Riverside Area Field Office was given jurisdiction over 31 reservations in southern California.

The records, 1887–1959 (206 ft. in FARC Los Angeles), including subject and decimal correspondence files and records concerning land transactions, rights-of-way, fiscal matters, health and medical service, dental service, and agricultural extension. There are also school census files and World War I draft registration records.

Rosebud Agency

The Rosebud Agency was the last in a series of agencies set up primarily for the band of Brulé Sioux led by Spotted Tail. The Upper Platte Agency was moved in December 1868 from the Platte River area to the mouth of Whetstone Creek on the Missouri River in present South Dakota, and the following year it was renamed the Whetstone Agency. In 1871 it was moved twice again, the second time to the White River near the Dakota-Nebraska boundary. In 1874 the name was changed to Spotted Tail Agency. After three more moves from 1875 to 1878, the agency was located on Rosebud Creek near its junction with the South Fork of the White River, and thereafter it was called the Rosebud Agency. From 1933 to 1967 the Rosebud Agency was also in charge of the Yankton Sioux.

The agency records, 1869–1966 (627 ft. in FARC Kansas City), include general correspondence and decimal files, student case files and school census reports, census rolls, probate files, police court records, case files and ledgers for individual money accounts and special deposits, and records concerning land, forestry, grazing, leases, births, deaths, marriages, and heirship.

Roseburg Agency

The Roseburg Agency was established in 1910 for nonreservation Indians in Oregon and northern California, but it was abolished in 1918 and its responsibilities were divided among the Warm Springs, Siletz, and Greenville Agencies.

The records of the Roseburg Agency, 1897-1921 (5 ft. in FARC San Francisco), among which are some of the Greenville Agency, include correspondence, administrative files, and census rolls.

Round Valley Agency

The Round Valley Agency was established in 1865, but as early as 1856 the Bureau had a farm at Round Valley which became the main reservation for the Indians of the Sacramento Valley area in 1862. Round Valley is located in the Coast Range in the northeastern corner of Mendocino County, Calif. There were Yuki, Yupu, Pit River, Konkau (Concow), Yokaia (Ukiah), Wailaki, Redwood (Whilkut), Pomo, Salan Pomo (Potter Valley), Little Lake Valley, Nomelaki, and other Indians living there. The Round Valley Agency was abolished in 1924, and its duties were transferred to the Sacramento Agency, but some records date as late as 1930.

The agency records, 1864-1930 (32 ft. in FARC San Francisco), include correspondence, reports, administrative files, census rolls, vital statistics records, farming and grazing leases, land allotment records, school reports, medical records, and individual Indian identification cards.

Sac and Fox Agency and Sanatorium

An agency was established in 1866 for the Sauk and Fox Indians living in Tama County, Iowa. When the Sac and Fox Sanatorium for tubercular patients was established in 1913, the agency was attached to it. The Sac and Fox Boarding School operated on the reservation from 1874 to 1911, and there were also a number of day schools.

There are records of the agency, sanatorium, and schools (153 ft. in FARC Chicago). Agency records, 1896-1947, include correspondence, reports, individual Indian case files and estate files, enrollment and census records, records of individual Indian accounts, other financial records, and records concerning Civilian Conservation Corps work, tribal laws and customs, World War II rationing, and the reservation postwar program. There are also records of the Mesquakie and Fox Day Schools, 1916-29, and records of the Sac and Fox Sanatorium, 1912-43, which include correspondence, individual Indian files, and clinical records.

Sacramento Area Office

The Sacramento Area Office was established in 1950, assuming control of the Sherman Institute and the California Agency. The California Agency had supervised the affairs of the Sacramento, Mission, and Hoopa Valley Agencies. Control of the Sherman Institute was transferred to the Phoenix Area Office in 1952.

Records of the area office and its predecessors, 1910-54 (54 ft. in FARC San Francisco), include administrative files and records concerning surveys and rehabilitation projects, agricultural activity, investigations, land, loans, payments to Indians, health, education, and fiscal matters.

San Carlos Agency

The San Carlos Agency was established in 1872 to administer the southern division of the White Mountain Reservation, to which Apache Indians in Arizona and some from New Mexico were being moved. In 1875 the San Carlos Agency took over the northern division of the reservation, for the White Mountain Apache, from the Camp Apache Agency. By 1876 the San Carlos Agency was in charge of all the Apache Indians in Arizona. In 1897 the reservation was divided again, and the Fort Apache Agency took over the northern part. The San Carlos Agency retained the southern part, or San Carlos Reservation. In 1919 the Rice Station Boarding School on the reservation, established as an independent school in 1900, was put under the agency. For many years there were some Mohave and Yuma Indians, as well as Apache, living on the reservation.

The agency records, 1911–51 (50 ft. in FARC Los Angeles), include correspondence, administrative records, ledgers of accounts of individual Indians, other financial records, and time records for firefighters.

Santa Fe Indian School

This nonreservation boarding school was opened in 1890. When the Pueblo and Jicarilla Agency was abolished in 1901, the school superintendent assumed responsibility for 11 northern pueblos and their day schools. In 1911 the pueblos and day schools were placed in the charge of the superintendent of the Pueblo Day Schools at Santa Fe. This jurisdiction was abolished in 1912, and the agency and day school duties were returned to the Santa Fe School. In 1914 these responsibilities were transferred to the Pueblo Agency and Day Schools. In 1930 the Northern Pueblos Agency was consolidated with the Santa Fe School, which in 1935 was placed under the United Pueblos Agency.

The records of the school, 1893–1934 (96 ft. in FARC Denver), include letters sent, 1890–1913, including letters sent concerning Pueblo day schools, 1900–1912; letters received, 1893–1925; student folders, 1910–34; and student enrollment books, 1894–1929. Some records created by the school are in the decimal file of the Northern Pueblos Agency.

Seminole Agency, Florida

In anticipation of the removal of the Seminole Indians in Florida, their agent was designated superintendent of emigration in 1834. He served until his death in 1835 and was not replaced. There was no regularly assigned agent in Florida after that, but the Bureau from time to time, however, did assign persons to field duties concerning these Indians. From the appointment of a special commissioner in 1913, there evolved a permanent Seminole Agency.

There is a cashbook, 1892–99, of J. E. Brecht, industrial teacher and special disbursing agent for the Seminole Indians in Florida. Agency records, 1934–52 (31 ft. in FARC Atlanta), include general files and Civilian Conservation Corps project records.

Shawnee Agency

The Shawnee Agency was established in 1901 for the Absentee Shawnee, Mexican Kickapoo, and Citizen Potawatomi Indians of Oklahoma, most of whom previously had been assigned to the Sac and Fox Agency. There had been a special agency for the Kickapoo and some of the Shawnee Indians since 1896. The Sac and Fox Agency, one of a succession of agencies starting as early as 1821 and located in Indian Territory and Oklahoma since 1869, was left in charge of the Sauk and Fox of the Mississippi and Iowa Indians. In 1919 the Sac and Fox Agency was consolidated with the Shawnee Agency. (The Shawnee Agency in Oklahoma should not be confused with the earlier Shawnee Agency in Kansas.)

Records of the Shawnee Agency in Oklahoma, 1870–1952 (505 ft. in FARC Fort Worth), incorporating records of the Sac and Fox Agency, include general correspondence, records relating to tribal committees, case files and accounts for individual Indians, land transaction files, allotment records, annuity payrolls, tribal census rolls, marriage cards and vital statistics records, heirship files and family histories, and records relating to Shawnee Civil War claims and Civilian Conservation Corps work.

Sherman Institute

The Sherman Institute, known at first as the Riverside School, a nonreservation boarding school at Riverside, Calif., opened in 1902. It took over but soon closed the Perris School, which had been opened in 1893.

The records, 1897–1959 (244 ft. in FARC Los Angeles), include files of students, containing applications, correspondence, and enrollment information, arranged alphabetically by name of student; general correspondence, including decimal files; financial records; and records concerning employees.

Sioux Sanatorium

The Sioux Sanatorium, Rapid City, S. Dak., for the care of tubercular Indians was opened in 1938 and transferred to the Public Health Service in 1952. The records, 1938–51 (40 ft. in FARC Kansas City), include decimal correspondence files, circulars and directives, and quarterly veterans reports.

Sisseton Agency

The Sisseton Agency was established in 1867 for the Sisseton and Wahpeton Sioux living on the Lake Traverse (now Sisseton) and Devil's Lake Reservations in Dakota Territory. A separate Devil's Lake Agency was established in 1871.

The records of the Sisseton Agency, 1888-1955 (91 ft. in FARC Kansas City), include general correspondence, correspondence concerning claims, ledgers of individual Indian accounts and special deposits, annuity payrolls, census rolls, Civilian Conservation Corps program records, student and school records, farm leases, heirship and probate records, land records, Indian language newspapers, and appropriation ledgers.

Southern Apache Agency

The Southern Apache Agency was established in 1852, with jurisdiction over the Mimbreño, Mogollon, Coyotero, and, for a time, the Mescalero Apache. Over the years the agency was located at various places in the vicinity of Ojo Caliente, New Mexico Territory. In 1873 it was moved to a new Apache reservation in the Tularosa Valley. The following year, the reservation and agency were moved to Ojo Caliente. Both were abolished in 1877, when the Indians were moved to the San Carlos Reservation in Arizona, but a man was left in charge of the property at the agency until the following year. The Southern Apache Agency was in the New Mexico Superintendency until the superintendency was abolished in 1874. Thereafter, the agent reported directly to the Bureau of Indian Affairs in Washington.

The records of the agency (9 in.), include letters received and two volumes of letters sent, 1873-78, and several account books, 1871-78. A ledger used by the Southern Apache Agency, 1870-74, is among the records of the New Mexico Superintendency described on pages 138 and 139.

Southern Pueblos Agency

The Pueblo Agency was abolished in 1919, and its responsibilities were divided between the newly created Southern and Northern Pueblos Agencies. The Southern Pueblos Agency assumed jurisdiction over the Laguna Sanatorium, the Navajo communities of Canoncito and Puertocito, and the pueblos and day schools in the vicinity of Albuquerque, where the agency was located. In 1924 the Laguna Sanatorium became an independent jurisdiction. The Southern Pueblos Agency was abolished in 1935, and its functions were transferred to the newly created United Pueblos Agency.

The records of the agency, 1911-35 (64 ft. in FARC Denver), include a decimal file, 1919-35; miscellaneous correspondence, fiscal reports, and other records, 1911-35; and a volume containing descriptions of day school buildings, 1911-27.

Southern Ute and Consolidated Ute Agencies

The Southern Ute Agency was established in southwestern Colorado in 1877 for the Capote, Wiminuche, and Moache Ute Indians formerly attached to the Abiquiu and Cimarron Agencies in New Mexico. From 1887 to 1891 the Jicarilla Apache also were assigned to the agency. In 1922 the Southern Ute and Ute Mountain Agencies were consolidated to form the Consolidated Ute Agency.

The agency records, 1878–1952 (75 ft. in FARC Denver), consist principally of a decimal file, which apparently was created by compiling records from various sources. There also are some copies of letters sent, land records, and records of the Fort Lewis School, Colo.

Spokane Agency

The Spokane Agency was established in 1912 primarily for the Spokan Indians living on the Spokane Reservation, which had been established in 1881 and administered by the Colville Agency. For a few months the Spokane Agency was responsible for some Kutenai, Kalispel, Wenatchi, and other Indians who were then assigned to other agencies. In 1924 Spokane was again consolidated with Colville, and thereafter it operated as a subagency. Some records dated before and after its period of independence have been incorporated with the agency records. These records, 1885–1950 (70 ft. in FARC Seattle), include general correspondence, school reports and censuses, road survey field notebooks, irrigation maps, census rolls, agreements for reimbursable services, and records concerning land, forestry, agricultural extension, irrigation, and individual Indian accounts.

Springfield (Hope) Indian School

The Springfield School was established as an independent boarding school for girls in 1902. From 1895 until 1902, as the Hope School, it had been attached to the Santee Agency; earlier it had been a contract mission school. In 1919 it was again named the Hope School, but it was discontinued the following year. It was reopened from 1921 until 1923, but there are no records for this period in the National Archives.

The records, 1901–20 (1 ft.), are a register of pupils, 1901–10; attendance records, 1909–14; rosters of employees; descriptions of buildings, 1918; and account books, including ledgers for funds of individual students.

Standing Rock Agency

The Standing Rock Agency, N. Dak., succeeded the Grand River Agency, established in 1869 for several bands of Sioux Indians. The agency was moved to Standing Rock in 1873 and renamed the following year. By that time it was responsible for Upper and Lower Yanktonai, Hunkpapa, and Blackfeet Sioux, who came to be known collectively as Standing Rock Sioux.

The agency records, 1870–1951 (433 ft. in FARC Kansas City), include general correspondence, school records, annuity records, records of individual Indian accounts and special deposits, census records, vital statistics, marriage and divorce records, heirship and probate records and certificates of guardianship, Civilian Conservation Corps project records, land records, grazing permits, and forestry and grazing reports.

Taholah Agency

The Taholah Agency was established in 1914 primarily for the Quinaielt Indians of Washington, who previously had been attached to the Cushman School. When the school was abolished in 1920, the Chehalis, Nisqualli, Skokomish, and Squaxin Island Indians were transferred to the Taholah Agency. In 1933 the Neah Bay Agency for the Makah, Quileute, Hoh, and Ozette Indians of far northwestern Washington, which had been established in 1861, was abolished and the Indians transferred to the Taholah Agency. By that time, most of the Indians except the Makah had moved to the Quinaielt Reservation. In 1950 the Taholah and Tulalip Agencies were merged to form the Western Washington Agency.

Records of the Taholah Agency, 1908–52 (152 ft. in FARC Seattle), include general correspondence and a decimal file, annual reports, school census cards, birth and death registers, tribal council records, field nurse case files, Makah tribal housing project records, timber sales records and other records concerning forestry and logging, and records concerning Civilian Conservation Corps and Work Projects Administration programs, land allotments and sales, health statistics, rehabilitation, fishing, and accounts of individual Indians. There are also allotment and appropriation ledgers.

Records created at Neah Bay, 1883–1938 (152 ft. in FARC Seattle), include general correspondence, birth and death registers, a register of Indian families, tribal council records, and records concerning land allotments, heirship cases, forestry, and individual Indian accounts.

Tomah Indian School and Agency

A nonreservation boarding school at Tomah, Wisc., was authorized in 1891 and opened in 1893. In 1911 the school was given agency duties for the Winnebago Indians of Wisconsin, previously assigned to the Wittenberg School. The agency duties were transferred to the newly established Grand Rapids Agency in 1916, but in 1927 that jurisdiction was consolidated with the school, which then regained its agency status. Between 1932 and 1935 Tomah took over responsibility for the Oneida, Stockbridge, and Munsee Indians from the Keshena Agency and for the Ottawa and Potawatomi and the Saginaw, Swan Creek, and Black River Chippewa, previously connected with the Mount Pleasant School. The Tomah School was closed in 1935, and in 1949 the Tomah Agency was incorporated into the Great Lakes Consolidated Agency.

The records of the school and agency, 1908–34 (7 ft. in FARC Chicago), consist chiefly of correspondence. Other records include student rosters and death certificates.

Truxton Canyon Agency

The Truxton Canon School was established as a boarding school on the Walapai Reservation in Arizona in 1901 and given agency duties for the Walapai and Havasupai Indians. Since 1895 an industrial teacher had been assigned these duties. From 1904 until 1933 there was a separate agency for the Havasupai. In 1937 the Camp Verde (Tonto and Yavapai Apache) and Yavapai Reservations were assigned to the Truxton Canon Agency. Truxton Canon was reduced to a subagency of the Colorado River Agency in 1951, but in 1964 it was restored to agency status as the Truxton Canyon Agency.

The agency records, 1895–1948 (12 ft. in FARC Los Angeles), consist mostly of correspondence and some financial records.

Tulalip Agency

The Tulalip Agency was established in 1861 for the bands of Indians who had agreed to the Treaty of Point Elliot in 1855, mainly those living on the eastern side of Puget Sound. The Indians included those living on the Tulalip, Port Madison, Swinomish, and Lummi Reservations and the Muckleshoot Reservation, who during some years were assigned to the Puyallup (Cushman) Agency. Tulalip was one of several successors to the Puget Sound District Agency, which had been established in 1851 for all of the Indians in the Puget Sound area. There was one agent for both Puyallup and Tulalip from 1865 to 1869, and there was a brief consolidation with the Puyallup and Skokomish Agencies in 1882. After the Cushman School was abolished in 1920, the Muckleshoot Indians were returned, and Clallam and other Indians were assigned to the Tulalip Agency. In 1950 the Tulalip and Taholah Agencies were merged to form the Western Washington Agency.

Agency records, 1854–1950 (215 ft. in FARC Seattle), include correspondence and accounts of the Puget Sound District Agency, 1854–61, and general correspondence, annual reports, school records, timber sale records, and other records concerning forestry and logging, birth and death and marriage registers, census rolls, records of tribal councils, physicians' reports, loan agreements, annuity payrolls, appropriation and allotment ledgers, and records concerning land, agricultural extension, road construction, dikes, social service, economic and social surveys, law and order, tribal industry, and individual Indian accounts.

Tule River Agency

The Tule River Agency, Calif., which was merged with the Mission Agency in 1887 and made part of the San Jacinto Agency in 1903, was reestablished as a separate jurisdiction in 1907. It was abolished in 1923, and the Indians of the Tule River Reservation and vicinity were assigned to the Sacramento Agency.

The only separate records of the Tule River Agency are some census and school census rolls, 1897–1920, with gaps (1 ft. in FARC San Francisco).

Turtle Mountain Agency

The Turtle Mountain Agency was established in 1910. Previously the Turtle Mountain Chippewa of North Dakota had been assigned to the Fort Totten Agency. Fort Totten was merged with Turtle Mountain in 1947 to form the Turtle Mountain Consolidated Agency, but they were separated again in 1949.

The records of the Turtle Mountain Agency, 1889–1950 (113 ft. in FARC Kansas City), include agency and school correspondence, ledgers of individual Indian accounts, annuity files, vital statistics, probate and heirship records, census records, and land transaction and lease case files.

Uintah and Ouray Agency

The Uintah and Ouray Agency in Utah, for the Uinta, White River, and Uncompahgre (Tabaquache) Ute Indians, was formed in 1886 by a merger of the Uintah and Ouray Agencies. In 1939 several reservations for Paiute Indians formerly assigned to the Paiute Agency were transferred to the Uintah and Ouray Agency.

Records of the agency, 1897–1949 (39 ft. in FARC Denver), include letters sent, including some concerning heirs of deceased Indians; letters received, reports, and other records; land management records; copies of annual narrative and statistical reports; annuity payrolls; and registers of vital statistics.

Umatilla Agency

The Umatilla Agency was established in 1861 for the Umatilla, Cayuse, and Wallawalla Indians living on the Umatilla Reservation in northeastern Oregon. In 1936 the Paiute Indians of Burns and some groups along the Columbia River in Oregon and Washington were transferred to Umatilla from the Warm Springs and Yakima Agencies.

The agency records, 1862–1952 (40 ft. in FARC Seattle), include general correspondence, school records, tribal rolls, and records concerning farming and grazing leases, the Civilian Conservation Corps program, individual Indian accounts, land allotments, heirship, family histories, medical treatment, law enforcement, court cases, and economic and social surveys.

United Pueblos Agency

The United Pueblos Agency was established in 1935 with headquarters in Albuquerque, N. Mex., by combining the Northern Pueblos and Zuni Agencies, the Albuquerque and Santa Fe Indian Schools, and the Albuquerque Sanatorium. It was responsible for the Pueblo Indians of New Mexico and the Navajo communities of Canoncito and Puertocito.

Among the agency records, 1935–52 (176 ft. in FARC Denver), the principal series is the general decimal file. There are also separate census records and reports, a decimal file for the Civilian Conservation Corps program, correspondence concerning Pueblo day schools, records concerning soil and moisture conservation, correspondence and reports created or received by the Pueblo Lands Board, and records created by the Interdepartmental Rio Grande Board.

Wahpeton Indian School

Wahpeton Indian School, one of the last nonreservation boarding schools to be established, was opened in 1908 at Wahpeton, N. Dak. The school records, 1910–63 (32 ft. in FARC Kansas City), include correspondence and decimal subject files, individual student records, property assignments and transfers, surgical contracts, accounting and fiscal records, reports of school inspections, campus news, and school calendars.

Walker River Agency

The Walker River Reservation for Paiute Indians was established in Nevada in 1859. Except for a few months in 1871, the reservation was under the supervision of the Nevada Agency until 1897, when it was transferred to the Carson School. A separate Walker River Agency was established in 1908. With the discontinuance of the Fallon and Bishop jurisdictions in 1925 and 1926, respectively, and the transfer of their duties to the Walker River Agency, it assumed responsibility for several groups of Indians in southern Nevada and in California, including Paiute, Monache, Shoshoni, and Washo. The Walker River Agency was abolished in 1935, and its duties were transferred to the Carson Agency.

The agency records, 1889–1926 (5 ft. in FARC San Francisco), include correspondence, registers of pupils' attendance, and medical records of the farmer in charge of the reservation and the reservation school before the establishment of the agency. There are also correspondence and administrative files of the agency.

Warm Springs Agency

The Warm Springs Agency was the successor of an agency established in 1851 for the Indians in Oregon east of the Cascade Mountains and known by many names. Beginning in 1860 the agent spent much of his time on the Warm Springs Reservation, which had been established in 1856. In 1861 the agent was specifically assigned to the Warm Springs Agency. Indians on the reservation included Warm Springs, Wasco, Tenino, Paiute, and John Day. When the Roseburg Agency was discontinued in 1917, Paiute Indians at Burns and Indians along the Columbia River were assigned to the Warm Springs Agency, but in 1936 this responsibility was transferred to the Umatilla Agency.

The agency records 1861–1952 (85 ft. in FARC Seattle), include general correspondence, decimal files, school attendance records, land and survey field notes, a tractbook, cattle sales reports, ledgers and abstracts of individual Indian accounts appropriation and allotment ledgers, censuses, a family history record, individual Indian history cards, court dockets, birth and death registers, medical reports, tribal council records, and records concerning lease payments, forestry, Civilian Conservation Corps programs, roads, and per capita payments.

Western Shoshone Agency

The Western Shoshone Agency for the Western Shoshoni and, later, some Paiute Indians in Nevada was established in 1878. A farmer in charge had been assigned to the Western Shoshoni in 1869. During 1871 and 1872 a special agent was assigned to them, but later the farmer in charge was reinstated.

The records of the agency, 1870–1925 (26 ft. in FARC San Francisco), include some correspondence and reports of the farmer in charge, 1870–78, with gaps, and correspondence, administrative files, school records, diaries, records of issuances to Indians, and other records of the agency.

White Earth Agency

The White Earth Agency was the successor to the Chippewa Agency, which was established in 1851. The Chippewa Agency had become responsible for the Indians in Minnesota known collectively as the Chippewa of the Mississippi, as distinguished from the Chippewa of Lake Superior at the La Pointe Agency. Some of its bands, however, were not Chippewa of the Mississippi. In 1872 the agency was moved to the White Earth Reservation. In 1873 a separate agency was established for the Red Lake Chippewa, and in 1874 an agency was established at Leech Lake for the Pillager and Lake Winnibigoshish Chippewa living in that area and the Chippewa of the Mississippi living at White Oak Point. The Chippewa Agency at White Earth then had charge of the other Chippewa of the Mississippi (including those who lived at Mille Lacs), the Otter Tail Pillagers, and the Pembina Chippewa. Beginning in 1878 the agency was called the White Earth Agency. In 1879 the Red Lake and Leech Lake Agencies were consolidated into the White Earth Agency.

In 1899 a separate agency was again established at Leech Lake for the Leech Lake, Cass Lake, Lake Winnibigoshish, White Oak Point, and Red Lake Chippewa, except those who had moved to the White Earth Reservation. The White Earth Agency was responsible for White Earth, Gull Lake, Removal and Nonremoval Mille Lac, Removal White Oak Point, Pembina, Removal Fond du Lac, Otter Tail, Removal Leech Lake, and Removal Cass and Winnibigoshish Chippewa. Most of these Indians lived on the White

Earth Reservation. The term "removal" denotes Indians who had moved from ceded reservations to White Earth, mainly under the direction of the Chippewa Commission. In 1922 the White Earth Agency was abolished, and the Indians were assigned to the new Consolidated Chippewa Agency.

The records of the agency, 1874–1922 (55 ft.), include a general series of correspondence with some annuity rolls, affidavits, receipts, application forms of different types, lists, minutes, and other records (19 ft.); letters received from the Commissioner of Indian Affairs, with registers; general letters sent to the Commissioner of Indian Affairs and others and letters sent concerning land, heirships, and education; stubs of land certificates, applications for allotments, allotment schedules, and records relating to investigations of allotments; logging and timber contracts and certificates of completion of timber contracts; annuity payment rolls; receipt rolls for goods issued to Indians; issue books; applications of Indians for lumber; medical reports; death certificates; police and court records; personnel and financial records; and school reports, applications for enrollment in nonreservation schools, school census reports, attendance reports, and questionnaires concerning former pupils and school facilities. For the White Earth Boarding School there are correspondence, class schedules and study programs, a register of pupils, attendance books, and rosters of employees. There are also some correspondence, 1910–14, of special agent John H. Hinton, who was appointed to investigate the fraudulent alienation of Indian allotments, and correspondence, docket books, and other records of examiners of inheritance, 1911–21.

Also with the records of the White Earth Agency are records of the Chippewa Commission, established in 1889 to negotiate with the Chippewa bands or tribes in Minnesota for the cession and relinquishment of all their reservations except White Earth and Red Lake and for the reduction of these reservations to the area actually needed by the Indians. An individual Indian could choose between receiving an allotment in severalty on the old reservation or moving to White Earth. The commission was to direct the removals and make the necessary allotments. It was also required to compile a census of the Indians. The Indians agreed to the cessions, but most of them decided to remain on their old land. In 1896 the commission was reduced to one member, and it was discontinued in 1900. The last commissioner transferred the commission's records to the White Earth Agency.

These records include correspondence, enrollment records, proceedings in enrollment cases, census rolls, a register of the arrival of Indians at White Earth, a record of goods issued to Indians, allotment schedules, a tractbook, last wills and testaments of Indians, rosters of employees, and account books.

See also the records of the Consolidated Chippewa Agency on pages 155 and 156.

Wind River Agency

The Shoshone and Bannock Agency, successor to the Fort Bridger Agency, was established in 1870 for the Shoshoni and Bannock Indians living on a reservation in the Wind River area of northwestern Wyoming Territory. Most of the Bannock moved to the Fort Hall Reservation in 1872, but "Bannock" was not deleted from the name of the agency until 1883. In 1878 some Northern Arapaho moved onto the reservation. In 1937 the agency was renamed the Wind River Agency.

The agency records, 1873–1952 (184 ft. in FARC Denver), include letters received and sent, decimal files, photographs of Indians, land records, and censuses.

Winnebago Agency

The Winnebago Agency evolved from the Prairie du Chien Agency, which was established in 1807. Over the years the Winnebago Agency also took over duties and records from agencies for the Omaha, Ponca, and Santee Sioux Indians. A full agency was established for the Winnebago Indians in 1848, the year they moved from Iowa to Minnesota. Until 1850 the agency also had charge of some Sioux and Chippewa Indians. After an uprising of the Sioux of the Mississippi of the St. Peters Agency, many of the Sioux and Winnebago Indians were moved in 1863 from Minnesota to Crow Creek in Dakota Territory. The Winnebago agent was put in charge of both tribes there. In 1865 the Winnebago Indians and Agency were moved to a new reservation in Nebraska, and the St. Peters agent was assigned to the Sioux at Crow Creek. In 1866 the Sioux, now known as Santee Sioux, also moved to a reservation in Nebraska, and thereafter their agency was usually called the Santee Sioux Agency.

In 1879 the Winnebago Agency was consolidated with the Omaha Agency, established in 1856 for the Omaha Indians, to form the Omaha and Winnebago Agency. They were separated in 1903, but from 1910 to 1914 the Omaha Agency was put under the Winnebago Agency. In 1925 the Omaha Agency was discontinued, and its duties were assigned to the Winnebago Agency.

The Ponca Agency was established in 1859. In 1877 the Ponca Indians and Agency were moved from Nebraska to Indian Territory. The following year some Ponca returned to Nebraska, and they were attached to the Santee Sioux Agency. From 1879 until 1903 the Santee Sioux Agency was also responsible for the group of Santee Sioux who had settled at Flandreau, S. Dak., and from 1895 until 1902 it was in charge of the Hope School. In 1917 the Santee Sioux Agency was consolidated with the Yankton Agency. In 1933 the Santee Sioux and Ponca Indians were transferred to the Winnebago Agency.

The records of the Winnebago Agency (in FARC Kansas City) incorporate many inherited from other agencies, and to a considerable extent more recent records are identified by the former agency names.

For the Omaha Agency, the records, 1867–1946, with gaps (29 ft.), include general correspondence and subject files, records of individual Indian accounts, census rolls, township plats and maps, annuity payrolls, a lease record book, land transaction books, and social and economic survey cards.

Identified as records of the Ponca Agency, 1860–72 and 1880–1947 (5 ft.), are general correspondence, records of individual Indian accounts, census rolls, family record books, vital statistics records, marriage registers, birth and death certificates, annuity payrolls, allotment rolls, and social and economic survey cards.

For the Santee Sioux Agency, the records, 1861–1947 (7 ft.), include census data, records of individual Indian accounts, Indian family records, plat books, allotment rolls and receipts, annuity payrolls, a marriage register, birth and death records, records concerning court claims, social and economic survey cards, and tribal fund vouchers.

For the Winnebago Agency itself, the records 1861–1955 (93 ft.), include general correspondence and decimal files, ledgers for individual Indian accounts and special deposit cards, case files for individual Indians, annuity payrolls, census rolls, birth and death registers, probate files, tractbooks, plats, and records concerning general and individual welfare, heirship, Civilian Conservation Corps work, and land transactions. A volume of letters sent by the Winnebago Agency, 1846–73, with gaps, is among the records of the Northern Superintendency.

Wittenberg Indian School

This school at Wittenberg, Wisc., a Lutheran mission school since 1887, was established as a Government nonreservation boarding school in 1895 and closed in 1917. From 1899 through 1910 the school superintendent also acted as agent for the Winnebago Indians living in Wisconsin. The records, 1895–1917 (9 in.), are a volume of letters sent, 1909–10; rosters of employees, 1895–1909; descriptions of buildings, 1915; account books; and rolls of births and deaths of the Winnebago Indians of Wisconsin, 1891–1903.

Yakima Agency

The Yakima Agency was established in 1859 primarily for the Yakima Indians living on their reservation in Washington.

The agency records, 1872–1952 (215 ft. in FARC Seattle), include general correspondence and decimal files, school records, farming and grazing leases, census rolls, cattle contracts, ledgers and case files for accounts of individual Indians, tribal council proceedings, birth and death and marriage registers, police and court journals, hospital reports, and records concerning heirship, land allotments, irrigation, forestry, road construction, credit, and traders' claims.

There are also records, 1906–56 (110 ft. in FARC Seattle), of the Wapato Irrigation Project, created primarily to provide water to the Yakima Reservation. They include correspondence, level and transit books, project folders, hydrographic data, water level records, crop reports, a census of water users, and fiscal records.

Yankton Agency

The Yankton Agency for the Yankton Sioux Indians of present South Dakota was established in 1859. From April 1877 until June 1878 the Yankton agent was also in charge of the Santee Sioux Agency and from 1917 until 1933 of the Santee Sioux and Ponca Indians of Nebraska. When the Yankton Agency was abolished in 1933, the Yankton Sioux were transferred to the Rosebud Agency and the Santee Sioux and Ponca to the Winnebago Agency. Yankton was reestablished as an independent jurisdiction in 1967.

The agency records, 1892–1965, with gaps (28 ft. in FARC Kansas City), include general correspondence, case files for individual Indian accounts, lease cards, Indian Reorganization Act vote ballots, an allotment register, and a tractbook.

Zuni Agency

The Zuni Agency was established in 1902. Previously the Zuni pueblo and school had successively been under the jurisdiction of the Pueblo Agency, the Pueblo and Jicarilla Agency, and the Albuquerque Indian School. In 1935 the agency was reduced to a subagency of the United Pueblos Agency, and it retained that status until about 1952.

The agency records, 1899–1934 (15 ft. in FARC Denver), include letters received and sent, 1899–1917 and 1926–27; a decimal file, 1926–35; agency and school reports, 1909–35; and a student record book, 1906–11.

Records of Other Field Offices

Other field office records include some correspondence, 1878–79, of special agent Alfred B. Meacham, who was in charge of making annuity payments to several tribes in Indian Territory. There are correspondence and other records, 1915–23 (4 ft. in FARC San Francisco), of Col. LaFayette A. Dorington, special agent and inspector, who conducted investigations at various agencies and schools in the Western States concerning such matters as poor administration, reported inefficiency or scandalous conduct of personnel, and troubles between Indians and agents and other persons. There is also correspondence, 1923–32 (4 ft.), of Herbert J. Hagerman, special commissioner to the Navajo Indians.

Records of the Board of Indian Commissioners

By an act of April 10, 1869 (16 Stat. 13, 40), the President was authorized, at his discretion, to organize a board of commissioners to which he could assign joint control with the Secretary of the Interior over the disbursement of any part of the appropriations for the Indian Service. By an Executive order of June 3, 1869, the President established the Board of Indian Commissioners and gave it the right to inspect the records of the Bureau of Indian Affairs, to visit and inspect superintendencies and agencies, to be present when goods were purchased for the Indian Service and to inspect them, and to make recommendations on matters pertaining to the administration of Indian affairs. In 1870 the Board's inspection of purchases was made mandatory. From 1870 to 1882 the Board also audited the accounts of the Bureau. In 1882 Congress restricted the authority of the Board to visiting and inspecting agencies and other units, inspecting purchases, and consulting with the Commissioner of Indian Affairs on the purchase of supplies. In practice the Board remained subordinate to the Secretary of the Interior and the Bureau of Indian Affairs; in its later years the Board limited its activities to inspections and surveys and to making recommendations. It was abolished by an Executive order of May 25, 1933.

There are minutes of the Board for its entire existence. Until 1899, its correspondence is divided into letters received and letters sent, each for the most part arranged in chronological order, but with most of the letters received, 1871–72, pasted into volumes alphabetically by initial letter of surname of writer. Letter books of letters sent continued to be used until 1909, but for the period 1899 to 1918 there is a series of general correspondence and other records (6 ft.) arranged into categories mainly by correspondent. These several series relate to such subjects as meetings of the Board, purchases, inspection trips, legislation, conditions among Indians, land allotments and other aspects of Indian administration, the examination of accounts, missionary activities, and appointments to the Board.

The decimal classification system adopted for general records in 1919 continued to be used until 1933. The major classifications and a few important subheadings are as follows:

000. Board
    010. Members (mainly correspondence with individual members)
    040. Operations (mainly correspondence concerning meetings and recommendations)
    005. Reports (correspondence concerning reports; few reports themselves)
100. General
    111.1 Secretary's Office
    111.2 Indian Office
200. Personnel (correspondence with individual persons and organizations)
300. Tribes, Schools, and Reservations

400. Administration
500. Industrial, Lands, Buildings, Roads
600. Legislation, Morals, Religion
700. Education, Health
800. Supplies, Equipment, Finance
900. Miscellaneous

Most of the records are in the 010, 200, and 300 classifications and are arranged by name of correspondent or by subject.

There are also 10 volumes of special reports, 1915-33, chiefly submitted by members and employees of the Board. Most are general reports with recommendations based on visits to reservations and field units of the Bureau, but some relate to specific subjects, such as tuberculosis among the Choctaw and Chickasaw of Oklahoma, Indian labor in Arizona, schools of the Five Civilized Tribes, annual extension conferences, Indians in eastern Canada, and the Pueblo Lands Board.

Other records concern an investigation of the administration of affairs of the Five Civilized Tribes in Oklahoma, 1925-26; a school survey, 1922; and a law and order survey, 1929-30. There are reports, 1925-31, of the Pueblo Lands Board, established to investigate ownership of lands within the boundaries of lands granted or confirmed to the Pueblo Indians of New Mexico; correspondence concerning exceptions to accounts, 1911-19; administrative records, 1919-33 (2 ft.); reference materials, ca. 1875-1933 (4 ft.); and newspaper clippings.

RECORDS OF THE OFFICE
OF THE SECRETARY OF THE INTERIOR
(RECORD GROUP 48)

Upon its establishment by an act of March 3, 1849 (9 Stat. 395), the Department of the Interior assumed the general supervision of Indian administration previously exercised by the Department of War. The Bureau of Indian Affairs, under the direction of the Secretary of the Interior, had primary responsibility for the actual conduct of Indian administration. In his supervisory capacity the Secretary was particularly concerned with such matters as legislation, estimates and appropriations, the negotiation and ratification of treaties, administrative organization, appointments and other personnel matters, and accounts. He had to approve deeds, patents, leases, census rolls, allotment schedules, and contracts, and for many years he had to authorize individual expenditures. He was the trustee for Indian trust funds, and he made recommendations to the Congress concerning individual depredation claims. On occasion he was required by the Congress to report on some particular matter.

Records of Divisions, 1849–1907

There are no general records of the Office of the Secretary of the Interior from its establishment in 1849 until a central filing system was started in 1907. Individual divisions and other units maintained their own records.

RECORDS OF THE INDIAN DIVISION

The Indian Division handled most of the Secretary's correspondence concerned with Indian administration, maintained related office records, and carried out legal duties. Much of its work pertained to matters brought to the Secretary's attention by the Bureau of Indian Affairs; when necessary, the Division referred the Secretary's decisions back to the Bureau for required action in the field. The Division was not formally established until about 1870; the work it performed previously had been assigned to a clerk at the Indian desk. It was also antedated by the Indian Trust Fund Divsion, which operated from 1867 to 1876, when the two divisions were combined. After 1898 its duties regarding the Indian Territory and the Five Civilized Tribes were transferred to the new Indian Territory Division. In 1907 the Indian Division was abolished as part of a reorganization of the Secretary's Office.

The general incoming and outgoing correspondence of the Division constitutes the most important source among the records of the Office of the Secretary for a broad study of Indian administration before 1907. Most of the letters received, 1849–80 (39 ft.), are arranged according to the name of the Government agency or official that sent them to the Department of the Interior and thereunder chronologically. The file headings used were: Executive Office (President), 1852–80; State Department, 1857–80; Treasury Department, 1850–80; War Department, 1849–80; Attorney General, 1852–80; Commissioner of the General Land Office, 1862–80; and Board of Indian Commissioners, 1873–80. Letters received from the principal correspondent, the Commissioner of Indian Affairs, 1849–80, were filed together except for communications transmitting for approval deeds for lands sold by Indians in Kansas, 1869–77, which were maintained separately. Placed in a miscellaneous category, 1849–78, are letters received from officials of other Federal agencies, Members of Congress, State and local officials, Indians, attorneys, businessmen, religious leaders, and private citizens. During 1879 and 1880 the miscellaneous letters were filed with letters from the Commissioner of Indian Affairs. Many of the letters received have been reproduced as M825, *Selected Classes of Letters Received by the Indian Division of the Office of the Secretary of the Interior, 1849–1880.*

The letters received, 1881–1907 (190 ft.), are arranged by year and thereunder by file number assigned in the order they were registered, chronologically by receipt. For the first two years of this period, one set of file numbers is used for the letters from the Commissioner of Indian Affairs and another for those from all other sources. After 1880, when immediate responsibility for inspectors was transferred from the Commissioner of Indian Affairs to the Secretary, inspection reports were filed with letters received by the Division.

Because the Bureau of Indian Affairs had immediate responsibility for the administration of Indian affairs, most of the correspondence with field officials and persons outside the Department was conducted by the Bureau, which in turn referred appropriate letters to the Office of the Secretary as enclosures. The Secretary's office often returned these letters after it had taken action upon them. Many other letters received directly by the Office of the Secretary were referred to the Bureau of Indian Affairs for action; therefore, a rather high proportion of letters received by the Division are now with the records of the Bureau of Indian Affairs.

Registers of letters received are used frequently to locate items in the files. There are general registers for 1849–80 and 1881–1900 and separate registers for letters from the Commissioner of Indian Affairs, 1849–53 and 1856–82. Three other series of registers cover shorter time periods. Research also is facilitated by index books for 1881–1900 and a card index for 1900–1907.

Letters sent were copied by hand in the years 1849 to 1903 (121 vols., 21 ft.) and by the press method 1854 to 1907 (168 vols., 26 ft.). Copies duplicate each other during the overlapping period. Each series is arranged in chronological order by date of letter except for certain years when letters to the Commissioner of Indian Affairs were copied into separate letter books. Handwritten letter books contain alphabetical indexes to addressees and subjects before 1881; sections for alphabetical indexes in the press copy books seldom were used before 1892, but thereafter until 1902 they are fairly complete. There are separate index books, 1849–61 and 1881–97, to the handwritten copies and a card index, 1897–1907, to the press copies. The handwritten letters and separate index books have been reproduced as M606.

The correspondence relates to the full range of Indian administration, including legislation, estimates and appropriations, negotiation and enforcement of treaties, investigations, depredation and other claims, education, health and sanitation, land sales and allotments, surveys, deeds, leases, mining, agriculture, irrigation, railroads, enrollment, annuity payments, trust funds, trade with Indians and the issuance of licenses to trade, military operations, liquor control, law and order, missionary work, attorneys, administration of the Indian field service, appointments and other personnel matters, contracts, authorizations for expenditures, buildings, supplies, and accounts.

Subject or special files containing letters received, copies of letters sent, reports, memorandums, printed matter, and other kinds of records cover the period 1833 to 1907 (3 ft.). Most of these records were either withdrawn from the general incoming correspondence of the Division or referred from the Bureau of Indian Affairs, but there also are records transmitted by special commissions. Files on Negro Seminole Indians, Osage Indians killed by the Kansas Militia, children rescued from Kiowa Indians, imprisonment of Kiowa chiefs, Crow Indian disturbances, Chippewa pinelands, railroads in Indian Territory, and the Indian school service are examples of the wide variety of subjects in this series. The activities of the Sioux Commission of 1863, the Peace Commission of 1867–68, and the Dawes Commission are documented. There also are files pertaining to negotiations with Indians, charges and investigations concerning Federal officials, claims, and many other subjects.

Other general records include abstracts of reports from the Commissioner of Indian Affairs to the Secretary, 1867–69; memorandums, 1888–1903; and a data book, 1887.

Apart from the general incoming and outgoing correspondence, the largest group of records are those relating to Indian tribal trust funds. These funds were of particular concern to the Office of the Secretary, for the Secretary rather than the Commissioner of Indian Affairs was the trustee for them. The funds, most often the proceeds of land sales, were usually invested in Federal and State bonds, commonly called stocks at the time. In 1876 the Congress transferred physical custody of the securities and authority to make purchases to the Treasurer of the United States, but the Secretary of the Interior continued to control the investments. In 1880 the Congress authorized the deposit of money in the Treasury at interest instead of investment in securities. It became standard practice to deposit the proceeds from matured bonds instead of reinvesting them, and by 1898 no bonds were held for Indian trust funds.

The segregation of trust fund correspondence from general correspondence of the Division was rather erratic; even during periods when separate records were kept, trust fund letters were placed with the general correspondence. There are letters received concerning trust funds, 1851–80 (4 ft.), with registers for 1849–55, 1861–64, and 1866–80. There are handwritten copies of letters sent, January 1857–October 1864, December 1865–February 1866, and December 1866–December 1880, and there are press copies for 1857–65 and 1866–80. After 1880 trust fund correspondence was handled as general correspondence. The correspondence relates to the sale of trust lands, establishment and investment of funds, collection and handling of income, claims, and other matters. Some letters received and other records, 1849–83, have been brought together into special files arranged alphabetically for the most part by name of tribe and thereunder by specific subject.

General ledgers, 1857–83, account for stock holdings and interest payments. There are also other ledgers and journals; a record of stock holdings, ca. 1875–81; interest payment statements, 1869–98; and appropriation warrants, vouchers, and other records concerning trust funds. Records about trust funds, particularly before 1867, also are among those of the Finance Division of the Bureau of Indian Affairs.

Indian inspectors were first appointed in 1873. They were responsible to the Commissioner of Indian Affairs until 1880, when they were put under the immediate supervision of the Secretary of the Interior. Letters sent to inspectors were copied in separate letter books from 1880 to 1882; thereafter, they were copied with the general correspondence of the Division. Most letters and reports received from inspectors also are with the general correspondence of the Division. Three closely related volumes indicate the scope of agency inspections: an index to reports from inspectors, 1879–83; a record of agency inspections, 1878–81; and a record of inspections, 1883–1907. Although the full inspection reports from 1881 are usually with the general correspondence, there are brief summaries of their contents arranged chronologically, 1882–94, and alphabetically by surname of inspector, August–November 1903.

Three series concerning Indian lands consist of records relating to Umatilla allotments, 1886–97; a record of ownership of Puyallup allotments, 1895–1906; and a register of sales of inherited land, 1902–6. Records relating to depredations are a register of claims, 1882–85, and letters sent transmitting claims to the Congress, 1873–82. A reference book concerning legislation was kept, 1882–84, and registers of bills received from the Congress for report were compiled, 1898–1903 and 1905–7. Other segregated records include proceedings of the Indian Peace Commission of 1867–68; a register of treaties, 1859–66; a record of claims for goods and services allowed by the Board of Indian Commissioners, 1873–80; and a roster of agency employees, 1894.

RECORDS OF THE INDIAN TERRITORY DIVISION

The Indian Territory Division was established in 1898 as a clerical and legal unit to handle increased Federal responsibilities for the Indian Territory and the Five Civilized Tribes. By 1898 the size of the Territory had been reduced to the eastern part of the present State of Oklahoma. Within its limits were the lands of the several small tribes of the Quapaw Agency and the Cherokee, Creek, Choctaw, Chickasaw, and Seminole. What was once the western portion of the Territory, inhabited by many other tribes, had been organized as Oklahoma Territory.

Before 1898 the Five Civilized Tribes largely governed themselves, although some control was exercised by the Union Agency. With the approach of statehood for Oklahoma and Indian Territories, the Secretary of the Interior acquired additional administrative duties for these tribes, although the Bureau of Indian Affairs continued to conduct actual field operations. In 1893 the Commission to the Five Civilized Tribes (Dawes Commission) was established to negotiate agreements with the Indians to exchange their tribal lands for individual allotments. The Curtis Act of June 28, 1898 (30 Stat. 495), provided for the preparation of rolls and allotments of lands by the Commission, the leasing of mineral lands, the creation of townsites, Federal control of tribal governments, and the increased jurisdiction of Federal courts in the Indian Territory. The Secretary or an Assistant Secretary had to approve leases, tribal acts, deeds and patents, and the rolls compiled by the Commission to the Five Civilized Tribes. Townsites, schools, railroads, telephone and telegraph lines, intruders on Indian lands, and tribal financial affairs were also handled by the Secretary. Officials to handle the increased Federal activities included an Inspector for Indian Territory, a superintendent of schools, and members of the several townsite commissions. In 1905 the Commission to the Five Civilized Tribes was reduced to a single commissioner, and in 1907 the position of inspector was merged with that of commissioner. The Indian Territory Division was abolished in 1907, the same year that Oklahoma attained statehood.

The correspondence of the Division was conducted with the Commissioner of Indian Affairs, the Commission and Commissioner to the Five Civilized Tribes, the Inspector for Indian Territory, the superintendent of schools, townsite commissioners, the President, members of the President's Cabinet, the Commissioner of the General Land Office, the Director of the Geological Survey, Members of Congress, other officials, attorneys, Indians, and businessmen. The correspondence relates to enrollment, tribal citizenship, land allotments, leases, townsites, removals of restrictions on the alienation of land, land sales, railroads, telephone and telegraph lines, intruders on Indian lands, congressional and tribal legislation, estimates and appropriations, claims, tribal financial affairs, schools, government organization in Indian Territory, employees, buildings, supplies, accounts, and many other subjects.

The main series of letters received, 1898–1907 (75 ft.), is arranged by year and thereunder by file number. Through 1902 the file numbers were assigned in chronological order by receipt. Thereafter even numbers were assigned to letters from officials and odd numbers were given to other letters, but they were still filed in numerical order. The result is that official and unofficial letters, often of considerably different dates, alternate and that toward the end of the letters for each year there are either all official or all unofficial letters.

Many records (31 ft.) were withdrawn from the general incoming correspondence and put into special files relating to particular subjects or, in a few cases, files of certain kinds of records. A file may be designated by the file number of the first letter in it (the "original file"), by a letter of the alphabet ("File A"), or simply by the subject. There is one file relating to the Mississippi Choctaw, chiefly concerning enrollment. It is followed by groups of files relating to townsites, minerals (mostly files for individual companies applying for leases), railroads, and Federal and tribal legislative acts. The titles of other files include *Delaware* v. *Cherokee Nation,* cattle, 98th meridian, Cherokee warrants, Creek warrants, Choctaw warrants, timber and stone, schools, Choctaw and Chickasaw freedmen, Cherokee freedmen, Old Settler Cherokee, Chickasaw Incompetent Fund, deeds for land in Quapaw Agency, boundary line between Choctaw Nation and Texas, Seminole roll, removals from Indian Territory and collection of taxes, noncitizen renters, Seminole boundary, sales of surplus land at Quapaw Agency, monthly reports of Dawes Commission, segregated Choctaw and Chickasaw asphalt lands, an 1893 report on allotments in the Cherokee Outlet, opinions of the Attorney General and Assistant Attorney General, opinions of the Comptroller of the Treasury, decisions of the Choctaw and Chickasaw Citizenship Court, Choctaw and Chickasaw financial affairs and elections, forest reserve, investigations of charges of fraud and irregularity, enrollment and citizenship, telephone and telegraph lines, lands and improvements of intermarried Cherokee, and Eastern Cherokee claims. They are arranged in the same manner as the general incoming correspondence.

There are indexes and registers covering both series and also an index to names of persons issued patents and deeds, 1902–5.

In the main series of letters sent (252 vols., 30 ft.), except for the first seven volumes covering the period August 2, 1898–May 5, 1899, press copies are arranged in even- and odd-numbered volumes according to the addressee. Until near the end of 1902, letters to the Commissioner of Indian Affairs and officials in Indian Territory were copied in even-numbered volumes and letters to others in odd-numbered volumes. After 1902 letters to all Federal officials were copied in the even-numbered volumes. There are more even-numbered volumes than there are odd-numbered volumes. There are indexes of varying detail to addressees and subjects in the individual volumes. There are also typed copies of the letters for the early years.

Other general records of the Division include memorandums of the Chief, orders and regulations, records concerning personnel, reference books concerning legislation and litigation and oil and gas, and congressional bills, reports, and documents.

The remainder of the records of the Division relate primarily to tribal enrollment and land. Most significant are the final rolls of the Five Civilized Tribes, 1899–1907 and 1914 (19 vols. and unbound papers, 3 ft.). These were the rolls prepared by the Commission and Commissioner to the Five Civilized Tribes and submitted to the Secretary of the Interior for approval. Approved and disapproved names are included. Most rolls give name, age, sex, degree of Indian blood, and roll and census card numbers of individuals. They are arranged by name of tribe and thereunder are divided into rolls for citizens by blood, citizens by marriage, and freedmen. There are separate rolls for minor children and newborn babies in many of the groups. There are also rolls for the Mississippi Choctaw and the Delaware Cherokee. There are two preliminary rolls for the identification of the Mississippi Choctaw, including an 1899 roll, with an index and report, that was disapproved by the Secretary in 1907. There is also a list of names struck from the rolls in 1907. The rolls have been reproduced as T529. The final rolls, including only approved names and not including the 1914 supplements, were published by authority of the Congress as *The Final Rolls of Citizens and Freedmen of the Five Civilized Tribes in Indian Territory*. A separate index volume also was published.

There are also a docket book for contested allotments, 1900–1907; a register of sales of allotted Creek lands, 1903–6; and a lease application docket book, 1898–1902.

RECORDS OF THE LANDS AND RAILROADS DIVISION

The Lands and Railroads Division was primarily concerned with the activities of the General Land Office. No series of records of the Division specifically concerns Indian lands, but there are occasional documents dispersed throughout the general correspondence and other records of the Division. In "railroad packages," 1849–1901, which relate to individual railroads, are some documents concerning surveys for routes and rights-of-way across Indian lands. In records relating to timber trespasses and fraudulent land entries, 1877–82, are documents concerning the illegal removal of timber from Indian lands. Among some records concerning investigations of inspectors and other small series are records concerning such subjects as the opening of the Cherokee Outlet and Cheyenne and Arapaho and other Indian lands, the Sioux Reservation in Dakota, and Chippewa Indians in Minnesota.

Of particular interest are letters received and other records, 1856–87, relating to the construction of wagon roads in the West under the direction of the Secretary of the Interior. Some of the roads crossed Indian reservations, and survey and construction parties sometimes encountered hostile Indians. As part of their work, the parties were expected to report on the general characteristics of the country through which they passed. Their reports, which often are in the form of daily itineraries or journals, include comments on the Indians they met. An itinerary of the El Paso-Fort Yuma Wagon Road expedition from Hopefield, Ark., to Fort Yuma, 1857–58, describes meetings, all peaceful, with Choctaw, Caddo, Delaware, Comanche, Apache, and Pima Indians. There are extended comments on the Choctaw and Apache, favorable about the former and scathing about the latter, for whom "utter extinction" is suggested. The Fort Kearney, South Pass, and Honey Lake Road party in 1857 was one that encountered hostile Indians, and its itinerary includes fairly gory descriptions of Indian attacks on emigrant wagon trains and the road party. Most of the records concerning wagon roads have been reproduced as M95.

RECORDS OF THE PATENTS AND MISCELLANEOUS DIVISION

The Patents and Miscellaneous Division, in addition to many other functions, handled business relating to the administration of Territories after 1873 and Departmental displays at public expositions.

The records concerning Territories, 1850–1911, consist chiefly of transcripts of executive proceedings, copies of the official correspondence of the Territorial Governors, and letters received by the Office of the Secretary of the Interior. The letters sent are in chronologically arranged volumes along with other letters handled by the Division. There are records for the Territories of Arizona, Colorado, Dakota, Idaho, Montana, New Mexico, Oklahoma, Utah, Washington, and Wyoming and the District of Alaska; they have been reproduced as NARS microfilm publications. Except for Alaska, information about Indians is only incidental, but item-by-item searches may turn up valuable data. For Oklahoma Territory there are records concerning the opening, sale, and leasing of Indian lands, and for Washington Territory there are a few letters concerning the alleged lynching of an Indian in British Columbia by residents of Washington.

For Alaska there are many records concerning the activities of the Office of Education, including the construction and operation of schools for Alaskan natives and the introduction and maintenance of reindeer herds. There are records concerning legislation and appropriations, destitute Indians and Army assistance for them, land claims, hunting and fishing grounds, timber, relations between natives and nonnatives, liquor control, hospitals, the preservation of deserted native villages, and many other subjects. For most of the records concerning Territories after 1907, see Records of the Office of Territories, Record Group 126, on pages 221 and 222.

Records relating to the ethnological exhibit at the Centennial Exhibition at Philadelphia in 1876 are in two packages labeled "Indian Collections" and "Bureau Display." There is also information about ethnological and other exhibits among the records pertaining to the World's Columbian Exposition at Chicago in 1893, the Louisiana Purchase Exposition at St. Louis in 1904, the Lewis and Clark Centennial Exposition at Portland in 1905, the Jamestown Ter-Centennial Exposition at Norfolk in 1907, and the Alaska-Yukon-Pacific Exposition at Seattle in 1909. At most of these expositions the Department directed an Alaska exhibit as well as a departmental one in the Government exhibit, and for the Louisiana Purchase Exposition there was an Indian Territory exhibit.

Other Division records include some letters received from the Commissioner of Indian Affairs, 1865–80, and a few records concerning pensions for Indians, 1872–74. There are occasional references to Indians among the records of Office of Explorations and Surveys, which studied possible routes for a railroad to the Pacific Ocean before the Civil War. There are also cartographic records of the Office of Explorations and Surveys described with other cartographic records of the Office of the Secretary on page 212.

RECORDS OF THE OFFICE OF THE ASSISTANT ATTORNEY GENERAL FOR THE DEPARTMENT OF THE INTERIOR

The position of Assistant Attorney General for the Department of the Interior was established in 1871. He was an official of the Department of Justice but served as chief legal adviser of the Secretary of the Interior. Records of the office include a volume of confidential correspondence, 1877–81, relating chiefly to alleged irregularities concerning public lands and the administration of Indian affairs. See also the records of the Office of the Solicitor on pages 209–211.

RECORDS OF THE APPOINTMENTS DIVISION

There are no records for employees of the Indian Service before 1907 that can be strictly construed as personnel files; the closest such materials are among the records of the Appointments Division. The business concerning appointments, promotions, reductions, transfers, removals, resignations, and other changes in the status of employees appointed by the President and the Secretary of the Interior was handled by this Division. It was not concerned, however, with the employees appointed at the Bureau level, which included the lesser field positions. The records of the Employees Section of the Bureau of Indian Affairs have information about such employees. Before 1907 no attempt was made to compile single consolidated files or folders for individuals, and available data on any one person ordinarily is dispersed among several series. In 1907 the Department began keeping official personnel files, and such records for separated employees after that year are in the custody of the National Personnel Records Center (Civilian Records), St. Louis, Mo. Other personnel-related materials, 1907–36, are among the central classified files of the Office of the Secretary discussed on page 207.

The Presidential appointment papers are a rich source of information about successful and unsuccessful applicants for positions with the Indian Service during the period 1849 to 1907. Most of the papers consist of applications and recommendations, but there are also letters of resignation, records concerning changes in the status of officeholders, charges, reports, petitions, and other kinds of materials. There are some records concerning offices rather than applicants or incumbents; in particular, there are records concerning the establishment, discontinuance, consolidation, and changes in headquarters or area of jurisdiction of Indian agencies and other field offices. There are also records concerning the designation of Army officers to serve as acting Indian agents or in other capacities and records concerning the replacement of Indian agents by superintendents appointed under civil service regulations. Most of the appointment papers for Indian agents and superintendents are with other papers for various Federal field positions, arranged according to the State or Territory where the office was held. There are not papers for every superintendent, agent, or unsuccessful applicant. Many of these records are included in NARS microfilm publications. Arranged in broad chronological periods are files for central office or special positions, such as Commissioner and Assistant Commissioner of Indian Affairs, Superintendent and Supervisor of Indian Schools, superintendents of individual schools, inspectors and special agents, and allotting agents. There are also files concerning the Board of Indian Commissioners, the Commission to the Five Civilized Tribes and other special commissions, townsite commissioners and appraisers for Indian Territory, and the appraiser for the Cherokee Outlet. There is a file of letters from various church denominations concerning appointments, 1869–78.

Dates of service for many officeholders concerned with Indian administration can be determined from the following series: Executive nominations, 1849–53 and 1857–94; temporary Executive commissions, 1849 and 1854–94; confirmed Executive commissions, 1849–50 and 1854–94; consolidated Executive nominations and commissions, 1893–1909; suspensions and removals, 1869–1914 and 1921–22; and Executive designations, 1869–86. There are indexes in individual volumes and an overall index for the years 1849–1914 and 1921–22. Published copies of the *Official Registers of the United States,* 1817–1919, and the *Registers of the Department of the Interior,* 1877–1909, also are with the records of the Division.

There are also series of orders, circulars, reports, lists, and correspondence, with information about personnel actions and the establishment and location of field offices.

RECORDS OF THE FINANCE DIVISION

Appropriation ledgers of the Finance Division contain a large number of entries concerning Indians, 1853–1923. Included are entries specifically for Alaskan Indians, 1895–1902, and Alaskan natives, 1905–18 and 1922–23. The four sets of ledgers in which these entries are found are Indian and pensions, 1853–86; civil and diplomatic appropriations, 1853–70; civil and miscellaneous appropriations, 1870–1923; and miscellaneous appropriations, 1880–1919. Entries in the first three sets give the date of the requisition for funds, the requisition number, the name of the person or firm requesting the funds, and a statement explaining how the funds were made available for the account. The fourth set gives the date of the voucher rather than the requisition date and the name of the person or firm in whose favor the voucher was made. See Catherine M. Rowland, comp., *Index to Appropriation Ledgers in Records of the Office of the Secretary of the Interior, Division of Finance, 1853-1923*, Special List 18 (1963).

Other financial records containing separate records for Indian affairs are statements of account current of the disbursing clerk, registers of requisitions, records of vouchers, and central office payrolls.

Records of the Office of the Secretary of the Interior Since 1907

In 1907 the Office of the Secretary of the Interior adopted a centralized recordkeeping system that provided for the maintenance of most of its records in one series. Some units and officials, however, continued to maintain records, and, as the organization of the Secretary's Office became more complex, more divisions and units began maintaining their own records.

GENERAL RECORDS

The central classified files, 1907-53 (1,618 ft.), are arranged by a numeric-subject classification system. Most of the records relating to Indians are classified under "Bureau of Indian Affairs" (5). Especially important is the subclass for agencies, schools, warehouses, and Indians of individual States (5-1). A typical heading such as Rosebud Agency has further subject breakdowns for accounts, allotments, claims, contracts, enrollment, expenditures, heirship, individual moneys, land purchases, land sales, lands, leases, patents, schools, taxation, tribal funds, tribal property, wills, and other subjects. Records within individual subject files (which may have several parts) are arranged chronologically. Other, more general subclasses were assigned numbers from 5-2 through 5-122. Among the more significant are "Conferences" (5-5), "General" (5-6), "Oil Situation" (5-8), "Removal of Restrictions" (5-10), "Administrative" (5-11), "Suppression of Liquor Traffic" (5-16), "Cooperation" (5-25), "Court Cases" (5-60), and "Rights of Way Through Indian Lands" (5-106). Some of the general subclasses have further subject breakdowns. Many general subclasses were discontinued after 1937, and the volume of records filed under those still used is much less.

Records useful for the study of high-level employees in the Indian Service before 1937 are classified under "Presidential Appointees" (22). There are also records concerning such positions during the same period under "Applications for Appointment" (24). Other records relating to Indians are classified under "Administrative" (1) for 1907-53, "General Land Office" (2) for 1907-36, and "Indian and Land Inspectors" (25) for 1907-24. More than 210 feet of central classified files relate to Indians.

A card index to subjects and names of correspondents in the central classified files covers the period 1907 to 1953. A list of file classifications and their subdivisions is available. General employment matters within the Indian Service are documented in records of the Division of Personnel

Supervision and Management, 1907–53, once part of the central classified files (chiefly 15–6).

Records concerning departmental consideration of congressional bills and resolutions affecting Indians are maintained as parts of two general series of legislation files, 1907–53 and 1953–58. They contain printed and draft copies of bills and resolutions, printed copies of congressional documents, and clippings from the *Congressional Record* as well as correspondence and other records. For 1907–53 the overall arrangement is similar to the central classified files. Again, records concerning legislation affecting the Rosebud Agency, for example, are under the 5–1 subclass. Within the various subject breakdowns for the Rosebud Agency, the records are arranged by Congress and thereunder by bill or resolution number. For 1953–58 the records are arranged by Congress (83d, 84th, and 85th). Thereunder there are some general records, including folders for proposed legislation concerning the Bureau of Indian Affairs. Most of the records are arranged by house of Congress, thereunder by type of legislation, and thereunder by number.

RECORDS OF OFFICIALS

Office files of various officials often are arranged at least in part according to bureaus, including the Bureau of Indian Affairs, and sometimes they include specific subject headings about Indians. Typically they do not have much information about any one subject, but they may reflect a more personal or political viewpoint than usually is found in Government records.

Records of Secretaries of the Interior Hubert Work, 1923–28, Harold L. Ickes, 1933–42, and Douglas McKay, 1952–56, include subject headings for the Bureau of Indian Affairs. Records, 1933–53, of Oscar L. Chapman, who was Assistant Secretary, 1933–46, Under Secretary, 1946–49, and Secretary, 1949–53, include headings for Alaska, Interdepartmental Committee on Alaska, Indians of Alaska, social security for Indians, Indian hospitals, the Bureau of Indian Affairs, the Indian Claims Commission, the Inter-American Conference on Indians, the Inter-American Indian Institute, and the National Indian Institute.

Records of Under Secretaries Abe Fortas, 1942–46, and Richard D. Searles, 1951–52, and of the Office of the Under Secretary, 1957–61, include some material on Indian affairs. For 1957 to 1960 there are records of the Office of the Under Secretary concerning the Rural Redevelopment Program in Alaska primarily for natives and, with Bureau of Indian Affairs participation, in Montana, New Mexico, Oklahoma, and Washington.

Records of First Assistant Secretary Theodore A. Walters, 1933–37, and Fred G. Aandahl, Assistant Secretary for Water and Power, 1953–60, include records about Indian affairs. The general office file of Assistant Secretary G. Girard Davidson, 1946–50, includes a general heading for Indian affairs and specific headings for the Flathead Irrigation Project,

Garrison Dam, and Navajo Tribe. Records, 1929–33, of Ernest Walker Sawyer, executive assistant to the Secretary of the Interior and special representative of the General Manager of the Alaska Railroad, relate chiefly to Alaska and include a series relating to reindeer. Records concerning Indians among those of the Special Advisor on Labor Relations, 1936–47, relate in large part to wage rates. The reference file of Saul Padover, Assistant to the Secretary, 1938–45, gathered chiefly in the preparation of publications, includes some material about Indians.

RECORDS OF THE OFFICE OF THE SOLICITOR

The Office of the Solicitor is a continuation of the Office of the Assistant Attorney General for the Department of the Interior established in 1871.The title was changed to Solicitor for the Department of the Interior in 1914. Until 1926 the Solicitor was an official of the Department of Justice, but his staff were employees of the Department of the Interior. The Solicitor is the chief legal officer for the Department. His office drafts and reviews legislation, prepares opinions on legal questions, including appeals from decisions of bureau chiefs, and handles litigation and claims against the Department.

There are general correspondence and other records of the Office for the years 1930–58 (73 ft.). Through 1938 the records are arranged for the most part chronologically, and to a considerable extent they are copies of records in the central classified files. Starting in 1939, they are arranged mostly by year and thereunder alphabetically by subject, with some subheadings, and thereunder chronologically. Sometimes, however, records on a subject over several years are grouped together under the last year, so there are a few records as early as 1927. Subjects include bureaus and other administrative units of the Department, units of the Office of the Solicitor, functions, programs, geographical areas, resources, acts of the Congress, companies, and legal cases. There is no general heading for the Bureau of Indian Affairs until 1945. Thereafter it was used every year until 1956, when "Branch of Indian Activities" (of the Solicitor's Office) was adopted as the main heading for records concerning Indian administration. The records relate to Federal and tribal legislation, land, heirship, mining claims, tribal enterprises, contracts and agreements, payment of income taxes by Indians, and many other legal subjects. For some years there are separate folders for such subjects as Yakima fishermen, Indian Claims Commission, Indian law survey, Indian voting (concerning the refusal of New Mexico to allow untaxed Indians to vote), Indian arts and crafts, reservations for Alaska Indians, appeals, and Fort Peck tribal elections. Until Alaska became a State, there are general and specific folders for Alaska, which relate in part to Alaskan natives.

With monthly narrative reports of chief counsels and other legal officers, 1946–54, are some memorandums concerning individual cases involving

Indians in Oklahoma. Correspondence with Kenneth R. L. Simmons, District Counsel at Billings, Mont., for the Irrigation Service of the Bureau of Indian Affairs, 1933-46, relates chiefly to legal matters concerning irrigation projects on Indian reservations. Correspondence with George W. Folta, Counsel at Large at Juneau, Alaska, 1940-47, relates in large part to legal matters concerning Alaskan natives. Records concerning water resources, 1944-52, include a mimeographed report about the Bureau of Indian Affairs program, including information about individual projects. Records of the Legislative Division, 1934-52, include information concerning proposed legislation for the Bureau of Indian Affairs. Records of the Property Acquisition Division, 1934-47, about Indians relate to irrigation, the Five Civilized Tribes Agency, miscellaneous cases, and opinions.

There are also several series of files concerning individual cases. Records of court cases, 1915-41, for the most part concern law and equity cases in the Supreme Court of the District of Columbia, now the U.S. District Court for the District of Columbia. There were numerous cases involving individual Indians and some concerning tribal matters relative to land title, control of accounts of individual Indians, heirship and guardianship, enrollment, irrigation and water rights, and other subjects. One case concerned Jackson Barnett, a Creek Indian made wealthy by the discovery of oil on his allotment. There was also a case in which patients at the Canton Asylum for Insane Indians when it closed protested being transferred to St. Elizabeths Hospital in Washington, D.C.

There is a series concerning Indian litigation cases, 1934-58 (7 ft.), in which the Justice Department, Bureau of Indian Affairs, and Office of the Solicitor participated, including some Indian Claims Commission cases. The cases concerned heirship, land allotments, condemnations, rights-of-way, leases, water and fishing rights, timber trespasses, damage and debt claims, and other subjects. There are other records, 1942-50, with an index and registers, for Oklahoma litigation case files. Most of these cases involved members of the Five Civilized Tribes and related to land or the determination of heirs. Frequently, the only action of the Department of the Interior was to decide that Federal intervention was unnecessary; removal to a Federal court normally was sought only when restricted Indian land was involved.

There are records, 1919-43, concerning a case in which the United States represented the Walapai Indians against the Santa Fe Railroad Company in a dispute over the railroad station at Peach Springs, Ariz. There are records, 1942-48 (3 ft.), including correspondence, proceedings of hearings and exhibits, and legal documents, concerning the claims of the natives of Hydaburg, Klawock, and Kake to exclusive possession of certain lands and waters in southeastern Alaska. Other records concern five cases presented to the Departmental Board of Appeals, 1941–47. Four of the cases concerned Indian lands; the largest group of records involved Blackfeet tribal leases.

RECORDS OF THE INSPECTION DIVISION

Records of the Inspection Division include general records, 1924–27, some of which concern Indian affairs, and Bureau of Indian Affairs inspection reports, 1907–24 (3 ft.), which consist of reports with exhibits about general inspections and conditions at agencies, schools, and reservations and about investigations of land allotments, liquor control, the conduct of employees, alleged crimes, and other more specific subjects.

RECORDS OF THE DIVISION OF INFORMATION

Records of the Radio Section of the Division of Information, 1938–47, include material on proposed radio programs about Indians and some scripts. Records of the Publications Section include a draft of that section of a history of the Department during World War II about the Bureau of Indian Affairs.

RECORDS OF THE DIVISION OF LAND UTILIZATION

The Division (originally Office) of Land Utilization existed from 1940 until 1953. It planned and coordinated land use activities within the Department and supervised and maintained relations outside the Department. It was concerned with soil and moisture conservation, forest conservation, water resources, fire control, noxious weed control, white pine blister rust control, forest pest control, and Civilian Public Service camps for conscientious objectors during World War II. Almost all of the records of the Division are in central classified files, 1937–56 (180 ft.), arranged by a decimal classification system. The pre-1940 records were maintained by the Division Director, Lee Muck, in his previous positions as Director of Forests for the Bureau of Indian Affairs and for the Department of the Interior. Post-1953 records were added by a unit of the Office of the Assistant Secretary for Water and Power Development. The organization of the decimal system is such that records concerning Indian activities are dispersed among many classifications, but often there are subheadings for Indian affairs within classifications. The 901 classification is a reading file of outgoing communications arranged for the most part alphabetically by office of addressee and thereunder chronologically. Decimal classifications noted on the records help identify related documents.

RECORDS OF THE DIVISION OF WATER AND POWER

The Division of Power was established in April 1941 to supervise and coordinate the work of the Department and its bureaus relating to electric power. It was replaced in 1950 by the Division of Water and Power, which also took over some duties from the Office of Land Utilization. The Division was abolished in 1953. The classified files and other records of the Division concerning Bureau of Reclamation projects contain some records, chiefly correspondence with the Bureau of Indian Affairs, concerning projects affecting Indian reservations, including Colorado River, Flathead, Fort Peck, and Yakima (filed under Klickitat). Some records concerning the development of Alaska relate in part to the natives, including their health, education, and welfare.

RECORDS OF COORDINATION AND PROGRAM STAFFS

Following World War II the Department of the Interior established units to coordinate programs, make studies, and determine priorities. In Washington there was the Coordination Committee, 1946–47; Program Staff, 1947–53; and Technical Review Staff, 1953–62. There were also field committees to help coordinate regional planning and an Alaska Field Staff to coordinate departmental programs in Alaska. Some programs concerned Indians, but, except in some processed reports, pertinent records are difficult to identify.There are some planning, programing, and budgeting records of the Office of Program Analysis for fiscal years 1966–71, with projections for fiscal years 1972 and 1973, which include segregated information concerning Indians.

CARTOGRAPHIC RECORDS

Maps relating to States and Territories include a General Land Office map of Oklahoma, 1914, annotated to show the locations of Indian tribes and reservations; military maps of Indian Territory, 1875, with annotations about Indian tribes; and a General Land Office map of Indian Territory, 1891, which shows boundaries of judicial districts. Records concerning Government reservations include a 1904 map showing Sully's Hill Park within the Devil's Lake Indian Reservation and an 1883 map showing boundaries of the Western Shoshone Reservation in Nevada and Idaho.

Cartographic records of the Office of Explorations and Surveys, 1849–57, consist of annotated printed topographic maps showing the general routes of surveys and explorations, manuscript topographic maps and profiles of routes of specific surveys, and an incomplete record set of published maps of general and specific surveys. Many of the general maps and some of the maps of specific routes show locations of Indian tribes and villages.

See Laura E. Kelsay, comp., *Preliminary Inventory of Cartographic Records of the Office of the Secretary of the Interior,* PI 81 (1954).

AUDIOVISUAL RECORDS

Among photographs illustrating reports of Territorial Governors, for Indian Territory, 1900, there are 15 photographs of Indians, including portraits of the chiefs of the Seminole, Creek, Cherokee, Choctaw, and

Chickasaw Nations. There are 21 motion pictures, mainly from the National Park Service, with sequences relating to Indians. These include a Bureau of Indian affairs film, "Rebuilding Indian Country," 1933; views of Papago and Sioux reservation life, 1937; films showing Indian dances and activities at Mesa Verde, Glacier, Grand Canyon, and Waterton-Glacier International Peace Parks; and films showing Indians in the Southwest and Minnesota and mound builder relics in Alabama. Thirteen sound recordings, 1939–41 and 1944, relate to Indians. One is a discussion of Indian self-government. In the second, Commissioner of Indian Affairs John Collier discusses the status of Indians and the work of the Bureau of Indian Affairs. In the third, Indians urge Americans to buy war bonds. The fourth is a discussion of Navajo progress and problems on the "What Price America" radio program. The remainder are from the radio program "Conservation Reporter" and deal with arts and crafts, the discovery of oil on Osage land, the registration of Indians for the draft, treaty gifts to the Iroquois, the loyalty pledge of the Shoshoni in Utah, and Indians in the defense effort.

RECORDS OF THE INDIAN ARTS
AND CRAFTS BOARD
(RECORD GROUP 435)

The Indian Arts and Crafts Board was established in the Department of the Interior by an act of August 27, 1935 (49 Stat. 891), to promote the development of Indian arts and crafts and the expansion of markets for them. Members of the Board serve part-time without compensation. A General Manager directs operations.

The records of the Board in the National Archives (33 ft.) include correspondence, memorandums, and other records concerning legislation, that created the Board, 1934–36; records concerning the establishment of standards for Indian crafts and assistance to Indian artists and craftsmen, including crafts cooperatives, 1936–48; records concerning the planning, organization, and operation of the exhibit of native American arts and crafts at the 1939–40 Golden Gate International Exposition, including the Covelo Indian market; records concerning a similar exhibit in 1941 at the Museum of Modern Art in New York City, 1939–41; and a card index to the correspondence of the Board, 1936–ca. 1942.

RECORDS OF THE BUREAU
OF LAND MANAGEMENT
(RECORD GROUP 49)

As the custodian of the public domain, the General Land Office handled the business of disposing of ceded and surplus Indian lands and the surveying, recording, and patenting of individual Indian allotments. From the establishment of the Federal Government until 1812, the Offices of the Secretary of the Treasury and the Register of the Treasury were directly responsible for the disposition of the public domain. The General Land Office was created by an act of April 25, 1812 (2 Stat. 716), within the Department of the Treasury and was transferred in 1849 to the new Department of the Interior. It was consolidated with the Grazing Service to form the Bureau of Land Management on July 16, 1946.

No single administrative unit of the General Land Office had overall responsibility concerning Indian lands. Eventually Division "K" became the nearest equivalent to such a unit, but business concerning Indian lands was handled by other divisions as well.

See Harry P. Yoshpe and Philip P. Brower, comps., *Preliminary Inventory of the Land-Entry Papers of the General Land Office,* PI 22 (1949).

Correspondence

A large number of letters relating to Indian lands are filed with the general incoming correspondence of the General Land Office and Bureau of Land Management, 1801–1965. Until 1845 this correspondence is arranged in alphabetical sections by surname of writer or designation of office and thereunder chronologically. After June 1845 the arrangement is by year and thereunder by registration number. Other relevant letters are among the letters received from the Treasury Department, ca. 1806–48; letters received concerning opinions of the Attorney General of the United States, 1815–43; and the letters received from Surveyors General, 1826–79. There are several series of indexes and registers to incoming correspondence, including registers specifically relating to Indian lands, 1835–63.

Copies of outgoing correspondence until 1908 are with the records of the divisions responsible for creating them. For the years 1908–48 the letters sent are centralized, arranged by day and thereunder by division.

Land Entry Papers and Related Records

Land entry papers are the documents accumulated to determine the entitlement of individuals to patents for title to tracts of land in the public domain. Through June 1908 most of the land entry papers are arranged by State and land office and thereunder by type of land entry. There are records specifically identified as relating to Indian lands for 25 of the 30 States in which most of the land was once part of the Federal public domain: Alabama, Alaska, Arizona, California, Colorado, Idaho, Illinois, Indiana, Kansas, Michigan, Minnesota, Mississippi, Missouri, Montana, Nebraska, Nevada, New Mexico, North Dakota, Oklahoma, Oregon, South Dakota, Utah, Washington, Wisconsin, and Wyoming. There are no such records for Arkansas, Florida, Iowa, Louisiana, or Ohio among those arranged by State. Land in the other 20 States was never part of the Federal public domain, and information concerning these areas should be sought from the archives or land agencies of the individual States.

Most of the land entry papers are in case files. There are two major categories for Indian lands—allotments of land to individual Indians and sales of tribal land. The files for allotments usually are in numbered sets for individual land offices with no tribal breakdown; most of these files were for allotments of public domain land to Indians who were not living on a reservation. These allotments were authorized by a provision of the General Allotment Act of 1887 (24 Stat. 388, 389). The usual basic document is a form with space for the application and supporting affidavit of the applicant, a corroborative affidavit signed by two witnesses, and an affidavit attesting to the nonmineral character of the land. General Land Office actions on the applications are noted on endorsement sheets.

Indian lands that were sold included entire reservations of tribes who had agreed to move elsewhere, parts of reservations ceded by Indians, and surplus reservation lands remaining after allotments had been made to individual Indians. The files relating to these sales are far more numerous than those relating to allotments, but usually they do not contain much information pertaining directly to the Indians. Rather, they document sales to individuals after the tribes had given up the land. Some former Indian land was disposed of as regular public domain land, for the most part by cash sale or homestead entry, although many of the homestead entries were canceled or commuted to cash sales. For most of the lands, however, there were special conditions of sale. Usually, preemption privileges were given to actual settlers, or settlement was a condition of the sale. Sometimes homestead requirements for residence and improvements were enforced, even though the entryman had to pay for the land. Payment in several installments, however, was allowed for some sales.

Proceeds from the sale of Indian land were used in a variety of ways. In some cases the money was placed in a trust fund for the tribe or distributed to individual Indians. In other cases the funds were used to settle claims against the tribe or to pay for improvements on land within the new limits of the reservation. Some of the money was deposited in the U.S. Treasury along with the proceeds from general land sales. The land entry papers, however, do not usually document what was actually done with the money after the sales.

For some States there are special records relating to Indian lands. Of particular interest are those for certain land offices in Alabama and Mississippi relating to the sale of land of individual Creek and Choctaw Indians at the time of their removal to Indian Territory.

Among the records not arranged by State and land office are several series of scrip and related records for Choctaw and mixed-blood Chippewa and Sioux Indians. Scrip was issued to people who qualified under provisions of various treaties and acts of the Congress, and it entitled them to select allotments from specified land. There is also an Indian reserve series, which consists of correspondence, reports, applications, contracts, plats, canceled patents, lists, schedules, accounts, and other records, ca. 1808-1921 (9 ft.), relating for the most part to land reserves for individual Indians as provided for by treaties and acts of the Congress. There are case files for individual reserves and more general records concerning the granting of reserves or allotments, sales, disputes, fraudulent claims, and other matters.

Among the records created in connection with the execution of special acts concerning land grants, disputed titles, and other land matters are files concerning allotments to Absentee Wyandot Indians, claims for reserves under the Treaty of Fort Jackson of 1814 with the Creek Indians, and warrants issued to members of the Lewis and Clark expedition. There also are records concerning lands for several Indian missions, including a file for a controversy between Baptist and Roman Catholic missionary societies over the sale of mission lands at Grand Rapids, Mich., as provided for by an 1836 treaty with the Ottawa and Chippewa Indians.

Another group of land entry papers are the records of private claims to land acquired before the United States assumed sovereignty over certain areas. The claims of the Pueblo Indians of New Mexico to the lands they occupied were adjudicated as private claims; records include case files for the individual villages, relating mostly to the determination of boundaries. Private land claims also involved Indian mission lands, particularly the Spanish missions in California, and land that was part of Indian reservations.

Beginning July 1, 1908, the General Land Office began arranging most case files for patented entries in one numerical series instead of by State and land office. There is, however, a separate series of records 1902-50 (102 ft.), relating to Indian fee patents. Fee patents, provided for by the General Allotment Act of 1887, gave Indians full control of their allotments, the main practical effect being that they could sell the land, after a 25-year trust period. Later acts extended the trust period for some Indians and reduced it for others. The application for a fee patent, often accompanied by the surrendered trust patent, had to be approved by the local Indian agent or superintendent, the Bureau of Indian Affairs, and the Office of the Secretary of the Interior before a patent could be issued by the General Land Office. By 1913 one form showed the actions of these several offices. Included among the General Land Office records are files for changes or cancellations of trust patents, approvals of sales of land belonging to minors and other Indians considered incapable of managing their own affairs, and patents for missionary groups.

Individual Indians sometimes acquired land by a standard purchase or homestead entry, and many of them received bounty land warrants entitling them to land as partial compensation for their military service. Records of such transactions, however, are intermingled with those for non-Indians.

Also among the records of the Bureau of Land Management are the abstracts of transactions received monthly from the registers and receivers of the district land offices. For some States, particularly in the West, there are tractbooks that indicate the disposal of each tract of public domain land. For some States the district office tractbooks are in a Federal archives and records center. These volumes are used mainly as finding aids for the case files, but a researcher interested in the disposition of part of an Indian reservation, for example, and not in the individual buyers might find them more convenient to use than the case files. For the Western States there are also record copies of patents, the documents that actually transferred title from the United States, but usually they do not contain any information not found in the case files. Central office tractbooks and patents for States east of the Mississippi River and Louisiana, Arkansas, Missouri, Iowa, and Minnesota are still in the custody of the Bureau of Land Management.

Other Records

Records of Division "B" (Recorder) concerning Indian scrip (6 in.) comprise a list of claims under the Choctaw treaty of 1830; an abstract of Choctaw scrip locations, 1846–61; an undated index to Sioux Half-Breed scrip; a location register of Sioux Half-Breed scrip and Chippewa scrip, 1854–1908; and an abstract of applications for Chippewa scrip made under an 1855 treaty, 1881–86. There is also a series of letters sent relating to Indian lands, private lands, and coal lands, 1903–7.

Among the records of Division "C" (Public Lands) are letters sent (2 ft.) relating to former Indian reservation lands, 1891–94; Indian lands, 1902–6; and Sioux Half-Breed, Chippewa, Kansas Trust, and other Indian scrip, ca. 1873–75.

With the records of Division "D" (Mails and Files) are two partially overlapping series of letters sent relating to Indians and private land claims, covering the periods 1835–91 and 1871–95 (6 ft.).

Records of Division "E" (Surveying) include special files concerning surveys of the Fort Peck, Navajo, Osage, Ponca, Pyramid Lake, Tule River, Walker River, and Zuni Indian Reservations as well as other Indian landholdings.

Among the records of Division "F" (Railroads, Rights-of-way, and Reclamation) are folders relating to railroad rights-of-way across Indian reservations, 1901–38 (30 ft.). The folders contain textual records and maps showing the locations of railroad lines and stations, pipelines, pumping plants, and reservoirs. Folders relating to highway rights-of-way, 1910–45, contain textual and cartographic records concerning public highways, wagon roads, and oil, gas, telephone, telegraph, and transmission lines.

With the records of Division "K" (Indian Lands by 1925) are Indian reserve files containing maps and printed materials as well as correspondence, 1907–55 (26 ft.), and schedules of classification and appraisal of ceded Indian reservation lands, 1883–1929 (2 ft.). Also pertinent are files concerning abandoned military reservations that were restored to the public domain by the General Land Office, 1822–1937 (63 ft.).

With the records of Division "M" (Accounting) are 3 feet of letters sent to the Commissioner of Indian Affairs, 1894–1908; Indian accounts, 1832–56; reports of adjusted Indian accounts, 1877–93; a schedule of patented Indian lands for the Winnebago Reservation in Minnesota and Sauk and Fox lands in Nebraska, 1863–65; a statement of proceeds from sales of lands within the Kiowa, Comanche, Apache, and Wichita Reservations, 1913–20; and statements of the disposal of public and Indian lands, 1885–1925.

Cartographic Records

Maps and plats of Indian reservations and of some of the boundaries of original and diminished reservations are among the records of the Bureau of Land Management. There are also several maps of Indian land boundaries that later became State boundaries, field notes of surveys of several Indian boundary lines, and other maps showing locations of Indian and military reservations.

There are manuscript plats and diagrams of Indian lands and boundaries for grants and reserves in Indiana, Michigan, and Ohio, 1807–49; a volume of diagrams, 1864, showing tracts of the Kansas Half-Breed lands; a volume of plats, 1857–65, of Sauk and Fox and Wyandot lands in Kansas and Omaha lands in Nebraska; two volumes of plats of "Indian Reservation Exteriors," showing the boundaries of Indian reservations in several States and the exterior lines of townships within some of the reservations, particularly in the Indian Territory, 1856–92.

There are township plats and diagrams, 1904–31, of lands in the following Indian reservations: Fort Peck and Flathead, Mont.; Devil's Lake and Fort Berthold, N. Dak.; Standing Rock, N. Dak. and S. Dak.; Cheyenne River, Rosebud, and Pine Ridge, S. Dak.; and Colville, Wash. Most are annotated to show the classification and status of lands offered for settlement. One set of plats for Fort Peck shows the acreage appraised in 1928. Manuscript and annotated maps and diagrams and statistical tables relate to lands within former Indian reservations, including Cheyenne River, S. Dak.; Oto and Missouri in Kansas and Nebraska; Fort Peck, Mont.; and early cessions and reserves in Michigan. Township plats of lands in the Moqui (Hopi) and Navajo Reservations in Arizona are annotated to show the area or estimated area of odd-number sections within the limits of the land granted to the Atlantic and Pacific Railroad, 1904-10; there are two manuscript plats and typed copies of field notes of the surveys of tracts of Cherokee Indian School lands in Swain County, N.C., 1951.

There are also railroad right-of-way maps involving Indian lands; a 3- by 5-inch card index for these maps is arranged alphabetically by name of railroad. Early maps of general routes, definite locations, and constructed lines are listed in an index volume that gives dates of statutes pertaining to each railroad. General routes of railroads in relation to Indian reservations are shown on maps of the United States, States, and Territories. A few county and State highway maps show Indian lands.

See Laura E. Kelsay, comp., *List of Cartographic Records of the General Land Office,* Special List 19 (1964).

RECORDS OF THE GEOLOGICAL SURVEY
(RECORD GROUP 57)

The Geological Survey was established in 1879 in the Department of the Interior to classify public lands and to examine the geological structure, mineral resources, and products of the national domain. It replaced four earlier surveys: the U.S. Geological and Geographical Survey of the Territories (Hayden Survey), 1867-79; the U.S. Geographical and Geological Survey of the Rocky Mountain Region (Powell Survey), 1869-79; the U.S. Geographical Surveys West of the One Hundredth Meridian (Wheeler Survey), 1872-79; and the Geological Exploration of the Fortieth Parallel (King Survey), 1867-79. The Hayden and Powell Surveys in particular included ethnological and archeological studies among their activities. Many of the findings of these surveys have been published, but there is supplementary material among the records in the National Archives. John Wesley Powell, Director of the Rocky Mountain Survey, was especially concerned with Indian vocabularies and linguistics, and he published works about them; these activities are documented in the records of the survey. Most of the early records of the Geological Survey and the records of its predecessors have been reproduced as NARS microfilm publications.

In the Maj. Joseph H. Wheat collection of Powell Survey photographic prints are 118 half-stereo prints of Indians in Arizona, New Mexico, Nevada, and Utah, 1872-74. Powell lists them in his handwritten catalog as ethnographic views. The catalog gives a short caption, the name of the tribe, and the tribe's location for each picture.

Under several classifications of the general files of the Geological Survey, 1912-69, and among the records of several of its divisions is information concerning work done on Indian reservations, including stream gauging, water supply studies, geological and topographical surveys, and mineral surveys. The Survey provided technical advice to the Bureau of Indian Affairs on such matters as water supply and irrigation projects, mineral development, and oil and gas leasing (particularly for the Osage Indians). Most of the records are administrative; there are some technical reports but little about the Indians themselves. A relatively high proportion of records concerning Indian reservations can be found in the series of reports, 1942–49, relating to stock water investigations, which usually involved locating sites for wells. There are also some records, 1933–37, of the Conservation Division, concerning public works on Indian lands in Oklahoma.

RECORDS OF THE FISH AND WILDLIFE SERVICE
(RECORD GROUP 22)

The records of the Fish and Wildlife Service in the National Archives of the United States include those of two predecessors, the Bureau of Fisheries (usually known until 1903 as the Fish Commission) and the Bureau of Biological Survey. They were merged in 1940 to form the Fish and Wildlife Service, which in 1956 was organized into two bureaus, the Bureau of Commercial Fisheries and the Bureau of Sport Fisheries and Wildlife.

The Bureau of Fisheries was given the added responsibilities of regulating the Alaskan fishery and fur seal industries in 1905 and 1908, respectively. Until 1903 the Treasury Department had had these responsibilities, and the Bureau acquired pertinent Treasury Department records, which have been reproduced as M720, *Alaska File of the Secretary of the Treasury, 1868–1903*. These and later records of the Division of Alaska Fisheries (or the Alaska Division) of the Bureau of Fisheries contain information about fishing rights of natives, areas set aside for their use, and illegal seal hunting and fishing by natives. The Bureau provided schools, medical service, food, fuel, clothing, and living quarters for the natives of the Pribilof Islands of St. George and St. Paul, principal hunting grounds for fur seals. There are census records for the islanders, including rolls; records, mostly reports, concerning schools and children sent to the Chemawa (Salem) Indian School in Oregon; records of medical and dental service, including reports on water supply, sewerage, sanitary facilities, housing, food supply, and the use of alcohol; and records concerning marriage laws, native bank accounts, and a church fund. Included are transcripts made during the winter of 1910–11 by Walter L. Hahn of notes from logs of agents on St. Paul written as early as 1872. There is a 112-page section on the natives, with subsections on education, intemperance, immorality, their relationship with the Greek Church, government, medical and sanitary conditions, and natural resources. Log books of the fur seal fishery in the Pribilof Islands, 1870–1961, are available on microfilm (in FARC Seattle). There are also records concerning surveys of native villages in Alaska, relating particularly to economic matters, such as employment, earnings, and living conditions.

In the general correspondence and other records of the Bureau of Biological Survey concerning game protection are some records about Indians, relating mainly to the application of game laws to Indians living on reservations. Under the predatory animal and rodent control category are records concerning a rodent control program on Indian reservations carried out in cooperation with the Bureau of Indian Affairs and the Civilian Conservation Corps (Emergency Conservation Work). There are occasional references to Alaskan natives among records concerning Bureau activities in Alaska.

The more recent records of the Fish and Wildlife Service, dating as late as 1970, continue the earlier series of its two predecessors. In particular, the general classified files of the Bureau of Fisheries, which include a major decimal classification for the Alaska Division, was continued by the Bureau of Commercial Fisheries. There are also records about river basin and recreation area development, which include material about Indian lands.

Audiovisual records include 40 photographs of Haida, Aleuts, Eskimos, unidentified natives, homes, villages, boats, implements, totems, graveyards, and methods of curing salmon in Alaska, 1888–90; these are included among eight albums of photographs made on cruises of the Fish Commission steamer *Albatross.* In the Biological Survey photographic subject file, there are 130 photographs, 1903–39, of Eskimos and Indians and their activities under the heading "Personal—Aleuts and Indians." There is also a photographic subject file of the Alaska Game Commission, which contains 10 photographs of Aleut chiefs and other natives, 1931–38, under the heading "People—Native."

RECORDS OF THE OFFICE OF TERRITORIES
(RECORD GROUP 126)

The Office of Territories was established within the Department of the Interior on July 28, 1950, by administrative order of the Secretary to carry out certain of his responsibilities in regard to the administration of Territories of the United States. Increasingly, the Office of Territories has been concerned with the development of the economic, social, and political life of the Territories and the coordination of Territorial affairs with the defense and foreign policies of the United States. The Office inherited records from its predecessor, the Department's Division of Territories and Island Possessions, created in 1934, which in turn had taken immediate custody of the central classified files of the Secretary's Office relating to Territorial matters, 1907–34. Earlier Department records concerning Territorial affairs are among the records of the Patents and Miscellaneous Division in the Records of the Office of the Secretary of the Interior, Record Group 48.

The records of the Office of Territories contain the largest collections of materials relating to Alaskan natives outside of the records of the Bureau of Indian Affairs and the Office of the Secretary of the Interior. Those concerning Eskimos, Aleuts, and various Indian groups are filed under the Alaska subject heading (9-1) of the central classified files for the period 1907 to 1951. Also included in the files are a few earlier related records.

The most significant files are identified as "Condition and Needs of Natives" (9-1-2), "Employment of Indian Police, Special Officers, and Game Wardens" (9-1-51), "Reservations—Reservations of Land for Use of Natives" (9-1-52), and "Alaska Indians" (9-1-82). Of the land reserves for which there are related records, that of Annette Island, containing the village of Metlakahtla, is the subject of the greatest number of files. Included among the records filed under the subheading "Alaska Indians" is an original report of June 30, 1885, submitted by a commission appointed to report on the natives. Other records relating to Alaskan natives are in files labeled "Game-Reindeer" (9-1-33), "Totem Poles" (9-1-36), "Salmon Fisheries" (9-1-37), and "Arts and Crafts" (9-1-91). When necessary, these files are further subdivided, and thereunder records within individual classifications are usually arranged chronologically.

There also are records relating to Arizona (9-2), New Mexico (9-5), and Oklahoma (9-6) Territories, but they include no specific subheadings for Indians, except for a small file for Arizona relating to the smuggling of arms to the Yaqui Indians of Mexico, 1907-9. These records have been reproduced as parts of M429, M364, and M828.

In a series of photographs relating to the Alaska Railroad, 1914-30, under the subject "Indians," are six photographs of a Knik village, church, and graveyard and one of a Talkentnai family, 1918. An album of photographic views of the Alaska Railroad and of Alaska contains five photographs of Eskimos and one of a Knik family, ca. 1915. Halftone illustrations for the *Thirteenth Annual Report on the Introduction of Domestic Reindeer into Alaska* include 15 of Indians, Eskimos, and Aleuts, mainly of groups of school children, ca. 1900.

See Richard S. Maxwell and Evans Walker, comps., *Preliminary Inventory of the Records of the Office of Territories,* PI 154 (1963).

RECORDS OF THE ALASKAN TERRITORIAL GOVERNMENT (RECORD GROUP 348)

The records of the Alaskan Territorial Government that are now part of the National Archives of the United States are microfilm copies (in FARC Seattle) of original records, 1884-1958, that have been transferred to the State of Alaska. They consist chiefly of records of the Offices of the Governor and the Secretary. Most of the documents are in general correspondence files, 1909-58, which are arranged according to a succession of filing schemes. There are files concerning Indian police, liquor, and other Indian affairs; the condition of Alaskan natives; the reindeer industry at Metlakahtla; fisheries and fur bearing animals; the desecration of Indian graves in Juneau; roads near native villages; land surveys of native villages; Indian citizenship and the organization of villages under territorial laws; and the education of natives.

RECORDS OF THE BUREAU OF RECLAMATION (RECORD GROUP 115)

The U.S. Reclamation Service was created in the Geological Survey in 1902, separated from the Survey in 1907, and renamed the Bureau of Reclamation in 1923. Its primary objective has been the development of water and related resources in arid regions, chiefly by the construction and, to some extent, the operation of irrigation works. The Bureau of Indian Affairs has directed most irrigation work done on Indian reservations. The Bureau of Reclamation did provide technical assistance, particularly in its earlier years. Until 1924 three projects in Montana—on the Blackfeet, Flathead, and Fort Peck Reservations—were controlled by the Bureau of Reclamation. The Wapato Irrigation Project, conducted by the Bureau of Indian Affairs for the Yakima Reservation in Washington, was considered a division of the Yakima Project of the Bureau of Reclamation. The Riverton Project was for ceded lands from the Wind River Reservation. Projects were considered but not undertaken for other reservations, such as the Crow Reservation in Montana and the Duck Valley Reservation in Nevada and Idaho.

In other places, Indian landholdings were within or adjacent to reclamation areas, and Indians might share in the benefits or suffer damages from irrigation projects; a proposed San Carlos Project called for the construction of a dam that would have flooded lands within the San Carlos Reservation.

The records of the Bureau of Reclamation in the National Archives include general administrative and project records, 1902–45; project histories, feature histories, and reports, 1902–60; and records of the Chief Engineer, 1902–52 (in FARC Denver). To a large extent the records are technical, relating chiefly to the construction and operation of the projects. However, for the Bureau of Reclamation projects on Indian reservations, there are records of more general interest (including letters from Indians), concerning land acquired from Indian allottees, rights- of-way across Indian lands, water services and the charges for them (particularly for the Wapato Project), delinquent payments, requests of missionary groups for free water, the employment of Indians on projects, squatters on lands to be irrigated, the irrigation of allotments leased from Indians, and claims for damages caused by irrigation work (including claims for cattle poisoned by eating TNT). For the Flathead Project there is testimony taken by a committee who asked Indian allottees and other settlers how they got water and what crops they grew; there are also reports of examinations of the allotments.

Under the 757 category of the numeric subject classification system used for general records, 1902-19, are 2 feet of records concerning the cooperation of the Bureau of Reclamation and the Bureau of Indian Affairs, primarily on projects controlled by the latter. The records are arranged by State and thereunder by reservation. They relate primarily to administrative and technical matters, but there are records about Indian water rights, the diversion of water before it reached the reservation, and the effects of projects on Indian lands. Classification 131.22 in the decimal system adopted by the Bureau of Reclamation in 1919 is for cooperation with the Bureau of Indian Affairs, but few records are filed under it either with the general records or with the records concerning individual projects.

Glass lantern slides, some colored, 1899-1915 (200 items), were made from photographs taken by Bureau photographers at projects on or near Indian reservations. They include photographs of Indians working on the projects, including members of the Apache, Blackfeet, Crow, Papago, Navajo, and Pueblo tribes.

Projects histories and reports of Reclamation Bureau projects, 1902-25, have been reproduced as M96. See Edward E. Hill, comp., *Preliminary Inventory of the Records of the Bureau of Reclamation,* PI 109 (1958).

RECORDS OF THE NATIONAL PARK SERVICE
(RECORD GROUP 79)

The National Park Service was established in the Department of the Interior by an act of August 25, 1916 (39 Stat. 535). Previously, since the establishment of Yellowstone Park in 1872, park administration was under the direct supervision of the Secretary of the Interior. The National Park Service inherited records of the Office of the Secretary relating to this work.

Many of the national parks, monuments, and other areas administered by the Park Service have some historical or prehistorical connection with Indians. Mesa Verde National Park and numerous national monuments, such as Bandelier, Casa Grande, and Gila Cliff Dwellings, feature ruins of prehistoric civilizations. Others, such as Tumacacori National Monument, were Indian missions. Still others, such as Custer Battlefield, Fort Laramie, and Lava Beds National Monuments, commemorate Indian-white conflicts, and other contacts. Other areas associated with Indians were proposed for inclusion in the National Park Service system but were not accepted.

The principal records of the National Park Service in the National Archives are letters received by the Office of the Secretary of the Interior relating to national parks, 1872-1907 (letters sent for these years are in bound volumes with letters relating to other subjects in Record Group 48), and two overlapping series of central files, 1907–39 and 1907–49, both arranged for the most part by park and thereunder by subject (the second uses a decimal classification system). Dispersed throughout these records is material relating indirectly to Indians—records about historical and archeological research, the preservation of ruins, and museums and other exhibits. Records relating more immediately to Indians are less common and more difficult to locate. Platt National Park, Okla., originally Sulphur Spring Reservation and located in the Chickasaw Nation, at first was administered through the Bureau of Indian Affairs and the Indian Territory Division of the Office of the Secretary of the Interior. At other areas, such as Canyon de Chelly, Mesa Verde, Great Smoky Mountains, and Custer Battlefield, the Park Service sought to acquire land from tribes or individual Indians. For Mesa Verde there are 65 pages of proceedings of a council held in 1911 at which Southern Ute Indians agreed to give up part of their reservation. The Indian agency superintendent, incidentally, acted as superintendent of the park for a time after its establishment. For Chaco Canyon there are some records concerning drilling wells for Indian use.

In the Henry G. Peabody collection of photographs, 1890–1935, are 75 photographs of Indians and their living conditions. They are in two sets of glass lantern slides. The first, "Indian on the Plains in 1870," contains 25 photographs of Arapaho, Comanche, Kiowa, and Wichita Indians; the second, "Indians of Desert, Mesa, and Canyon," consists of 50 photographs of Pueblo, Navajo, Hopi, and Havasupai Indians taken by Peabody, 1899–1902.

See Edward E. Hill, comp., *Preliminary Inventory of the Records of the National Park Service,* PI 166 (1966).

RECORDS OF THE BUREAU OF MINES
(RECORD GROUP 70)

A motion picture film, "Arizona and Its Natural Resources," 1939, shows Apache Indians rounding up cattle, Hopi Indians making pottery and religious dolls, and Navajo Indians herding sheep, preparing food, and weaving cloth in front of their brush homes.

RECORDS OF THE OFFICE OF THE SECRETARY OF WAR
(RECORD GROUP 107)

The Office of the Secretary of War was created by an act of August 7, 1789 (1 Stat. 49). Its functions in the early years were to recruit, provision, and regulate the military and naval forces of the United States, to administer the awarding of pensions and bounty lands for military service, and to oversee Indian affairs. The Department of the Navy was separated in 1798. Administration and supervision of military and Indian affairs, pensions, and fortifications and arsenals soon proved too great a task for one office, and between 1812 and 1850 the Congress created a number of separate bureaus, among them the Adjutant General's Department, the Quartermaster's Department, the Pay Department, the Medical Department, the Ordnance Department, and the Engineer Department to take over functions formerly handled by the Secretary. Later from time to time additional bureaus were created to handle other duties of the Office of the Secretary of War, and, as the bureaus began to function, correspondence was routed more frequently to them and the files of the Secretary gradually became less comprehensive.

Some functions originally performed by the Secretary of War's Office were transferred to other agencies outside the War Department. Although there had been a Military Bounty Land and Pensions Branch and a Pension Office in the Secretary's Office, in 1833 a Commissioner of Pensions was authorized by the Congress to perform duties under the direction of the Secretary of War in relation to the various pension laws. In 1843 duties relating to the granting of military bounty lands were assigned to the Commissioner, and in 1849 his office was transferred to the Interior Department. The Bureau of Indian Affairs was established in 1824 and continued in the War Department until 1849, when it was transferred, with most of its records, to the newly created Department of the Interior.

Letters Sent

Many of the letters sent by the Secretary of War relate to the administration of Indian affairs and concern such subjects as the conduct of Indian wars and campaigns, the appointment of Indian agents, negotiations with Indian delegations in Washington, D.C., the making of treaties, atrocities committed by Indians and non-Indians, and intrusions by miners and others onto Indian reservations. The letters sent were maintained in several different series; those that have been microfilmed include M6, *Letters Sent by the Secretary of War Relating to Military Affairs, 1800–1889*; M127, *Letters Sent by the Secretary of War to the President, 1800–1863*; M370, *Miscellaneous Letters Sent by the Secretary of War, 1800–1809*; and M7, *Confidential and Unofficial Letters Sent by the Secretary of War, 1814–1847*. Available as a finding aid is M420, *Indexes to Letters Sent by the Secretary of War Relating to Military Affairs, 1871–1889*. A series of letters sent by the Secretary of War relating to Indian affairs, 1800–1824, is among the records of the Bureau of Indian Affairs.

Letters Received

The Secretary of War received letters and reports from officials of subordinate bureaus of the War Department, officials of other executive departments, Army officers and civilian agents in the field, Governors of States and Territories, the President, Members of Congress, and private persons. Many of the letters, particularly in the first several decades of the 19th century, relate to campaigns against Indians and Indian affairs in general. Included are letters concerning the enlistment and payment of bounties to Indian soldiers, mining permits in Indian territory, positions as Indian agents, the removal of miners and other intruders from Indian lands, investigations of atrocities committed by or against Indians, and reports from officers engaged in Indian campaigns and from officials of the Bureau of Indian Affairs. There are, for example, several long letters from William Henry Harrison and others concerning campaigns against the Indians on the Northwest frontier around Vincennes, including a 3-page transcript of the "Minutes of a Council held at Fort Wayne on the 21st Day of June 1805 by General Gibson and Colonel Vigo, present the Delawares, Eel River and Miamie Indians."

The major series of letters received by the Secretary of War have been reproduced as NARS microfilm publications, including M221, *Letters Received by the Secretary of War, Main Series, 1801–1870*; M492, *Letters Received by the Secretary of War, Irregular Series, 1861–1866*; M494, *Letters Received by the Secretary of War from the President, Executive Departments, and War Department Bureaus, 1862–1870*; and M222, *Letters Received by the Secretary of War, Unregistered Series, 1789–1861*. Indexes are reproduced as M495, *Indexes to Letters Received by the Secretary of War, 1861–1870*. The registers of letters received, containing abstracts of the letters, are available as M22, *Registers of Letters Received by the Office of the Secretary of War, Main Series, 1800–1870*; M491, *Registers of Letters Received by the Secretary of War, Irregular Series, 1861–1866*; and M493, *Registers of Letters Received by the Secretary of War from the President, Executive Departments, and War Department Bureaus, 1862–1870*. Many letters received by the Secretary of War relating to Indian affairs, 1800–23, are among the records of the Bureau of Indian Affairs, but they are registered in the main series of registers of the Office of the Secretary.

Reports

An 11-volume series of reports to the Congress from the Secretary of War, 1803–70 (available as M220) contains copies of letters and accompanying reports and inquiries. One report of particular interest is the 38-page "Extract from a journal of an expedition from San Diego, California, to the Rio Colorado from September 11 to December 11, 1849, by A. W. Whipple, Lieut., U.S. Topographical Engineers" (printed in *Reports of Explorations and Surveys to Ascertain the Most Practicable and Economical Route for a Railroad From the Mississippi River to the Pacific Ocean, Made Under the Direction of the Secretary of War* (H. Ex. Doc. 91, 33d Cong., 2d sess.)). The report describes Indian life in detail, including the behavior of Christian Indians, crops, living conditions, foods, and dress and lists the Indian language equivalents of common English words. One list, for example, gives the Yuma Indian equivalents of 250 common English expressions. A smaller series of *Reports for Use in Replies to Congressional Resolutions, 1827–1828* (2 vols.), includes extensive tables of expenditures by Indian agents and commissioners. The tables are arranged by name of Indian agent or commissioner, and they list the amount of money disbursed, the name of the person receiving the money, the reason for the expenditure, abstracts of provisions issued to Indian tribes, and miscellaneous remarks by the agent or commissioner.

Other Records

A volume reproduced as M1062, *Correspondence of the War Department Relating to Indian Affairs, Military Pensions, and Fortifications, 1791–1797*, includes copies of letters and messages sent by the Secretary of War concerning southern Indians, 1792; letters received from the Mohawk Indian chief Joseph Brant, 1792; letters from the U.S. agent to the Creek Indians, 1792; letters from Gov. William Blount of Tennessee relating in a large part to Creek and Cherokee hostilities, 1792; and letters from Maj. Gen. Anthony Wayne, commander of an expedition against northwestern Indians, 1794; and letters regarding other Indian-related subjects. The records have been published in the first volume of *American State Papers: Indian Affairs*.

RECORDS OF THE HEADQUARTERS OF THE ARMY
(RECORD GROUP 108)

An act of May 28, 1798 (1 Stat. 558), authorized the President to appoint a commander of the armies of the United States. Gen. George Washington served in that capacity until his death in 1799, and then there was a lapse in the position until the appointment of the second commanding general in 1821. From that time until the office was abolished in 1903, the Army had a commanding general, except for 1846–49 and March-July 1862. The records of Washington's term as commanding general were destroyed in the War Department fire of 1800, and thus the records of the Headquarters of the Army begin in 1821.

The Military Establishment generally was subordinate to the commanding general in matters regarding its military control. He was concerned with Indians through the issuance of instructions on military strategy and operations against them; the maintenance of order in towns, reservations, and frontier settlements; the protection of special exploring expeditions in the West; and the supply, inspection, and garrisons of military posts. The correspondence of the Headquarters of the Army includes communications to and from the Secretary of War, Members of Congress, chiefs of the War Department and other departmental bureaus, staff and line officers, military commanders in military departments and divisions, Governors of States and Territories, Indian agents, and private persons.

See Aloha South, comp., *Records of the Headquarters of the Army*, Inventory 1 (1970).

Letters Sent

Typical letters from the several series of letters, telegrams, and endorsements sent by Headquarters (approximately 100 volumes and unbound papers) discuss the raising of Indian troops, Indian scouts, and State troops to fight hostile Indians; the protection of the Santa Fe route and the Arkansas and Missouri frontiers from the Indians; and the removal of Indians from Wisconsin to Nebraska. Most of the letters sent are available as M857.

Letters Received

There are approximately 100 feet of letters and telegrams received, most of which were entered in 106 registers. Many letters entered in the registers of letters received, however, were forwarded to other offices for action, and thus are not now among the records of the Headquarters of the Army. Most of these forwarded letters are among the records of the Office of the Secretary of War or the Office of the Adjutant General.

Letters were received from Federal and State officials and from private persons on a wide variety of subjects concerning Indians. Included are applications for positions as sutlers and Indian agents and letters concerning the expulsion of miners from Indian lands, grievances against Indians, the transportation of Indians to reservations, the sale of whiskey to Indians, the protection of Indians from settlers and from other Indians, atrocities committed by Indians and Mexicans, the guarding of railroads, and requests for the establishment of military posts. Some of the best sources of information about Indians are reports, included in the letters received, concerning expeditions, inspections, and local disturbances. There is a journal-type description of the land and people from an 1831 expedition "for the purpose of exploring that part of the country comprised between the Eastern line of the Osage Reservation and the Arkansas River." A long inspection report, 1842, suggests detailed plans for the defense of the frontier and notes that "9/10 of our conflicts with the Indians . . . have arisen, either directly or indirectly, from the lawless intercourse which has been suffered to exist between them and our licensed and unlicensed traders, which has resulted in constant scenes of drunkenness and fraud . . ." and suggests "a cordon of posts separating the Indians from that class of white and colored people who respect no law."

Descriptive Volumes of Posts

A descriptive volume concerning military posts in the Departments of California and the Columbia, 1868, lists for each post the State or Territory, latitude and longitude, military district, garrison units, supply depot, and nearest roads, trails, rivers, lakes, mines, towns, and Indian tribes. At the end of the volume are tables of distances from military posts and towns west of the Mississippi and a brief list of hostile Indian tribes. Another descriptive volume for posts in the District of Texas, 1868, includes maps and drawings of the district and of each post described as well as a table of distances between posts and towns and a list of military units serving in the district.

RECORDS OF THE WAR DEPARTMENT GENERAL AND SPECIAL STAFFS (RECORD GROUP 165)

An act of February 14, 1903 (32 Stat. 830), provided for a War Department General Staff composed of officers detailed from the Army at large. The General Staff was established as a separate and distinct staff organization with supervision over most of the branches of the military service, both line and staff. It was under the direction of the Chief of Staff, who in turn acted under the direction of the President or the Secretary of War. The duties of the General Staff were to gather information and to prepare plans for the national defense and for the mobilization of the military forces in time of war, to investigate and report all questions affecting the efficiency of the Army and its state of preparation, and to render professional aid and assistance to the Secretary of War, general officers, and other senior commanders.

Among the correspondence of the Chief of Staff, 1907–18, are records (2 in.) relating to the incarceration of Apache Indians at Fort Sill, Okla., 1911–12 (files 6080, 7223, 7481, 7809, 7816, and 8493), and the return of these prisoners to Arizona and New Mexico, 1907–14 (files 934 and 8128); correspondence relating to proposals for the formation of Army units composed of Indians, 1911–17 (file 6623); and documents relating to the troubles with the Ute Indians in Utah, 1907 (files 1332, 1530, 1714, 1768, and 2809).   There are 43 photographs, most dating from the late 19th century, principally of individual chiefs, other Indians, and groups from several tribes.

RECORDS OF THE ADJUTANT GENERAL'S OFFICE, 1780's–1917 (RECORD GROUP 94)

The Office of the Adjutant General dates from 1775 when an Adjutant General was appointed by the Continental Congress. From the disbanding of the Army in 1783 until 1792, there was no permanent position of Adjutant General in the War Department. An act of March 5, 1792 (1 Stat. 241), created the position of adjutant, who was also to serve as an inspector. The dual functions of the office were continued in an act of March 3, 1813

(2 Stat. 819), which established separate Adjutant General's and Inspector General's Departments administered by one Adjutant and Inspector General. The full separation of the two offices dates from an act of March 2, 1821 (3 Stat. 615), which provided for an adjutant general and two inspectors-general.

Acting under the direction of the Secretary of War, the Adjutant General's Office was the administrative and recordkeeping agency of the War Department. It was charged with the command, discipline, and administration of the Military Establishment, including such duties as recording, authenticating, and communicating orders, instructions, and regulations issued by the Secretary of War; preparing and distributing commissions to Army officers; consolidating the general returns of the Army and Militia; and recruiting. In its recordkeeping capacity, it also acquired custody of many War Department records, including correspondence and reports submitted by Regular and Volunteer Army officers, records of discontinued commands, and noncurrent records of War Department bureaus. Most of the command and bureau records are in other record groups according to the agency that created them.

See Lucille H. Pendell and Elizabeth Bethel, comps., *Preliminary Inventory of the Records of the Adjutant General's Office*, PI 17 (1949).

Correspondence

Before 1900, the Adjutant General's Office maintained separate correspondence series consisting of copies of letters sent and files of incoming letters received. Incoming letters were abstracted and entered in registers from 1812 to 1889 and indexed by name and subject beginning in 1861. The registry system, however, is inconsistent and incomplete before 1816 and not of much use as a finding aid to correspondence before 1822. In addition, during the period from the Civil War to the end of the 19th century, various divisions were created within the Adjutant General's Office, each of which maintained its own correspondence and registry system. A general correspondence system was initiated in 1890, in which both incoming and outgoing letters were filed together. After that time, one consolidated name and subject index was maintained, which is more complete than the earlier volume indexes. Most of these records are available as NARS microfilm publications, including M565, *Letters Sent by the Office of the Adjutant General (Main Series), 1800–1890*; M566, *Letters Received by the Office of the Adjutant General, 1805–1821*; M567, *(Main Series) 1822–1860*; M619, *(Main Series) 1861–1870*; M666, *(Main Series) 1871–1880*; M689, *(Main Series) 1881–1889*; M725, *Indexes of Letters Received by the Office of the Adjutant General, Main Series, 1846, 1861–1889*; and M698, *Index to General Correspondence of the Adjutant General's Office, 1890–1917*.

The correspondence of the Adjutant General's Office provides perhaps the richest single source among War Department records for information concerning Indians and Indian-white relations. Researchers should consult it before searching other records, because material may be available here in the most convenient and comprehensive form. Beginning in the early 19th century, related documents pertaining to particular subjects were frequently placed in consolidated files, a practice that became increasingly prevalent after the Civil War and particularly in the general correspondence period after 1890. The consolidated files vary in size from several documents to many linear feet. While some of the data may be duplicated in records of lower level commands, a great deal more effort may be required to compile it from these sources. In addition, consolidated files often provide the best opportunity for obtaining a comprehensive view of all levels of Army participation in a given situation. Because the Adjutant General's Office was the final referral point for reports and correspondence, its files often contain material from all command levels—regimental and post commanders in the field, departmental and district commanders, and higher officials in the War Department.

In addition to letters and reports received, the correspondence files of the post-1890 period often contain useful information compiled by the Adjutant General's Office in answering requests pertaining to Indians. In some instances, older documents used to furnish information for the reply were filed in the general correspondence with other papers concerning the inquiry and were not returned to their original location. For example, Brig. Gen. James H. Carleton's report of November 22, 1863, relating to the removal of the Navajo Indians to the Bosque Redondo, New Mexico Territory, is now filed among the general correspondence rather than with the earlier letters received. Much of the information furnished relating to inquiries in this period, particularly those pertaining to the military service of individuals or organizations, is among the correspondence of the War Department's Record and Pension Office. In addition, papers originally received by one office quite commonly were transferred to the files of another. In one unusual instance, letters originally received by the Adjutant General's Office pertaining to the Mountain Meadows massacre of 1857 are now among the correspondence of the Record and Pension Office (R and P file 751395).

Some of the consolidated files pertaining to Indians among the letters received and general correspondence of the Adjutant General's Office have been listed below and described briefly. Some large consolidations relating only peripherally to Indians and many smaller consolidations have not been included. Also, many relevant letters and reports exist as single file items, each of which must be located by using correspondence indexes and registers. Through 1890 the letters sent complementing the letters received are in separate copybooks.

"Daisy," a White Mountain Apache. Apache society, like that of the Navajo, was matriarchal in nature. The two groups were so closely related that the word "Apache," meaning "enemy," was first applied by the Zuñi Indians to the Navajo. Record Group 165, Carter Collection

Acoma pueblo, N. Mex., photographed by Ansel Adams in 1936. 79-AAA-1

A group of Omaha Indians in cadet uniforms at the Carlisle School, ca. 1880. The U.S. Government operated the school from 1879 to 1918. The school's objective was the education of Indian children in "civilization." 75-IP-1-10

Chief Joseph of the Nez Percé. Joseph was one of the most formidable Indian strategists opposing the U. S. Army during the post-Civil War Indian wars. 111-82275

Painting of a Hidatsa (Crow) warrior in the costume of the dog dance, by Charles Bodmer, ca. 1833. Bodmer accompanied Prince Maximilian of Wied-Neuwied on a 3,000-mile journey to study the American Indian. 106-IN-202

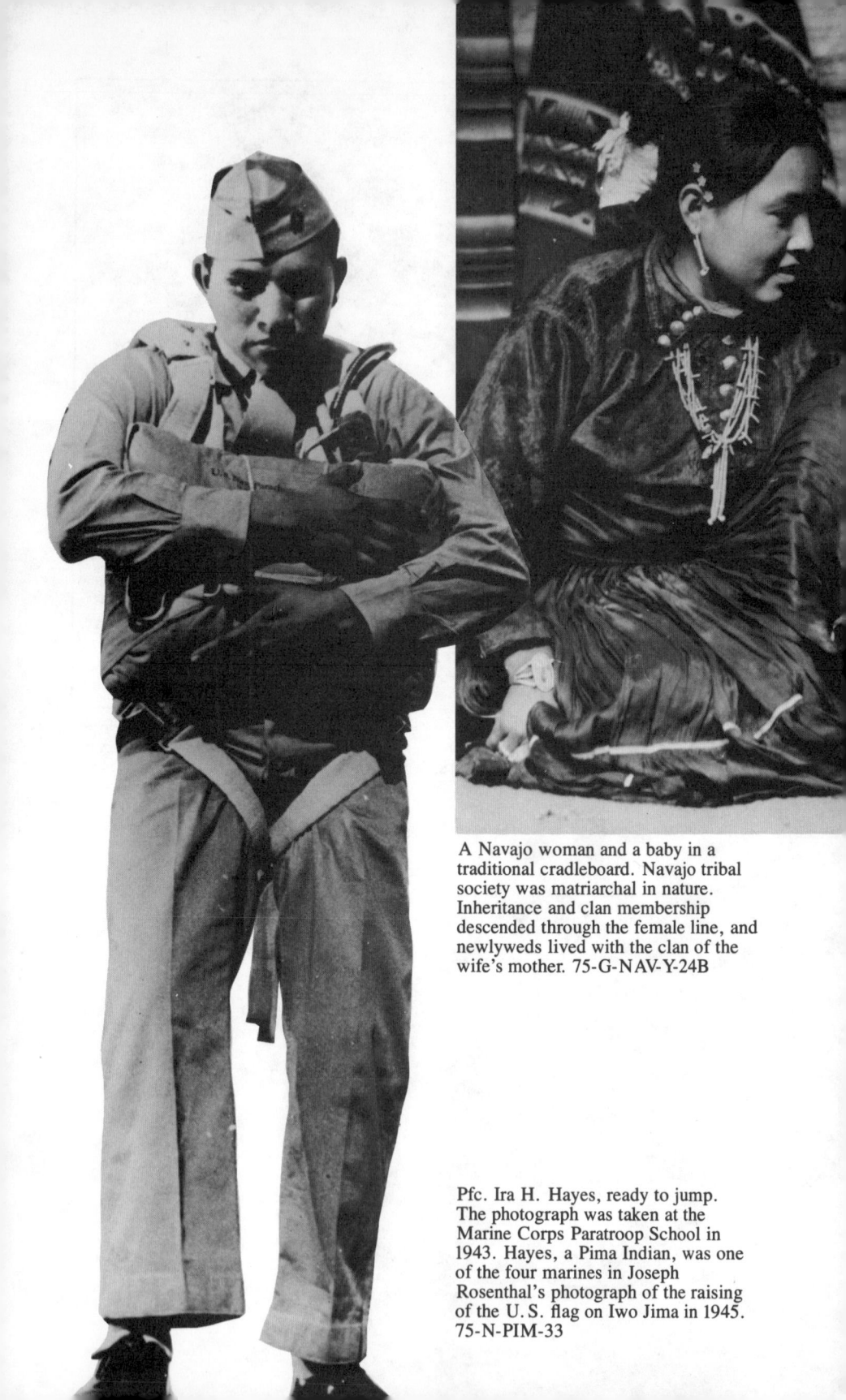

A Navajo woman and a baby in a
traditional cradleboard. Navajo tribal
society was matriarchal in nature.
Inheritance and clan membership
descended through the female line, and
newlyweds lived with the clan of the
wife's mother. 75-G-NAV-Y-24B

Pfc. Ira H. Hayes, ready to jump.
The photograph was taken at the
Marine Corps Paratroop School in
1943. Hayes, a Pima Indian, was one
of the four marines in Joseph
Rosenthal's photograph of the raising
of the U.S. flag on Iwo Jima in 1945.
75-N-PIM-33

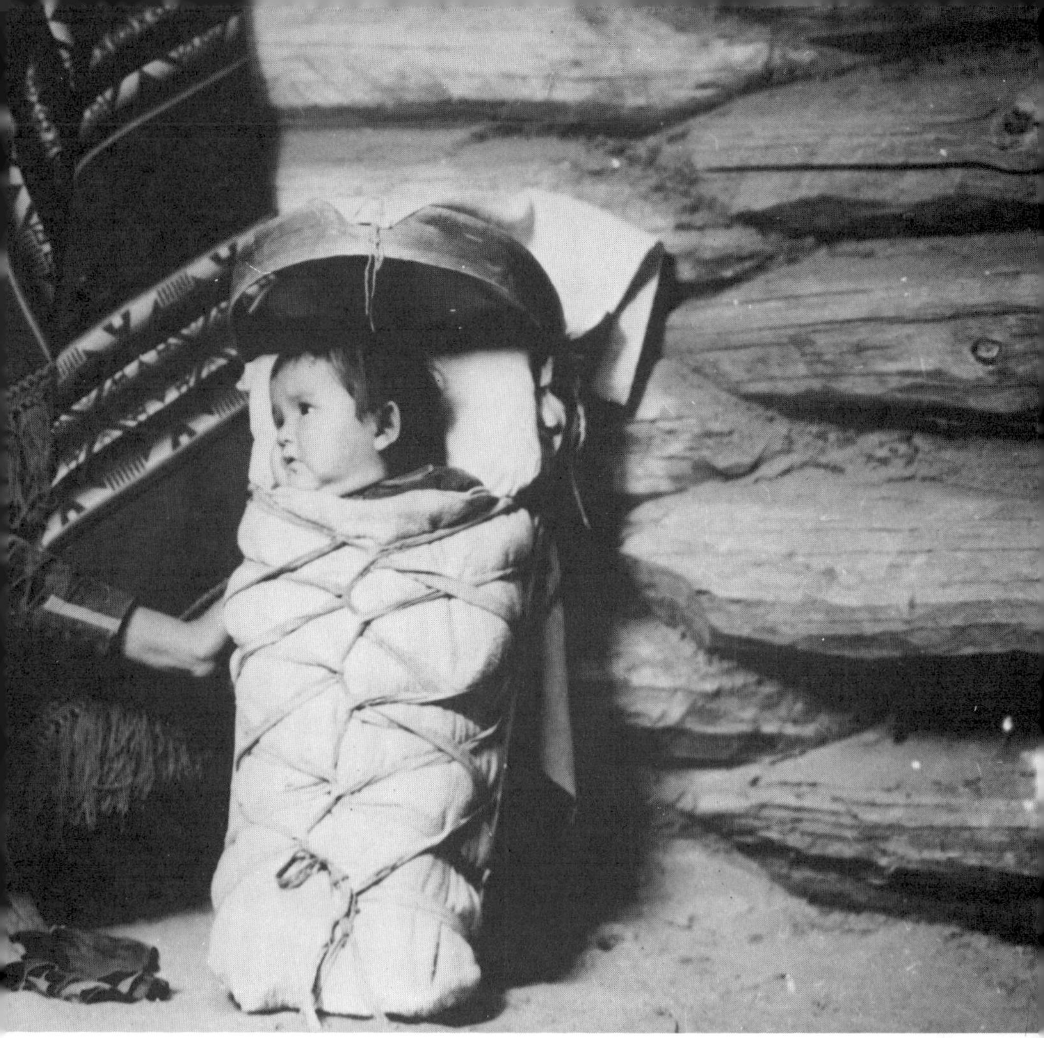

Fishermen from the Tulalip Agency, Wash.,
take a skate from the Swinomish tribal fishtrap, 1938.
75-N-TUL-14

Hopi snake dance, ritual of prayer for rain. Rain was invoked using snakes purified and carried in the priest's mouth, sprinkled with meal, and released to the four cardinal points of the compass. The dance is still a popular tourist attraction, though taking photographs of it has been forbidden since the early 20th century. 106-IN-268

A Zuñi pueblo, probably photographed by John Hillers in 1879. Hillers accompanied John Wesley Powell on his various geographic and geologic expeditions and later photographed various Indian pueblos and ruins for the Bureau of Ethnology. 106-IN-2384CQ

Overleaf: Natchez, Geronimo, and other Apache on their way into exile. After his surrender to the Army, Geronimo and some of his followers were imprisoned for a time in Florida. Here, Natchez (fourth from right, front row), Geronimo (third from right, front row), Geronimo's son (second from right, front row), and others rest from their train ride on the way to Florida. 106-BAE-2517A

A Flathead delegation and an interpreter photographed in Washington, D.C., by C. M. Bell, 1884. Such delegations visited Washington frequently throughout the 19th century. 106-INE-31

Navajo Indians shearing sheep. The Navajo were a pastoral tribe, unlike the Plains tribes, whose economy depended on the buffalo. 111-89583

An Indian family at a buffalo lodge. The family life of the Plains Indian, including the buffalo hide tepee, the curing of buffalo meat ("collops"), and the use of buffalo rope, is captured in this photograph of an Indian family at a buffalo lodge. The photograph was donated by Capt. R. G. Carter to the U.S. Army Signal Corps. 111-80663

A Yuma Apache camp, probably photographed in Arizona in the 1880's. The photograph was presented to the U.S. Army Signal corps by Lt. Gen. Nelson A. Miles, whose military reputation was based in part on his campaigns against warriors of the Apache tribes, including Geronimo. 111-85745

The Seminole chief Osceola, painted by George
Catlin, ca. 1837. Osceola led his tribe in armed
resistance against the U.S. Army in the second
Seminole war and was finally captured by the
Army while negotiating under a flag of truce in
1837. 111-SC-93123

Geronimo and his family in their fields. In contrast to his
early resistance to white ways, Geronimo later embraced
them, riding in automobiles and attending President
Theodore Roosevelt's inauguration in 1905. 111-90639

Drawing entitled "Blackfeet Indians on Horseback." 111-92842

Indian camp at the Pine Ridge Agency, S. Dak., Jan. 17, 1891, photographed soon after the Battle of Wounded Knee (Dec. 20, 1890). 111-99687

Eskimo mother and child, photographed at Nome, Alaska, ca. 1915, by H. G. Kaiser. 126-ARA-2-235

Three Marine Corps reservists, photographed at Camp Lejeune, N.C., Oct. 16, 1943. From left to right: Minnie Spotted Wolf (Blackfoot), Celia Mix (Potawatomi), and Viola Eastman (Chippewa). 208-NS-4350-2

SELECTED CONSOLIDATED FILES PERTAINING TO INDIANS FROM THE LETTERS RECEIVED BY THE OFFICE OF THE ADJUTANT GENERAL, "MAIN SERIES," 1821–89, NARS MICROFILM PUBLICATIONS M567, M619, M666, M689

M567—LETTERS RECEIVED, 1822–1860

File Number	Roll Number	File Description
14 S 1824	12	Correspondence relating to Col. Henry Leavenworth's expedition against the Arikara Indians in 1823.
104 A 1832	66	Copies of orders and communications issued by Brig. Gen. Henry Atkinson to the Army of the Frontier in connection with the Black Hawk war. See also file 105 A 1832 on the same roll.
234 T 1839	197	Report of Gen. Zachary Taylor relating to operations in Florida, from the opening of the campaign in the fall of 1838 to May 1839, with enclosures.
69 B 1840	202	Series of resolutions and related papers adopted by the General Assembly of the State of Missouri relating to the conduct of the Missouri Volunteers during the Florida campaign of 1837–38 against the Seminole Indians.
26 W 1842	260	Reports of Gen. W. J. Worth and other officers relating to the operations of the Army in Florida, October–December 1841.
478 H 1853	483	Reports relating to the Indians living on the west coast, 1853.
216 R 1856	546	Correspondence relating to the massacre of Lt. John L. Grattan and 20 soldiers near Fort Laramie on August 19, 1854.
270 P 1858	586	Records relating to an Indian war in Washington Territory and to treaties of peace signed with the Indians, 1858.
83 I 1859	603	Copy of a communication from the Postmaster General and correspondence relating to attacks on the overland mail route to Santa Fe by the Kiowa Indians, 1859.

M619—LETTERS RECEIVED, 1861–1870

File Number	Roll Number	File Description
87 N 1864	283	Communications relating to the Navajo campaign and affairs in the Department of New Mexico, August 1863–January 1864.
255 N 1864	285	Report, with enclosures, by a board of officers appointed to investigate the complaints of Charles Poston, Superintendent of Indian Affairs for Arizona Territory, against certain Army officers in the District of Western Arizona, 1864.
280 N 1864	286	Papers relating to the procurement and issuance of commissary stores for captive Navajo Indians in the Department of New Mexico, 1864. See also file 2143 S 1865 on roll 417.
145 I 1865	367	Papers relating to the investigation of charges made against Maj. Gen. Alfred Sully and his administration of Indian affairs on the upper Missouri River, 1865.
5 I 1866	483	Papers relating to the 1862 Sioux uprising in Minnesota, 1862–1916.
91 I 1866	484	Papers relating to the confinement of the Navajo Indians on the Bosque Redondo Reservation, New Mexico Territory, and to the transfer of their custody from the War Department to the Department of the Interior, 1866–67.
102 M 1867	560	Papers relating to the Fetterman massacre near Fort Phil Kearny, Dakota Territory, on December 21, 1866.
223 M 1867	561	Papers relating to the relocation of the Navajo Indians on a military reservation at the Bosque Redondo, New Mexico Territory, 1863–67. Some of the papers relate to the cost of feeding the Navajo Indians during this period.
590 M 1867	563	Reports of the campaigns of Gen. Winfield S. Hancock and Col. George A. Custer against the Sioux and the Cheyenne Indians, March–May 1867.

File Number	Roll Number	File Description
		See also files 523 M 1867 on roll 562 and 1093 M 1867 on roll 565.
625 P 1867	573	Correspondence relating to unratified treaties made with the Apache Indians by Lt. Col. Guido Ilges, 14th Infantry, 1866–67.
798 P 1867	574	Report of Lt. Col. Robert N. Scott concerning the Indian tribes living near the boundary between British Columbia and Alaska, November 12, 1867.
42 I 1868	629	Correspondence relating to the implementation of the Medicine Lodge treaties with the Kiowa, Kiowa-Apache, Comanche, Cheyenne, and Arapaho Indians, July–September 1868.
807 M 1868	639	Report of Lt. Gen. William T. Sherman stating the reasons for the removal of the Navajo Indians from the Bosque Redondo Reservation, New Mexico Territory, June 24, 1868.
1275 M 1868	642	Reports relating to Indian tribes (Kickapoo, Lipan, and Mescalero Apache) inhabiting the territory of Mexico adjacent to the United States, 1868–69.
1285 M 1868	642	Papers relating to the engagement on the Arickaree Fork of the Republican River, Kansas, between scouts under Maj. George A. Forsyth and a band of Sioux and Cheyenne Indians, September 17–20, 1868.
523 P 1868	650	Reports of Capt. Charles A. Whittier and Lt. Wager Barnet concerning military posts, settlements, and Indians in Arizona Territory and conditions in Sonora, Mexico, June 1868.
504 R 1868	656	Reports of expenditures made by War Department bureaus and commands in suppressing Indian hostilities during the years 1866 to 1868.
645 W 1868	671	Papers relating to the cost of providing subsistence stores for certain bands of Ute and Apache Indians in the Department of New Mexico, 1866–68.

File Number	Roll Number	File Description
106 I 1869	711	Papers relating to the military expedition against the Piegan Indians and to other matters concerning Indians in Montana Territory, 1869–70.
207 M 1869	718	Reports of minor clashes with Kiowa and Pawnee Indians in western Kansas, January–April 1869.
703 M 1869	722	Correspondence relating to policy in regard to Indians who refused to go on reservations, May–August 1869.
942 M 1869	724	Reports by Maj. Alexander Moore, 38th Infantry, of an expedition against the Apache Indians, April–May 1869.
925 P 1869	737	Report of Bvt. Col. Reuben F. Bernard relating to the engagement between troops of the 1st and 8th Regiments, Cavalry, and Chiricahua Apache at Chiricahua Pass, Arizona Territory, on October 20, 1869. For other reports of actions against the Apache at this time, see file 841 P 1869 on the same roll.
65 I 1870	791	Papers relating to the claim of Yankton Indians for services as scouts in 1864 under Gen. Alfred Sully, 1870–92.
120 I 1870	792	Papers relating to the removal of intruders from lands belonging to the Cherokee Nation in the Indian Territory, 1870–71.
186 I 1870	792	Papers relating to the removal of trespassers from the Miami Indian Reservation in Kansas, 1870.
488 M 1870	799–800	Papers relating to the return of the Kickapoo and the Seminole (Negro) Indians from Mexico to the United States, 1870–85.
98 P 1870	807	Reports relating to a proposal to establish a reservation for the Apache Indians in the White Mountains area of Arizona Territory, November 1869–March 1870.
507 P 1870	808	Reports of operations against the Apache Indians in the Department of Arizona, April–June 1870.

File Number	Roll Number	File Description
102 R 1870	812	Copies of report by Generals Sheridan and Custer and by other officers relating to activities against the Indians in the Military Division of the Missouri, 1868–69. For 1870 reports of Indian matters in the division, see file 786 M 1870 on roll 802.

M666—LETTERS RECEIVED, 1871–1880

File Number	Roll Number	File Description
113 AGO 1871	2	Correspondence relating to the provision of food and ammunition for hunting to nearly 3,000 starving Indians of the Arapaho, Cheyenne, and Sioux tribes under Chief Red Cloud at Fort Laramie, Wyoming Territory, 1871–72.
557 AGO 1871	4	Report by Brig. Gen. John Pope, commanding the Department of the Missouri, of a possible war with the Cheyenne and Arapaho Indians in the spring of 1871. Included is correspondence relating to conditions at the Cheyenne and Arapaho Agency and to the agent's defense of his policies against charges by the military officers of inefficient administration.
1305 AGO 1871	10	Correspondence relating to the arrest of Kiowa Chiefs Satanta, Satank, and Big Tree, who were charged with attacking a corn train of 12 wagons. The arrest was made by troops under Gen. William T. Sherman at Fort Sill, Indian Territory, May–June 1871.
1339 AGO 1871	10	Correspondence relating to the request of financier Jay Cooke that 800 to 1,000 troops be sent to Dakota and Montana Territories to protect the Northern Pacific Railroad engineer–surveying parties, 1871.
1839 AGO 1871	15	Correspondence relating to the massacre of 23 Apache Indians at Camp Grant, Arizona Territory, on April 30, 1871, by a party of citizens from Tucson.

File Number	Roll Number	File Description
2019 AGO 1871	16	Correspondence relating to activities of the Santee, Yankton, and other Sioux Indians in 1871 and 1872 in various locations (including the settlement on the Milk River, Montana Territory), and to the attack on Gallatin Valley, Montana Territory, by Sioux tribes from the Big Horn area.
2418 AGO 1871	20–22	Papers relating to the war with the Modoc Indians in northern California, 1871–73.
2465 AGO 1871	24	Correspondence relating to the selection by Vincent Colyer of the Board of Indian Commissioners of sites for Apache Indian reservations at Tularosa Valley and White Mountain, New Mexico Territory, and at Camp Grant and Camp Verde, Arizona Territory, 1871–72. Included is the order by Gen. George Crook that the Apache move onto the reservations by February 15, 1872, or be considered hostile.
2564 AGO 1871	25	Correspondence relating to recommendations that the military posts at Cheyenne River, Grand River, Lower Brulé, and Whetstone Agencies in Dakota Territory be moved or discontinued, April 1872.
3314 AGO 1871	32	Correspondence relating to requests for the establishment of a military post at Beaver City in southern Utah, 1871–72. Included is information relating to the Mormons and the Mountain Meadows massacre in 1857.
3971 AGO 1871	37	Correspondence relating to the successful removal of intruders from lands set aside for the Osage and Cherokee Indians in Kansas, November 1871–May 1872.
3996 AGO 1871	37	Correspondence pertaining to a letter from the Superintendent of Indian Affairs for Montana regarding illicit trading with the Indians, 1871–72.

File Number	Roll Number	File Description
1119 AGO 1872	55	Correspondence relating to the proposed establishment of temporary posts along the Texas frontier to protect U.S. citizens against raiders from Mexico, 1872–73 ("Mexican Border Papers").
1388 AGO 1872	58	Correspondence relating to reports by William H. Miller, subagent of the Whetstone Agency, Sioux Indian Reservation, Dakota Territory, that the commander of the agency refused to provide a guard to protect property under the charge of the agent, 1872.
1582 AGO 1872	60	Correspondence relating to raids by Comanche and Kiowa Indians in Texas, 1872–73 (including the Kiowa demand for the release of Chiefs Satanta and Big Tree), and to the scouting expedition under Col. Ranald S. MacKenzie to the Brazos River, June–September 1872.
1603 AGO 1872	61	Correspondence relating to the attack on a Miniconjou Sioux war party by Capt. Charles Meinhold's Company of the 3d Cavalry on the South Fork of Loup River, Nebraska, and to the subsequent award of the Medal of Honor to three members of the company and to William F. ("Buffalo Bill") Cody, who accompanied the party as a guide, 1872.
2770 AGO 1872	73	Correspondence relating to Ute Indians who had left their agencies at Uintah, Utah Territory, and White River, Colorado Territory, and were congregating in the San Pete Valley. The correspondence also deals with the suspected influence of Brigham Young and the Mormons in inducing the Indians off the reservations and with military efforts towards securing their return.
3323 AGO 1872	80	Correspondence relating to the attack on the escort party of the surveyors of the Northern Pacific Railroad by Arapaho, Cheyenne, and Sioux warriors on

File Number	Roll Number	File Description
		August 14, 1872, at the mouth of Pryor's River in the Yellowstone Valley. Included is a journal kept by Maj. John W. Barlow relating to the escort of the surveying party, July 27–October 1, 1872.
3512 AGO 1872	81	Correspondence and reports of Col. David S. Stanley relating to his escort of Northern Pacific Railroad engineers surveying the proposed railroad route from Heart River, Dakota Territory, to the mouth of Powder River, 1872. For additional reports by Colonel Stanley, see file 3159 AGO 1873 on roll 120.
3699 AGO 1872	83	Correspondence relating to events at the Red Cloud Agency, including Chief Red Cloud's refusal to move to White River and the capture by troops from Fort Laramie of 450 Indian ponies grazing illegally on the south side of the Platte River on the Fort Laramie Military Reservation, 1872.
4148 AGO 1872	86	Papers relating to the attack by troops under Col. Ranald S. MacKenzie on a village of about 200 Comanche Indians near McClellan Creek, Tex., on September 29, 1873.
5103 AGO 1872	95	Correspondence relating to the discovery of valuable mines on the Ute Reservation in Colorado, the extension of the deadline for the removal of intruders on the reservation, and a dispute over pasturage between ranchers and a band of Ute Indians near Spanish Peaks, 1872–73.
5147 AGO 1872	95	Correspondence relating to the issuance of rations to Ocheo, leader of a band of Paiute Indians, and to the refusal of the Paiute to return to Yainax, Oreg., 1872–73. For additional correspondence relating to the Paiute, see files 3313 AGO 1873 on roll 121 and 7111 AGO 1879 on roll 536.

File Number	Roll Number	File Description
5176 AGO 1872	96	Correspondence relating to the scouting expedition of Lt. Charles Morton in Arizona Territory, June 6–19, 1872, during which the troops fought four battles with a band of Tonto Apache, and to the subsequent recommendation of the men on the march for the Medal of Honor, 1872–76.
1433 AGO 1873	108	Correspondence pertaining to a communication from Col. J. Reynolds, 3d Cavalry, commanding at Fort McPherson, Nebr., regarding a talk held with Chiefs No Flesh and Pawnee Killer, 1873.
1780 AGO 1873	110	Correspondence pertaining to Clarke and Bill, merchants at James River Crossing, Minn., who were involved in the liquor trade with the Indians and complained against their arrest and the seizure of their stock, 1873.
2933 AGO 1873	118	Correspondence and a report of proceedings of a board of investigation relating to the murder of Lt. Jacob Almy by Indians in May 1873 at the San Carlos Agency.
3326 AGO 1873	122	Correspondence pertaining to supplies delivered to Army officers to issue to Indians at Camps Apache and Beale's Springs and at Mojave Reservation in Arizona Territory, 1873–76
3383 AGO 1873	123	Correspondence relating to the agreement with Cochise, chief of the Chiricahua Apache, negotiated by Gen. Oliver O. Howard and to Gen. George Crook's criticism of the agreement and his request to be allowed to subdue Cochise with force, 1873–74.
4028 AGO 1873	126	Correspondence relating to Cheyenne raids in the territory between the Kansas Pacific Railroad and the northern frontier of Texas, 1873.
4477 AGO 1873	130	Correspondence relating to plundering by the Mescalero Apache Indians in

File Number	Roll Number	File Description
		southern New Mexico and to the attack by Capt. George W. Chilson's troops on a party of Mescalero Apache at the western base of the Guadalupe Mountains, New Mexico Territory, 1873.
4603 AGO 1873	131	Correspondence relating to a Department of Justice opinion categorizing Alaska as Indian country and stating that spirituous liquor could not be introduced there without an authorizing order from the War Department, 1873–75.
4667 AGO 1873	132	Correspondence relating to the proposal by the licensed Indian trader at Fort Benton, Montana Territory, that Indians be permitted to trade there, 1873–74.
4746 AGO 1873	133	Correspondence relating to the removal of nearly 1,000 Winnebago Indians from Wisconsin to Nebraska, December 1873–January 1874.
554 AGO 1874	142	Papers relating to requests for military aid to quell riots and murders caused by cattle herders and Indians in Lincoln County, New Mexico Territory, 1874. For more information on the Lincoln County war, see file 1405 AGO 1878 on rolls 397–398.
563 AGO 1874	143	Correspondence relating to increased Sioux Indian activities in the Department of the Platte, 1874, including the murder of Lt. Levi H. Robinson near Laramie Peak, Wyoming Territory, and to the request for the establishment of a military post to protect the Red Cloud and Whetstone Agencies.
1224 AGO 1874	147	Correspondence relating to disturbances at the Standing Rock Indian Agency, Dakota Territory, including the arrest of Chief Rain-in-the-Face of the Hunkpapa band of Sioux for the murder of two men on Col. David S. Stanley's Yellowstone expedition, and to the request for

File Number	Roll Number	File Description
		troops to enforce the enrollment of Indians at the agency, 1874.
1848 AGO 1874	153	Correspondence relating to the Indian situation at Camp Gaston, Calif., and the Hoopa Valley Reservation, 1874.
2815 AGO 1874	159–164	Papers relating to the 1874–75 campaign against Arapaho, Cheyenne, Comanche, and Kiowa bands in Indian Territory (the Red River war).
3198 AGO 1874	167	Correspondence pertaining to inspections by military officers of flour for the Indian Service at Milk River and Blackfeet Agencies, Montana Territory, Fort Berthold, Dakota Territory, 1874–75.
5009 AGO 1874	181	Correspondence relating to reports that miners had been working in the Black Hills country of the Sioux Indian Reservation, 1874–75.
56 AGO 1875	185	Correspondence relating to permission given by the Indian agent at Wichita Agency, Indian Territory, for his charges to go north to hunt and to the protest lodged by Lt. Col. T. H. Neill, the commanding officer at Cheyenne River Agency, Dakota Territory, 1875.
546–AGO 1875	187	Correspondence pertaining to military operations at Fort Stanton, New Mexico Territory, and to the Indians of that reservation, 1875.
1452 AGO 1875	193	Correspondence relating to the appointment of the military commandant as the Indian agent for Alaska and to his imposition of restrictions on trade, 1875–76. Also included is Gen. Oliver O. Howard's report of a tour in Alaska, June 1875.
1504 AGO 1875	194	Correspondence relating to the ouster of James E. Roberts as Indian agent at Fort Apache, Arizona Territory, and the removal of the Apache Indians from there to the San Carlos Indian Agency by San Carlos Agent John P. Clum, 1875–76.

File Number	Roll Number	File Description
1653 AGO 1875	195–211	Papers relating to raids into Texas made between 1875 and 1884 by parties of Indians and Mexicans from the Mexican side of the Rio Grande ("Mexican Border Troubles").
3517 AGO 1875	221	Correspondence relating to requests for military protection of the Crow Indian Agency, Montana Territory, from Sioux attacks, 1875. Also included is a report by Capt. George L. Tyler of a fight between Crow, Grosventre, and Nez Percé Indians and the 1,200 to 1,500 Sioux Indians below the mouth of the Big Horn River in June 1875.
3538 AGO 1875	220	Correspondence relating to a letter of the Commissioner of Indian Affairs recommending that a small guard be furnished for duty at Cimarron Agency, New Mexico Territory, to prevent depredations by Indians in that vicinity, 1875.
3945 AGO 1875	224	Correspondence relating to a communication from the agent for the Cherokee Nation, Indian Territory, stating that hostile feelings existed between the rival Indian factions, 1875.
4228 AGO 1875	225	Correspondence relating to charges against Capt. John S. Poland, commander of the U.S. Military Station at Standing Rock Indian Agency, Dakota Territory, of arbitrary action in assuming control of trading and other activities of the Indians and businessmen at the agency, 1875–76.
4354 AGO 1875	226	Correspondence relating to the removal of agent William F. M. Arny of the Navajo Indian Agency, Fort Defiance, Arizona Territory, after a council of the principal chiefs of the Navajo Nation at Fort Wingate, New Mexico Territory, in July 1875 and to the appointment of Alexander G. Irvine as his successor, 1875–76.

File Number	Roll Number	File Description
4608 AGO 1875	227	Correspondence relating to telegrams from Col. Ranald MacKenzie, commander at Fort Sill, Indian Territory, accusing the Interior Department of failing to furnish supplies to the Indians, 1875.
4720 AGO 1875	228	Correspondence pertaining to a threatened general Indian outbreak in eastern Nevada and measures to prevent it, 1875.
5650 AGO 1875	233	Correspondence relating to the fight between Company H, 5th Cavalry, and a band of 60 warriors of the Northern Arapaho south of the buffalo station on the Kansas Pacific Railway on October 28, 1875.
6160 AGO 1875	238	Papers relating to military expeditions against the Sioux Indians in the Big Horn, Powder River, and Yellowstone River areas, November 1875–July 1876.
265 AGO 1876	247	Correspondence relating to proposals to sell liquor in the Cherokee Nation, Indian Territory, 1876–78.
1929 AGO 1876	259	Correspondence relating to the total number of Indian scouts authorized to be employed by the Army and to requests for permission to enlist scouts in various departments, 1876–78.
2440 AGO 1876	264	Papers relating to Gen. George Crook's charge that Col. Joseph J. Reynolds and Capt. Alexander Moore failed to carry out orders in an attack on the village of Chief Crazy Horse near Powder River, Montana Territory, in March 1876, and the subsequent general courts-martial of Reynolds and Moore.
2576 AGO 1876	265	Correspondence relating to the removal of the Chiricahua Apache Indians to the San Carlos Indian Agency, Arizona Territory, 1876–77.
3570 AGO 1876	271	Correspondence relating to Gen. George Crook's battle with the Sioux and Cheyenne Indians under Chief Crazy Horse

File Number	Roll Number	File Description
		at Rosebud Creek, Montana Territory, June 1876.
3597 AGO 1876	271	Correspondence relating to the claim of Young Joseph and his band of Nez Percé Indians to the Wallowa Valley, Oreg.; the appointment of a commission to negotiate with Young Joseph; and the removal of the Indians to the reservation at Boise, Idaho Territory, 1876–77.
3770 AGO 1876	273	Papers relating to the defeat of Gen. George A. Custer and his whole command by Sitting Bull's band of Sioux Indians in the battle on the Little Big Horn River, Montana Territory, June 25–26, 1876.
3820 AGO 1876	274	Correspondence pertaining to the offer of volunteer military service by Montana citizens in response to the Custer defeat, 1876.
4163 AGO 1876	277–292	Papers relating to military operations in the Departments of the Platte and Dakota against the Sioux Indians ("Sioux War Papers"), 1876–96.
4408 AGO 1876	294	Correspondence relating to the proposed prohibition of the sale of arms and ammunition to Indians by traders, 1876–78.
1281 AGO 1877	321	Correspondence pertaining to the message of the Governor of Arizona concerning Indian depredations and his request for the removal of the commanding general of the Department of Arizona, 1877.
1322 AGO 1877	322	Correspondence, reports of surveys, and maps of the three wagon roads through the Sioux Reservation in Dakota Territory provided for by the agreement in 1876 with the Sioux. The three routes were from Bismarck to Deadwood City, from Fort Pierre to Deadwood City, and from Fort Niobrara, Nebr., to Custer City.

File Number	Roll Number	File Description
1469 AGO 1877	323	Correspondence relating to timber cutting by whites on the Sioux Reservations in Dakota Territory, 1877–80.
1927 AGO 1877	326	Correspondence relating to the arrest and removal of Geronimo's band of renegade Chiricahua Apache Indians from Ojo Caliente, New Mexico Territory, to the San Carlos Indian Agency, Arizona Territory, 1877.
2526 AGO 1877	330	Correspondence relating to the appointment of military officers to witness deliveries by contractors at Indian agencies. Also included are reports of the appointed officers, 1877.
3369 AGO 1877	335	Correspondence pertaining to a report from the commanding officer at Fort Reno, Wyoming Territory, alleging a deficiency of Indian supplies at the Cheyenne and Arapaho Agency and starvation among the Indians, 1876–78.
3464 AGO 1877	336–340	Correspondence relating to the war with the Nez Percé Indians in 1877, including the battle at Bear Paw Mountain, Montana Territory.
3897 AGO 1877	345	Correspondence relating to intruders on the Klamath Indian Reservation, Oreg., and the possible necessity of removing the Indians, 1877–86.
4966 AGO 1877	361	Correspondence pertaining to troop operations commanded by Lt. J. W. Summerhayes to recover stock from Pima Indians in Arizona and to charges by Gen. A. V. Kautz, commanding the Department of Arizona, that the agent for the Pima, Maricopa, and Papago tribes was inattentive to his responsibilities.
4976 AGO 1877	362	Correspondence relating to the Indians in the area of Fort Benton, Montana Territory, including such matters as the sustenance of a band of Assiniboin and a band of Grosventre Indians and the ex-

File Number	Roll Number	File Description
		pulsion of a group of Canadian mixed-blood Indians who had settled on the Milk River, 1877–79.
5705 AGO 1877	366	Correspondence relating to military operations against the Warm Springs Indians who fled from the San Carlos Indian Agency, Arizona Territory, 1877–79.
7316 AGO 1877	377–379	Correspondence relating to the war with the Bannock Indians and associated tribes, the Paiute, Klamath, and Umatilla, 1877–79.
7441 AGO 1877	381	Correspondence relating to requests for a military post in the Black Hills to protect settlers and the subsequent selection of a site for a military reservation at Bear Butte, Dakota Territory, 1877–78.
125 AGO 1878	389	Correspondence and reports relating to the inspection of beef cattle at the Kiowa and Comanche Agency, Indian Territory, 1878.
710 AGO 1878	392	Correspondence pertaining to the detailing of Army officers as acting Indian agents at the Yankton, Crow Creek, Lower Brulé, and Cheyenne River Agencies, Dakota Territory, 1878–84.
1036 AGO 1878	394	Correspondence pertaining to affairs at Standing Rock Agency, Dakota Territory, including the butchering of hogs and the cutting of timber, 1878.
1089 AGO 1878	395	Correspondence relating to the Ute Indians of Colorado and to the November 1878 agreement under which they relinquished their rights to 12 million acres of land.
1405 AGO 1878	397–398	Papers relating to the use of U.S. troops to suppress lawlessness in Lincoln County, New Mexico Territory ("Lincoln County War"), 1878–81. For earlier correspondence, see file 554 AGO 1874 on roll 142.
1499 AGO 1878	400	Correspondence and claims for com-

File Number	Roll Number	File Description
		pensation, 1878–96, for losses sustained during the Nez Percé Indian War in Idaho in the summer of 1877.
1620 AGO 1878	401	Correspondence concerning the removal of Ute and Apache Indians from the Cimarron Agency, New Mexico Territory, to the Southern Ute Agency, Colo., and the Mescalero Agency, New Mexico Territory, 1878.
3042 AGO 1878	406	Correspondence about Maj. Gen. Philip H. Sheridan's contention that Indian raids along the Rio Grande were committed by Indians from the Fort Stanton Reservation, New Mexico Territory, and his proposal to give the Army exclusive control over them, 1878.
3930 AGO 1878	414	Correspondence pertaining to a complaint by Col. Elias C. Boudinot, Cherokee Nation, Indian Territory, against the seizure of his hotel by the Fort Gibson post trader and his request for War Department intervention on his behalf, 1878–84.
4613 AGO 1878	419	Reports from division and department commanders to the Joint Congressional Committee on the Indian Bureau Transfer, showing the number of troops at Indian agencies in each division or department and the estimated cost for maintaining these troops, 1878.
5641 AGO 1878	423	Correspondence relating to the September 1878 consolidation of the Kiowa and Comanche Indian Agency with the Wichita Agency, Indian Territory, and to subsequent reports of dissatisfaction and unrest, 1878, 1879, and 1881.
5900 AGO 1878	425	Correspondence relating to the request of the Commissioner of Indian Affairs for 15 to 20 cavalrymen to be stationed at Tularosa, New Mexico Territory, to deal with Indian stragglers and to stop the liquor traffic in the vicinity, 1878.

File Number	Roll Number	File Description
6310 AGO 1878	427	Correspondence relating to the arrest of Chief Moses and the attempts to relocate his band of Indians on the Yakima Reservation, 1878–79.
6470 AGO 1878	428–430	Papers relating to military operations against the Northern Cheyenne, 1878–79. Included is a report by a board of officers on the arrest and confinement of a number of Cheyenne Indians in the vicinity of Fort Robinson, Nebr.
8705 AGO 1878	449	Correspondence relating to the confinement of nearly 150 Northern Cheyenne at Fort Robinson, Nebr., their refusal to return to the Indian Territory, their escape from the fort, and the attack by Capt. Henry W. Wessell's Company, 1878–79.
71 AGO 1879	454	Papers pertaining to the inspection of flour and beef cattle at the Kiowa and Comanche Agency, Indian Territory, 1879.
2653 AGO 1879	471–488	Papers relating to the intrusion by unauthorized persons or "boomers" into Indian Territory, including Oklahoma, the Cherokee Outlet, and the part of the Territory known as Greer County, Tex., 1879–93.
3417 AGO 1879	493	Correspondence relating to a request by a U.S. marshal for military assistance in arresting white outlaws in the Choctaw Nation, Indian Territory, 1879.
4278 AGO 1879	513–517	Papers relating to the Ute Indian uprising of 1879 at the White River Agency, Colo., and the subsequent military operations and reprisals, 1879–83.
5141 AGO 1879	522	Correspondence relating to the 1879 war with the bands of Indians in central Idaho known as the Sheepeaters ("Sheepeaters' War").
6058 AGO 1879	526–528	Papers relating to military operations against Chief Victorio's band of Mescalero Apache in southern New Mexico,

File Number	Roll Number	File Description
		1879–81 and one letter dated March 13, 1886.
7076 AGO 1879	535	Correspondence relating to charges of illegal trading with Indians against the post trader at Fort Yates, Dakota Territory, 1879–81.
7111 AGO 1879	536	Correspondence pertaining to complaints by citizens and miners of harassment by roving Paiute bands, 1878–80.
2608 AGO 1880	560	Correspondence relating to dissatisfaction among Indians of the Navajo Agency, Arizona Territory, with their agent, Galen Eastman; the assumption of military control by Capt. Frank T. Bennett, 9th U.S. Cavalry, both there and at Moqui Pueblo Agency; and the eventual reassignment of both agencies to Eastman, 1880.
3153 AGO 1880	565	Correspondence pertaining to complaints of the Sioux Indians at Standing Rock Agency, Dakota Territory, about the number of troops at the reservation, the amount of timber cut there, and the cattle still due them for the seizure of their ponies by the Army, 1880–83.
3619 AGO 1880	568	Correspondence relating to unauthorized white settlement on the Sioux Reservation at Fort Pierre, Dakota Territory, 1880.

M689—LETTERS RECEIVED, 1881–1889

File Number	Roll Number	File Description
1504 AGO 1881	9	Papers relating to the mortal wounding of a Navajo Indian in Farmington, New Mexico Territory, by Frank Meyers and the subsequent investigation by Army officers that disclosed an absence of law and order in the vicinity because of the outlaw bands, January–May 1881.
1528 AGO 1881	9	Correspondence pertaining to important mines discovered at Cataract Creek, Arizona Territory, on the Havasupai Indian Reservation and the difficulties oc-

File Number	Roll Number	File Description
		casioned by the invasion of white miners. Also included are papers pertaining to the survey of Havasupai lands.
4327 AGO 1881	36–39	Papers relating to the battle between the command of Col. Eugene A. Carr, 6th Cavalry, and Apache Indians at Cibecue Creek, Arizona Territory, in August 1881 and a court of inquiry at Fort Grant, Arizona Territory, to investigate charges of negligence against Colonel Carr, 1881–83.
4414 AGO 1881	41	Papers relating to aid for destitute Walapai and Navajo Indians, July 1881–August 1891.
4746 AGO 1881	44	Correspondence and reports mainly concerning efforts to capture hostile Apache Indians who were terrorizing the border region of the District of New Mexico, July–December 1881.
5200 AGO 1881	48	Correspondence relating to a request from the Department of the Interior that the War Department help move Little Chief and certain members of his band of Northern Cheyenne from the Cheyenne and Arapaho Agency, Indian Territory, to the Pine Ridge Agency, Dakota Territory, August 1881–August 1883.
5517 AGO 1881	51	Correspondence relating to the intrusion of miners and ranchers on Chief Moses' reservation in Washington Territory, September 1881–February 1884.
5957 AGO 1881	54	Papers relating to engagements against Indians in Texas and New Mexico from 1850 to 1856 compiled in reply to a pension claim filed by the widow of William R. Talbot, Company G, 2d Dragoons. Included are evaluations as to whether the fighting constituted a war and efforts to define the limits of the areas involved, September 1881–December 1898.

File Number	Roll Number	File Description
6067 AGO 1881	56	Correspondence pertaining to the Paiute Indians in California, Nevada, Oregon, and the Territory of Washington, including their migration from the Yakima Agency, Washington Territory, to reservations at Malheur River in Oregon and Fort McDermitt and Pyramid Lake in Nevada. A number of the documents deal with the destitute condition of Indians, 1881–88.
364 AGO 1882	77	Papers and a report of March 4, 1882, from the Secretary of War relating to a statement of expenditures for Indian wars and for the observation and control of Indians from July 1, 1871, to June 20, 1882.
442 AGO 1882	78	Report by the Secretary of War and other papers relating to the status of Indian prisoners held under War Department orders, January–February 1882.
663 AGO 1882	81	Papers relating to the Frelinghuysen–Romero Agreement of July 29, 1882, providing for reciprocal crossings of the international boundary by troops of the United States and Mexico in pursuit of hostile Indians, February 1882–June 1887.
1076 AGO 1882	85	Papers pertaining to actions taken by the sheriff of Chouteau County, Montana Territory, and special deputy U.S. marshals in collecting taxes and fines from Indians and Canadian mixed-bloods and in driving the mixed-bloods back to Canada, 1882.
1280 AGO 1882	88	Correspondence relating to a planned reduction of beef rations for the Arapaho, Cheyenne, Comanche, and Kiowa agencies; the fears of Army officers, particularly of Capt. G. M. Randall, commander at Fort Reno, Indian Territory, that such a reduction would lead to an outbreak of violence; and the subse-

File Number	Roll Number	File Description
		quent efforts of some officers to obtain a satisfactory quantity of beef for the Indians to avoid endangering the entire frontier with an uprising, March–September 1882.
1513 AGO 1882	92	Correspondence and reports relating to unrest among the Indians of the Navajo Reservation, Arizona Territory, including the recommendation that Indian Agent Galen Eastman be replaced because of his inability to deal with the situation. The file also includes information about Navajo Indians who had gone to the San Juan River Valley, New Mexico Territory, and the efforts of the Army to return them to the reservation, April–November 1882.
1749 AGO 1882	96–97	Papers relating to outbreaks of violence, including several murders, in New Mexico and Arizona by Chiricahua Apache who escaped from the San Carlos Reservation, Arizona Territory, and to their pacification.
2180 AGO 1882	101	Papers concerning the threatened starvation of Indians on the Mescalero Apache Reservation, New Mexico Territory, after the Congress failed to appropriate funds for rations and the subsequent efforts by Army officers and the Department of the Interior to obtain rations, May 1882–August 1884.
2809 AGO 1882	108	Papers and reports relating to surveys of the boundaries of the White Mountain Reservation in Arizona Territory and of the Mescalero Apache Reservation in New Mexico Territory and to an Executive order reducing the area of the latter, June 1882–December 1884.
3875 AGO 1882	123	Papers relating to a potential Piegan Indian outbreak at the Blackfeet Agency, Montana Territory, due to insufficient food rations, 1882–83.

File Number	Roll Number	File Description
5171 AGO 1882	138	Correspondence relating to the illegal sale of liquor in Indian Territory, 1882-83.
5942 AGO 1882	147	Correspondence relating to disorders near Okmulgee, Indian Territory, among the Creek Indians who rebelled against their leaders and to efforts of the Army to restore order, December 1882-November 1883.
1066 AGO 1883	173-202	Papers relating to the uprising of the Chiricahua Apache under Geronimo, Chatto, and Natchez and to their subsequent surrender and imprisonment in the East, 1883-1906. Included are records pertaining to the disposition of surrendered Chiricahua, September 19, 1885-April 8, 1886; the movement of U.S. troops into Mexico; and the death of Capt. Emmet Crawford from wounds received from Mexican troops. For other papers relating to Captain Crawford, see file 4061 AGO 1883 on roll 231. For later documentation (not microfilmed) pertaining to the Apache prisoners, see 445841 AGO, described on page 263.
1181 AGO 1883	204	Correspondence relating to Chief Moses' trip to Washington, D.C., to confer with the Secretary of War and other officials over a dispute between farmers and Colville, Moses, and Okinagan Indians in Washington Territory, May-September 1883.
1233 AGO 1883	205	Papers pertaining to fighting between war parties of Cree Indians from Canada and herders in Montana Territory, 1883.
3111 AGO 1883	224	Correspondence relating to the plan to visit Indians in Montana and Dakota by members of the Senate Committee on Indian Affairs and to the request of Sen. H. L. Davis that the Army provide transportation and other necessary aid during their tour, July 1883-May 1885.

File Number	Roll Number	File Description
1759 AGO 1884	271	Papers relating to reports from post officers of attempts by white men to dispossess nonreservation Indians settled along the Columbia River and other places within the Military District of the Columbia and to an Interior Department order, May 31, 1884, to U.S. land offices, instructing land agents to refuse to file all entries by whites for lands then settled by Indians, April 1884–March 1885.
1882 AGO 1884	273	Papers pertaining to Indian depredations near Mitchell's ranch, New Mexico Territory, and measures taken to suppress them, 1884.
2016 AGO 1884	275	Correspondence relating to the death of Running Buffalo, a Cheyenne Indian, killed by a herder named Horton near Fort Supply, Indian Territory, in May 1884; the resulting conflict with the Indians; and the propriety of granting leases to cattlemen to drive livestock herds through Indian lands, May 1884–February 1885.
2487 AGO 1884	279	Correspondence relating to the May 1884 killing of Sioux Chief White Thunder by Thunder Hawk and Spotted Tail at the Rosebud Agency, Dakota Territory, as a result of an old feud, June–October 1884. Includes correspondence relating to disturbances at the Pine Ridge Agency, Dakota Territory, resulting from the arrival of T. A. Bland, publisher of the magazine *Council Fire*.
127 AGO 1885	331	Report of Lt. H. T. Allen's reconnaissance voyage to Alaska Territory, October–December 1884, and papers relating to an expedition by Lieutenant Allen and his party to the district of the Copper and Tanana Rivers to investigate the character and disposition of the natives,

File Number	Roll Number	File Description
		December 1884–May 1885. Included are copies of Lieutenant Allen's reports of March and April 1885.
722 AGO 1885	336	Papers pertaining to an investigation into the shooting of an Indian by a white at an Indian camp in Grant County, Oreg., 1885.
1153 AGO 1885	341	Correspondence and several reports relating to a suspected outbreak of inter-tribal warfare, reported by Joseph Terrill, who lived near Fort McKinney, Wyoming Territory, involving Arapaho, Blackfeet, Cheyenne, Crow, Piegan, Shoshoni, and Sioux Indians in Wyoming and Montana, February–May 1885.
3140 AGO 1885	362–363	Correspondence relating to disturbances caused by Indians of the Cheyenne and Arapaho Agency, Indian Territory, June 1885–September 1886, and Lt. Gen. Philip H. Sheridan's report, July 24, 1885.
7125 AGO 1885	402	Papers relating to a recommendation by Gen. F. C. Armstrong, U.S. Indian Inspector, that troops be sent to preserve order among Northern Cheyenne Indians at Tongue River, Montana Territory, and papers relating to attacks by Rosebud Indians in the Tongue River area against their agency, November–December 1885.
2104 AGO 1886	446	Papers pertaining to the appointment of Capt. J. M. Bell as temporary Indian agent at Pine Ridge Agency, Dakota Territory, 1886.
2458 AGO 1886	452	Correspondence and reports relating to the condition of the Chief Moses and Joseph Indians in the Department of the Columbia, including a request that the Department of the Interior supply agricultural implements to them, May 1886–May 1887.

File Number	Roll Number	File Description
3395 AGO 1886	466	Papers relating to Richard Fitzpatrick's claim for damages caused by Indian depredations during the Seminole war and for losses sustained on account of U.S. troops quartered on his plantation in southern Florida from 1838 to 1842. Included are copies of reports and correspondence concerning military operations in Florida in 1838 and military maps of Florida. The papers are dated July 1886–February 1887.
5269 AGO 1886	483	Report by Lt. J. T. Haines, 5th Cavalry, and copies of correspondence from the Department of the Interior relating to efforts to bring back Indians who left the Sac and Fox Indian Agency, Indian Territory, September 1886–January 1887.
5304 AGO 1886	483	Papers relating to intertribal hostilities among the Blood, Piegan, Grosventre, and Crow Indians in the border region of the Department of Dakota, October 1886–August 1887.
5939 AGO 1886	489	Reports, recommendations, and other papers relating to efforts by the Army and the Department of the Interior to return Jicarilla Apache Indians, camped near Espanola, New Mexico Territory, to the Mescalero Reservation and to adjust their grievances, October 1886–June 1888.
477 AGO 1887	513	Papers relating to the protection of the Klamath Indian Reservation, Oreg., against poachers, cattlemen, and settlers. Reports and correspondence from the Department of the Interior are included, January 1887–December 1888.
827 AGO 1887	517	Correspondence and reports relating to problems caused by white settlers in the San Juan River country on the Navajo Reservation in the District of New Mexico, February–November 1887.

File Number	Roll Number	File Description
880 AGO 1887	526	Reports from officers in the Department of California and from officials of the Interior Department relating to the encroachment of white settlers and cattlemen on the Round Valley Indian Reservation, Calif., April–December 1887.
2889 AGO 1887	533	Papers and copies of reports relating to white intruders on the Coeur d'Alène Reservation, Idaho. Included is a transcript of the field notes by Darius F. Baker, U.S. Deputy Surveyor, on the survey of the boundary lines of the reservation.
3264 AGO 1887	536	Reports of Gen. Nelson A. Miles and other persons concerning operations in Arizona against renegade Apache from the San Carlos Reservation and the condition of the tribes there, June 1887–May 1889. Included is a letter from Maj. Gen. George Crook giving his views on the management of the Mohave, Yuma, and Tonto Apache.
3324 AGO 1887	537	Papers relating to the removal of Pine Ridge Cheyenne from the Tongue River Agency in Montana, where they had traveled to hold a sun dance, June–October 1887. For additional records on this subject, see file 2493 AGO 1889 on roll 683.
3470 AGO 1887	538	Papers pertaining to an anticipated visit of Sioux Indians at the Crow Agency, Montana Territory, and a request by the Commissioner of Indian Affairs that they be intercepted, 1887.
4668 AGO 1887	548	Papers pertaining to a party of Comanche Indians from Indian Territory who visited the Mescalero Reservation in New Mexico. Other documents deal with general policies of allowing Indians to leave their reservations for visits, 1887.
4686 AGO 1887	549	Report of 1st Lt. George R. Burnett, 9th Cavalry, September 10, 1887, and other

File Number	Roll Number	File Description
		correspondence concerning trouble between the Colorado militia and Colorado ("Colorow"), chief of the Ute Indians, and efforts of U.S. troops to bring the Ute back to the Uintah and Ouray Reservation, August–September 1887.
5199 AGO 1887	554	Papers relating to the protection of the Indians who accepted allotments of land in severalty on the Yankton Reservation, Dakota Territory, and to the removal of intruders on the Pipestone Reservation, Minn., September–October 1887.
5681 AGO 1887	557	Papers relating to the Crow Indian outbreak led by Deaf Bull in the vicinity of the Crow Agency, Mont., and to the subsequent investigation and imprisonment of the Indians involved, October 1887–June 1890.
6839 AGO 1887	567	Papers relating to the death of Mary Wagnor, allegedly killed by Indians in the Rogue River Valley, Oregon Territory, in 1856. Included are 42 reports and enclosures filed by Lt. Col. R. C. Buchanan concerning his operations in the area during the Rogue River Indian war, 1855–56.
7007 AGO 1887	569	Correspondence, December 1887–December 1889, relating to Senate resolutions of December 20, 1887, and January 29, 1889, directing the Secretary of War to supply all records pertaining to Capt. Lawrence Hall's Company of Oregon Volunteers, which participated in the Cayuse Indian war of 1848 in the Oregon Territory. The requested information was furnished December 7, 1889, and published as *Letter From the Secretary of War Transmitting Report of Capt. W. E. Birkhimer,* Senate Executive Document 6, 51st Congress, 1st session.

File Number	Roll Number	File Description
3089 AGO 1888	634	Papers pertaining to Indian problems in the Departments of the Platte and Dakota. Included are documents concerning citizens' protests against troop removals, Indians under Lost Bull who left the Tongue River Agency in Montana, and Sioux from Pine Ridge Agency, Dakota Territory, who left for Tongue River to participate in a sun dance, 1888.
3340 AGO 1889	636	Report of Lt. Col. Simon Snyder, 10th Infantry, July 30, 1888, and related correspondence and telegrams concerning disturbances caused by renegade Indians in the vicinity of the San Carlos Reservation, Arizona Territory, July–September 1888.
7 AGO 1889	663	Correspondence and a printed report of the Secretary of War relating to the service of Volunteers from Washington and Idaho Territories in the Nez Percé war of 1877.
281 AGO 1889	665	Correspondence of the acting Indian agent of Hoopa Valley Agency regarding the Lower Klamath Indians and land speculators and the request of the Commissioner of Indian Affairs for the removal of intruders from Indian land, 1889.
299 AGO 1889	665	Papers relating to attempts by the Army to remove the heirs of Henry Harris, a white settler and U.S. citizen, from the Cherokee Nation, Indian Territory, January–March 1889.
567 AGO 1889	667	Correspondence relating to the attempted removal of cattlemen and their herds from Indian Territory and the problem of opening Oklahoma for public settlement, February 1889.
1253 AGO 1889	676	Correspondence relating to the encroachment of white settlers on the Sioux Reservation.

File Number	Roll Number	File Description
3551 AGO 1889	696	Papers pertaining to the Flathead Indians in Montana and their strained relations with local authorities and citizens. There are also documents relating to the activities of the troops sent to investigate the problem. See also file 5435 AGO 1889 on roll 716.
4310 AGO 1889	701	Reports of Capt. Quinton Williams, Inspector of Indian Supplies, on the destitute condition of Indians of the Shoshone (Wind River) Reservation, Wyoming Territory, and copies of correspondence from the Department of the Interior relating to this matter, July–September 1889.

SELECTED CONSOLIDATIONS ILLUSTRATIVE OF THE ARMY'S ROLE IN INDIAN AFFAIRS, 1890-1917, FROM THE GENERAL CORRESPONDENCE OF THE ADJUTANT GENERAL'S OFFICE

Papers pertaining to the Sioux campaigns of 1890 and 1891. Included is material about the ghost dance or messiah craze leading to the military intervention that culminated with the death of Sitting Bull, December 15, 1890, and the battles at Wounded Knee Creek and Drexel Catholic Mission, December 29 and 30, 1890. This file also includes the transcript and related documentation pertaining to the investigation of the Wounded Knee conflict conducted by Maj. J. Ford Kent and Capt. Frank D. Baldwin at the behest of Maj. Gen. Nelson A. Miles. These investigatory records have been reproduced as M983, *Reports and Correspondence Relating to the Army Investigations of the Battle at Wounded Knee and to the Sioux Campaign of 1890-1891* (file 5412–PRD–1890, 13 ft.).

Correspondence pertaining to the 1891-95 experiment in enlisting Indians in companies of Regular Army regiments (file 1222–PRD–1891, 3 ft.).

Correspondence, 1891, pertaining to Army officers who witnessed the issuance of annuity goods to Indians at agencies in the Dakotas, Indian Territory, Montana, and Wyoming (file 19219–PRD–1891, 2 in.).

Correspondence, 1892-93, pertaining to the subsistence, land titles, and general living conditions of Indians at the Cheyenne and Arapahoe Agency at Fort Reno, Oklahoma Territory (file 27769–PRD–1892, 3 in.).

Correspondence, 1894, pertaining to Grosventre Indians who left their agency at Fort Berthold, N. Dak., and who were to be returned by the military authorities (file 3596–PRD–1894, 1 in.).

Correspondence, 1895, relating to the Bannock Indian problems of that year. The Bannock left their Fort Hall Reservation and were charged with wanton killing of game in Wyoming. U.S. troops proceeded to the scene in an effort to prevent further conflicts between Indians and settlers (file 23148–AGO, 4 in.).

Correspondence, 1898, relating to an outbreak among the Pillager band of Chippewa Indians at Leech Lake, Minn., October 1898, and the efforts of U.S. and Minnesota Volunteer troops to deal with the situation (file 132734–AGO, 2 in.).

Correspondence, 1900-1901, pertaining to the influx of whites upon Kiowa, Comanche, and Apache lands in Oklahoma and the efforts of the Army to maintain order when reservation lands were opened to settlers in 1901 (file 331932–AGO, 1 in.).

Correspondence and other papers, 1902-15, relating to the internment of Apache prisoners at Fort Sill, Okla. This file is a continuation of 1066–AGO 1883 described on page 255. Included are periodic reports on reservation conditions, transcripts of conferences held with the Apache, maps of the Fort Sill reservation, and copies of congressional bills and documents. Later documentation pertains to the transfer of some of the Indians to the Mescalero Agency in New Mexico and to the awarding of land allotments to those remaining in Oklahoma (file 445841–AGO, 2 ft.).

Correspondence, 1903, of Maj. George L. Scott, acting agent of Leech Lake Agency, Minn., relating to the restless condition of the Indians and the necessity of sending for U.S. troops (file 506437–AGO, 1 in.).

Correspondence, 1903, pertaining to a conflict between a hunting party of Sioux Indians and civil authorities 40 miles from Newcastle, Wyo. (file 507742–AGO, 1 in.).

Correspondence, 1904-8, relating to difficulties with the Ute Indians. Included in this file is information pertaining to unrest at the Uintah and Ouray Agency in Utah during 1904 and 1905, to Ute Indians who left Utah in 1906 and were charged with killing livestock and destroying property in Wyoming, and to the efforts of the Army in securing the return of the Indians to their reservation and in dealing with their destitution (files 904009 and 1168758–AGO, 9 in.).

Correspondence, 1906-9, relating to the stationing of troops to prevent hostilities during the opening of the Shoshone (Wind River) Indian Reservation in Wyoming (file 1139753–AGO, ½ in.).

Correspondence, 1906-8, pertaining to difficulties with the Hopi Indians in

1906, their subsequent imprisonment at Fort Huachuca, Arizona Territory, and the expenses later incurred by the Army in transporting them from the prison to the Moqui Reservation at the expiration of their term (file 1171383–AGO, 1 in.).

Correspondence, 1911-17, pertaining to the proposed organization of Indian cavalry regiments (file 1669226–AGO, 2 in.).

Correspondence, 1913, pertaining to an expedition of the 12th U.S. Cavalry Regiment against Indians of the Navajo Reservation near Gallup, N. Mex., who were defying civil authorities who had issued warrants for their arrest (file 2098002–AGO, 1 in.).

Papers pertaining to issuing pensions for Indian war veterans who served from 1859 to 1891. Included is information compiled by the Adjutant General's Office relating to various Indian campaigns of this period, including file references to pertinent documents (file 2371356–AGO, 3 in.).

Orders

WAR DEPARTMENT ORDERS

War Department orders, which emanated from the Adjutant General's Office, are useful in studying War Department policies regarding Indians. Among the records of the Adjutant General's Office, the earliest orders, 1797-1808, are those issued by the ranking officer of the Army, Brig. Gen. James Wilkinson, a few of which pertain to Indian policies. For example, a general order issued at Washington on August 28, 1800, forbade military commanders serving on the frontier to issue rations or make presents of public property to Indians except in cases of extraordinary emergency or absolute necessity. Wilkinson's order book has been reproduced as M654, *Gen. James Wilkinson's Order Book, December 31, 1796-March 8, 1808.*

General policies pursued by the Army toward the Indians were sometimes embodied in general orders, the medium used to transmit instructions or directives to the entire Army command. For example, General Order 59, October 8, 1841, specified that in accordance with a Presidential directive, soldiers discharged from the Army at posts in Indian country ordinarily would be required to leave the vicinity within a reasonable time. Similarly, General Order 9, February 5, 1874, specified that arms, ammunition, and other ordnance stores were not to be issued to Indians other than those employed as scouts by the War Department; in dire emergencies, departmental commanders could sell arms and ammunition to settlers in exposed frontier communities. The enlistment of Indians in Regular Army infantry and cavalry regiments was authorized in General Order 28, March 9, 1891. Legislation, Presidential directives, and opinions of the Attorney General were frequently published as general orders, as were charges and findings of military courts of inquiry that investigated Army Indian campaigns. Information relating to the court that examined the campaigns of Brig. Gens. Winfield Scott and Edmund P. Gaines against the Seminole and Creek Indians in 1836 was published as General Order 13, March 21, 1837. Similarly, information about the 1837 court of inquiry into the conduct of Brig. Gen. John E. Wool regarding the Cherokee in Alabama was published as General Order 63, October 2, 1837.

General orders are unnumbered and incomplete before 1822 and exist primarily in manuscript form before 1833. After that date, printed copies of orders issued usually are available. Individual volumes of orders are indexed by name before 1860; afterwards, published name and subject indexes are available.

Special orders and general court-martial orders are less significant with respect to Indians and Indian-white relations. The former were used to convey information relating to a specific individual or subject not of concern to the entire Army command. Special orders exist in manuscript form beginning in 1822; from 1861 they were printed. There are name and subject indexes. General court-martial orders summarized the charges, specifications, and findings of courts-martial and exist in printed form for the period 1864 to 1894.

ORDERS OF SUBORDINATE COMMANDS

The records of the Adjutant General's Office include a large collection, possibly the most complete of its kind, of orders of various Army commands. In most instances, the original copies of the orders are filed with the records of the command in Records of U.S. Army Continental Commands, 1821-1920, Record Group 393. Of particular value concerning Indians are the orders of the Right Wing, Western Department, and Headquarters, Northwestern Army, from April to October 1832 during the Black Hawk war (vol. 13); orders of the Army of Florida and the Army of the South from December 1835 to August 1842 in the second Seminole war (vols. 9-12); and orders of Headquarters, Army of the South, and Headquarters, II Army Corps of the Southern Army, and the Army of East Tennessee and the Cherokee Nation from May 1836 to June 1837 during the Cherokee removal (vol. 13).

Returns

Army regulations and War Department general orders required the submission of monthly returns from commanders of regiments, posts, departments, corps, divisions, and brigades. Commanders of detached forces participating in active campaigns also were required to submit returns. This record group contains both Regular and Volunteer Army returns dating from the 1790's, but the former are more significant regarding Indians.

Many types of returns have been reproduced on microfilm, including M617, *Returns From U.S. Military Posts, 1800-1916*; M665, *Returns From*

Regular Army Infantry Regiments, June 1821-December 1916; M744, *Returns From Regular Army Cavalry Regiments, 1833-1916*; and M727, *Returns From Regular Army Artillery Regiments, June 1821-January 1901.*

Returns were basically statistical reports submitted monthly on forms, which furnished such information as the names of commanding and subordinate officers, the location of a regiment or command, the number of officers and enlisted men constituting a regiment, command, or post garrison, and, by the mid-19th century, a brief summary of activities ("record of events") in which the regiment or command participated or which transpired in the vicinity.

The returns contain brief accounts of the scouts, battles, or campaigns of particular regiments, but their primary value as a research tool is for locating more substantive documentation. With the names of post or regimental commanders and the dates of engagements, as well as other factual data, reports can be located among the War Department records. The different types of returns and the information available from each are further discussed below.

POST RETURNS

There are returns for posts located in Indian areas of the frontier, for example, Fort Gibson, Indian Territory, April 1824-October 1897 (M617, rolls 404-406); Fort Laramie, Wyo., June 1849-March 1890 (rolls 595-597); and Fort Abraham Lincoln, N. Dak., December 1872-August 1913 (rolls 628-630). There also are returns for posts, often temporary, which were established during Indian campaigns, for example, Fort Na-Ches, Washington Territory, established during Maj. Edward J. Steptoe's campaign against the Yakima Indians (roll 1527) and forts established during the Florida Seminole wars. Indian reservations under military control also submitted monthly returns, for example, Crow Creek Agency, Dakota Territory, February 1864-April 1871 (roll 274); Grand River Agency, Dakota Territory, May 1871-May 1875 (roll 413); Pine Ridge Agency, S. Dak., November 1890-June 1891 (roll 1532); Red Cloud Agency, Dakota Territory, November 1877-May 1879 (roll 1535); San Carlos Agency, Arizona Territory, October 1882-June 1900 (rolls 1091 and 1092); Spotted Tail Agency, Dakota Territory, December 1877-July 1878 (roll 1543); Fort Sumner (Bosque Redondo Reservation), New Mexico Territory, December 1862-June 1869 (roll 1241); Whetstone Agency, Dakota Territory, June 1870-April 1872 (roll 1424); and Yankton Agency, Dakota Territory, December 1865-March 1866 (roll 1550). Most of the information available on the reservation returns relates to the troops of the garrison, but occasionally other data can be gleaned. Several of the Fort Sumner returns in 1864 indicate the number of Indian captives on the post. The "record of events" part of a return submitted from the Pine Ridge Agency in December 1890 contains a brief summary of the military engagements at Wounded Knee Creek on December 29 and at White Clay Creek on December 30. Listed elsewhere on the return are the names of the men killed in the battles.

REGIMENTAL RETURNS

The returns of infantry and cavalry regiments are of primary interest regarding Indian campaigns in which the Regular Army participated. As in the case of post returns, the "record of events" part of the regimental returns contains summaries of scouts, engagements, and campaigns. The names of men killed and wounded in engagements generally are listed under "losses." A field return of the 7th U.S. Cavalry Regiment for June 1876 (M744, roll 72), for instance, contains a brief summary of the Battle of the Little Big Horn, June 25 and 26, and a list of the men killed and wounded. Information regarding casualties also is recapitulated in annual and quarterly returns of alterations and casualties, which were filed with the other returns of the regiment.

RETURNS OF EXPEDITIONS AND CAMPAIGNS

Returns for expeditions and campaigns date from the early 19th century to 1916, but few predate the 1850's. Returns are available for such operations as the Bannock war of 1878, the Black Hawk war, the Florida Seminole wars, the Sioux expedition of 1855-56 under Col. William S. Harney, and the Sioux campaign of 1890-91. Generally the returns were submitted to the Adjutant General's Office by the field commanders, and they encompass all the troops under the commander's immediate control. In format, these returns resemble those prepared at the regimental level.

COMPILATIONS FROM RETURNS

Regimental and expedition returns were used by the Adjutant General's Office and others to compile data on the activities of Regular or Volunteer Army troops that participated in various campaigns or wars. Such compilations were prepared by the Adjutant General's Office on the troops that served in the Black Hawk war of 1832 (1 vol.) and the second Seminole war of 1835-42 (1 vol.). In both cases the regimental return format was followed closely. In 1850-51, a more comprehensive compilation (1 vol.) was prepared by Lt. Col. Joseph H. Eaton, containing information about battles and engagements with Indians and British troops from 1790 to 1842. Described are the Indian campaigns of Brig. Gen. Josiah Harmar, Maj. Gen. Arthur St. Clair, Maj. Gen. Anthony Wayne, and others during the 1790's; the Battle of Tippecanoe in 1811; Indian engagements during the War of 1812; Gen. Andrew Jackson's 1817-18 campaigns against the Seminole Indians; Col. Henry Leavenworth's campaigns of 1823 against the Arikara and Blackfeet tribes; the Black Hawk war of 1832; and various engagements in the second Seminole war. Available information includes the place and date of each battle, name of the commanding officer, troops engaged, number killed and wounded, and a brief summary of the engagement. In the late 19th century a compilation was prepared that listed the names of men killed in battle or who died in service during the second Seminole war and gives the date, place, and cause of death for each.

Medical Records

Medical records include reports from surgeons accompanying field expeditions, 1868-89. Documents for a given engagement may include lists and statistical reports of the killed and wounded, newspaper clippings, and narrative reports of surgeons. Among the reports are those for the Battle of the Washita, Indian Territory, November 27, 1868 (file F–421); the Modoc expedition of 1872-73 (files F–431–435); the Big Horn campaign of 1876 (files F–461–464); the Nez Percé campaign of 1877 (files F–478–483); the Cheyenne outbreak at Fort Robinson, Nebr., January 9-22, 1879 (file F–492); the Battle of Milk River, Colo., September 29, 1877 (file F–501); and the engagement at Cibecue Creek, Arizona Territory, August 30, 1881 (file F–529).

Field records of hospitals consist primarily of registers of sick and wounded patients and of such other materials as prescriptions and casebooks. Most of the records date from the Civil War period. There are some records for hospitals located on Indian reservations administered by the Army, but Indian patients do not appear to have been recorded until the 1880's. An exception is Fort Sumner (Bosque Redondo Reservation), New Mexico Territory, for which there is a register of Indian patients, September 1864-February 1866. By the 1880's names of Regular Army Indian scouts appear as patients in post hospital registers. The registers generally indicate the name of the patient, the date of admission, the nature of the ailment, and the date and nature of the disposition of the case. Also by the 1880's, the hospital registers contained monthly consolidated reports of the medical department, which occasionally include information, primarily statistical, about Indian civilians on the post as well as Indian births, illnesses, and deaths.

Records Relating To Military Service

There is a large volume of records pertaining to soldiers who participated in Indian campaigns in the Regular or Volunteer Army. Volunteer organizations for which records are available include the 1st Illinois Mounted Volunteers, who served in the Black Hawk war; the 1st and 3d Colorado Cavalry Regiments, who participated in the campaign against the Cheyenne in 1864, culminating in the Sand Creek massacre; and the 1st New Mexico Cavalry Regiment, which participated in the Navajo campaign of 1863 and 1864 under Col. Christopher Carson. There is also a large volume of material pertaining to military service performed by Indians as scouts, guides, and soldiers in Regular and Volunteer Army organizations, beginning with Will Shorey's Corps of Cherokee Scouts in 1800. Also available are records of the Cherokee, Choctaw, and Creek organizations that fought in the War of 1812 and in the first Seminole war of 1817-18; Menominee and Potawatomi in the Black Hawk war; friendly Creek Indians in the Creek war of 1836; Choctaw, Creek, and Delaware in the second Seminole war; Pueblo who accompanied the Navajo expedition of 1849; and the 1st, 2d, and 3d Indian Home Guard Regiments who fought for the Union in the Civil War.

Before the Civil War, Indians who served with the Army were either enlisted in Volunteer organizations or hired in civilian capacities by Army officers in the field. An act of July 28, 1866 (14 Stat. 332), authorized the President to enlist and employ up to 1,000 Indian scouts; after this date Indian scouts served as part of the Regular establishment. Indian service in infantry and cavalry regiments was authorized by General Order 28, Headquarters of the Army, Adjutant General's Office, dated March 9, 1891, and was tried experimentally for several years. The different types of records pertaining to military service have been categorized and described below.

ARMY ENLISTMENT REGISTERS AND PAPERS

Enlistment papers generally were prepared for each soldier who enlisted in the Regular Army. In completing an enlistment paper, the enlistee indicated by his signature or mark his willingness to perform military service for a specified period. Usually, the papers also included information about the enlistee's age, place of birth, physical attributes, marital status, occupation, and date and place of enlistment. Enlistment papers for Indians were, for the most part, maintained separately in a single series, 1866-1914 (15 ft.), although some are dispersed among series pertaining largely to non-Indians.

The information from each enlistment paper was abstracted and entered into registers, which also contain information about service performed after enlistment, including the date of termination of service and the reason. Enlistment registers for Indians also were maintained separately. The enlistment registers have been reproduced as M233, *Registers of Enlistments in the United States Army, 1798-1914*; the volumes pertaining to Indian scouts appear on rolls 70 and 71.

MUSTER ROLLS

Muster rolls were lists of soldiers present or accounted for in a particular unit, in most cases a company. They were also prepared at the regimental level to indicate field and staff officers. Muster rolls were submitted on forms supplied by the Adjutant General's Office and covered 2-month periods. They were used from the Revolutionary War until 1912; the rolls among the records of the Adjutant General's Office date from 1791. Muster rolls provide the name, rank, enlistment data, and pay of each individual. Frequently, space was allowed on the rolls for comments about the state of discipline, military instruction, military appearance, arms, accouterments, and clothing of the unit as a whole. The "record of events" section, when properly completed, gave a brief account of the unit's activities over the 2-month period. Muster rolls for organizations of Indian scouts for the period 1866 to 1912 are filed together (25 ft.) and include rolls for units from Arizona, California, Montana, Nebraska, North Dakota, Oklahoma, Oregon, South Dakota, Texas, Utah, Washington, and Wyoming. Papers filed with the muster rolls are described in the section for miscellaneous series on pages 278 and 279.

COMPILED MILITARY SERVICE RECORDS

Information about the military service of Volunteer soldiers was abstracted from original records, such as muster rolls and returns, by the Record and Pension Division of the Adjutant General's Office beginning in 1890. The records pertaining to a particular war, campaign, or period are filed together. The records are arranged by organization, and jacket files for each individual are in alphabetical sequence. The individual files or compiled military service records consist largely of abstracts on cards, which give information such as might be obtained from muster rolls. Some files, however, also contain original records, such as casualty sheets, statements of death, statements of effects, pay or clothing receipts, enlistment and discharge papers, and copies of orders and correspondence. Examples of files available are those for Indian campaigners Col. John M. Chivington (with the records of the 1st Colorado Cavalry Regiment) and Col. Christopher Carson (with the records of the 1st New Mexico Cavalry Regiment). The records of the latter regiment and other Volunteer organizations from New Mexico during the Civil War period have been reproduced as M427, *Compiled Military Service Records of Volunteer Union Soldiers Who Served in Organizations From the Territory of New Mexico*; the Carson file appears on roll 4.

Filed first with the cards for each regiment are caption and record-of-event cards that contain histories of the organization. The cards pertaining to the Union regiments during the Civil War have been reproduced as M594, *Compiled Records Showing Service of Military Units in Volunteer Union Organizations*. The records pertaining to Indian Home Guard regiments appear on roll 225, and the records also can be used to furnish information about non-Indian organizations that participated in Civil War Indian campaigns.

There are numerous indexes to the compiled military service records, many of which have been reproduced on microfilm. General indexes that cover all State organizations for a particular war or period include M602, *Index to Compiled Military Service Records of Volunteer Soldiers Who Served During the War of 1812*; M629, *Index to Compiled Service Records of Volunteer Soldiers Who Served During Indian Wars and Disturbances, 1815-58*; and M694, *Index to Compiled Service Records of Volunteer Soldiers Who Served from 1784 to 1811.* There are also numerous indexes pertaining to the organizations of particular States in a given war or campaign, many of which are available on microfilm.

OTHER RECORDS

Files pertaining to the Volunteer service of Indian and other troops in Indian wars and campaigns are among the correspondence of the Enlisted Branch, Volunteer Service Division, and Record and Pension Office of the Adjutant General's Office. Files pertaining to the military service of Regular Army officers, including those who fought in Indian wars, are among the correspondence of the Commission Branch, 1863-70, and the Appointment, Commission, and Personal Branch, 1871-94, of the Adjutant General's Office. Most of the pertinent information available from these files relates to administrative aspects of the careers of white Army officers who fought in Indian campaigns, because Indians were seldom commissioned in the Regular Army. In an unusual instance, Ely Parker held such a commission as a member of the staff of Lt. Gen. Ulysses S. Grant during and immediately following the Civil War, and his file is among the correspondence of the Appointment, Commission, and Personal Branch (file dividual Regular and Volunteer Army physicians and civilian contract physicians. These records furnish information about those doctors who participated in Indian wars and campaigns.

Generals' Papers and Books

This collection was assembled after the Civil War from some records that had always been in War Department custody and from others that were obtained from private sources. Most of the records document the Civil War careers of prominent Union officers and contain little information about Indian affairs. In a few instances, however, the books and papers of certain officers include earlier and later materials that contain significant information about War Department involvement with Indian problems. Much of the material, including that described below, apparently was created and maintained by the officer as his personal record.

MAJ. GEN. THOMAS S. JESUP

The books and papers of Maj. Gen. Thomas S. Jesup (13 vols. and 22 ft.) date from 1818 to 1852, but the great preponderance is for the period 1836 to 1838, when, as commander of the Army of the South, Jesup directed first the removal of the Creek Indians from Alabama and, subsequently, the military operations against the Seminole in Florida. The Jesup materials cover the entire spectrum of military operations in both campaigns.

The largest series of records consists of incoming letters. Other series include copies of letters sent, orders issued, returns, muster rolls of Regular and Volunteer Army troops in Florida, and lists of Indians and blacks captured by the Army there. The letters received are divided into subseries according to correspondent: officers of the Regular and Volunteer Army; officers of the Navy and Marine Corps; infantry, dragoon, and artillery officers; and officials of the War Department. Other subseries contain letters from nonmilitary correspondents, including the Governors of Alabama, Florida, and Georgia and Indian chieftains. The subseries overlap to a degree so that letters from a particular officer may be found in more than one group.

Examples of letters received illustrate the information available. Letters from Maj. H. J. Wilson, superintendent of Creek emigration in 1837, deal with outrages committed in Alabama upon the families of friendly Creek Indians fighting with the Army in Florida and with various problems associated with the removal of the Creek from Alabama to the West. Letters from Opothle Yoholo, the Creek chieftain, also relate to the emigration of his people and to their service in Florida. Other letters and papers relate to the Creek relinquishment of Alabama lands to whites. Letters received from quartermasters include many pertaining to the procurement of supplies and transportation for the campaigns in Florida. Among the letters from ordnance officers are those of Capt. Julius A. de'Lagnel, commander of the Black Creek Ordnance Depot in East Florida, pertaining to the procurement of ordnance and ordnance supplies and the development and use of new weapons, including the 12-pounder mountain howitzer. There are letters from Lt. Col. William S. Harney, commander at Fort Mellon, East Florida, among the letters received from dragoon officers. Harney's correspondence concerns scouts, expeditions, and the attitude of Indians toward emigration and the status of their blacks. Letters of Col. Archibald Henderson, commander of the Marine Corps detachment in Alabama, and Lt. Col. Samuel Miller in Florida are among the letters received from Marine Corps officers. The correspondence from naval officers includes letters from those of the West India Squadron conducting patrolling operations and other officers engaged in riverine and inland operations.

MAJ. GEN. HENRY W. HALLECK

Most of Halleck's papers and books (about 90 vols. and 5 ft.) are from the Civil War period, but of most significance concerning Indians are the copies of letters sent for the years 1865 to 1869, when he commanded the Military Division of the Pacific. Many of the letters to subordinate command officers and War Department superiors relate to important Indian matters—for example, those to Maj. Gen. Jefferson C. Davis, commander of the District of Alaska in 1867, which concern Indian policies to be pursued there. The Halleck letters are important not only for their content but also for their uniqueness, as there are no copies of them among the materials for the Pacific Division in Records of U.S. Army Continental Commands, 1821–1920, Record Group 393.

SMALLER COLLECTIONS

There are some pertinent materials in the smaller groups of papers. Among the papers of Maj. Gen. Philip H. Sheridan (4 in.), for example, are several letters pertaining to the campaigns against the Cheyenne Indians, 1868–69, including one Lt. Col. George A. Custer wrote in November 1868.

Records of the Military Reservation Division

The Military Reservation Division of the Adjutant General's Office was established in 1882 and discontinued in 1890. It was charged with handling all correspondence relating to the establishment, occupation, maintenance, and abandonment of military posts, including those on the frontier, and in this capacity created the records described below. There is, however, much information in the records which both predates and postdates the Division's existence.

An outline index of military forts and stations, reproduced as M661, *Historical Information Relating to Military Posts and Other Installations, ca. 1700–1900*, consists of 26 volumes that provide brief data concerning individual posts. Information for a given post may include the dates of establishment and abandonment, its geographical location, the physical appearance, and the forces that garrisoned it. There are also bibliographic references to primary and secondary printed sources, lists of published works on Indian wars from the Pequot war to the third Seminole war, and a list of Indian trading houses, giving the name, location, date of establishment, and references to relevant public documents, 1795–1826 (vol. "X" reproduced on roll 8).

More detailed information is in the reservation files, 1800's–1916 (30 ft.). In many instances, original documents such as correspondence, reports, orders, maps, plats, and blueprints are in files for a given installation, and these may have information about Indians in the vicinity. In the file for the San Carlos Agency, Ariz., for example, is a memorial from the Arizona Legislative Assembly to Congress, requesting that a new post be established in the vicinity of Gibson's Well as an additional safeguard against Indian depredations. Similarly, the Camp Stambaugh, Wyo., file includes a petition from residents of Sweetwater County, requesting that a cavalry force be stationed in the immediate vicinity to deal with Indians who had been raiding settlers engaged in mining, 1868–69. The file for Fort Bidwell, Calif., includes information about the Paiute Indians and other tribes whose reservations fell within the surveillance of the fort. Of most significance in this regard is Capt. Jesse M. Lee's 1890 report on the possible abandonment of the post. He discussed the extent and character of Indian and white settlements and Indian attitudes toward whites. Lee also solicited statements from both groups concerning their attitudes toward the military in general and the abandonment of the post in particular. Appendixes to this document include a report of Lt. Nat P. Phister about the messiah craze and a report concerning Indian troubles in the area since 1878. Also in the Fort Bidwell file are many letters and petitions from local citizens about the discontinuation of the fort. These documents also include some information about living conditions of Indians and whites.

Miscellaneous Series

A general information index (33 ft.) was compiled by the Adjutant General's Office beginning in the late 19th century as a reference to sources of information on significant persons or subjects about which inquiries had been received or were expected. The index consists primarily of alphabetically filed cards bearing references to pertinent War Department records and printed materials. Information about Indians can be located under "Indians" and under the names of tribes, battles, and individuals. In a number of instances, original records or printed materials also have been filed in the index. For example, a copy of extracts from the journal of Captain Spalding of the ship *Lausanne*, containing information about the Indians of the Fort Vancouver area, has been filed under "Oregon."

Records and printed materials that were too bulky to be filed in the general information index but were needed for ready reference were placed in one of a numbered series of miscellaneous files (19 ft.), for which there are usually entries in the index. The files include journals, inspection reports, correspondence, maps, printed materials, and photographs. Files concerning Indians are listed below:

Journal of a march by Company B, 10th U.S. Cavalry Regiment, from Fort Dodge, Kans., to Camp Wichita, Indian Territory, April 17, 1869–May 5, 1869. This briefly mentions a conflict with Wichita Indians at Beaver Creek on April 30, 1869 (file 22).

Papers dated 1871 and 1872 relating to the intrusion of settlers upon Osage and Cherokee lands in Kansas and the efforts made toward removing them (file 25).

Copies of treaties between the United States and various tribes of eastern, midwestern, and western Indians, 1837–58 (file 26).

Original maps of the Little Big Horn battlefield. Two were compiled by the chief engineer of the Military Division of the Missouri in 1876 and 1877, and the other was compiled by Lt. Edward Maguire, Corps of Engineers, in 1876. This file also includes copies of newspaper and magazine articles (1920's and 1930's) relating to the Battle of the Little Big Horn and the Sioux campaign of 1876 (file 53).

Photostatic copies of letters from Capt. Frederick W. Benteen to his wife, July 1876, containing information about the Battle of the Little Big Horn (file 53½).

Blueprint map of the trail of Sitting Bull from the Little Big Horn battlefield to Canada, based upon information he furnished at Fort Randall, Dakota Territory, in December 1881 (file 105).

Reports of scouting expeditions from Fort Griffin, Tex., in pursuit of Indians, during June and July 1873 (file 120).

Report by Lt. Bernard Sharp, 3d U.S. Infantry, relating to the Indians in the Copper River Valley near Fort Liscum, Alaska, February 20, 1905. Included is information about various aspects of Indian culture and life (file 125).

Two compilations of engagements between Indians and U.S. troops, the first covering the period 1837 to 1866 and the second, 1866 to 1891. The latter, which is more complete, was published as a memorandum of the Adjutant General's Office in 1891. Both compilations list the actions chronologically and give brief information about the location, troops engaged, commanding officers, and casualties. The file also includes an unpublished essay by Capt. Philip Rease, "The American Indian as a Warrior, With an Account of Some of Our Early Indian Wars," written 1898; it covers the period 1605 to 1792 and contains information about the relations of colonial settlers with Indians (file 126).

Proclamations by Gov. Henry Connelly of New Mexico Territory, September 14, 1862, and September 21, 1863, relating to a proposed expedition against the Navajo Indians (file 160).

A map of the Battle of Wounded Knee Creek, S. Dak., December 29, 1890, showing the location of the fight with Big Foot's band and troop positions when the first shots were fired. The map was prepared from sketches made by Lt. S. A. Closman, acting engineer officer, Division of the Missouri, by Pvt. James Hade, 6th U.S. Cavalry Regiment (file 209).

Report of Maj. Gen. Alexander Macomb, October 22, 1815, on conditions in the Fifth Military Department, including Indian affairs, with references to a Kickapoo Indian killed by American soldiers and the adverse reaction to the incident by the British commander at Malden. This file also includes a report by Judge Benjamin Parke, June 10, 1816, relating to his negotiations with Wea, Kickapoo, and Mississinewa Indians over lands ceded to the United States in Indiana Territory and reports and correspondence, 1816 and 1819, from Col. Duncan L. Clinch relating to the destruction of the Negro Fort on the Apalachicola River (file 218). See also pages 356 and 357.

Brig. Gen. Alfred Sully's journal of an expedition from Fort Pierre, Dakota Territory, against the Sioux during August and September 1863, including a brief account of the battle at White Stone Hill, September 3, 1863 (file 219).

Photostatic copy of a document alleged to be secret articles of a treaty of peace and friendship concluded August 7, 1790, between the United States and the Creek Nation (file 222).

Reports pertaining to the Powder River Indian Expedition in Dakota and Montana Territories from June 20 to October 7, 1865. Included is a report dated November 1, 1865, from Maj. Gen. Grenville M. Dodge, commander of the Department of the Missouri and of U.S. forces in Kansas and the Territories. There are also other reports from the subordinate military commanders (file 224).

Photostatic copy of an 1859 map, showing the site of the Mountain Meadows massacre, which took place in Utah Territory on September 13, 1857 (file 241).

Maps (mostly photostatic copies) of Indian campaigns and battles, 1874–79. Included are maps of the campaign of 1879 in the country between Big Creek and Salmon River, Indian Territory; the Battle of Powder River, March 17, 1876, drawn by Capt. Anson Mills; Crazy Horse's village and vicinity, drawn by 2d Lt. Charles Morton, 3d Cavalry; the campaigns of troops under the command of Col. Nelson A. Miles, 1876–78; and Capt. Anson Mills' expedition of September 1874 (file 246).

A published map of the route followed by the 7th U.S. Cavalry Regiment under Lt. Col. George A. Custer to the Battle of the Washita, Indian Territory, which occurred on November 27, 1868. This map was made under the supervision of Robert Bruce, who consulted Gen. Edward S. Godfrey, a survivor of the fight; it was intended for publication in the *Cavalry Journal*, October 1928 (file 247).

Reports of scouting expeditions, June–July 1873, conducted by detachments of the 4th U.S. Cavalry Regiment from camps on the Nueces River and Elm Creek and at Live Oaks and San Picho, Tex.; the 10th U.S. Cavalry Regiment from Fort Richardson, Tex.; and the 9th U.S. Cavalry Regiment from Fort Concho, Tex. There is also a report by Capt. E. M. Heyl, 4th U.S. Cavalry Regiment, on escorting a surveying party of the Texas and Pacific Railroad in 1872 and 1873, during which time Indians were encountered (file 264).

A published map of the Department of the Columbia compiled in 1877 by Lt. Robert Fletcher to show the locations of troops under the command of Brig. Gen. Oliver O. Howard during the Nez Percé Indian campaign (file 276).

Printed maps of Indian country and reservations, including a map of part of the Indian country lying east and west of the Mississippi River to 46° of north latitude, compiled by U.S. Geologist G. W. Featherstonhaugh for the Topographical Bureau; a map of a reconnaissance of the Minnay Sotor

Watapah or St. Peters River, Minn., to its sources, 1835, by G. W. Featherstonhaugh, with Indian place names; and a map of the Indian Territory showing reservation boundaries, published by G. W. and C. B. Colton in 1883 (file 281).

Inspection reports by Col. W. G. Freeman of the 8th Military Department, 1853; Col. Joseph K. F. Mansfield of the Department of New Mexico, 1854; the Department of the Pacific, 1855; and the Department of Texas, 1856 (file 282).

Records pertaining to the second and third Seminole wars, including maps showing military operations, 1835–39 and 1855–56; a list of forts and military camps on the Caloosahatchee River, 1835–42 and 1855–58; and correspondence and reports related to military operations, 1835–37 and 1840–41. Those of the 1840–41 period pertain primarily to proposals by Col. J. H. Sherburne for using balloons and ending the war. There is a pencil sketch of a balloon ascension over an Indian encampment (files 119, 284, and 286).

Casualty lists, primarily for engagements during the Sioux campaign of 1876 and the Nez Percé campaign of 1877. Available are lists for engagements at Rosebud Creek, Montana Territory, June 17, 1876; Little Big Horn River, Montana Territory, June 25 and 26, 1876; North Fork of the Powder River, Wyoming Territory, November 25, 1876; White Bird Canyon, Idaho Territory, June 17, 1877; Cottonwood Creek, Idaho Territory, July 3, 1877; Clearwater, Idaho Territory, July 11–12, 1877; Big Hole, Montana Territory, August 9, 1877; Camas Meadow, Montana Territory, August 20, 1877; Bear Paw Mountain, Montana Territory, September 30–October 1, 1877; Milk River, Colo., September 29–October 5, 1879; Cibecue, Arizona Territory, October 2, 1881; Wounded Knee Creek, S. Dak., December 29, 1890; White Bear Creek, S. Dak., December 30, 1890; and Leech Lake, Minn., October 5, 1898 (file 299).

Post-Revolutionary War manuscripts, 1784–1811 (2 ft.), consist primarily of documents relating to the pay and supply of Volunteer troops mustered into U.S. service after the Revolution. They document the logistical and financial aspects of some of the Indian campaigns. The collection evidently was assembled by the War Department during the late 19th and early 20th centuries from materials received from various Government agencies and documents already in its custody. The types of documents include correspondence, abstracts, warrants, receipts, vouchers, claims relating to pay for services performed or goods furnished, and organizational and supply returns. The documents are arranged according to the State or Territory to which they pertain, and a card name index is available to locate manuscripts about specific individuals. Among the Indian campaigns for which some information is available are those conducted against the Cherokee in South Carolina, Georgia, and Tennessee in the 1790's;

those led by Gens. Josiah Harmar, John Sevier, Arthur St. Clair, and Anthony Wayne, 1784–93; and that of William Henry Harrison in 1811, culminating in the Battle of Tippecanoe. This series has been reproduced as M904, *War Department Collection of Post-Revolutionary War Manuscripts.*

The papers relating to Indian prisoners, 1860–65, originated largely in the Department of the Northwest and the District of Minnesota and were sent to the Adjutant General's Office by the Department of Dakota. They relate mainly to the Sioux wars of 1862–64. Many of the documents are morning reports of Indian prisoners at Fort Snelling, Minn. There is also a list of 326 Indian prisoners at Mankato on January 12, 1863, and other documentation concerning their imprisonment. An inventory of property of the families of condemned Indians at a camp near Fort Snelling, dated January 8, 1863, lists the names of individuals and the number of horses, oxen, wagons, and chains and yokes that belonged to each. Other papers include statements made by various Indians to military authorities and letters, many of them from Indians and written in Indian languages, to Brig. Gen. Henry H. Sibley. There are a few items relating to Indians in other areas of the West, including a list, dated May 5, 1860, of Delaware Indians employed in an expedition against the Kiowa; 1865 correspondence relating to the imprisonment, trial, and death of Curley Headed Tom, an Indian who had resided on the Hoopa Valley Reservation in California; and a letter pertaining to Indian prisoners at Fort Wingate, New Mexico Territory, in May 1864.

Records in book form of Civil War Union Volunteer organizations include those created at regimental and company levels, such as copies of letters sent, orders issued, descriptive books, and morning reports. Not all types of records are available for each organization, but frequently a researcher can obtain information about a particular unit or certain individuals within the unit. There are book records for Union Civil War Indian organizations; the 1st, 2d, and 3d Indian Home Guards; and other organizations that participated in Civil War Indian campaigns. These records are closely related to the regimental papers described below.

Filed with the muster rolls of Indian and white Volunteer Army organizations that participated in Indian campaigns are correspondence, reports, and other papers. (The muster rolls are described on pages 269 and 270.) Many of the regimental papers are of considerable significance with respect to the information they provide about the organization's involvement with Indians. Filed with the muster rolls for the period 1791 to 1811 are papers pertaining to discharges, pay, supplies, various types of returns, and copies of orders. Of perhaps greater significance are documents relating to the Indian expeditions of Maj. Gens. Arthur St. Clair and Anthony Wayne in the 1790's, many of these records apparently were assembled for the Congressional Committee of Inquiry Into the Causes of the Failure of St. Clair's Expedition Against the Indians in 1791. Filed with the muster rolls of the Indian war period, 1811–58, is approximately 1 foot of 1832 correspondence between Regular and Volunteer Army officers and War Department and State officials pertaining to the Black Hawk war. There are also papers concerning the "Heatherly War" of July 1836, when troops of the 1st Regiment of Dragoons participated with Volunteers from Clay County, Mo., in an expedition against the Sauk, Fox, and Iowa Indians following the killing of two white men by Potawatomi. The records include a memorandum book kept by Alexander Doniphan, the militia commander, his later account of the campaign, and copies of correspondence of Brig. Gen. Henry Atkinson, Lt. Col. Stephen Watts Kearny, and Capt. Matthew Duncan of the 1st Dragoons about the incidents. Records relating to the Cherokee disturbances in Tennessee in 1823–24 include letters to Capt. Joseph C. McMinn, U.S. Indian agent for the Cherokee Nation, authorizing him to raise troops to expel intruders from the Indian lands. A file of material pertaining to the Mormon suppression of Indian hostilities in 1853 includes documents, such as bills and payrolls, that show the expenses incurred by Utah Territory. A letter from Brigham Young to Secretary of War Jefferson Davis, September 11, 1855, pertains to the reimbursement of Utah Territory by the U.S. Government.

For the Civil War period, regimental papers are regularly filed with muster rolls and returns. For example, papers for the 3d Indian Home Guard Regiment include correspondence, orders, and battle and casualty reports. Papers for the 1st New Mexico Cavalry Regiment contain the same kinds of materials and, in addition, reports of scouts, proceedings of courts-martial, lists of prisoners and deserters, and regimental and company rosters. Many of the letters and reports among the organization's regimental papers were taken from the files of the Department of New Mexico and relate to the pursuit and capture of Navajo Indians during the 1863–64 campaign.

RECORDS OF THE OFFICE OF THE
QUARTERMASTER GENERAL
(RECORD GROUP 92)

The first Quartermaster General, appointed by a resolution of the Second Continental Congress on June 16, 1775, took charge of supplying camp equipment and the means of transportation for the Army. A Commissary General of Stores and Purchases procured subsistence stores for Army personnel, and a Clothier General provided their clothing until 1781 when the Treasury Department began procuring these items under a contract system. Between 1785, when the Congress eliminated the Office of the Quartermaster General, and 1818, when it created a Quartermaster Department and a Subsistence Department, quartermaster generals were regarded as field staff officers who served with the principal armies in time of war.

During these years various officials in the Treasury and War Departments, mainly stationed at Philadelphia, were concerned with supplies, including annuity goods for Indians and the procurement of goods for and the disposal of goods received from Government-operated trading factories, particularly before the Office of Indian Trade was established in 1806 (see page 18). There are records of these offices relating to Indian goods among the records of the Office of the Quartermaster General, particularly the letters sent, ledgers, and other records of the Purveyor of Public Supplies, established in the Treasury Department in 1795. There also are records of the Military Storekeeper at Philadelphia, the Superintendent of Military Stores, and the Quartermaster Officer at Philadelphia, who was known as the Military Agent until 1812.

The Office of the Commissary General of Purchases, established in 1812, and the Clothing Bureau, established in 1832, were gradually phased out of existence, so that by 1842 the functions of both of these agencies and their records were transferred to the Office of the Quartermaster General and its field establishments. The Office was responsible for administering the system of supply for the Army and overseeing the accountability of officers and agents charged with monies or supplies until 1912, when the Subsistence, Pay, and Quartermaster Departments were merged to form the Quartermaster Corps.

The Quartermaster Department participated directly in matters relating to Indians: supplying the Army units engaged in hostilities with Indians, buying land from them, hiring Indian scouts, and transporting Indian prisoners. Because the Department was responsible for food, clothing, housing, and transportation, its operations often affected materials most necessary to the Indians' survival. As the Army moved westward and more and more Indians were located on reservations, the quartermaster in the field often became one of the sources of supply for Indians living on reservations or under the supervision of an Indian agent.

The following series or groups of series are examples of records that may be of value to the researcher in Indian affairs. Although the correspondence series are not described, it should be pointed out that among the letters sent (reproduced as M745) and the letters received, 1818–70, there are many letters concerning Indian matters, as there are in the correspondence series of the several branches and divisions of the Office after 1870.

Special Files, 1794–1913

CONSOLIDATED CORRESPONDENCE FILE, 1794–1890

The records in this file (1,276 ft.) came from the Commissary General of Subsistence, the Commissary General of Purchases, and other War Department officers and Government bureaus and from post, department, and depot quartermasters. There are various types of records, including letters, reports, issuances, statements, lists, newspaper clippings, maps, and sketches. Numerous consolidations of records within the file detail aspects of the relationships between Indians, the Army, and the civilian population. The following are some of the types of file headings under which there is material concerning Indians: (1) the names of Indian tribes, (2) the names of wars or campaigns, (3) subjects closely related to Indian affairs, such as Indian agencies, reservations, expeditions, Indian scouts, prisoners, supplies, and annuities, and (4) the names of particular geographic areas or military commands, such as a military post, where one might find reports by the post quartermaster concerning Indian depredations in the vicinity or concerning the amount and kind of subsistence stores issued to Indians nearby. The file "Indian Department" also contains information about Indian affairs for the period 1802 to 1809.

The consolidated file is a helpful research source, but the records are rarely comprehensive in their coverage of a particular subject. In order to gain an adequate grasp of the subjects included in the file, it is necessary to consult the correspondence and other series from which these records were removed.

SPECIAL SUBJECT FILES, 1865–82

In a series of correspondence (2 in.) relating to the cost of maintaining troops at various Indian agencies (file 3373 QMGO 1878), there are letters and reports pertaining to the cost of maintaining troops at frontier posts and in the field for service against hostile Indians. In some cases the records provide evidence of the cost of supporting Indians. These records were created in response to an inquiry by a joint congressional committee in 1878, which was investigating the feasibility of transferring the Indian Bureau from the Department of the Interior to the War Department.

A Senate resolution of June 21, 1879, requested the President of the United States to inform the Senate of the number of soldiers, civilians, and Indians killed and wounded and the estimated value of property destroyed in the various Indian wars between 1865 and 1879. Among the correspondence of the Quartermaster General is a series of letters, telegrams, reports, and computations (6 in.) that were created in accumulating the information called for by this resolution. These records constitute part of the raw material used by the War Department to formulate its report, which was transmitted to the Senate by President Rutherford B. Hayes on January 5, 1881. They provide statistical information on the lives lost and the property destroyed as well as evidence of the manner in which the data for the report was gathered.

REPORTS OF PERSONS AND ARTICLES HIRED, 1818–1913

Quartermasters assigned to military commands, expeditions, or installations were required to submit monthly reports (which total 1,526 ft.) to the Quartermaster General listing, for persons employed by them, name, occupation, number of days employed, rate of compensation, date of contract, amount of money paid for the service, and a brief remark on the nature of the duties. Typically quartermasters would hire clerks, teamsters, interpreters, wagonmasters, storekeepers, engineers, blacksmiths, carpenters, and scouts. Since Indians from time to time filled some of these positions, the reports can be used to study the types of jobs for which Indians were hired as well as the amount of compensation they received. Quartermasters serving with units participating in Indian campaigns submitted reports, which may provide information on persons and articles employed for engagements with hostile Indians.

There are several finding aids that may be useful for research among the reports of persons and articles hired. A card index (15 ft.) to the names of scouts mentioned in some of the reports includes the names not only of the scouts but also of wagonmasters, guides, dispatchers, mail carriers, spies, interpreters, couriers, and trailers. Another card index (8 in.) pertains to reports made by important unit commanders and the commanders of expeditions. This index is especially useful for locating reports from campaigns and expeditions, such as the Indian expedition of 1865, the Modoc Indian war, MacKenzie's expedition, the Indian expeditions of 1876–77, Custer's expedition of 1874–76, and the Powder River expedition. The index also contains cards for some reports filed by quartermasters at western posts that were often involved with Indian disturbances. There are, for example, index cards for Fort Abraham Lincoln, Dakota Territory; Fort Dodge, Kans.; Fort Keogh, Montana Territory; Fort Klamath, Oreg.; Fort Lewis, Colo.; and San Carlos, Arizona Territory. A list of Indian scouts (1 in.) whose names appear in reports, 1868–70, includes names that are not found in the card index.

Records of Officers

QUARTERMASTER GENERAL—BRIG. GEN. THOMAS S. JESUP

Resource material for a study of Indian affairs along the western frontier from 1818 to 1846 and in Florida during the Seminole campaigns of the late 1830's and early 1840's is in the letters and reports sent by Quartermaster General Jesup (2 ft.) for the periods 1818–36 and 1839–46. There are letters referring to funds allotted to individual quartermasters during Indian hostilities; the amounts and types of provisions, supplies, and equipment furnished and the means of transporting such goods; the hiring and use of spies and interpreters; claims arising from Indian hostilities; purchases of timber and other goods from Indians; the leasing or purchase of land for military installations from Indians; and pay for Indians who rendered service in frontier campaigns.

General Jesup commanded the Army in Florida from 1836 to 1838, and some of his letters and reports written to the Secretary of War, Members of Congress, and heads of Government offices after he returned to Washington as Quartermaster General contain reflections on events and conditions that he experienced in Florida. In his 1841 letter to the Chairman of the Senate Military Affairs Committee, William C. Preston, for example, he tells how, following the battle of Locha Hatchee in 1838, his contacts with a group of Seminole Indians were assisted by a black slave. These contacts were instrumental in the peaceful removal of these Indians to Arkansas.

A larger collection of General Jesup's records, most of which pertain to his Seminole and Creek war activities, 1836–38, is among the collection of generals' papers and books in Records of the Adjutant General's Office, 1780's–1917, Record Group 94. See pages 271 and 272.

QUARTERMASTERS

Among the records of quartermasters in the field are those of such officers assigned to Army organizations or installations which, because of their duties or location, had frequent contacts with Indians. Typically, these records consist of correspondence, reports, returns, receipts, and financial records concerning accounts, purchases, and disbursements; records of supplies, subsistence, and equipment received, issued, used, or transported; and registers and lists of persons employed. In these records are general comments on the disposition of various Indian tribes and more specific information about particular acts of Indian hostility, Indians employed in the Quartermaster Department, business transactions between quartermasters and Indians, and occasions when quartermasters issued subsistence stores to destitute Indians.

The following brief descriptions indicate some of the types of information available among the records of several quartermasters whose assignments placed them in close contact with Indians.

PATRICK H. BRESLIN

Lieutenant Breslin was assistant quartermaster and assistant commissary of subsistence during the Big Horn expedition. A series of letters and telegrams received and reports retained by Breslin (8 in.) provides information on the activities, equipment, and supply of troops participating in this expedition of 1874.

ABNER R. HETZEL

In several series of letters sent and received by Hetzel, Quartermaster to the Army of the Cherokee Nation, 1830–47 (5 ft.), and a series of miscellaneous papers, 1836–45 (6 in.), there are letters that provide information on the operations of the Army in the Cherokee country, the supply of troops and garrisons, the mustering and equipping of Volunteers, the financing of quartermaster operations during active hostilities, transportation for Indians emigrating to the West, and other activities pertinent to "preventing and suppressing Indian hostilities." Among Hetzel's records is a volume containing abstracts of disbursements, 1838–47. They delineate the types of supplies and services used in actions against hostile Indians as well as those used in the accomplishment of routine quartermaster functions. Included are the names of persons or firms providing supplies and services and the amount paid by the Quartermaster Department.

JUSTUS MCKINSTRY

Among the letters sent by McKinstry (3 vols.) are ones written while he was at the quartermaster depot in San Diego, Calif., 1851–54. A number of these letters refer to the activities of the Yuma, Cahuilla, and "Liguina" Indians who inhabited parts of southern California. For instance, in a letter to the Quartermaster General, June 28, 1852, he reported on the resources of the country, "the disposition of the Indians, and how. . .they might be controlled."

W. M. D. MCKISSACK

A series of letters sent by McKissack (1 vol.) includes numerous letters giving detailed descriptions of Indian depredations in the Southwest during the Mexican War. In one such letter McKissack informed the Quartermaster General of attacks on provision trains, the robbing and killing of teamsters, the burning of wagons, and the stealing of 175 mules, all of which he attributed to the Pawnee.

W. F. SWASEY

The letters sent by Assistant Quartermaster and Acting Commissary of Subsistence Swasey (4 vols.) include letters that refer to the activities of the Hupa and Klamath Indians in the vicinity of Fort Humboldt, Calif. Many of these letters pertain to capturing and moving Indian prisoners, issuing stores to them, or reimbursing civilians who provided food to Indian prisoners on their way to Fort Humboldt.

Cartographic Records

General cartographic records, 1820–1951, include maps showing Indian lands and cessions and a sketch of a proposed road through the Choctaw country in Indian Territory.

RECORDS OF THE OFFICE OF THE
COMMISSARY GENERAL OF SUBSISTENCE
(RECORD GROUP 192)

The Office of the Commissary General of Subsistence was in charge of purchasing and issuing rations for the Army from 1818 until 1912, when the Office was abolished and its functions transferred to the Office of the Quartermaster General. This record group consists of 842 cubic feet of correspondence, reports, compilations, provision books, records of contracts, accounts, and other records, 1818–1912, with a few documents dating as early as 1812. The records contain information concerning furnishing subsistence—basically food—to Indian enlistees and their families, Indian prisoners, Indians being moved, and destitute Indians. Such information is usually found among the letters received on forms that list the cost and quantity of goods furnished. There are also records concerning the purchase of provisions from Indians.

For the most part information about Indians is widely dispersed, but there is a volume with a record of subsistence stores furnished to Indians, 1827–30, in which are itemized the types and amounts of food issued to Indians at certain military posts. There is also a provision book, 1875–81, in which are recorded the amounts of different kinds of rations issued and, occasionally, the cost of the rations, the place where the goods were received, and the name of the officer who received them. In a volume entitled "Refundments to Appropriations for Subsistence of the Army," 1876–89, are entries concerning refunds to Army accounts of amounts chargeable to the Department of the Interior for the issue of subsistence to Indians.

From 1830 to 1836 the Office of the Commissary General of Subsistence was in charge of Indian removal, but the records concerning this activity are now in Records of the Bureau of Indian Affairs, Record Group 75. Many other records taken from the files of the Office of the Commissary General of Subsistence are now in Records of the Office of the Quartermaster General, Record Group 92. See page 279.

RECORDS OF THE OFFICE OF THE
CHIEF OF ENGINEERS
(RECORD GROUP 77)

The present Corps of Engineers originated in an act of the Congress of March 16, 1802 (2 Stat. 132), which authorized the President to establish such a corps at West Point to constitute a military academy. Orders of April 3, 1818, which directed the Chief Engineer as the commanding officer of this corps to fix his headquarters in Washington, resulted in the establishment of the War Department office now known as the Office of the Chief of Engineers. In the same year the Army's topographical engineers, established by an act of the Congress of March 3, 1813 (2 Stat. 819), were placed under the supervision of the Chief Engineer. The topographical engineers remained under the jurisdiction of the Chief Engineer until 1831, when a general order issued by the Secretary of War made the Topographical Bureau an independent office of the War Department. The Army Reorganization Act of July 1838 (5 Stat. 256) granted the topographical engineers the status of a corps equal to that of the Corps of Engineers. On March 3, 1863, by "An Act to promote the efficiency of the Corps of Engineers" (12 Stat. 743), the Topographical Corps was once again merged with the Corps of Engineers.

In addition to such military duties as producing and distributing Army maps, building roads, planning camps, and constructing and repairing fortifications and other installations, the corps has had civil duties most notably maintaining and improving inland waterways and harbors and flood control projects.

Letters received by the central office, 1826–66, include a few widely dispersed documents relating to Indians. There are, for example, some letters of 1832 relating to the furnishing of steamboats to move the Choctaw Indians to their new home west of Arkansas. In several reports submitted in 1849, Lt. W. H. C. Whiting related his encounters with Indians in Texas. In a journal of his reconnaissance from San Antonio to Bexar to El Paso del Norte, Whiting related his encounters with Lipan, Comanche, and Apache Indians. In a journal of a march from San Antonio to El Paso, he described his experiences with Apache Indians under Chief Gomez and his councils with the Indians in which he attempted to convince them of the good intentions of the Government. In a letter of June 19, Whiting reported on recent Indian depredations in Texas and urged the establishment of moving companies of dragoons on the southwestern frontier as the best possible means of dealing with the situation.

In a two-volume series of reports on fortifications and topographical surveys, 1812–23, there is a copy of Capt. Hugh Young's "Topographical Memoir on East and West Florida With Itineraries," submitted in 1818. Part of the report deals with the Seminole Indians in East Florida, with comments as to their different tribal groups, customs and manners, wars and treaties, councils, marriages, trade, amusements, the influence and rank of women, property, the power of chiefs, burials, religion and superstitions, and holidays.

In an unregistered series of reports and histories received, 1817–94, there are a few items relating to Indians. A letter written December 20, 1800, by Uriah Tracy, relating to an inspection of the posts of the Northwest Territory, condemns the Government for not fulfilling the terms of a treaty, criticizes dishonest traders, recommends the type of gifts to be given Indians, and discusses the British policy toward Indians. In his report of February 1821 on the exploration of western rivers, Col. Stephen H. Long describes the various Indian tribes encountered, their languages, living conditions, and attitudes toward whites. John L. Sullivan's report of December 1824, describing the first expedition of the Pacific Fur Company, refers to the Flathead and Shoshoni Indians in Idaho. In a memoir dated October 1857, Capt. T. J. Cram describes an attack upon Indians in Idaho.

Dispersed among later general correspondence, particularly in the correspondence concerning rivers and harbors, 1923–42 (1,328 ft.), is information concerning flood control and other projects affecting Indian lands. Much of the material relates to negotiations between the Office and the Bureau of Indian Affairs for the use of Indian land and to the damages and benefits that might result from the various projects. There are also records on these subjects among those of Engineer divisions and districts in several Federal archives and records centers.

Among the letters received by the Topographical Bureau, 1824–64 (66 ft.), are several reports that refer to Indians. The Pawnee and Osage Indians are mentioned in Capt. Nathan Boone's report, dated August 1843, of his march from Fort Gibson to the southwest prairies. A peace talk with a band of Comanche Indians led by Wolf Shoulder is described in Lt. James H. Simpson's report of August 14, 1849, on the exploration and survey of a route from Fort Smith, Ark., to Santa Fe. A similar report by Simpson, dated April 1850, contains a survey of the New Mexican Indians and a comparative vocabulary of six different linguistic groups. In the report of his expedition in 1858 from Fort Dalles to Fort Walla Walla, Lt. John Mullan discusses the Whitman massacre.

There is also one separate series of records of the Topographical Bureau relating to the migration of Indians from Ohio to Missouri under the direction of Lt. Col. John J. Abert in 1832 and 1833 (1 in.). In addition to the correspondence of Abert, there are deeds to the land sold by Indians to the Government, a list of the number of Indians east of the Mississippi River and the number who had already migrated west, a table showing the land held by each Indian tribe south and west of the Missouri River and between Ponca Creek and the Red River, and a list of Indian treaties. Many of these documents are incomplete.

Cartographic Records

The headquarters map file includes manuscript and annotated maps of military and civilian geographical explorations and surveys beginning in the late 1700's, showing the locations of Indian tribes and bands.

The first Government-sponsored exploring expedition was carried out between 1804 and 1806 by Lewis and Clark, who had been authorized by President Jefferson to explore the Louisiana Purchase, report on its resources, and find a route across the vast area. Copies of two maps of the expedition in the headquarters map file show the general locations of Indian tribes, bands, and villages, some with numbers of "souls," tents, or lodges. These maps are identified as "A map of part of the Continent of North America Between the 35th and 51st degrees of North Latitude, and extending from 89° of West Longitude to the Pacific Ocean" and "A Map of Lewis and Clark's Tract Across the Western Portion of North America, from the Mississippi to the Pacific Ocean, by order of the Executive of the United States in 1804, 5 & 6."

The Corps of Topographical Engineers, established in 1813, conducted many expeditions and reconnaissances in the West and produced maps that show not only important information about the topography of the country but also the location of Indian tribes and villages, sometimes giving the estimated population and noting especially the number of warriors. Outstanding among the exploring expeditions were Maj. Stephen H. Long's expedition to the Rocky Mountains, 1819–20; Capt. John C. Fremont's expedition to the Rocky Mountains, 1842, and to Oregon and northern California, 1843–44; and explorations for a railroad route from the Mississippi River to the Pacific Ocean, 1853–57. Examples of maps produced on such expeditions among the records of the Office of the Chief of Engineers are a "Map of the Country situated between the Meridian of Washington City and the Rocky Mountains exhibiting the route of the late Exploring Expedition commanded by Maj. Long, together with other recent surveys and explorations by himself and others" and a "Map of an Exploring Expedition to the Rocky Mountains in the year 1842 and to Oregon and Northern California in the years 1843–44 by Brevet Capt. J. C. Fremont of the Corps of Topographical Engineers. . . ."

Lt. G. K. Warren's "Map of the Territory of the United States from the Mississippi to the Pacific Ocean . . . To accompany the Reports of the Explorations for a Railroad Route, . . ." compiled from 1854 to 1857, included the results of Topographical Engineer expeditions over a period of 15 years. This was the first reasonably accurate map of the West. Included in the wealth of information on it are the names of mountains, rivers, forts, towns, and Indian tribes. Published in 1857, the map was recompiled and redrawn by Edward Freyhold from 1865 to 1868 under the direction of the Chief of the Corps of Engineers. Changes were made to include information obtained from further explorations between 1857 and 1868. Published copies of the new edition, annotated in 1873 to show Indian reservations and additions to and corrections of railroads, are in the headquarters map file of the Office of the Chief of Engineers.

Maps of civilian explorations in the Indian country include a copy of Josiah Gregg's map of the "Prairies," about 1840, and J. N. Nicollet's map of the sources of the Mississippi and the Red River of the North, 1836–37. Nicollet was assisted, 1838–40, by Lt. John C. Fremont in a survey over the same area. The more detailed "Map of the Hydrographical Basin of the Mississippi River" resulted from this expedition. These and other maps of civilian explorations show names of Indian tribes and villages.

Several maps showing explorations in the Indian country west of the Mississippi River are among the record set of published maps of the Office of the Chief of Engineers.

The headquarters map file of the Office of the Chief of Engineers also includes a group of I.R. (Indian Relations) maps that date from about 1820 to 1880. Most of these maps are manuscript or annotated. Several early maps show areas ceded by Indian tribes in treaties or purchased from them. Many of the maps are of the areas west of Missouri and Arkansas that were assigned to the different tribes of emigrant Indians. Included are the surveys of Isaac McCoy in 1832; a copy of a map compiled by William Clark, St. Louis Superintendent of Indian Affairs, in 1833; and an annotated published map of Indian Territory and part of Kansas in 1866, showing Indian lands and reservations. There is also a tracing of an 1859–60 map of the Yellowstone and Missouri Rivers, revised to 1876 and annotated to show Indian reservations, exploration routes, and battlegrounds. There are four annotated copies of a map of the "Territory of the United States from the Mississippi River to the Pacific Ocean, . . . " 1865–68, one of which is annotated to show Indian reservations established by treaty or Presidential order from 1866 to 1870 and another to show Indian reservations and proposed reservations to January 1873.

Audiovisual Records

Among photographs made by Timothy H. O'Sullivan during the U.S. Geographical Surveys West of the One Hundredth Meridian (Wheeler Survey) are 30 items showing Zuñi, Navajo, Ute, and Coyotero and Jicarilla Apache Indians and their activities and homes in New Mexico and Arizona Territories, 1871 and 1873–74.

RECORDS OF THE OFFICE OF THE
JUDGE ADVOCATE GENERAL (ARMY)
(RECORD GROUP 153)

An Office of the Judge Advocate of the Army was established in the Continental Army in 1775. From 1797 to 1821 Judge Advocates for the Army were authorized by Federal law, and in 1849 an Office of the Judge Advocate for the Army was established by statute. A law of 1862 designated the position as Judge Advocate General and provided that all records of courts-martial and military commissions be forwarded there. Until 1835 such records had been filed in the Office of the Secretary of War and, subsequently, in the Office of the Adjutant General. The 1862 act also provided that each army in the field should have a judge advocate. In 1864 the Judge

Advocate General became the head of the new Bureau of Military Justice. In 1884 the Judge Advocate General's Department was established by consolidating the Bureau of Military Justice with the Corps of Judge Advocates. The primary functions of the Judge Advocate General were to administer military justice and to render opinions on questions of law referred to him by the Secretary of War, Adjutant General, or Commanding General of the Army.

Case Files Of Military Courts And Commissions

The case files dating from 1809 are relatively complete. Typically, each file contains a transcript of the court proceedings; in some instances related documentation, such as correspondence, also is included. Most indexing is by name of the court-martialed defendant, so that his name and the approximate date are necessary to locate the files.

The most significant case files pertaining to Indians are those of military courts of inquiry convened to investigate specific engagements or campaigns. Such a court convened at Frederick, Md., November 28, 1836, to inquire into the lack of progress by Brig. Gens. Winfield Scott and Edmund P. Gaines in their campaigns against the Seminole Indians in Florida and the Creek Indians in Georgia and Alabama. The files include extensive supporting documentation, primarily correspondence (files CC–197, 198, and 199). Similarly, a court of inquiry convened at Knoxville, Tenn., October 2, 1837, to examine the policies pursued by Brig. Gen. John E. Wool with regard to the Cherokee Indians in Alabama. The supporting documents include a letter from President Andrew Jackson to Wool, September 7, 1836, containing instructions for the removal of the Cherokee Indians to the West (file CC–278). A court of inquiry convened at Denver, Colorado Territory, in February 1865, to investigate the conduct of Col. John M. Chivington, 1st Colorado Cavalry Regiment, during the campaign against the Cheyenne Indians in 1864, particularly the massacre at Sand Creek, Colorado Territory, November 29, 1864 (file MM–2867). Similarly, a board of inquiry convened at Fort Phil Kearny, Dakota Territory, in April 1867 to investigate the destruction of troops commanded by Capt. William J. Fetterman in an engagement with Sioux Indians, December 21, 1866. In addition to the transcript of the investigation, the case file includes reports by Col. Henry B. Carrington, commander at Fort Phil Kearny, and other officers of the 18th Infantry Regiment, June 1866–January 1867 (file OO–2236). *M592, Proceedings of a Court of Inquiry Concerning the Conduct of Maj. Marcus A. Reno at the Battle of the Little Big Horn River on June 25 and 26, 1876* (file QQ–979), includes much detailed information about the battle.

Indians who served in the Volunteer or Regular Army of the United States were subject to trial by court-martial, as were all other soldiers. Some soldiers of the 3d Indian Home Guard Regiment were tried at Fort Gibson, Cherokee Nation, in July 1864 for desertion, absence without leave, and murder (file NN–3003). In November 1881, Apache Indian scouts charged with mutiny and murder against soldiers of the 6th Cavalry Regiment at Cibecue Creek, Arizona Territory, on August 30 were tried by a military court at Whipple Barracks (file QQ–2821). Further information about the Cibecue Creek incident is available in the case file for a subsequent court of inquiry (file QQ–3410). The court met in August 1882 to investigate the conduct of Col. Eugene A. Carr, 6th U.S. Cavalry, during the affair.

Indians who did not serve in the Army were nevertheless, on occasion, tried in military courts. There is, for example, a file pertaining to trials by military commissions of Sioux Indians Tahta-e-chash-na-manne (Medicine Bottle) and Shakopee (Little Six) at Fort Snelling, Minn., in 1864 and Wowi-na-pa at Fort Abercrombie, Dakota Territory, in 1863 (file NN–3132). These Indians had participated in the Sioux wars against the Federal Government.

White soldiers accused of misconduct involving Indians were also subject to trial by court-martial. A court of inquiry was convened at Camp Apache, Arizona Territory, May 10, 1877, to investigate allegations made by John Clum, U.S. Indian agent at the San Carlos Reservation, against Capt. William S. Worth, 8th U.S. Infantry Regiment. Worth was charged with giving liquor, guns, and ammunition to the Indians and with other offenses detrimental to maintaining good order at the reservation (file QQ–270).

Occasionally, Army officers involved in the peacetime administration of Indian affairs found their policies subject to investigation by military courts and commissions. For example, an 1884 court of inquiry investigated the policies pursued by Capt. Emmet Crawford, military administrator of the San Carlos Reservation in Arizona Territory. The investigation revealed considerable information about the lives of the Chiricahua Apache on the reservation and their relations with the military and civil authorities. Subjects investigated included the issuance of cattle and other goods under the auspices of the Bureau of Indian Affairs, the trial of an Indian by a military court, the attitude of the Indians toward the military officers, and the selection of Indian children to attend the school at Carlisle, Pa. (file RR–440).

Correspondence

Copies of outgoing correspondence are relatively complete from 1842. Files of incoming letters are less complete, many evidently having been transferred to other offices. In his outgoing correspondence, the Judge Advocate General rendered opinions and furnished information on various legal questions affecting the status of Indians and their relationships with non-Indians. Generally the reply was given in response to an incoming inquiry, such as from the Adjutant General's Office. In August 1881, for example, the Judge Advocate General stated that "in trials by courts martial Indians are competent witnesses, provided they understand the obligation of an oath, believe in a future state of rewards and punishments and in a Supreme being." Another ruling in 1881 provided that the President could employ military forces to arrest persons cutting timber or taking coal on the Cherokee Reservation. In a 1907 opinion, the Judge Advocate General ruled that Ute Indians who recently had surrendered to the Army in Wyoming were to be considered prisoners of war to the extent of clothing and feeding them but that the expenses were not to be borne by the War Department. Other opinions rendered through correspondence dealt with such questions as the status of Indians who had enlisted and served in the Army, the introduction of liquor on Indian reservations, and the imprisonment of Indians by the Army at the request of civil authorities.

Opinions of the Attorney General

The records consist of copies of opinions and decisions of the Attorney General, with a few of the Secretary of War, 1821–70. Generally, the rulings were made at the request of the War Department and concerned legal questions that confronted it, some of them dealing with various Indian matters. In August 1833, for example, Attorney General Roger B. Taney ruled that the President could direct the marshal of the district to use military force in removing intruders from Creek and Cherokee lands in Alabama. Other opinions dealt with Indian titles to land, the seizure of goods illegally introduced into Indian country, the subsistence of Seminole and Creek Indians removed to the West, and bounties due to soldiers of the Indian Home Guard who had served during the Civil War.

RECORDS OF THE OFFICE OF THE
INSPECTOR GENERAL
(RECORD GROUP 159)

An Inspector General's Department was established under the War Department by an act of March 3, 1813 (2 Stat. 819). However, not until 1863 did the Adjutant General direct the Inspector General in Washington, D.C., to receive reports from inspectors in the field regarding their stations and activities, and not until 1864 were all inspection reports regularly submitted to the Inspector General's Office. Previously, inspection reports had been sent to the Adjutant General's Office or the Headquarters of the Army. Consequently, the records of the Inspector General's Office in this record group contain no inspection reports predating 1863, except for a small collection dating from 1814 to 1842. These early reports originally were among the records of the Adjutant General but were transferred to the Office of the Inspector General in 1894. The entire series has been reproduced as

M624, *Inspection Reports of the Office of the Inspector General, 1814–1842.*

Inspection Reports

Most of the material pertaining to Indians is found in reports submitted from 1865 to 1880. During this period, inspection reports were considered correspondence and filed as letters received. There are approximately 60 linear feet of such correspondence for the period from 1863 to 1894. Often, reports are filed by the military department or division in which they originated rather than by the surname of the individual who submitted the report. Inspection reports were not made exclusively by officers of the Inspector General's Office. Often an inspecting officer would request reports from other officers in the field and would forward them with his own to Washington. Occasionally an officer not of the Inspector General's Office would forward a report directly to the Inspector General.

Information about Indians is in a number of different types of reports. Officers inspecting western military posts frequently reserved portions of their reports for comments on the Indians inhabiting the post or surrounding area. Indian reservations under military control, such as Grand River, Whetstone, and Lower Brulé, Dakota Territory, also were inspected and reports were submitted. (Some of these reports reveal certain attitudes on the part of the inspecting officer. Capt. Henry Clayton, commander at Grand River Agency, reported in 1871 to Col. James A. Hardie regarding the Sioux that "their principal occupations are dancing and eating rations furnished by the Indian Bureau. Their disposition is proud, cunning and idle, and they are not inclined to follow the example set by their neighbors, the 'Rees,' and enter the first state to civilization by industrious farming.") Inspection reports of western military commands also contain information about the Indians in a particular geographical area and some contain data about the names and numbers of the tribes, their location, disposition toward whites, and way of life. Other inspection reports relate to Indian campaigns, and a few have recommendations for overall changes in the administration of Indian affairs. Below is a list of representative inspection reports containing information about Indians.

Maj. Gen. Edmund P. Gaines' report of June 6, 1828, regarding the administration of Indian affairs; Gaines viewed the policies pursued as "radically defective" and suggested improvements (M624, roll 2).

Reports submitted by Col. Randolph B. Marcy, August 15, 1864, and February 22, 1865, on the cattle stolen from loyal Cherokee, Creek, and Choctaw Indians by U.S. troops and citizens of Kansas (files M–70–IGO–1864 and M–20–IGO–1865).

Col. James A. Hardie's report of May 1865 on the Department of New Mexico, containing information and statistics about the Navajo Reservation at Fort Sumner, New Mexico Territory (file H-40/5-IGO-1865).

Maj. Gen. John Pope's report of October 23, 1865, on the Department of the Missouri, with particular emphasis on Indian affairs (file M-75-IGO-1865).

Maj. Gen. Irvin McDowell's report of March 23, 1866, on the District of Arizona. The report briefly mentions Indians on the Colorado River, including the Cocopa, Yuma, Yavapai, Mohave, Walapai, and Chemehuevi tribes; South Gila Indians, including the Papago, Pima, and Maricopa tribes; and Apache Indians, including the Tonto, Pinal, Coyotero, Sierra Blanco, and Sonora tribes (file C-17-IGO-1866).

Maj. Gen. Henry W. Halleck's report of August 4, 1866, of a personal tour of inspection in Nevada, Oregon, Idaho, and Washington, with extensive comments on the hostile Indians in the area (file P-22 1/2-IGO-1866).

Col. D. B. Sackett's report of October 26, 1866, on the territory between the Mississippi River and the Pacific Ocean. This report contains information about the Bannock, Snake, Pend d'Oreille, Flathead, Crow, Grosventre, Blackfeet, and Sioux tribes (file S-42-IGO-1866).

Reports submitted in 1867 pertaining to the cost of feeding and supplying Navajo Indians at Fort Sumner, New Mexico Territory, in 1866 and 1867 (files M-8 1/2-IGO-1867 and M-33-IGO-1867).

Reports submitted in 1867 pertaining to the administration of Indian affairs at Maxwell's Ranch, New Mexico Territory, including a report by Col. Christopher Carson denying any irregularities (file M-34-IGO-1867).

Documents submitted in late 1868 and early 1869 relating to the subsistence of Navajo Indians in New Mexico Territory. Included are reports, correspondence, contracts, and proposals for furnishing foodstuffs (file I-2-IGO-1868).

Reports and correspondence submitted in early 1869 about the furnishing of foodstuffs and other supplies to Crow Indians in Montana Territory (file I-1-IGO-1868).

Capt. Murray Davis' report of November 12, 1868, pertaining to Indian affairs at the Hoopa Valley Reservation (file P-23/19-IGO-1868).

Col. N. H. Davis' report of December 16, 1868, relating to Fort Lowell, New Mexico Territory, and the Indians in the vicinity, including Moache, Capote, and Wiminuche Ute; Jicarilla Apache; and Navajo (file M-4-IGO-1869).

Col. N. H. Davis' report of February 28, 1869, recommending the issue of food and supplies to settlers in the Solomon, Saline, and Republican Valleys in Kansas who had suffered from Indian depredations. Included is a list numbering males, females, and children in each stricken family; noting the losses sustained; and estimating the cost of the rations needed to relieve destitution (file M–19–IGO–1869).

Lt. Col. Roger Jones' report of August 25, 1869, regarding Indians living on the Klamath Reservation in Oregon (file P–16–IGO–1869).

Col. N. B. Sweitzer's report of September 18, 1869, giving a general classification of the Indian tribes living or roaming in the Department of the Platte (file P–21–IGO–1869).

Reports received by Col. James A. Hardie in 1871 pertaining to affairs at the Grand River, Whetstone, Cheyenne River, and Lower Brulé Indian Agencies (file M–49–IGO–1871).

Col. D. B. Sackett's report of June 30, 1873, relating to Arizona, "with some notes on its Indians" (file A–59–IGO–1873).

Col. James A. Hardie's report of June 14, 1873, relating to an inspection of Fort Colville, Washington Territory, with remarks about the Indians of the area (file C–10–IGO–1873).

Col. James A. Hardie's report of September 30, 1873, of a tour of inspection of the Department of the Columbia with extensive comments regarding the Indian population. The enclosures to this report include statistical charts relating to the Indians of the Washington and Oregon Superintendencies, which indicate the tribes and their habitats, disposition, numbers, names of agents and agencies, and names of principal chiefs and headmen (file C–25–IGO–1873).

Col. N. H. Davis' report of July 15, 1873, relating to the Indians at Fort Abraham Lincoln, Camp Stevenson, and Camp Hancock, Dakota Territory (file D–35–IGO–1873).

Col. N. H. Davis' report of October 8, 1873, which includes sketches of the military stations and buildings at Grand River and Lower Brulé Indian Agencies (file D–52–IGO–1873).

Reports received by Col. N. H. Davis in 1873 from officers and post commanders concerning the Indian situation at Forts Ellis, Shaw, and Benton, Washington Territory; Forts Buford, Stevenson, Abraham Lincoln, Rice, Randall, Pembina, and Totten and Indian agencies at Cheyenne River, Grand River, and Lower Brulé, Dakota Territory; and Fort Ripley, Minn. (file D–57–IGO–1873).

Col. James A. Hardie's reports of May 30 and September 30, 1873, relating to his investigation of the Modoc campaign of 1873. Enclosures to the reports include maps showing the Tule Lake area and defensive fortifications used by the Modoc. There is also a report by Maj. Edwin C. Mason regarding the murder of Gen. Edward R. S. Canby by the Indians (files P-4-IGO-1873 and C-25-IGO-1873).

Reports received by Col. N. H. Davis in 1874 from commanding officers at Camps Gaston and Wright, Calif.; Camps McDermitt and Halleck, Nev.; and Fort Hall, Idaho Territory. Included is information about irregularities at the Hoopa Valley Reservation (file D-81-IGO-1874).

Reports received by Col. N. H. Davis in 1874 relating to Indian tribes in Alaska (file D-3-IGO-1875).

James A. Hardie's report of September 26, 1875, of an inspection in the Department of Arizona, with remarks about the Indian tribes. A report by Capt. H. C. Egbert regarding the Indians of the Fort Yuma area and their habits, mode of life, religion, amusements, manufactures, clothing, and personal appearance is enclosed (file H-36-IGO-1875).

Col. Randolph B. Marcy's report of July 25, 1878, recommending the transfer of the Indian Bureau from the Department of the Interior to the War Department (file 616-IGO-1878).

Col. John Gibbon's report of October 8, 1879, relating to an inspection of Fort Keogh, Montana Territory, with comments about the Indians on the post (file 1032-IGO-1879).

Maj. A. A. Arnold's annual report of inspection of the Department of Arizona, August 20, 1882, with comments about Indians. Enclosed is a printed pamphlet by 1st Lt. George S. Wilson, *The Indian Question: An Attempt to Answer One Phase in Detail* (Whipple Barracks, Arizona Territory, 1882). This publication contains overall recommendations regarding Indian policy (file 909-IGO-1882).

Papers, 1912-13, relating to allegedly poor living conditions of Indians at Tanana, near Fort Gibbon, Alaska. The data was collected in response to an article about the Tanana Indians that appeared in the May 1912 issue of *The Spirit of Missions*. The article attempted to place partial blame for the Indians' problems on the military garrison. The file includes reports by the post commander and post surgeon, photographs, including some of Indian cabins, and a copy of the magazine containing the article (file 16465-IGO).

Records Relating to Dakota, Montana, and Modoc War Claims

These records (3 ft.) were created and received by Col. James A. Hardie, who investigated the claims in the 1870's. The claims were for goods and services furnished and Volunteer Army service performed by State and Territorial governments and private citizens in Dakota Territory during the Indian war of 1862, in Montana Territory during the Indian hostilities of 1867, and in Oregon and California during the Modoc war of 1872-73. Included is correspondence received and sent by Hardie during this period relating to the claims; a file of the *Yreka Union* newspaper, December 7, 1872–May 24, 1873, containing articles about the Modoc war; a map of Utah and Colorado prepared by order of Lt. Gen. William T. Sherman; letters received from Dr. J. B. W. Gardner at Camp Apache, Arizona Territory, containing information about the Indians there; and indexes, lists, and miscellaneous papers pertaining to claims and Volunteer Army service.

RECORDS OF THE OFFICE OF THE PAYMASTER GENERAL (RECORD GROUP 99)

The 559 cubic feet of records in this record group consist chiefly of correspondence and related records, 1799–1912, and ledgers and other account books, 1791–1917. The records primarily concern paying Army troops, including Indian scouts and interpreters, soldiers of the Indian Home Guard during the Civil War, and other Indians serving with the Army. There also are records about the pay of Army officers detailed as acting Indian agents and about costs resulting from Indian disturbances.

See Roland C. McConnell, comp., *Preliminary Inventory of the Records of the Paymaster General,* PI9 (1948).

RECORDS OF THE OFFICE OF THE CHIEF OF FINANCE (ARMY) (RECORD GROUP 203)

Before World War I there was no centralized agency for handling the finances of the War Department. There was, however, a Division of Requisitions and Accounts in the Office of the Secretary of War that kept a current general account of the status of appropriations, compiled annual estimates, and accounted for War Department funds drawn from the Treasury.

This record group includes letters sent by the Secretary of War concerning financial matters, 1800–1912, and accounting records of the Division of Requisitions and Accounts dating from the year 1792. They include much information about financial matters involving Indians and Indian administration, particularly before the Bureau of Indian Affairs was transferred from the Department of War to the Department of the Interior in 1849. Usually the information is more accessible in other sources, but occasionally these records can be useful on particular matters. One item of interest is a register of claims for pay by Volunteers in the Rogue River Indian war of 1854.

See Richard W. Giroux, comp., *Preliminary Inventory of the Records of the Office of the Chief of Finance (Army),* PI 142, revised by Maizie H. Johnson (1962).

RECORDS OF THE OFFICE OF THE
CHIEF SIGNAL OFFICER
(RECORD GROUP 111)

In the Signal Corps collection of historical photographs, 1917-39, are photographic copies of artworks dating from the French and Indian War and photographs dating from the 1860's. Approximately 600 of these items relate to Indians, from 1833 to 1910. Many are filed under "Indians," which is further subdivided by tribe or activity. Others are under such subjects as "Modoc War" or "General Crook's Expedition Against Geronimo." Most of those for Eskimos are filed under "Alaska-Point Barrow." A name and place index is available.

In an album of photographs made for the Valdez, Copper River, and Yukon Railroad, 1902, are 19 photographs of individuals and groups of natives living in this area of Alaska. In the Brady collection of Civil War photographs, 1861-74, are photographs of Indians identified as Hole-in-the-Day, Red Lion, and Spotted Leopard and a delegation on the White House grounds. It also includes photographs of Col. Ely Samuel Parker. A graduate of West Point and a member of Gen. U. S. Grant's staff, he was a grandnephew of Red Jacket and was later Commissioner of Indian Affairs.

There are also two educational films that show Indians in the Far Western States and Pueblo and Navajo Indians in the Southwestern States, 1942; a film of Crow Indians dancing for Marshal Foch in Montana and Sioux Indians greeting him in Bismarck, S. Dak., 1921; and two *Screen Magazine* films, each showing an Indian reservation, 1945.

RECORDS OF THE SELECTIVE SERVICE SYSTEM
(WORLD WAR I)
(RECORD GROUP 163)

The subject index to the records of the Office of the Provost Marshal General, the director of the World War I Selective Service System, indicates that there are about 165 documents relating to Indians dispersed among the records. They relate particularly to such subjects as registration on reservations and the exemption of noncitizen Indians from military service. Local board records concerning individual registrants are in FARC Atlanta.

RECORDS OF UNITED STATES
ARMY CONTINENTAL COMMANDS, 1821-1920
(RECORD GROUP 393)

From 1813 to 1921 the U.S. Army, for the purposes of administrative control, was organized into commands designated as geographical or territorial divisions and departments. These varied in name, jurisdiction, and total number, as reorganizations occurred frequently over the years. At times departments reported to divisions, and at other times they reported directly to the War Department. The military divisions were established to handle problems requiring an effort greater than one department could produce. From 1867 to 1891 the Military Division of the Missouri coordinated the efforts of three departments (Missouri, Dakota, and Platte) against the hostile Indians in the Middle West. The Department of Texas was added to the division in 1871. Each department and division had an organization of staff officers corresponding to the War Department bureaus, to which the staff officers were responsible for the technical aspects of their duties.

The territorial departments sometimes were divided into districts to authorize and enable the district commander, when necessary, to concentrate sufficient troops to take care of some crisis. Except for the brief periods when these districts existed, all of the posts, camps, forts, stations, and barracks, the troops stationed at them, and other miscellaneous elements, such as briefly organized U.S. troops and the many expeditions, were responsible to the departmental commander. The staff officers at the posts were responsible to their departmental counterparts for the technical aspects of their duties.

The records of U.S. Army continental commands are of the same types as those of the Adjutant General's Office, but they are organized separately for each individual command that created them. There are few consolidations of related records or records that summarize information, and, consequently, for many subjects the command records are harder to use than those of the Adjutant General's Office. The command records, on the other hand, include records that were not sent to the Adjutant General's Office, especially orders of lower level commands.

There are more than 10,000 cubic feet of these command records, divided into thousands of series created by hundreds of different commands. The more significant records of departments and divisions, districts, and military installations are discussed in this guide in sufficient detail to give some idea of the extent and nature of the records relating to Indians. Subject areas of particular interest to a command are emphasized, and more attention is given to special series of records than to the basic series of letters, orders, and other records, which usually were much the same for all commands. Not discussed are records, such as those of staff officers, that are predominantly technical or administrative, although these sometimes include information about Indians.

Although the field commands were primarily concerned with Indian wars and campaigns, the Army was interested in peaceful solutions to problems with Indians and performed duties other than policing and fighting them. Consequently, the correspondence series contains much correspondence with Indian agents and superintendents, commissioners, Indian chiefs, Interior Department officials, State and Territorial governors, and other officials.

See Elaine Everly, Alice Haynes, Maizie Johnson, Sarah Powell, Harry Schwartz, John Scroggins, Aloha South, and Evelyn Wade, comps., *Preliminary Inventory of the Records of United States Army Commands, 1821-1920*, PI 172 (1973).

Geographical Divisions and Departments

There are headquarters records of most of the geographical divisions and departments. Those with significant records concerning Indians are reasonably complete and can be used to study the daily production and flow of letters, reports, orders, and instructions relating to the business of the command. For example, in the records of the Department of the Columbia there are letters and endorsements sent, registers of letters received, letters received with accompanying indexes, and general and special orders for the period 1865 to 1913. There are also quarterly tabular statements of scouts and expeditions containing names of the posts from which parties were sent, the names of officers in command, organizations involved, expedition strength, inclusive dates, routes, distances traveled, and results. There also may be reports of persons killed or captured by Indians, court-martial records involving Indians, monthly reports of prisoners, recruiting records, and descriptive books.

In addition to the general headquarters records and the records of the staff officers, there are many special collections of records concerning relations with Indians and records of specific field expeditions. As a further example in the Department of the Columbia records, there are collections of records created by the department relating to the Modoc war of 1873, and there are also records created by the field headquarters of the Modoc expedition.

For each department and division the type and volume of headquarters correspondence is indicated, and illustrations of matters involving Indians are given. This is followed by a brief description of some of the special collections or series of records, if any exist, among the records of the department. The following select list of Indian expeditions and campaigns shows the commanding district and department.

Date	Name	District	Department
1850	Pit River Expedition	—	Pacific
1855	Sioux Expedition, Nebraska Territory	—	West
1855	Yakima Expedition, Washington Territory	—	Pacific
1858	Seminole or Florida War	—	Florida
1858	Expedition against Northern Indians, Washington Territory	Columbia River	Pacific
1858	Puget Sound Expedition	—	Pacific
1859	Colorado Expedition	—	Pacific
1862	Sibley's Indian Expedition	—	Northwest
1862–65	Sioux Indian Wars in Minnesota and Dakota	Minnesota	Northwest
1862	Owens Lake Expedition	—	Pacific
1864	Northwest Indian Expedition	Iowa	Northwest
1864	Sand Creek Massacre	Colorado	Kansas
1865–68	Indian Wars in Southern Oregon and Idaho, Northern California and Nevada	Boise and Owyhee Humboldt and Nevada	Columbia Pacific
1865	Connor's Powder River Expedition	Plains	Missouri
1866	Fetterman Massacre	Mountain	Platte
1867	Piney Creek "Wagon Box Fight"	Mountain	Platte
1867	Kansas Expedition	Upper Arkansas	Missouri
1868	Battle of the Washita	—	Missouri
1868	Republican River	—	Missouri
1873	Modoc Expedition	Lakes	Columbia
1873	Modoc War	Lakes	Columbia

Date	Name	District	Department
1873	Yellowstone Expedition	—	Dakota
1874	Sioux Expedition, Wyoming Territory	—	Platte
1874	Black Hills Expedition	—	Dakota
1874–75	Indian Territory Expedition	—	Missouri and Texas
1875–77	Sioux War	—	Dakota and Platte
1876	Big Horn and Yellowstone Expedition	—	Dakota and Platte
1877	Nez Percé Campaign	Yellowstone Clearwater	Dakota and Platte Columbia
1878–79	Cheyenne Outbreak	—	Platte and Missouri
1878	Bannock Campaign	—	Platte and Columbia
1879	Ute War, Colorado	—	Platte and Columbia
1880's	Apache Campaigns (Geronimo, Victorio)	—	Missouri and Arizona
1890	Sioux Outbreak and Battle of Wounded Knee	—	Platte and Dakota Missouri and Columbia

10TH MILITARY DEPARTMENT, 1846–51

The 10th Military Department originally consisted of Oregon Territory and as much of Mexican Upper and Lower California as became subject to the authority of the United States. After August 1848 it was limited to the former province of Upper California, which became the State of California. Most of the records (13 vols. and 3 ft.) of this department have been reproduced as M210.

The correspondence series includes complaints from civilians about stolen horses, poisoned arrows, Indian depredations, and losses sustained. There are many reports of trips made to study the Indian situation, instructions pertaining to the treatment to be accorded Indians, and letters describing Indian attitudes to the Roman Catholic missions. More specifically, there is a letter to Gen. Stephen Kearny in May 1847 complaining that Indians from different villages were camping on the writer's farm to organize themselves for defense against the Californians.

DEPARTMENT OF ARIZONA, 1870–93

The headquarters correspondence containing letters sent (28 vols.) and letters received (123 ft.) is particularly helpful for studying the campaigns against the Apache Indians. After the letters received for 1886 are a number of detailed reports submitted by officers who headed expeditions during the Apache campaign of 1885–86. There are also useful specific collections.

Records of the U.S. troops stationed in the field in southwestern Arizona under Col. Eugene A. Carr contain letters, telegrams, and endorsements sent (11 vols.) and letters received (2 ft.). This correspondence details the movements of these troops, who were engaged in scouting operations against Victorio and his band of Chiricahua and Mescalero raiders, during the period 1878 to 1880. In addition to the correspondence series, there are issuances (4 vols.) and a small body of miscellaneous records (6 in.) consisting mostly of scouting reports.

During September and October 1881, Colonel Carr commanded another body of U.S. troops, this time in the District of Apache, who were primarily engaged in scouting operations in the field and policing the Fort Apache Reservation. In the records of the department are letters, telegrams, and endorsements sent and received (3 vols.).

During the same period a similar body of troops operated for the same purpose in the District of the Verde, for which there is a similar set of correspondence books (3 vols.). The operations were continued at Camp Price from March to October 1882. There is a single volume of letters, telegrams, and endorsements sent by the headquarters for operations against the Chiricahua at Willcox, Arizona Territory, during October 1881.

By far the largest collection within the department records is a series of correspondence relating to the Apache campaign of 1886 (9 ft.). It consists primarily of registered and unregistered letters, telegrams, and reports forwarded from various camps and posts in the field to departmental or field headquarters relating to the pursuit, surrender, and disposition of Geronimo and his Chiricahua Apache followers. Included are a large number of field operation reports submitted by officers commanding scouting parties and troop detachments in the field, circulars, and regimental, field, and court-martial orders. There are also reports from the Governor of Sonora and other Mexican officials to Gen. George Crook and his successor in command of the department, Gen. Nelson Miles, concerning the movement of Geronimo and the Chiricahua across and below the Mexican border.

Most of the correspondence is dated 1886, but there are some letters, telegrams, and reports as early as May 1885, when Geronimo left the Fort Apache Reservation with Mangus, Chihuahua, and Natchez. There are a number of dispatches between General Crook and General Sheridan relating to the surrender terms offered Geronimo in March and April 1886, as well as correspondence between Generals Crook and Miles after the former was relieved of command of the department.

Most of the letters sent and received in this series, however, are between General Miles and the various officers of the War Department and subordinate officers in the Department of Arizona and on detached service. There are a number of telegrams and letters between General Miles and Capt. Henry W. Lawton, 4th Cavalry, who led troops across the Mexican border and captured Geronimo in August 1886, along with letters, telegrams, and reports sent and received by headquarters concerning the imprisonment and final surrender of Geronimo's band in September 1886.

Closely connected with this large series are the letters and telegrams sent (3 vols.) by Gen. Nelson Miles from departmental headquarters in the field during the summers of 1886, 1887, and 1888. Those of the first summer cover the Apache campaign, May–July 1886, and include directions from General Miles to subordinate officers in the field, as well as reports on the progress of the campaign to Headquarters, Division of the Pacific. The letters and telegrams sent during June 1887 and August 1888 include reports to Headquarters, Division of the Pacific, and to subordinate officers in the department concerning conditions on the San Carlos Reservation. There is also a copy of General Miles' annual report of affairs in the department for 1886.

Included in the miscellaneous records of the department (1 ft.) are a list of letters received in 1881 containing reports of attacks made by Apache raiders within the department, a summary of actions taken by Indian agents and the Army at the San Carlos Reservation in 1877–78, and reports submitted by various officers on the attempted arrest of the Apache medicine man Nakaidoklini at Cibecue by forces led by Col. Eugene A. Carr in

August 1881. There are also manuscript reports (5 in.) including some telegrams and letters, 1880–85, which relate primarily to conditions at the Fort Apache (White Mountain) and San Carlos Reservations during August and September 1881, following the Cibecue incident.

DEPARTMENT OF THE COLUMBIA, 1865–1913

The headquarters correspondence series (84 vols. and 225 ft.) are important sources for material on the Modoc war of 1873, the part of the Nez Percé campaign in 1877 under the command of Gen. Oliver O. Howard, department commander, and the Bannock campaign the following year.

In a collection of letters received from Indian agents, December 1876–April 1878 (3 in.), are registered letters sent to the department headquarters in compliance with a request by General Howard that all Indian agents in the department make informal monthly reports of conditions at their agencies. The largest number of reports was received for December 1876, when the reporting system was begun.

A series of selected letters relating to the Indians in Oregon (4 in.) describes relations with the various Indian tribes there, ca. 1863–72. There are copies of letters and reports sent between the department and J. W. Perit Huntington and Alfred B. Meacham, both of whom served as superintendent of Indian affairs for Oregon during this period. There are also letters from officers serving in the districts and from the Governor of Oregon and a number of petitions and complaints against the Modoc received at headquarters in early 1872 from citizens of Jackson County, Oreg. A report accompanied by a lengthy transcript of a conversation among Maj. Elmer Otis, 1st Cavalry, two Indian agents, Captain Jack, and a group of about 30 Modoc in April also is included.

There are a number of series connected with the Modoc campaign, including a single volume of letters, endorsements, and issuances of the department commander, Gen. Jefferson C. Davis, in the field, April–July 1873. Among the department headquarters records is a small compilation of letters received by the department, 1863–73 (4 in.), which relate to the Modoc Indians. Of particular interest is a letter stating the comments believed to have been made by Captain Jack before his trial for the murder of Gen. Edward R. S. Canby. There is also a small series of field returns of troops operating against the Modoc. In addition, there are a volume of letters and endorsements sent and a volume of orders issued by the Modoc expedition, December 1872–June 1873, under the command of Maj. John Green, 1st Cavalry.

Two volumes of records relate to field headquarters before and during the Nez Percé campaign. One consists of letters and telegrams sent and field orders issued, April–July 1877. During this period General Howard traveled to Fort Walla Walla, Washington Territory, to plan for the proposed Army occupation of the Wallowa Valley, and to Fort Lapwai, Idaho Territory, to meet with the Nez Percé leaders. The other volume contains orders and circulars issued by field headquarters, July–September 1877.

There are a number of series relating to the Bannock campaign, June–August 1878, including telegrams sent and registers of letters received by field headquarters (2 vols.), as well as letters received and the reports of troops and staff operations (1 ft.). The telegrams were sent by General Howard and his aide-de-camp, relaying information and instructions to subordinate officers in the field and at posts. The letters received frequently reported movements of the Indians and requested instructions. In the operations reports are annual reports for 1878 submitted by the chief quartermaster, chief commissary of subsistence, and acting assistant inspector general, as well as reports submitted by commanding officers of companies of the 1st Cavalry and the 8th and 21st Infantry Regiments.

Capt. W. H. Winters, 1st Cavalry, commanded troops sent to remove Paiute prisoners from Camp Harney, Oreg., to the Yakima Reservation in Washington Territory. Two volumes of letters and endorsements sent to headquarters and orders issued relate to the progress of Winters' mission and to relations between certain Indians and white settlers in Washington Territory from January to May 1879. A few letters describing the relations between Indians and white settlers in the Territory during 1879 also are among the letters sent to headquarters by another expedition led by Maj. John Green, 1st Cavalry, from May to October 1879 (1 vol.).

DEPARTMENT OF DAKOTA, 1866–1911

The department letters sent (30 vols.) are incomplete, but the letters received (132 ft.) contain many valuable communications from the division commanders, subordinate officers, and field commanders relating to the many campaigns and expeditions under the jurisdiction of the department. These include the Yellowstone expedition of 1873, the Black Hills expedition of 1874, the Big Horn and Yellowstone expedition of 1876, the Nez Percé campaign of 1877, and the 1890 operation against the Sioux. Also among the headquarters records are several series relating to Indians generally: a volume of letters sent by the department headquarters in the field in the summers of 1867 and 1868 during operations against Indians in Montana Territory; a special collection of letters received from district offices, 1863–66, that relate to Sioux Indian matters (1 in.); and reports of two scouting expeditions against Indians in the vicinity of Sweetwater Bridge, Dakota Territory, in 1867.

In a volume of letters and telegrams sent in 1873 by the Yellowstone expedition under Col. George A. Custer are a few relating to two encounters with Indians on the Yellowstone River. Filed among the letters received, 1872–73 (8 in.), by the expedition is a copy of a report prepared in 1872 by the commander of the Middle District, Department of Dakota, regarding the difficulties encountered by the Army in persuading the Sioux to abide by their treaty obligations.

There is also a volume of issuances of the Black Hills expedition under Colonel Custer, issued June–August 1874, while on a reconnaissance through the Great Sioux Reservation.

In a volume of letters, endorsements, and telegrams sent by the Big Horn and Yellowstone expedition, May–October 1876, there are communications from the expedition commander, Gen. George Crook, to the Division of the Missouri at Chicago, the Department of Dakota, and other officers. Most of the letters relate to Crook's movements against the Sioux on Rosebud Creek in June 1876 and to his plans for an attack after the Sioux were joined by the Cheyenne.

In a volume of letters sent by the commanding officer of a troop of Indian scouts attached to Fort Keogh, Mont., from March to December 1890, there are letters sent by 1st Lt. E. W. Casey, 22d Infantry, to the Commanding General of the Army, the Commissioner of Indian Affairs, department headquarters, Indian agents, and staff officers at posts. These relate to an experiment launched at Fort Keogh of enlisting, organizing, and equipping a company of Northern Cheyenne and Sioux Indian scouts. Some of the letters contain descriptions of the Indians living on reservations within the department and of the past history of relations between these Indians and the Army.

EASTERN DIVISION, 1837–42

With effort, a few items relating to Indians can be found among the headquarters records of the Eastern Division. For example, in the headquarters records in a series of letters sent by Maj. Gen. Winfield Scott, there is a letter of July 30, 1839, to the Secretary of War describing Scott's talk to a group of 200–300 Winnebago Indians at the post at Niagara Falls, N.Y., in which he mentioned the Government's concern over their violation of an 1832 treaty and its plan to relocate them southwest of the Missouri River.

The most important series of the records of the division, however, is one relating to the removal of the Cherokee Indians in 1838 (2 ft.), which consists primarily of correspondence received but includes a few letters sent by Maj. Gen. Winfield Scott, commander of the Army of the Cherokee Nation in 1838. The correspondents included the Secretary of War, heads of War Department bureaus in Washington, D.C., subordinate Regular Army and Volunteer officers in the field, State officials, private citizens, and Cherokee leaders such as John Ross. Other documents include copies of orders and statements or invoices pertaining to supplies and equipment used for troops and Indians. There are a few documents for 1836 and 1837, when Brig. Gen. John E. Wool and Col. William Lindsay, respectively, commanded the military forces in the Cherokee Nation. The documents relate largely to the procedures followed by the Army in removing the Cherokee from North Carolina, Georgia, Tennessee, and Alabama to the West in 1838 and include some reports from officers who led migrating parties late in the year and observations made by Scott to the Secretary of War.

DEPARTMENT OF FLORIDA, 1856–58, AND U.S. TROOPS IN FLORIDA, 1850–56

Much of the information relating to the attempts by the Army and special Indian agents to remove the remaining Seminole Indians from Florida between 1850 and 1858 is among the letters, endorsements, and memorandums sent and received and orders issued by the headquarters of U.S. troops in Florida and the successor command, the Department of Florida (6 vols. and 9 ft.). Among the letters sent and received, 1850–56, are references to meetings with various Seminole leaders, including Sam Jones and Billy Bowlegs, and to the Seminole's feelings toward the Army and the various special Indian agents stationed in Florida.

A letter sent to the Adjutant General of the Army in March 1852 reports the conduct of the Indian delegation that returned to Florida to attend an Indian council held at Fort Myers, at which it was to be decided whether the remaining Seminole would migrate. A group of letters received at headquarters from the War Department, January–March 1850, concerns payments made to Seminole tribal chieftains by special Indian agents at certain Army posts to persuade the Indians to leave Florida.

Much of the correspondence and many of the orders issued by headquarters for the period December 1855 to April 1856 relate to preparations made by the Regular or Volunteer Army forces to remove forcibly the Seminole from the State. Letters and orders of departmental headquarters, for the remainder of 1856 through February 1858, relate to the Florida campaign to remove the Seminole along the southwest coast. The letters sent and received between March and April 1858, concern the gathering of the Seminole for removal to Indian Territory.

A three-volume "Memoir of Reconnaissances with Maps during the Florida Campaign" for the period January 1856 to February 1858 was prepared under the direction of Maj. Francis N. Page, who served as adjutant general of the Department of Florida during the campaign. The oversized maps and the sketches accompanying the memoir contain considerable detail of the country scouted during the various expeditions into southwestern Florida.

DEPARTMENT OF KANSAS, 1864–65

In the headquarters correspondence of this department are many communications with Army headquarters in Washington, D.C., and with district commanders in the department primarily concerned with Indian problems: Col. John Chivington, Colorado; Gen. James G. Blunt, Upper Arkansas; and Gen. Robert B. Mitchell, Nebraska.

Among the department records is a small series of letters and telegrams sent by department field headquarters, July–September 1864 (1 in.), during an expedition against the Indians on the upper Arkansas River who were believed responsible for the killings at Fort Larned in 1864. There is also a series of telegrams received by the Army of the Border, October 1864 (1 in.), containing reports of attacks on coaches and killings believed to have been committed by Indians in the western part of the department.

DIVISION OF THE MISSOURI, 1866–91

The headquarters correspondence of the division (27 vols. and 130 ft.) can be most useful because throughout its existence the Division of the Missouri, as the superior command of the Departments of Dakota, the Missouri, and the Platte, was involved with the Plains Indians; as the superior command of the Department of Texas beginning in 1870, it was confronted with Indian problems in Texas and New Mexico. However, as the coordinator of Indian matters in this vast area, the division's correspondence is most likely to be found in the consolidated correspondence of the Adjutant General's Office. Furthermore, it is the only command whose own records include a consolidated file of any size. As a consequence, searches in the general correspondence of the division headquarters may not prove as fruitful as anticipated.

Among the headquarters records is a volume of letters, telegrams, and endorsements sent by Gen. Nelson Miles, division commander, and his aide-de-camp, in the field between December 1890 and January 1891. The early letters relate to disturbances at Pine Ridge, Cheyenne River, Standing Rock, and other agencies connected with the rise of the ghost dance religion among the Sioux and Cheyenne. A number of letters of instructions to be followed in the case of an uprising were addressed to Gen. John R. Brooke, commander of the Department of the Platte, at Pine Ridge. There are also Miles' letters to Col. Eugene A. Carr, 6th Cavalry commander, explaining the mission and strategy of the Army's campaign against the Sioux and Cheyenne; to the Commanding General of the Army expressing views on the Army's role in implementing the Indian policy of the Federal Government; and to the Sioux chieftains who fled to the Badlands after the Battle of Wounded Knee.

Brought together in a series (5 ft.) are manuscript and printed copies of annual reports submitted to division headquarters by commanding officers of the Departments of Dakota, the Missouri, the Platte, and Texas for various years, between 1871 and 1887. These reports usually contain considerable information on Indian affairs. The annual reports of the Department of Dakota for most years have, as appendixes, reports of conditions within each district and at each post and Indian agency within the department. Letters, tables, lists, returns, and other related material have been attached to some of the other departmental reports.

By far the most important series in the records of the Division of the Missouri is the compilation of letters received that constitutes the special file. Almost all of the more than 30 files in this series, 1863–85 (21 ft.), relate in some way to Indian affairs within the division. Below is a brief description of some of these files.

INDIAN AFFAIRS IN NEW MEXICO, 1863–67 (½ in.)

These letters, orders, reports, and other documents received at division headquarters relate to conditions at the Bosque Redondo Reservation for the Navajo and Apache and to Indian affairs generally in the Department, later District, of New Mexico. Included is General Order 3, issued by the Department of New Mexico in February 1864, which contains a synopsis of the Indian scouts or expeditions made within the department in 1863.

INDIAN WAR, 1867 (4 in.)

This collection contains copies of letters that passed through the division office from many sources: the Departments of Dakota, the Platte, and the Missouri; subdistricts; and post commanders. There are many reports of proceedings of councils held in the field by Gen. Winfield Scott Hancock, commander of the Department of the Missouri, with head chiefs of several Indian tribes, including the Arapaho, Apache, Cheyenne, and Kiowa.

SEMINOLE-NEGRO INDIANS, 1872–76 (4 in.)

The subjects of these letters and reports are the Seminole-Negro Indians who had migrated from Arkansas to Mexico and again crossed the border in the spring of 1870 to settle at Forts Clark and Duncan in the Department of Texas. Much of the correspondence is between the Headquarters of the Army and the Interior Department concerning whether these people were to be considered "Indians" and settled on reservations.

YELLOWSTONE EXPEDITION, 1873 (4 in.)

These letters relate to the expedition under Col. David S. Stanley organized to escort parties of the Northern Pacific Railroad during the exploration, survey, and location of that road. Many of the letters relate to supplies and equipment, such as horses and wagons, but there is a copy of Col. George A. Custer's report of August 15, 1873, in which he tells of his engagements with Sioux Indians on August 4 and 11, 1873.

BLACK HILLS EXPEDITION, 1874–75 (6 in.)

For 1874 there are letters received relating to miners prospecting in the

Black Hills. For March–October 1875 there are letters and reports received by the Department of Dakota and forwarded to the division from Col. George Custer, commander of the Black Hills expedition, and other officers, including post commanders, relating to the Indians and movements of the expedition. The expedition had been organized to prevent any violation of the Indian Intercourse Act by parties of miners attempting to enter the Black Hills.

INDIAN TERRITORY EXPEDITION, 1874–75 (2 ft.)

The letters and telegrams in this file were received by the Department of the Missouri, the Department of Texas, and the Division of the Missouri during the expedition under Gen. Nelson Miles, which was launched after Kiowa, Cheyenne, and Comanche attacks on posts, agencies, and settlements along the Kansas and Colorado frontiers in the summer of 1874. Included are several letters concerning the Army's attempt to get the Interior Department to grant approval for an invasion of the Kiowa, Cheyenne, and Comanche reservations in retaliation for the attacks on white settlements.

INDIAN PONY FUND, 1874–79 (4 in.)

These letters and reports pertain to money derived from the sale of horses and mules captured by the Army from hostile Indians and deposited in accounts for the purchase of cattle and sheep for Indians on the reservations.

SIOUX WAR, 1875–77 (2 ft.)

At the beginning of this file is a register of the letters in it, which date from October 15, 1875, to November 1, 1877. The letters include one from Gen. Alfred H. Terry reporting the disaster that befell General Custer and his command on June 25, 1876, and the movements of the rest of the expedition until June 27, 1876. There is correspondence from the Indian agent at the Cheyenne River Agency, relating to the differences between the orders given by the commanding officers to the military and to the agent for the control of the Indians. A letter received through the Department of Dakota from the Standing Rock Agency, September 1876, reports the surrender of Kill Eagle, Little Wound, and 27 men who were in the Little Big Horn fight. A letter from Gen. George Crook, commander of the Big Horn and Yellowstone expedition, reports the movements of the expedition, June 20–September 25, 1876. The 1877 correspondence includes reports on the movements of hostile Indians, reports of the surrender of more hostile Sioux, and many communications from General Crook, then commanding the field headquarters of the Department of the Platte.

BIG HORN AND YELLOWSTONE EXPEDITION, 1876 (1 report)

This report of Gen. George Crook, commander of the expedition, is his official report of his engagement with hostile Sioux on Rosebud Creek,

June 17, 1876. It includes reports of the subordinate officers and a list of persons killed and wounded.

YELLOWSTONE EXPEDITION, 1876 (10 in.)

Composed mainly of telegrams and a few letters sent to Gen. Philip Sheridan, commander of the Division of the Missouri, this file relates to Gen. George Crook's Yellowstone expedition in 1876. Telegrams from March through July from posts along Crook's route report the progress of the march; others are from troop commanders continuously informing Sheridan of troop dispositions, Indian movements, affairs at Indian agencies, and fights with Indians. About July 6, the telegrams begin to relate mainly to Custer's disaster and rumors of it; they include a copy of Gen. Alfred H. Terry's written instructions to Custer.

SALE OF LIQUOR IN INDIAN TERRITORY, 1877–78 (4 in.)

Most of the letters in this file are either requests for permission to sell liquor for medicinal purposes in Indian Territory or complaints of abuses on the part of liquor licensees in Indian Territory. Among the letters of complaint is one sent to the Secretary of War (and later forwarded to the Division of the Missouri) by the Governor of the Chickasaw Nation and the Delegate and the Principal Chief of the Choctaw Nation.

NEZ PERCÉ WAR IN MONTANA, 1877–78 (1 ft.)

This file contains mostly telegrams received from the field during the campaign, but it also includes letters and several reports of operations.

CHEYENNE OUTBREAK, 1878–79 (1 ft.)

These letters, telegrams, and reports received by the Department of the Missouri, Department of the Platte, and Division of the Missouri concern the campaign conducted against the Northern and Southern Cheyenne who broke away from their reservations in 1878. Of particular interest are the proceedings of a board of officers investigating the arrest and escape of renegade Cheyenne Indians from Fort Robinson in January 1879 at the conclusion of the campaign. Among those testifying were Indians who took part in the incident.

WHITE RIVER INDIAN TROUBLES, 1879 (8 in.)

The letters, telegrams, and reports in this file were received from Col. Wesley Merritt, commanding the expedition; departmental headquarters of the Platte and the Missouri; district headquarters of New Mexico; and the Headquarters of the Army in Washington, D.C. They relate to the ordering of troops to put down an uprising among the Southern Ute in Colorado.

INDIAN TERRITORY LETTERS, 1879 (8 in.)

These letters, telegrams, and reports concern the Army's enforcement of President Rutherford B. Hayes' proclamation of April 26, 1879, forbidding emigrants to trespass on Indian Territory. Also included are a number of letters relating to encounters in September and October with Victorio's Apache band.

VICTORIO PAPERS, 1880 (8 in.)

These letters, telegrams, and reports were received from headquarters of the departments, various troop headquarters in the field, Headquarters of the Army in Washington, Mexican officials, and others concerning the pursuit and final destruction of Victorio and his band.

DEPARTMENT OF THE MISSOURI, 1861-98

The letters sent by the department headquarters (79 vols.) and the letters received (255 ft.) are important sources of information for many Indian campaigns and Indian tribes. The boundaries of the department changed frequently; but, generally, after 1865 the Department of the Missouri embraced Missouri, Kansas, New Mexico, Colorado, and Indian Territory. The departmental correspondence, consequently, is a source of information for Connor's Powder River expedition in the summer of 1865, the Battle of the Washita in 1868, Forsyth's scouts on the Republican River in 1868, the Indian Territory expedition of 1874 under Gen. Nelson Miles, the Cheyenne outbreak of 1878-79, the White River Indian troubles (Ute war) in Colorado in 1879, and other incidents. There is much correspondence with agents at the various agencies and various Indian commissioners and other officials of the Department of the Interior.

The headquarters records include a special file containing correspondence and reports relating to selected subjects (9 in.), one of which is Indian affairs. It includes a copy of the report of Gen. Alexander M. McCook of his journey with a congressional delegation to investigate the management of Indian affairs in the Territories west and south of the Missouri River in 1865; reports of Indian depredations in the vicinity of Julesburg, Colorado Territory, and Fort Laramie and South Pass, Dakota Territory, between February and October 1865; and reports and orders relating to the Department of Kansas Indian expedition in 1864. There also is a series (3 in.) of letters and telegrams received at headquarters relating to the removal of the Indian company (Co. I) of the 12th Infantry and certain Apache Indian prisoners from Mt. Vernon Barracks, Ala., to Fort Sill, Indian Territory, in 1894.

There are two volumes of letters, telegrams, and reports sent and received, July-October 1865, by Gen. Grenville M. Dodge, commander of the U.S. forces in Kansas and the Territories that were sent into the field against the Indians in Kansas, Iowa, and Nebraska and Colorado and Dakota Territories. Much of the correspondence relates to the protection of the overland routes from attack by the Cheyenne, Arapaho, and Sioux tribes and to the Powder River expedition led by Brig. Gen. Patrick E. Connor. Information on the expedition in Connor's letters and telegrams to Dodge at headquarters in the field was usually relayed to Gen. John Pope, commander of the Department of the Missouri. Dodge, in turn, forwarded Pope's instructions to Connor and to other officers of the expedition.

Among the records of the department are letters and telegrams sent, March–July 1867 (2 vols.), by department headquarters in the field known as the Kansas expedition. These letters and telegrams relate to the movements of Gen. Winfield Scott Hancock, departmental commander, and Lt. Col. George A. Custer against the Southern Cheyenne, Kiowa, and Comanche. General Hancock's letters to the Division of the Missouri contain interesting observations on the Indians met by the expedition and descriptions of the Indian villages through which he passed. Most of the telegrams are addressed to division headquarters and relate to plans for the expedition and anticipated movements in the field, including the movements of Custer's command.

There are also letters and endorsements sent and special orders issued (3 vols.) by the headquarters of Col. Nelson A. Miles' column of the Indian Territory expedition of 1874–75. Most of the letters and endorsements were sent to headquarters of the Department of the Missouri; they include vivid descriptions of several of the engagements with Indians, as well as Miles' own evaluations of the success of the expedition against the Kiowa, Cheyenne, and Comanche.

Also among the Department of the Missouri records are several small series of letters sent and received and orders and circulars issued, May–September 1880 (2 vols.), by the Fort Garland column during the Ute Indian campaign in Colorado and Utah.

DEPARTMENT OF NEW MEXICO, 1853–66, AND THE 9TH MILITARY DEPARTMENT, 1848–53

The 9th Military Department, with headquarters at Santa Fe, New Mexico Territory, was established shortly after the Mexican War to protect settlers and roads from Indian raiders. The troops had to contend with the Ute, Navajo, and Jicarilla, Mescalero, and Gila Apache Indians. By 1851 the department commander had been instructed to organize campaigns against the Indians. The letters sent by the department and its successor, the Department of New Mexico (10 vols.), and the letters received (3 ft.) document these campaigns. In addition, they describe many meetings with Indian agents in an attempt to execute the Government's Indian policies. There is much correspondence between Gen. James Carleton, department commander in the 1860's, and the War Department, the Governors of California and Arizona, the subordinate district offices, the Headquarters of the Army, and the superintendents of Indian affairs relating to hostile and friendly Indians, Indian attacks and depredations, the construction of dwellings for Indians, Indian delegations and councils, the guarding of roads and Indian prisoners, Apache hostilities, the surveying of reservations (such as Bosque Redondo), and the unsuccessful resettlement of the Navajo at Bosque Redondo.

In addition to headquarters correspondence, there are a number of other series with records concerning Indian affairs. Among letters and routine reports received, 1863-68 (8 in.), there is a report entitled "Numbers, Manners, Habits, and Customs of the Navajo and Apache Indians on the Bosque Redondo Reservation in New Mexico," prepared by Maj. Henry D. Wallen, 7th Infantry, in April 1864. Also in this series are reports of scouts after Indians made by detachments of troops from Fort Stanton, New Mexico Territory, in April and May 1866, and a statement of provisions issued to Indians at Fort Sumner, New Mexico Territory, in July 1866.

There is a series of records relating to Indian affairs, 1850-66 (6 in.), which contains reports to headquarters of progress made at the Navajo Indian Farm in 1865; reports and journals of scouts, marches, and Indian depredations within the department; copies of treaties made, in 1853 and 1855, with Apache, Ute, and Navajo bands in various parts of New Mexico; and the testimony of Indians examined by Gen. James H. Carleton in relation to murders committed near Red River, New Mexico Territory, in the spring of 1866.

Another series of miscellaneous records, 1850-66, contains the report of an expedition ordered from Fort Union, New Mexico Territory, to search for Indians accused of robbing a train on the Cimarron Route of more than 100 horses in 1862.

There are also two volumes of records of the Navajo expedition commanded by Col. Christopher Carson of the New Mexico Volunteers between July 1863 and June 1864. Most of the correspondence consists of letters sent by Colonel Carson to department headquarters, to the commanding officer of Fort Wingate, New Mexico Territory, and to various officers commanding in the field regarding the movements of the Indians; Navajo killed, captured, and taken prisoner; and descriptions of the country in which the Indians were located. There are also general and special orders and circulars issued by Carson directing movements in the field.

DEPARTMENT OF THE NORTHWEST, 1862-65

Throughout its existence this department was involved in the Sioux Indian war in Minnesota and Dakota. The years are covered fully by letters sent (3 vols.) and received (3 ft.) that document the problems of this department. The correspondence with Col. Henry H. Sibley, commander of the District of Minnesota and of many summer expeditions, with the Secretary of War and the Headquarters of the Army testify to the unfortunate Indian policy undertaken in Minnesota. The correspondence includes many reports relating to Sibley's meetings with the Sioux, scouts, skirmishes, the location of the Sioux, methods of pursuing the Indians, instructions for operating in Indian country during the summers, complaints that traders were selling arms and ammunition to the Indians, and the need for regulations. The most informative items are the annual reports, which relate in detail the operations of Sibley and Gen. Alfred Sully during each year.

Included with the department records are letters sent and received (4 in.) by Col. Henry H. Sibley's expedition to put down the Santee Sioux uprising in the fall of 1862. Sibley sent letters to officers commanding in the field and at posts in Minnesota, the Governor and the adjutant general of the State, and Gen. John Pope after he had assumed command of the Department of the Northwest. In these letters Sibley discussed plans of attack against the Sioux, the need for men and supplies, the terms offered to the "peace" faction of the Sioux, and the work of the military commission that he created at the close of the expedition to try the Sioux involved in the outbreak. Most of the letters received by Sibley were from the Governor and the adjutant general of the State. Others were received from headquarters of the department, other Minnesota public officials, and officers at posts and in command of forces in the field relating to the Sioux uprising and the terms for peace.

DEPARTMENT OF OREGON, 1858–61

The letters sent (2 vols.) and letters received (5 ft.) reveal the large amount of time and effort spent on the problems associated with the Indians in the Pacific Northwest. Although some of the correspondence relates to roads, supplies, and posts, much of it concerns Indian affairs. Many of the letters sent to the Headquarters of the Army are expository. There are long reports relating to treaties made with the Indians, such as the Spokan, Coeur d'Alène, and Nez Percés; explaining the differences between the Pacific Northwest Indians and the Plains Indians; exposing the tensions between the Indians and the Colville miners in Washington Territory; describing meetings with Indian chiefs; and presenting accounts of Gen. William Harney's trips through the department. Among the most interesting letters are those between the department and Pierre J. De Smet, a Jesuit missionary.

DEPARTMENT AND DIVISION OF THE PACIFIC, 1848–66

The records of the Department of the Pacific include those of the Department of California, the Pacific Division, and the Pacific Department, for the name and jurisdiction of this command changed frequently. The headquarters of this succession of commands is well covered by letters sent (8 vols.), registers of letters received, and letters received (31 ft.). Much of this correspondence is related to Indian affairs.

Among the letters received are many important items; for example, a report on Tulares Valley, Calif., that includes a description of the living conditions of the various Indian tribes in the area and another report that describes an attack on friendly Indians by some California Volunteers. In an 1853 letter, Col. B. L. E. Bonneville wonders, from both the military point of view and that of humanity to the Indians, whether ". . . the citizen can lawfully locate his claim for settlement anywhere he pleases in the territory, spreading alike over that claimed by all Indian Tribes; or, are there any limits assigned for the settlement of the white?" Many letters request assistance against the Indians; some describe the destitute condition of friendly Indians and their worsening situation. There are many letters from superintendents of Indian affairs regarding Indian policy.

Except for the period of the short-lived Department of Oregon, this command had jurisdiction along the entire West Coast. Consequently, there are many letters and reports received from subordinate commanders relating to expeditions, campaigns, wars, and negotiations with the Indian tribes of the area, including the Pit River expedition of 1850, the Yakima expedition of 1855–56, the expedition against the Northern Indians in 1858, the Colorado expedition of 1859, and the Puget Sound expedition of 1858.

In addition to the headquarters correspondence, there are several special collections among the records of this department. One series (part of a volume) contains reports from subordinate officers within the department during 1853 and 1854 that describe the many Indian tribal groups living in California and in Oregon and Washington Territories. In addition to providing information of a "military character," such as types of arms, total population and number of warriors, and attitudes toward whites, they describe the language and social and religious customs of the Indians. Sometimes statistical information accompanies the narratives. Among the groups described are the Nez Percé, Cayuse, Yakima, Wallawalla, Spokan, and "Root-Diggers."

Among the miscellaneous records of the chief quartermaster, 1853–59, is a report on Fort Humboldt, Calif., June 30, 1853, in which general conditions among Klamath, Trinity, and other Indian groups in the vicinity are described. There is also comment on the Indians' disposition toward white immigrants and the Army.

There are two series (2 vols.) of letters sent and orders issued during an expedition commanded by Lt. Col. William Hoffman, 6th Infantry, along the Colorado River through land occupied by Mohave Indians and into Utah Territory in the spring of 1859. A number of letters were sent by Hoffman from Camp Colorado, Utah Territory, reporting interviews and negotiations with the Mohave chieftains. A report submitted by Hoffman at the conclusion of the expedition describes the surrender of six bands of Mohave Indians.

In the letters received by the Column from California, October 1861–August 1862, there are scattered references to Pima and Apache Indians in Arizona. There is also a series of miscellaneous records of the Column from California in 1862 that includes several letters received relating to the Pima and Apache and to the Army troops entering the Pima villages.

Among the headquarters records are letters sent and orders issued (4 vols.) by the 2d Cavalry (California Volunteers) detachment while on the Owens Lake and Owens River expeditions, June–September 1862. Encounters with the Owens Lake Indians and their means of subsistence are described in the letters sent by headquarters of the Owens Lake expedition during June 1862. Attempts made in June and July 1862 to make peace with the Owens River Indians also are described in the letters. Several of the general orders issued relate to conduct toward the Indians, including the order issued July 9, 1862, that announced the peace treaty with the Indians in the Owens River Valley and prohibited the soldiers from molesting Indians living in the Owens River Valley.

The letters sent (1 vol.) by the 1st Cavalry Regiment and the 1st Infantry Regiment of Oregon Volunteers, July 1862–January 1866, contain many references to the Klamath, Modoc, and "Snake" Indians living in the areas surrounding Camp Baker and Fort Klamath, Oreg. Among the subjects mentioned are the exclusion of the Klamath Indians from the white settlements in the vicinity of Camp Baker, the return of fugitive Indians from the Smith River Reservation, the peace treaty made by the Klamath, Modoc, and "Snake" Indians with the U.S. Government in October 1864, and the later dissatisfaction of the Modoc with that treaty.

DEPARTMENT OF THE PLATTE, 1866–98

The main series of letters sent (27 vols.) by the department and the letters received (208 ft.) document the many campaigns in which the department was involved. There is correspondence with the Mountain District which was involved in the Fetterman massacre and the Piney Creek "Wagon Box Fight," with the Sioux expedition into Wyoming Territory in 1874, and with the various participants in the Sioux campaigns of 1890–91.

There are two series of telegrams received (3 vols.) by Gen. George Crook, department commander, at field headquarters during the period 1877 to 1879. The telegrams relate to such subjects as the movements of the Nez Percé during the campaign of 1877, the operations carried on by various commands in the Division of the Missouri against the Cheyenne from September to October 1878, and the departure of the Bannock from their reservation in March 1879.

Included with the headquarters records is a volume of telegrams sent by General Crook's aide-de-camp, January 1877–May 1878, from headquarters in the field. The telegrams relate to the war against the Northern Cheyenne and Sioux in Nebraska and in Montana, Wyoming, and Dakota Territories and various other subjects, such as the proposed arming of the Arapaho and Sioux to hunt in 1878.

There is also a series of reports of scouts and reconnaissances, maps of marches, and requests for maps, 1868–81, which were referred to the Chief Engineer's Office (1 ft.). This series is a source of some interesting maps and accounts of marches and encounters with the Indians, as well as personal observations submitted by officers serving in the department.

Among the general and special orders received from the districts in 1872 (1 vol.) are special orders issued by the District of the Republican relating to the issuance of subsistence stores to Indians, including those invited to meet the Grand Duke Alexis of Russia at Red Willow Creek, Nebr. There are also orders relating to Indian affairs among the general and special orders of the District of the Black Hills, 1875–77 (3 vols.).

There are several series of letters, telegrams, and endorsements sent and received (13 vols. and 2 ft.) by Gen. John Brooke from headquarters in the field at Pine Ridge Agency before and after the Battle of Wounded Knee Creek, from November 1890 to January 1891. Letters and telegrams were received before the battle from division headquarters, department headquarters at Omaha, headquarters of the Department of the Missouri, subordinate officers in the field, Rev. John Jutz at Holy Rosary Mission, and other missionaries and private citizens reporting conditions with respect to the Sioux who had fled to the Badlands and the Indians still remaining at the reservations. Many of the letters sent and received concern the spread of the ghost dance religion and the effect of the capture and death of Sitting Bull on the Indians at the Pine Ridge, Rosebud, and Standing Rock Agencies. Among the letters received is a note, December 29, 1890, from Col. James W. Forsyth, commanding the 7th U.S. Cavalry at Wounded Knee, in which he described the "hot fight" precipitated by his troops in "attempting to disarm the persons of the bucks." Many of the letters, telegrams, and endorsements sent and received after the battle contain instructions to officers in the field regarding tactics for removing the Indians from the Badlands.

There are also copies of letters, telegrams, and endorsements sent (2 vols.) by the Medical Director's Office at Pine Ridge on the day of the battle, as well as lists showing the number of Army and Indian casualties.

Between February and August 1874 an expedition was sent into Wyoming Territory to protect the Red Cloud and Spotted Tail Agencies from hostile Indians. Most of the letters and endorsements sent and received and orders issued by the Sioux expedition (4 vols.) pertain to Indian affairs at the agencies, particularly the relocation of the Spotted Tail Agency. Some of the letters received from the field camps, particularly those from Capt. H. M. Lazelle near the Spotted Tail Agency, describe the attitude of the Indian chieftains toward the presence of the expedition forces and the relocation of the agency.

The events of the Bannock uprising at Jackson Hole, Wyo., in July 1895 are well documented in the letters, telegrams, memorandums, orders, reports, and other records in a series relating to the Bannock Indian troubles (4 in.). In addition to the correspondence and orders, there are other records pertaining to the Bannock at the Fort Hall Agency and the events at Jackson Hole, such as a typed summary of press reports and official correspondence received in connection with the incident, a collection of contemporary newspaper clippings, and the reports of scouts made in the vicinity of Jackson Hole in August 1895.

DEPARTMENT OF TEXAS, 1853-58, AND THE 8TH MILITARY DEPARTMENT, 1851-53

Dispersed throughout the correspondence of this department (1 vol. and 3 in.) are references to Indian problems, especially Kiowa and Comanche raids and occasionally Lipan and Kickapoo raids. Consequently, the correspondence frequently contains petitions for protection from Indians, plans for placing Indians on reservations, and letters relating to operations against the Indians. There is a small series of reports of reconnaissances conducted by topographical engineers between 1849 and 1852, in which are described various camps and fords used by the Indians in the Southwest. Maps accompany some of the reports.

DEPARTMENT OF TEXAS, 1870-1913

The headquarters correspondence includes letters sent to 1898 (33 vols.) and letters received (104 ft.). The letters received provide very uneven coverage, the years from 1883 to 1890 being covered by 3 feet and the period 1890 to 1899 by 26 feet. Many of the letters received relating to Indians between 1870 and 1876 have been segregated into an Indian file (3 ft.). This file includes numerous reports of marches, expeditions, and scouts after Indians. A copy of a report submitted in June 1870 by Col. James Oakes, post commander at Fort Richardson, to the chairman of the Committee on Indians and Frontier Protection of the Texas State Senate recounts the depredations occurring within the department during 1869 and 1870. There are also many reports of attacks made on white settlements between 1870 and 1873 by Kiowa and Comanche who fled from the reservation near Fort Sill, Indian Territory, and crossed the Red River into Texas. Included are copies of proceedings of councils held at Fort Sill in October 1874 to consider the problem of the Indians leaving the reservation for Texas. In the letters received for 1873 are several references to raids by Kickapoo and Mescalero Apache Indians from Mexico across the Nueces River into Texas.

Letters and telegrams reporting operations in the field were received from the Southern and Fort Sill columns during the campaign against the Kiowa, Cheyenne, and Comanche Indians in Texas and Indian Territory in the fall of 1874. There are also a number of letters referring to Seminole-Negro Indians at Fort Duncan, Tex., in 1871 and a penciled report that is alleged to be the statement made December 31, 1883, by Chief Zele, Warm Springs Apache, to Capt. Emmet Crawford describing the movements of Geronimo and Juh in Mexico.

There is also a series of quarterly reports of persons killed or captured by Indians, submitted by Texas posts, 1872–78.

DEPARTMENT OF UTAH, 1858–61

No letters received and only three volumes of letters sent exist for this department.

In a volume of letters sent by the Utah Forces under the department, commanded by Gen. William S. Harney, is a letter to the Headquarters of the Army at the conclusion of the 1858 expedition in which Harney asks permission to lead an expedition the following spring to meet with the Cheyenne chieftains and negotiate a peace treaty and to establish peaceful relations with the Pawnee.

There is correspondence, April–July 1859, relating to the recovery of children who survived the Mountain Meadows massacre of September 1857. In a letter of April 7, 1859, Col. Albert S. Johnston, the departmental commander, reported dispatching an expedition to Santa Clara, Calif., to protect travelers passing over the southern route and to inquire into the murders alleged to have been committed by Indians the previous fall. A number of other letters for 1859 also relate to military protection of travelers against Indian raids. Among the letters sent, August 1860–July 1861, are some relating to the Army's role of protecting the mail and express routes from Indian attack, as well as references to measures to be taken to conciliate the Indians in Utah Territory.

WESTERN DIVISION AND DEPARTMENT, 1820–54

Among the records of the Western Department, 1821–37, is a volume of orders issued by Gen. Henry Atkinson, June 1819–January 1826, while he was commander of the 9th Military Department. Several references to the Winnebago and Missouri Indians are in the volume. There are also references to relations with the Osage and other Indian tribes among the letters received, 1825–31, while Atkinson alternated as commander of the Western Department, the Northwestern Frontier, and the Right Wing of the Western Department.

In a series of records identified as correspondence and reports relating to special subjects, 1831–51, are two items of interest: a manuscript copy of a "Treaty with the Comanche and Wichitaw Nations and their associated Bands or Tribes of Indians," signed August 24, 1835, and copies of bills for the expenses of the removal of the Cherokee to the West during 1838–39.

DEPARTMENT OF THE WEST AND WESTERN DEPARTMENT, 1853–61

Among the Department of the West records are two series of letters, endorsements, and memorandums sent by the Sioux expedition commanded by Gen. William S. Harney from April 1855 to July 1856. Among the letters sent is Harney's account of the battle with Little Thunder's band of Brulé Sioux on Blue Water Creek, Nebraska Territory, on September 3, 1855; it was waged in retaliation for the massacre by the Sioux in 1854 of a detachment of troops led by 2d Lt. John L. Grattan, 6th Infantry. In some of his letters to the Assistant Adjutant General of the Army, Harney expresses his views on the management of Indian affairs.

Geographic Districts

Although a few were established earlier, many geographical districts were established during the Civil War, usually to meet emergencies involving Confederate forces or hostile Indians. After the war several districts were formed to meet border threats from Mexicans, but most were created to face Indian problems.

The names, locations of headquarters, and areas of jurisdiction changed as the districts were abolished and reestablished. For example, in the Pacific Northwest between 1855 and 1865, the major problem was the Indians, including Yakima, Klikitat, Wallawalla, and Umatilla. Under the Department of the Pacific, a Columbia River District (also known as the Northern District) was established at Fort Vancouver, Washington Territory, and later moved to Fort Walla Walla. A Puget Sound District was established at Fort Steilacoom. In 1858, these districts were abolished when the Department of Oregon was established for the same area. This department became the District of Oregon in 1861 under a newly created Department of the Pacific and then became the Department of the Columbia in 1865. To meet the problems of the hostile Paiute and "Snake" Indians in the Department of the Columbia during the years 1865 to 1869, a District of Boise (changed to Owyhee in 1867) was established; to meet the hostile Modoc between 1867 and 1873, the District of the Lakes was established; and to meet the Nez Percé problem between 1877 and 1879, the District of Clearwater was formed.

The volume of records varies greatly for the different districts, and for some there are no records. Usually records consist of letters, telegrams, and endorsements sent; registers of letters received; letters received; and orders.

Duplicate copies of orders are not often found among the records of superior commands and War Department bureaus, but duplicate district letters, or letters not properly filed with the district records, may very likely be among the records of subordinate commands and units or among the records of superior commands and War Department bureaus.

Only those districts that played an important role in Indian affairs or for which there is a significant volume of records are treated in this guide. They have been grouped by geographical area as follows: Pacific Northwest, California-Nevada, Arizona-New Mexico, Texas, Arkansas-Oklahoma, Kansas-Nebraska, and Dakota-Northwest. The dates are those of the records and not necessarily those of the existence of the districts. It is neither feasible nor necessary to try to point out all the pertinent records; many of them are duplicated elsewhere. The intention of this section of the guide is to indicate the volume of correspondence and to give an idea of the nature of the information to be found.

PACIFIC NORTHWEST AREA

COLUMBIA RIVER DISTRICT (NORTHERN), 1855–57

In a single volume of letters sent, and a few letters received, there are letters relating to friendly and unfriendly acts of Indians, murders, movements of whites fearful of Indian hostilities, the Yakima expedition, interviews with members of Indian tribes of the Yakima Nation, and attempts to induce the Indians to sue for peace. There is a long report of October 31, 1856, describing a meeting of chiefs and the attitudes of the Indians toward the whites and the treaties of 1855, by which the Indians gave up their land.

PUGET SOUND DISTRICT, 1855–57

In a packet of letters received (7 in.) and a volume of letters sent are reports from the Governors of Oregon and Washington Territories relating to Indian difficulties, including the unwillingness of the Indians to abide by the treaties and sell their land; reports of scouts and Indian movements; and a lengthy report of an expedition to the Stuck River area. The district commander was reminded by the Department of the Pacific that, if the whites attacked the Indians, the authority of the Indian agent ceased and the whole power of peace and war was vested in the military. There are reports of visits to Indian reservations, instructions for attacking Indians, narratives of events, and a description of the Indian attack on Seattle, January 26, 1856.

DISTRICT OF OREGON, 1861–65

The correspondence series of letters and endorsements sent and registers and letters received are quite complete (7 vols. and 8 ft.). They relate to such subjects as the establishment and garrisoning of posts to protect settlers and

Indian agents, fear of Indian outbreaks (especially among friendly Indians, because thousands of miners were entering Nez Percé country), and the sale of liquor to Indians.

DISTRICT OF BOISE, 1865–67, and DISTRICT OF OWYHEE, 1867–69

This district was established at Fort Boise, Idaho Territory, because of the hostile "Snake" and Paiute Indians. There are only a few letters received (3 in.); but among the complete series of letters sent (2 vols.) are reports of Indian scouts, operations against Indians, stolen cattle, hostile Indians, and false alarms. Some of the expedition reports—for example, that of Gen. George Crook in January 1867—are lengthy recitals of miles covered, places marched to, and conditions prevailing. Letters also relate to the employment of Indian scouts to hunt hostile Indians, hostilities between two mining companies at Silver City, Idaho Territory, and meetings with Indian parties seeking peace.

DISTRICT OF THE LAKES, 1868–73

With headquarters at Camp Warner, Oreg., the district commander had responsibility for the Indian difficulties on the Oregon-California border, primarily with the Modoc. In the letters and endorsements sent (2 vols.) are many long reports of trips through Indian country, such as that through Modoc country in March 1872, which describes many meetings with Modoc chiefs and the prevailing alarm among the whites. A report of April 15, 1872, describes in detail the Indians within the district—the principal bands and their feelings—and includes a history of Captain Jack's Modoc band at the Klamath Reservation and the district commander's recommendations. There is also a summary report of the Lava Beds operations south of Tule Lake, Calif., and an expedition report of the troops engaged in the battle at the Modoc Caves, January 17, 1873. Interesting also are the letters indicating the divided opinion among the military officers as to Captain Jack's intentions.

Of interest are the two volumes of letters sent and received by the Modoc expedition under Col. A. C. Gillem, February–May 1873. Included are many operational reports and correspondence relating to the murder of Gen. Edward R. S. Canby, commander of the Department of the Columbia, by Modoc Indians on April 11, 1873.

DISTRICT OF CLEARWATER, 1877–79

Of most interest in the records of this district are the field records (1 ft.) of the troops involved in the Nez Percé campaign on the Clearwater River, Idaho Territory, between July and September 1877, which include letters, telegrams, and a map. The district headquarters correspondence (3 vols. and 1 ft.) contains the usual reports of scouts, Indian depredations, and rumors. In 1879 there are many references to settlers in the area around

Coeur d'Alene, Lewiston, and Colfax, who dreaded an amicable settlement with the Indians lest it avert an Indian outbreak. They wanted war and envied the eastern Oregonians who had had an Indian war in 1878 in the eastern part of the State. The settlers made money in wartime; one reportedly held $25,000 worth of Government vouchers from the 1878 summer campaign and hoped to do as well in the summer of 1879.

CALIFORNIA-NEVADA AREA

DISTRICT OF SOUTHERN CALIFORNIA, 1861–66

Among the letters and endorsements sent (5 vols.) and the letters received (1 ft.) are numerous demands from citizens for escorts and guards; reports of Indians captured, Indians fired upon by citizens, and the unfriendly acts of Indians, such as their closing off railroad tracks; and letters describing secessionist sympathizers' practice of inciting Indians to attack whites. Many letters are requests from Superintending Agent George M. Hanson of the Bureau of Indian Affairs for troops to protect Indians and employees from whites, or his complaints about the outrages committed by whites on Indians. There are also reports of inspections of "corrals" erected at posts for the confinement of Indians. These were unhealthy, dirty, and crowded and generated disease among both Indians and soldiers, according to the inspectors. Copies of treaties made with the Indians also are included.

DISTRICT OF CALIFORNIA, 1864–66

Among the letters and endorsements sent and registers of letters received (5 vols.) and the letters received (2 in.) is correspondence with the Governor regarding the placement of troops to prevent organizations of disloyal Indians from meeting, petitions requesting protection from Indians, reports of expeditions against the Indians and the arrest of murderers, reports on the confinement of citizens who exulted over Lincoln's assassination, reports of the abandonment of Chico, Calif., after its destruction by Indians, and reports of secessionists stirring up the Indians. There is a long report of an expedition to the Sink of Carson and the Truckee (Pyramid Lake) Reservation, which describes many peaceful Indians coming to the reservation in spite of white settlers' statements that war was imminent. There is also correspondence related to Indian complaints about untruthful Indian agents and the bad treatment of Indians by dishonest agents and swindlers.

DISTRICT OF NEVADA, 1865–70

Among the letters and endorsements sent (5 vols.) and the letters and telegrams received (2 ft.) is the usual correspondence relating to Indian scouts, Indian murders and reports of Indian engagements, depredations, operations against hostile Indians, and other such matters.

ARIZONA-NEW MEXICO AREA

DISTRICT OF ARIZONA, 1862-70

Among the letters and endorsements sent and registers of letters received (15 vols.) and letters received (3 ft.) is correspondence from the Bureau of Indian Affairs relating to the establishment of posts, instructions to Indians, and requests for the removal by the Army of intruders from the reservation of the Pima and Maricopa Indians. Most of the purely military correspondence pertains to the expected subjects: scouts in search of hostile Indians, expeditions after the murderers of whites, escaped Apache prisoners, enlistment of Indian scouts, mail escorts killed by Indians, and the stealing of cattle by Pima and Maricopa Indians. There is also correspondence relating to Indian farms, as at Fort Goodwin and Fort McDowell, and the duties to be performed by the farm commander as opposed to the post commander. In addition to the regular correspondence series, there are reports of expeditions (1 vol.) and a packet of quarterly reports of scouts and combats (1 in.).

DISTRICT OF NEW MEXICO, 1865-90

Under the Department of the Missouri, the District of New Mexico was the headquarters for the Apache campaigns, especially in the 1880's when Col. Ranald S. MacKenzie was district commander. The records for this district are far more voluminous than those for any other. In addition to headquarters correspondence, consisting of letters, endorsements, and telegrams sent and registers of letters received (92 vols.) and letters and telegrams received (50 ft.), there are correspondence series for staff officers (those for the quartermaster being the most voluminous) and for quartermaster agents in the field.

There is much correspondence with the Governors of New Mexico and Colorado, as well as with the Department of the Missouri, subordinate posts, the superintendent of Indian affairs, and Indian agents. Many of the letters relate to suggested methods of handling Indian problems and problems stemming from overlapping responsibility—the Bureau of Indian Affairs claiming sole control when the Ute and Apache were quiet, and the War Department only when they were at war. Much of the correspondence with post commanders includes directions for making the Indians self-sufficient in agriculture. Explicit directions are given for clearing land, plowing, cultivating, planting, seeding, fencing, and planting orchards.

The annual reports are particularly helpful in that they summarize scouts against Indians and Indian depredations and describe the numbers and condition of the various tribes. Other letters describe roads, land fertility, the availability of water for agriculture, the selection of areas for reservations, the removal of Apache and other Indians, and issuing licenses for trading with the Indians.

TEXAS AREA

DISTRICT OF THE PECOS, 1878-81

This district, with headquarters at Fort Concho, Tex., was primarily involved with the Mescalero Apache. The records consist of letters, endorsements, and telegrams sent (7 vols.) and letters and telegrams received (3 ft.) and relate to scouts, new roads, border raids, Indian trails, and Indian movements. A report of the expedition to the Mescalero Agency in New Mexico Territory in 1880 describes the many difficulties encountered. There are also reports covering the chase of Victorio from August to October 1880, the supplying of Mexican forces, and the pursuit into Mexico of the Indians who attacked the picket post near Ojo Caliente (Hot Springs), Tex. There is a long report, dated September 20, 1880, which covers the period after May 1880, relating to plans for coping with Victorio's band and the district commander's trip to western Texas. The annual reports recapitulate the operations of the command.

ARKANSAS-OKLAHOMA AREA

FRONTIER DISTRICT, 1865-66

Among the letters received (3 in.) by the Frontier District are complaints that refugee Creek and Cherokee Indians were driving off stock while returning to their own country. There are reports of visits with Gov. Peter P. Pitchlynn of the Choctaw Nation and Gov. Winchester Colbert of the Chickasaw Nation, who complained of their inability to enforce the laws because of refugee Cherokee and others stealing cattle and defacing the land. Indians were reported to be without food and clothing for the winter.

DISTRICT OF THE INDIAN TERRITORY, 1867-69

The records of this district, established in 1867, consist of letters and endorsements sent and registers of letters received (6 vols.) and letters received (3 in.). Although much of the correspondence relates to roads and mail stations, there are many letters and reports to the Department of the Missouri relating to visits to various parts of the district, the friendly exchange of information with Indians, and troubles among Indians, among Indians and agents, and among Indians and traders. Other reports relate to the best location of posts for practical defense and for preventing or correcting troubles with or among the Indians. Many letters relate to meetings with Indians and the surrender of bands and lodges. Of particular interest is the district commander's reports of his talks with the surrendering Cheyenne Indians, in which he learned their version of Colonel Custer's operations at the head of the Washita.

KANSAS–NEBRASKA AREA

DISTRICT OF COLORADO, 1862–65

This district, with headquarters at Denver, Colorado Territory, was established in 1862 under the Department of the Missouri but operated under the Department of Kansas during 1864. The district was under the command of Col. John M. Chivington, Colorado's "Fighting Parson," who is remembered primarily for the Sand Creek massacre of 1864.

The headquarters records contain letters, endorsements, and registers of letters received (7 vols.) and letters received (5 in.), among which are letters relating to rebel sympathizers, fears of Indian outbreaks, plundering by the Arapaho and Cheyenne, the organizing of operations against the Indians, Indians being terrorized by white men, Ute hostilities, and the "state of feverish excitement" of the people of Colorado. There is a report on the operations in June 1863 against the Ute who were hampering the operation of the Overland Stage Line. Colonel Chivington wrote that he did not countenance exhibiting heads and making his officers "baptized heathens washed to fouler stains," and that the presence of four cavalry companies and a battery of artillery "had a most salutary influence" in making a satisfactory treaty with the Ute. The correspondence contains many reports by Chivington on the Sand Creek massacre.

DISTRICT OF NEBRASKA, 1862–66

Under the Department of Kansas in 1864 and otherwise under the Department of the Missouri, the district had a primary duty to assist the Indian agents. In the correspondence, consisting of letters, endorsements, and telegrams sent and registers of letters received (15 vols.), there are letters relating to the movements of the Sioux, anticipated hostilities, and crop failures. In a lengthy letter of October 14, 1864, there is a report of an expedition made in September along the Platte River and of the conditions of the Indians encountered.

DISTRICT OF THE PLAINS, 1865

In the spring of 1865 Gen. Grenville M. Dodge, commander of the Department of the Missouri, was charged with the responsibility for the overland mail route as far as Salt Lake City. As a consequence, the Districts of Utah, Colorado, and Nebraska were consolidated into the District of the Plains under Gen. Patrick Connor. In cooperation with the Districts of Arkansas and Iowa, the District of the Plains troops were to march against Indian camps on the Powder River in northeastern Wyoming. This became known as Connor's Powder River expedition of 1865. The correspondence of the district was carried on at headquarters at Fort Laramie. After Connor left on the expedition in July, the correspondence of the adjutant, Capt.

George Price, consisted largely of information relayed between Dodge and Connor.

DISTRICT OF THE UPPER ARKANSAS, 1866–69

Established under the command of Col. Innis R. Palmer, the district faced problems with the Plains Indians. In the headquarters records are letters and endorsements sent and registers of letters received (13 vols.) and letters received (3 ft.) that refer to the usual rumors, depredations, and outrages and escorts for citizens and survey parties. There are reports of meetings with the Pawnee and Cheyenne chiefs (including Black Kettle) and agreements reached. Colonel Palmer believed the most effective method of achieving peace was to drive out the whiskey peddlers, stating that "whenever a military post is established there just off the military reservation—appears the miserable 'whiskey ranch,' the owner of which is ready to sell his villainous stuff to Indian or white men, and to purchase stolen government property or soldiers clothes." Colonel Palmer doubted that peace would last, considering the opinion of one sutler he quoted: "We don't want no peace with the Indians Genl,—we rather have war for it makes things kind o'lively out here, in the money way."

In the summer of 1868 the district took to the field under district commander Gen. Alfred Sully. The field headquarters letters (2 vols.) are filled with information received from the Indians. It was as a part of this operation that Colonel Custer fought the Battle of Washita River late in 1868.

DISTRICT OF KANSAS, 1867–69

The correspondence of this district consists of letters and endorsements sent and a register of letters received (3 vols.) and letters received (6 in.). Some of the letters sent relate to the propriety of delivering goods to Indians who had been loyal and abstained from hostilities during the Civil War and to sending detachments to the Republican River. In addition to the usual letters relating to encounters with Indians, Indian attacks and murders, and the sending of detachments to protect settlers and restore confidence, there are numerous letters relating to the payment of "head" money or annuities by the Superintendent of Indian Affairs, Central Superintendency, and references to the fact that most, if not all, of the money paid was owed to the post or agency trader.

DISTRICT OF THE PLATTE, 1865–66

Headquarters for this district were at Fort Laramie, which had been the headquarters for previous subdistricts of the Districts of the Plains and Nebraska, and the records are the creation of three successive commands: the North Subdistrict of the Plains, the West Subdistrict of Nebraska, and the District of the Platte. The correspondence consists of letters, endorsements, and telegrams sent and a register of letters received (5 vols.) and letters received (4 in.). A letter of May 27, 1865, relates to the capture of Two Face and Black Foot, chiefs of the Oglala Sioux, along with their band, and to the execution of the chiefs. Other letters tell of Indian attacks and depredations and of councils with Indians. Others detail the destitution of Indians and the issuance of food and clothing by the Army because the Indian agent had none to issue. There are many letters to the Commissioner of Indian Affairs in Washington, such as reports on hazardous missions to hostile Sioux performed by Indians in the dead of winter in 1866. Numerous interviews with the Sioux chiefs were reported throughout the spring.

DISTRICT OF THE UPPER MISSOURI, 1865–67

This district was established in the fall of 1865 as the District of Dakota, under Gen. Alfred Sully, with headquarters at Sioux City, Iowa, under the Department of the Missouri. In December 1865, headquarters were moved to Clinton, Iowa, and the district became the District of the Upper Missouri; in March 1866 it was placed under the Department of the Platte. In the correspondence, consisting of letters and endorsements sent and a register of letters received (3 vols.) and letters received (3 in.), are letters relating to the reestablishment of religious missions in Indian country, forthcoming Indian hostilities, and the pitiful condition of Sioux bands in the winter of 1865–66. Indian affairs are well covered in the annual report for 1866; in a lengthy report of November 2, 1865, describing the Indian agents' haphazard method of distributing food to the Upper Sioux and the many rumors of fraud; and in a report of General Sully's visit to the Santee Sioux imprisoned at Davenport, Iowa.

MOUNTAIN DISTRICT, 1866–67

The Mountain District, commanded by Col. Henry Carrington, was established in the Department of the Platte for the purpose of erecting posts along the Bozeman Trail. Leaving Fort Laramie, Carrington went to Fort Reno and then on to the Piney Creek tributary of the Powder River where he erected his headquarters post—Fort Phil Kearny. When the Indians attacked a wood train some 6 miles from the fort in December 1866, William J. Fetterman, a member of the command, against Carrington's orders went to relieve the train and thereby initiated the Fetterman massacre.

In addition to the report of this massacre by Carrington's successor, Gen. H. W. Wessells, there are reports of scouts, the location of Indians, and their attitudes, including a report of affairs in August 1867 at Fort C. F. Smith, the scene of the Hayfield fight. Two letters dated August 4 give the district commander's version of the August 2 "Wagon Box Fight." In the correspondence, consisting of letters and endorsements sent, a register of telegrams received and sent, and letters received (5 vols.) are many letters relating to Indian chiefs, Sioux skirmishes, and Indian depredations. There are several long reports that detail operations against hostile Indians, the character of Indian warfare, and the U.S. forces required.

DAKOTA-NORTHWEST AREA

DISTRICT OF MINNESOTA, 1862-73

After the Santee Sioux uprising in the fall of 1862, the District of Minnesota was established in the Department of the Northwest under Col. Henry H. Sibley with headquarters at St. Paul. The records of the district include letters, endorsements, and telegrams sent and received, issuances, a daily journal of the Indian expedition of June–September 1863, and a few records of the second and third subdistricts (15 vols. and 6 ft.).

In the correspondence there are letters sent relating to Sioux war preparations in the spring of 1863, reports of scouts and escorts, and requests for guards. Although most of the letters are addressed to subordinate post commanders and the department commander, there are some letters to the Governor of Minnesota. Some of these reveal concern that the citizens of Minnesota might execute prisoners being guarded by U.S. soldiers or that a mixed-blood Sioux condemned to death by a military commission might not be pardoned by President Lincoln. Of special interest are the annual reports prepared for the department commander and a letter of July 3, 1864, which reports on matters connected with the Indian war on the frontiers of Minnesota, Iowa, and the Territory of Dakota, which began with the Sioux outbreak of 1862.

DISTRICT OF IOWA, 1863-65

In 1863 a District of Iowa was established. Most of the correspondence (5 vols.) covers the period from June to December 1863. Of primary interest is the daily journal of the Northwest Indian expedition against the Sioux in the fall of 1864.

MIDDLE DISTRICT, 1867-79

After the Department of Dakota was created in 1866, the District of Minnesota was transferred from the Department of the Northwest to this Department, and in 1867 three additional districts were created: the Middle District, the District of Southeastern Dakota, and the District of Montana. First established at Fort Stevenson, the Middle District was moved in 1869 to Fort Sully, 6 miles from the Cheyenne River Agency, under Col. D. S. Stanley. While the district was commanded by Col. George A. Custer in 1874 and 1875, the headquarters were at Fort Abraham Lincoln. The records consist of letters and endorsements sent and received (10 vols. and 2 ft.). There is considerable correspondence with the Commissioner of Indian Affairs and Indian agencies. In addition to the usual reports of Indian attacks and operations against the Indians, there are letters relating to dishonest contractors who provided foul food for Indians, the knavery or in-capacity of Indian agents, the complaints of Indians against agents, and the building of blockhouses at posts to house howitzers. There are numerous letters relating to the treatment of Indians at the agencies and the Indians' reactions. Letters to the superintendent of Indian affairs concern the Sioux at the Cheyenne River and Grand River Agencies, who preferred to talk with Army officers rather than agents, because they had not received what they were promised in the peace treaty. There are instructions to command-ing officers ". . . to give all proper protection to the agent, his employees, and the property of the U.S. in the agent's charge. . . ." The annual reports are particularly interesting.

DISTRICT OF SOUTHEASTERN DAKOTA, 1867–69

Some of the more frequent problems mentioned in the correspondence (5 vols. and 4 in.) were the arrival of mail, illegal expeditions of settlers, fail-ures of corn and other crops and the consequent need for Indian rations, and the care of orphaned children, the aged, and the sick at military posts while the Indian men were out hunting for food.

DISTRICT OF MONTANA, 1867–79

In a volume of letters sent, 1870–79, and one of endorsements sent, 1867–68, are references to the Blackfeet Indians' stealing property and sell-ing it in Canada to the Hudson's Bay Company, the hostile Piegan, opera-tions out of Helena and Fort Pease in 1876, and, especially, operations against the Nez Percé in the summer of 1877.

SOUTHERN DISTRICT, DEPARTMENT OF DAKOTA, 1874–79

In a single volume of letters and endorsements sent are references to In-dian attitudes and conditions at several agencies and suggestions for ways of living with the Ponca and Pawnee Indians. Particularly good are the annual reports for 1877 and 1878. The first discusses in detail the situation at the Cheyenne River Agency, new agencies being established, and the amount of food being raised at the agencies; the latter reports at length on the opera-tions of the district against the Cheyenne, October 5–20, 1878.

DISTRICT OF THE BLACK HILLS, 1872–75

Among the letters sent in the records of the district (2 vols.) are many relating to attempts to carry out the Government's policy of placing all Cheyenne and Arapaho on the reservation of the Southern Cheyenne and Arapaho in Indian Territory. Post commanders were to forbid the Indians to trade at or anywhere near the posts or to come to the post, and they were to give the Indians no supplies.

ROCKY MOUNTAIN DISTRICT, 1868

The Rocky Mountain District, with headquarters at Fort Sanders, under Col. John Gibbon, was concerned primarily with protecting Union Pacific Railroad property and employees from hostile Indians. The letters, telegrams, and endorsements sent and registers of letters received (5 vols.) relate to the railroad's problems with hostile Indians and lawless white men, to following and attacking Indians, to anticipated Indian hostilities, and to the defenses of the district posts.

DISTRICT OF THE YELLOWSTONE, 1877–81, AND YELLOWSTONE COMMAND, 1876–77

Under the Department of Dakota, this district was operated by Col. Nelson A. Miles from headquarters at Fort Keogh and the Tongue River Cantonment, Montana Territory, against the Nez Percé. The records contain letters, telegrams, and endorsements sent and received (24 vols. and 7 ft.) that well document the operations against the Nez Percé and include reports of the pursuit of them; depredations against miners, scouts, and wagon trains; and descriptions of the Indian situation after 1877. More specifically, the correspondence reflects concern about future Sioux hostilities, Indian strength, the whereabouts of the Indian chiefs, the possible employment of Crow Indians as auxiliaries against the hostile Sioux, and the desirability of a large military command sufficient to separate hostile Indians from friendly ones. In addition to the scout reports and reports concerning expeditions to determine the practicality of establishing signal stations, there are letters relating to the poor and destitute Nez Percé after the 1877 hostilities, their willingness to surrender, and the resulting possibility of detaching the Nez Percé from the hostile Sioux.

Military Installations

Separate from the records of geographical divisions, departments, and districts are the records of military installations that played important parts in controlling and protecting Indians in the last half of the 19th century. These installations—which included posts, subposts, cantonments, camps, barracks, forts, depots, stations, and Indian agencies—were administered by commanders who came under the jurisdiction of the Territorial department commanders. In addition to the usual staff officers serving under the post commanders, line officers were designated at several of the posts to serve as commanding officers of companies of Indian scouts.

Besides the usual letters sent and received and orders issued by post headquarters, at the posts where Indian scouts were employed various scout records were maintained, such as descriptive books, clothing account books, morning reports, enlistment papers, and final statements. Many of the posts also retained copies of tabular statements of campaigns, expeditions, and scouts against hostile Indians and monthly reports and returns of enlisted scouts.

Conceivably, records of some 130 installations may relate in some degree to Indians and Indian-white relations, but the fullest treatment in this guide has been reserved for only the more pertinent records. Posts have been grouped together by geographic area, but this arrangement does not necessarily coincide with the geographical boundaries of military divisions, departments, and districts in which these posts were located. Special series or collections of pertinent post records have been described separately from the routine post series.

Reports and correspondence found among a post's headquarters records sometimes are duplicated at a higher level of command, primarily because the post commander reported directly to and received instructions from department headquarters on important decisions and actions. Rarely are the special collections among the records of post headquarters duplicated at a higher level of command, nor is there such duplication of information concerning the daily contacts of the Army, the Indians, and the white settlers, which constitutes perhaps the greatest value of the post records.

PACIFIC NORTHWEST AREA

The years between 1850 and 1880 were a period of unrest in the Pacific Northwest. Volunteer troops founded many of the posts in Oregon at which Regular Army troops were sometimes later garrisoned. Some of the posts at which Regular Army troops were stationed in Oregon and for which there are records were Fort Dalles, Fort Klamath, and Camp Warner. The records of Fort Dalles are quite fragmentary, but the records of the other two posts are more complete.

There are scattered references to Indian affairs among the records of Fort Klamath for the 1860's and 1870's. Among the letters received for 1864 is a copy of the articles of agreement made between the chiefs and headmen of the Klamath, Modoc, and "Snake" tribes and the U.S. Government concerning the setting aside of reservation land in Oregon. Among the letters received by post headquarters in 1876 are a letter and a rather long report about an investigation made in June 1878 into the death of Tecumseh, a Klamath Indian, believed to have been caused by a mixed-blood, Tom McKay. These papers had been forwarded to department headquarters and returned with an endorsement by Gen. Oliver O. Howard.

The letters received by Camp Warner for 1866 include letters and orders relating to the establishment of the post, among them the special order issued June 21, 1866, by the headquarters of the District of Boise, which directed the troops at Warner's Lake to establish a camp, scout the area, and prevent the Indians from digging roots and hiding in the canyons and swamps. Among the letters received between 1866 and 1871 are reports of scouts after Indians and copies of issuances with directions for the scouts. The letters received, 1871-74, include a copy of remarks made by Sarah Winnencas (Winnemucca?), the daughter of a Paiute chieftain, who traveled to San Francisco in July 1871 to request Army assistance for her tribesmen during the coming winter. Of interest are the endorsements on these remarks made by the division and department commanders.

The surviving records of posts established in Washington Territory to handle Indian unrest are more numerous and include records of Fort Steilacoom, Port Townsend, Fort Spokane, Fort Walla Walla, Vancouver Barracks, and the post on San Juan Island known as Camp Pickett. The letters received by Fort Steilacoom, 1854-68, include a number of letters from the Governor and the superintendent of Indian affairs of Washington Territory and private citizens of the Territory reporting outrages committed by Indians and requesting military escorts and the dispatch of troops to certain areas. Reports of marches, scouts, and movements of Volunteer Army troops are among the letters received, 1855-57. For 1858 there are several letters received pertaining to conditions on San Juan Island, Whidbey Island, and Lummi Island as well as reports of the movements of northern Indians. Both the letters sent and received, 1859-67, refer to the northern Indians.

Among the records of Fort Walla Walla are a number of letters sent relating to the Army's prohibition of the return of settlers to the Walla Walla Valley in 1856. Other letters sent by post headquarters between 1856 and 1863 concern the effect of the Mormon war in Utah on the Indians living on the Columbia River and the views of the commanding officer of the post and the Governor of Washington Territory with respect to dealing with the Indians. Several of the letters received in 1856 relate to the council to be held that September at which leaders of the Nez Percé and other tribes were to be present. The headquarters records of the post also include orders issued during the Nez Percé campaign in 1877.

The letters sent by Port Townsend include several reports made in 1857 by the post commander to Headquarters, Department of the Pacific, regarding the character of the Skokomish, Clallam, Makah, and other tribes living in the vicinity of the post and the relationships among the tribes. Also discussed in the reports are the fears of white settlers of attack by Indians and preventive measures against such attacks. Reference is made in the letters sent to the troubles on San Juan Island in 1858, and there are letters sent during the Puget Sound expedition, August-September 1858. There are scattered references to Indian matters in the letters sent for 1859 and 1860.

Many of the letters sent by Camp Pickett on San Juan Island, 1860-61 and 1863-67, concern the illegal sale of whiskey to Indians. The letters received for 1859 also include references to Indian affairs on the island. The records of Vancouver Barracks provide very little information concerning

Indian affairs at that post, but reference is made in the letters sent for 1877 to Indian prisoners brought there during the Nez Percé campaign. There are also copies of orders for the months of June to October 1877, when almost all of the troops at the post were ordered into the field against the Nez Percé.

The records of Fort Spokane include a series relating to Indian scouts, 1885–91 (3 in.), composed of muster rolls of detachments of Indian scouts, scouts' clothing account statements, enlistment papers, and a few letters. There is also correspondence concerning Indian relations, 1879–81 and 1883–85 (4 in.), consisting of letters and reports that apparently were removed from the main series of headquarters correspondence. Most of the documents relate to Indian affairs at the Columbia and Colville Reservations in Washington Territory between 1880 and 1885. A part of the series is a collection of letters, telegrams, and reports sent and received by the headquarters of Fort Spokane and Camp Chelan about attempts by whites to settle within the limits of the reservation set aside for Chief Moses and his people.

CALIFORNIA–NEVADA AREA

Included are records of Fort Halleck and Fort McDermitt, established in Nevada between 1865 and 1867, and of Fort Gaston, Fort Bidwell, and Camp Wright, established in California between 1858 and 1863 to provide defense both for and against Indians in those areas. Only negligible amounts of records remain for many of the California and Nevada posts that played important roles in the defense of the overland emigrant and mail routes and white settlements. These include Fort Churchill, Fort McGarry, Camp Winfield Scott, and Camp Ruby in Nevada and Fort Crook, Fort Humboldt, and Fort Yuma in California.

Almost all of the information pertaining to Indians among the records of the California and Nevada posts is located in the main correspondence and issuance series of the various post headquarters. Among the letters and telegrams sent, 1867–71 and 1875–77, by Fort Halleck, Nev., are reports of scouts and references to relations between white settlers and Shoshoni, "Snake," and Paiute Indians. Among the letters received for roughly the same time period are scattered references to incidents involving Indians.

The letters sent by Fort McDermitt, Nev., 1865–68, include a number of reports of scouts against hostile Paiute Indians, and the letters sent, 1872–75, include references to Indian prisoners at the post and relations between the Paiute and the white settlers. There is also a report of an interview between Winnemucca, head chief of the Paiute, and the commanding officer of the post in May 1873 at Barren Valley, Oreg. The letters received by Fort McDermitt, particularly for the years 1872 and 1873, also contain a number of references to the Paiute at the Pyramid Lake Reservation and to the movements of Chief Winnemucca and his band.

The letters sent by Camp Wright, Calif., 1862–69, provide much information concerning relations between the Army, white settlers, and Indians in the Round Valley. There is also a small group of letters received in 1861 concerning the Indians of San Diego County. A number of the letters sent from 1870 to 1872 concern conditions among the Indians at the Round Valley Indian Reservation and the troops sent out from the post to scout for renegade Indians and return them to the reservation. Many of the letters sent in 1887 concern white trespassers on reservation lands.

A number of the letters sent and received between 1864 and 1866 by Fort Gaston, Calif., pertain to the Indians on the Hoopa Valley Reservation and the Redwood Indians on the Mendocino Reservation. The letters received, 1879–86, contain several references to the Klamath Indian Reservation at Requa, Calif., and to attempts by whites to settle within its boundaries.

References to Indian affairs, particularly to relations with the Paiute, are dispersed throughout the letters sent by Headquarters, Fort Bidwell, Calif., during 1864 and 1865. Included is a report of an expedition into Honey Valley and Surprise Valley, which comments on Indian–white relations there. Also among the records of Fort Bidwell is a volume with narrative reports of scouts for the period July 1871 to January 1877. The scouting parties were sent into areas occupied by friendly as well as hostile Indians.

ARIZONA–NEW MEXICO AREA

There are records for most of the military posts established in Arizona and New Mexico Territories, between 1846 and 1877, which served as centers of operations during the campaigns and expeditions against the Apache, Navajo, Kiowa, Comanche, and other tribes. These posts also defended the mining districts and emigrant routes of the Southwest, and troops stationed there kept intruders from encroaching on the Indian reservations. The Arizona posts included Forts Mojave, Bowie, Huachuca, Lowell, Grant, and Apache, which were established between 1859 and 1877; posts at Date Creek and San Carlos and the Post of Verde, which were established between 1866 and 1871; several temporary camps established between 1867 and 1878, including Camps Beales Spring, Colo., Crittenden, and Supply; and Whipple Barracks, which was established in 1863. The New Mexico posts established between 1846 and 1874 whose records are among the holdings of the National Archives include Forts Marcy, Bayard, Selden, Sumner, Bascom, Cummings, Craig, Conrad, McRae, Defiance, Stanton, Union, and Wingate and the posts at Las Cruces and Ojo Caliente.

The records of most of the permanent posts extend, with some gaps, from the early 1860's to 1890 and thereafter. For some of the posts, especially those that existed for only brief periods, fragmentary or negligible amounts of records remain, as is the case with Forts Bascom, Defiance, and Conrad; Camps Beales Spring and Crittenden; and the post at Date Creek. Although

most of the letters sent and received and orders issued by the post headquarters relate to routine events and administrative matters, during the periods
of the major Indian campaigns and expeditions there usually can be found
letters and orders pertaining to operations in which troops from these posts
were engaged. For example, the letters sent and received by Forts Union and
Wingate, 1862–65, contain many references to movements against the
Navajo and to the expedition launched by the New Mexico Volunteers.
Most of the record series for the posts at Bosque Redondo (Fort Sumner)
and San Carlos relate in some way to Indian affairs at those reservations.
The letters sent for Fort Sumner provide valuable documentation with re-
spect to conditions among the Navajo and Apache Indians. There are nu-
merous letters and telegrams sent and received by San Carlos during the
Apache campaigns of the 1880's.

There are special series of post records relating to Indian affairs, among
them a small series of narrative reports of scouts conducted from Fort Craig
in 1866. There are muster rolls of detachments of Indian scouts at Camp
McDowell in 1868 and at Fort Wingate from 1910 to 1912. Also among the
records of Fort Wingate is a list of Indian scouts copied in the descriptive
book of noncommissioned officers and enlisted men at the post between
1894 and 1906. Morning reports of Indian scouts for various times are
among the post records of San Carlos, Fort Apache, and Fort Grant. There
also are guard reports of Indian prisoners for 1882 to 1889 at San Carlos
and a descriptive book of Indian scouts at Fort Grant for the same years. In
addition to these series, the following special collections of post records relate to Indian affairs.

FORT APACHE

In a volume of reports received at post headquarters from detachment
commanders, February 1893–September 1896, there are accounts of troops
and Indian scouts sent to drive off intruders and to search for renegade Indians, including "Massy" (Massai) and "Kid," on the Fort Apache Reservation. There also are reports of reconnaissances into areas sparsely inhabited by Indians. Some letters of instructions to commanders also have been
copied into the volume.

FORT BOWIE

There is a series of narrative reports of scouts, 1869–72 (2 in.), against
hostile Chiricahua, Pinal, and White Mountain Apache in the vicinity of the
Gila River and the Santa Catalina Mountains. There also are a few reports
of scouts for later periods.

A series of correspondence relating to Cochise, September–October 1872
(1 in.), consists mostly of letters received by the commanding officer at
Camp Bowie from Gen. Oliver O. Howard who, serving as special commissioner, was negotiating peace terms with Cochise's band in the Dragoon

Mountains. Included is Howard's order of October 12, 1872, setting aside the Chiricahua Reservation for the southern Apache.

POST AT LAS CRUCES

Among the events briefly described in a register of post events, January–August 1865 (1 vol.), are incidents involving Indians, such as the entry made on June 22, 1865: "News of Navajo and Apache Indians leaving the Bosque Redondo arrived at 4 p.m." Also recorded were Indian expeditions leaving from the post, movements of troops engaged in expeditions, and reports received from them.

FORT CUMMINGS

In a series of narrative reports of scouts against hostile Indians, 1880–82 (1 vol.), is an interesting account by Lt. D. N. McDonald, January 23, 1882, of a scout that he led across the Mexican border while following an Indian trail. McDonald and his troops were arrested in Ascensión, and the Mexican officials attempted to disarm the Indian scouts accompanying him. Letters substantiating the account also are copied in the volume.

FORT STANTON

The register of letters received by post headquarters, 1866–68, contains a small number of narrative reports of scouts against Indians from Fort Stanton in 1868. The register for 1878 contains complete copies of letters received between 1875 and 1878 relating to the Indians at the Mescalero Agency near the fort. The registers for the period 1881–86 also contain copies of letters pertaining to the Indians at the Mescalero Agency and reports of scouts.

FORT SUMNER

A series of letters received and miscellaneous records (including letters, returns, and subsistence reports) provides descriptions of the condition and number of Navajo and Apache captives at Bosque Redondo from 1865 to 1868. A volume of miscellaneous records relating to Indians, 1865–68, includes various orders, an 1865 agreement between Jose Gallegos and the military authorities to furnish instructions for irrigating Indian lands, accounts of the post Indian fund, reports of produce raised on Indian farms, and a list for June 1865 to July 1866 of food supplies issued to Indians, civilians, and military detachments by the post commissary of subsistence. Another volume includes morning reports for November 1866 to October 1867 giving statistics on the number of Indian captives.

TEXAS AREA

Between 1848 and 1858 the U.S. Army established a number of posts and camps in Texas. These installations, along with the posts established before and during the Mexican War, protected frontier settlements, overland routes, and communication lines against Indian attacks. There are records for some of these posts and camps, including Forts Belknap, Bliss, Brown, Clark, Chadbourne, Davis, Duncan, McKavett, Mason, Ringgold, and San Antonio and the subpost of Phantom Hill. Also available are the records of Forts Concho, Griffin, and Richardson, established during 1867–68 to serve as lines of defense against the Kiowa and Comanche Indians who raided into Texas from the north, and the records of Fort Elliot, established in 1875. There also are records created by various temporary posts and camps established in Texas during the 1860's and 1870's as bases of operation against hostile Indians.

With few exceptions, the records of the Texas posts do not antedate 1865, and they continue through the 1880's. There usually are gaps in the various series, and for some posts and camps only fragmentary records remain, as with Forts Mason, Chadbourne, and Belknap and the Phantom Hill subpost. The main series of headquarters records contains most of the references to the many scouts and expeditions against the Apache and other tribes, the 1874–75 campaign against the Kiowa and Comanche, and the Kickapoo, Lipan, and Seminole-Negro Indians who crossed the Mexican border into Texas. The descriptions that follow are of special collections of post records that contain letters, reports, or other documents pertaining to Indians.

FORT BLISS

A series of letters received from Mexican Army officers relating to Indian affairs and the movements of Mexican troops, 1880 (1 in.), contains requests from Mexican officials for permission to cross the border into Texas to pursue Victorio and his band. Other letters relate to the depredations inflicted on frontier towns by the Apache.

FORT CONCHO

There are three series of narrative reports of scouts submitted to post headquarters at different times between 1867 and 1889 (3 vols.). Most of these are reports of marches, escort duties, and scouts against Indians in the vicinity of the Concho, Colorado, and Pecos Rivers. Sometimes maps or sketches accompany the reports.

FORT DAVIS

There are narrative accounts of scouts and expeditions during 1881 and 1882 (1 vol.) against hostile Apache Indians by detachments of troops from Fort Davis and its subpost. Included is an account of an expedition during May and June 1882 to watch for hostile Apache who attempted to cross the Rio Grande from Mexico into Texas.

FORT DUNCAN

References to Indian affairs are scattered among several series of the post records of Fort Duncan. Some of the letters sent pertaining to civil affairs, 1869–70, concern Indian parties crossing the Rio Grande and stealing horses in the vicinity of the fort. The registers of letters received for the period 1868 to 1883 contain a number of complete letters pertaining to actions taken by U.S. and Mexican officials with respect to hostile Indians and letters received from commanders of detachments sent to scout for Indians. A series of miscellaneous records contains a copy of a reciprocal agreement with Mexico regarding the pursuit of Indians across the border, which was signed and exchanged on July 29, 1882.

FORT GRIFFIN

There are copies of the enlistment papers of Tonkawa Indian scouts at Fort Griffin, 1870–77 (4 in.), showing the branches of service and regiments to which they were assigned.

Of the letters sent and received by the commanding officer of the Tonkawa scouts, 1867–78 (3 in.), most were forwarded through post headquarters and relate to such subjects as the clothing, arming, and mounting of the scouts. There are also a few letters of complaint filed by Texas citizens against some of the Tonkawa at Fort Griffin. Descriptive lists and discharge papers of certain Tonkawa scouts also are a part of this series.

FORT MCKAVETT

There is a substantial collection of narrative reports to post headquarters of expeditions and scouts, 1870–80 (2 vols.). Sketches of the country passed through accompany several of the reports.

FORT RICHARDSON

In a series of reports of scouts and marches, 1872–74 (1 vol.), there are narrative accounts of pursuits of Indians along the Red River. There also are a list of persons killed or captured by Indians near the fort between 1871 and 1874 and an unidentified newspaper account, dated August 28, 1874, of the killing by Indians of a white family.

FORT RINGGOLD

A descriptive book of Seminole-Negro Indian scouts, 1894–1905, shows that most enlisted for service at Fort Ringgold. A small number of them served with the U.S. Army in Texas beginning in the early 1870's.

OKLAHOMA-KANSAS-NEBRASKA-COLORADO AREA

Throughout the headquarters records of most of the posts established by the Army in Oklahoma (Indian Territory), Kansas, Nebraska, and Colorado between 1842 and 1880 are references to the Plains tribes, including the

Cheyenne, Kiowa, Comanche, Arapaho, Osage, Pawnee, and Ute. The records created by several posts during their involvement with these tribes in the 1860's and 1870's no longer remain or are extremely fragmentary, as with Forts Riley, Larned, and Scott and Camp Zarah in Kansas; Forts Kearney and Robinson in Nebraska; Forts Lyon, Morgan, and Garland in Colorado; and Fort Sill in Indian Territory. The records of Fort Niobrara, Nebr., Fort Leavenworth, Kans., and Fort Reno, Indian Territory, are, with few exceptions, concerned only with administrative or routine post matters.

Many of the letters sent and received and orders issued by post headquarters of Forts Larned, Dodge, Hays, and Harker in Kansas; Forts Hartsuff and McPherson in Nebraska; and Forts Lyon and Sedgwick in Colorado, for the period between 1863 and 1869, relate to depredations by the Cheyenne, Arapaho, Kiowa, and Comanche Indians and operations against them. There also are reports received at these posts concerning the whereabouts of certain Indian leaders and the locations of Indian villages. Correspondence and issuances also exist relating to the campaign against the Kiowa, Cheyenne, and Comanche Indians in 1874–75 and to later campaigns against the Cheyenne.

The correspondence of several of the posts relates to Indian reservation lands. Letters sent by Fort Scott, Kans., between 1869 and 1872 concern the operations of troops sent to remove trespassers from the Osage Reservation. Also among the records of Fort Scott is a small collection of letters received in 1870, while the post served as headquarters of troops in southeastern Kansas, which concerns intruders on the reservation of the Miami Indians. The letters sent by Camp Sheridan, Nebr., in 1874 and 1875 relate primarily to the commission that was to determine the location of the Spotted Tail Agency. Many of the letters sent by the camp on the White River, Colo., pertain to general conditions among the White River Ute after 1880. The post records include letters, endorsements, and issuances, 1879–80, while the camp served as headquarters of the Ute expedition. There also are letters sent referring to the condition of the Ute at the Los Pinos Agency among the headquarters records of Fort Crawford, Colo.

Among the letters received by Fort Reno, Indian Territory, in 1889 are several pertaining to the "boomers," who were allowed to cross into Indian Territory in April that year to buy land. The letters received by Fort Supply, Indian Territory, for the following year include a collection of letters pertaining to the enforcement of the President's proclamation of February 17, 1890, barring intrusions into the Cherokee Outlet.

Descriptive books, enlistment papers, morning reports, clothing reports or clothing account books, and final statements pertaining to Indian scouts are among the records of Fort Niobrara, Nebr., and Forts Reno and Supply, Indian Territory. The following are descriptions of the records of Fort

Gibson, Indian Territory, and series of records particularly significant to Indian affairs of the posts that already have been mentioned.

FORT GIBSON

The letters received series, 1833–57 (3 ft.), is rich in materials pertaining to the living conditions of the Indians in Arkansas and Indian Territory and to the role of the Army in administering the tribes. The coverage is somewhat uneven, however, with considerably more letters for some years than others. In addition to incoming letters, there are drafts and copies of letters sent by the post commander, copies of orders, and many other types of papers.

The correspondents include high officials of the War Department, such as the Secretary of War and the Adjutant General; the Bureau of Indian Affairs; Indian agents; Indian chiefs, particularly John Ross of the Cherokee; white citizens; U.S. marshals; and other Government officials. Also included is a letter of February 1833 from Sam Houston concerning the Comanche of Texas. Among the subjects dealt with are intertribal and intratribal conflicts, particularly the hostilities among various Cherokee factions; intertribal and intratribal councils and meetings, such as that held in June 1839 in an effort to unify the Cherokee who recently had emigrated from the East with those already in the West and the May 1845 council of Choctaw, Chickasaw, Caddo, Quapaw, Shawnee, Kickapoo, and Peoria Indians held at Deep Creek; intrusions of Indians and whites on Indian lands, such as Seminole intrusions on Cherokee lands in 1846; depredations committed by Indians and whites; destitution among the various tribes, such as that alleged by John Ross to exist among the Cherokee in April 1839, because of insufficient rations, and that reported by the Seminole agent in March 1842, caused by lack of building and farming implements; crimes committed by and against Indians or on Indian reservations and requests for military aid in making arrests; rations and supplies; the illegal introduction of liquor among the Indians; black slaves belonging to Indians and whites; elections and other political developments among the Cherokee; expenses of the Cherokee in emigrating west; and friction between Army officers and Indian agents in administering Indian affairs.

Included in a series of Indian papers, April 1840–August 1851 (1 vol.), are emancipation papers of black slaves granted freedom from their Seminole masters, letters received from Headquarters of the Army in Washington concerning Seminole-Negro Indians, letters sent and received concerning the Cherokee Nation, and requests from whites for permission to take up residence among the Cherokee. There also are letters relating to the sale of black slaves by Cherokee, Creek, and Seminole Indians.

FORT DODGE

A series of copies of treaties between the United States and various Indian tribes, 1865-66 (2 in.), includes a treaty with the Cheyenne and Arapaho tribes, concluded October 14, 1865; a treaty with the Apache, Cheyenne, and Arapaho tribes of October 17, 1865; a treaty with the Comanche and Kiowa tribes of October 18, 1865; and a treaty with the Cherokee Nation of July 19, 1866.

A series of reports and journals of scouts and marches, 1873-79 (1 vol.), contains some detailed narrative accounts of various expeditions in search of hostile Indians undertaken by troops from Fort Dodge. There are numerous references to raids on settlements and encounters with Indians along various routes in Kansas. There is also a small series of reports from detachments sent out from Fort Dodge in 1868.

FORT SUPPLY

The series of letters received relating to Indian affairs, 1869-85 with gaps (5 in.), touches on various matters, including murders, massacres, and kidnappings committed by Indians; attacks on Indians; the illicit sale of liquor and arms to reservation Indians; and renegade Indians. Most of the letters received for 1871 are from Brinton Darlington, U.S. Indian agent at the Cheyenne and Arapaho (Upper Arkansas) Agency. Several of the letters for 1885 relate to Indian scouts.

There also is a series of letters received from the Indian Territory expedition, 1874-75 (2 in.), by the commanding officer at Camp Supply from Lt. Col. Nelson A. Miles, requesting food, clothing, ammunition, forage, and other supplies.

CAMP ON WHITE RIVER

There are narrative reports of scouts and reconnaissances, 1882-83 (1 in.), into the White River region inhabited by Ute Indians to determine the feasibility of building roads and bridges in the area. One scout was made explicitly for the purpose of determining the "temper and intentions" of the White River Ute.

DAKOTA-NORTHWEST AREA

There are post headquarters records for most of the military posts and camps established throughout the Dakotas, Montana, and Minnesota during the latter half of the 19th century. As their records reveal, these posts were established because of the emigration of settlers to these areas by overland routes and by way of the Missouri River; the discovery of gold in Dakota, Idaho, and Montana Territories; the construction of the Northern Pacific Railroad; and the removal of the Sioux, Cheyenne, and other tribes to reservations.

Before 1880 the need for protection against hostile Sioux and other tribes led to the establishment of Forts Abercrombie and Randall in Dakota and Forts Ridgely and Snelling in Minnesota. Between 1864 and 1870, Forts Buford, Hale, Pembina, Ransom, Rice, Sisseton, and Stevenson were established in Dakota Territory and Forts Benton, Ellis, Logan, and Shaw and Camp Cooke in Montana Territory, primarily to protect emigrants from hostile Indians but also to provide neutral areas in which Indians could hunt, trade, or settle their differences. The remaining posts and camps established in Dakota, Montana, and Minnesota during the 1870's and 1880's, including Forts Bennett, Yates, Maginnis, Missoula, Keogh, Custer, Assinniboine, Abraham Lincoln, Meade, and Seward and Camp Poplar River, served as important bases of operations during the campaigns and expeditions against the Sioux, Cheyenne, Nez Percé, and other tribes.

In addition to the records of Fort Yates located at the Standing Rock Agency, Fort Hale at the Lower Brulé Agency, and Fort Bennett at the Cheyenne River Agency, there are headquarters correspondence, issuances, and other records of military installations at other Indian agencies in Dakota Territory, including Crow Creek, Spotted Tail, Pine Ridge, and Red Cloud. There also are records of various temporary posts and camps established between 1860 and 1890.

The records of most of the posts and camps extend through the early 1890's although not all series of records are complete for the entire period of an installation's existence. Information pertaining to Indian affairs generally is concentrated in the main series of headquarters records. Forts Abraham Lincoln, Buford, Keogh, and Stevenson maintained descriptive books of Indian scouts and, with the exception of Fort Stevenson, also retained copies of enlistment papers of scouts. Clothing account books for Indian scouts were kept at Forts Bennett and Buford. Copybooks of letters sent on routine matters by the commanding officers of Indian scouts are among the records of Forts Bennett and Stevenson. The descriptions that follow are of other special collections of records that concern Indian affairs at some of the posts.

FORT BENNETT

Registration of the Indians at the Cheyenne River Agency was undertaken by Army officers in December 1876, and a register was compiled (1 vol.). Members of the Sans Arcs, Two Kettle, Miniconjou, and Blackfeet Sioux bands were listed under the names of the head chiefs. The number of male and female children and the number of horses owned are shown for each member. Also listed were the whites and mixed-bloods married to Indians at the reservation, the bands who left for the hostile camp after being registered, and the bands who left the agency refusing to be registered.

FORT BENTON

A series of letters and endorsements sent pertaining to Indian affairs, November 1878–November 1880 (1 vol.), contains copies of a number of letters sent by the commanding officer of the post regarding the sale of ammunition to the Indians in the vicinity of Fort Benton. Other subjects touched upon are the loss of horses by the Sioux and Grosventre Indians and the presence of British mixed-bloods and Nez Percé Indians nearby.

FORT RANDALL

A small series of narrative reports of scouts, expeditions, and reconnaissances made by detachments of troops from Fort Buford, 1868–81 (1 in.), includes a copy of the proceedings of a council of Indians representing the Grosventre, Mandan, and Arikara tribes at Fort Berthold in May 1871. There also are a few copies of statements and confessions made by Indians in a series of affidavits and statements, 1862–82.

FORT BUFORD

There is a series of printed and manuscript copies of treaties with the Ponca, Omaha, Iowa, Kickapoo, Oto, Missouri, Delaware, Sauk and Fox, and Yankton Sioux Indians, 1817, 1825, 1854–55, and 1857–58 (1 in.). There also is a manuscript list or census of certain mixed-blood Indians who drew rations at the post in July 1868. The census records age and sex.

UTAH-IDAHO-WYOMING AREA

The military posts in what are now the States of Utah, Idaho, and Wyoming were established between 1858 and 1881, to control various Indian tribes and to guard Indian reservation lands, mining districts, and railway construction crews. The records of the Utah posts, including Forts Cameron, Douglas, Rawlins, and Thornburgh, provide very little information about their involvement with Indians. The records of major Idaho and Wyoming posts, however, are relatively complete and provide more information concerning Indians.

Most of the information pertaining to Indians among the Idaho and Wyoming post records is in the main series of letters, endorsements, and telegrams sent and received and orders issued by post headquarters. The letters sent by Fort Lapwai, Idaho Territory, 1866–71, contain scattered references to conditions on the Nez Percé Indian Reservation. The letters sent for 1874 and 1875 include several relating to white trespassers on the reservation lands, and the letters received, 1876–80, provide information concerning the troubles among the settlers, the Army, and Chief Joseph's band before the start of the Nez Percé campaign. There also are letters and orders received from the field headquarters of the Department of the Columbia during the campaign in 1877 and a volume of telegrams sent and received by the post from 1877 to 1880 concerning field operations. The post records of Fort Lapwai also include a small collection of letters received from various sources, including the Indian agent at the Nez Percé Reservation concerning the removal of William Caldwell from the reservation in 1874.

The letters sent by Fort Hall, Idaho Territory, 1870–76, contain a number of references to conditions prevailing among the Bannock and Shoshoni Indians at the Fort Hall Agency. The main correspondence and issuance series for Fort Sherman relate almost entirely to routine post matters, as do the records of Boise Barracks, with the exception of the letters, endorsements, and telegrams sent from April to December 1878 regarding the Bannock and Paiute campaign. There is only a negligible amount of records for Camp Lyon, Idaho Territory.

The greatest amount of information pertaining to Indian affairs among the Wyoming post records probably is in the records of Fort Laramie, which at times was within the boundaries of both Nebraska and Dakota Territories. There are many references to the Sioux and Cheyenne in the letters sent from 1855 to 1869, which include the letters sent during the 1855–56 Sioux expedition in Nebraska Territory. There also are telegrams sent and received for the period 1866 to 1879 concerning operations during various Indian expeditions.

The post records for Fort Sanders, Wyoming Territory, include copies of telegrams received during the Big Horn expedition of 1874 and the Big Horn and Yellowstone expeditions of 1876–77. The letters sent by Fort Washakie, Wyoming Territory, for 1878 include a number of letters received from the Indian agent at the Shoshone and Bannock Agency (Wind River Reservation). There also are a number of letters sent from the post pertaining to conditions among the Shoshoni Indians at the reservation in 1888. There are occasional references to Indians in the main correspondence series of Forts Fred Steele, Bridger, McKinney, and Fetterman, Wyoming Territory. Only fragmentary records remain for Camps Stambaugh and Walback and Forts D. A. Russell, Reno, and Casper, Wyoming Territory.

In addition to the records that already have been described for these posts, there are a few special collections of post records for Forts Laramie and Fetterman, Wyoming Territory.

FORT LARAMIE

Most of the contents of a volume of letters and orders received by Col. William Hoffman, February–December 1856, came from the Sioux expedition in Nebraska Territory and relate to the Indians in the vicinity of the post.

FORT FETTERMAN

Three daily journals of events occurring at the post, October 1868–June 1877, cite incidents relating directly or indirectly to Indians, such as the entry for June 21, 1875: "A party of citizens, (6), from direction of Laramie encamped near post yesterday. They state that they are prospecting the country in the vicinity, and disclaim any intention of going into B. H. [Black Hills] Indian Reserve unless they get authority to do so." Also recorded in one of these volumes are clothing accounts of Indian scouts for the period March to July 1874.

Cartographic Records

Among the cartographic records of various departments and divisions are maps showing operations against hostile Indians and maps of Indian agencies and reservations.

RECORDS OF UNITED STATES REGULAR ARMY MOBILE UNITS, 1821–1942 (RECORD GROUP 391)

By the end of the 19th century, the Regular Army mobile units consisted of 7 artillery regiments, 10 cavalry regiments, 25 infantry regiments, and 1 battalion of engineers, plus a few Signal Corps and Indian scout companies. Before the designation of the first six cavalry units as such in 1861, each of these units had one or more different designations. In describing the records, the units are referred to by their designation at the time the records were created. For instance, the 1st Cavalry is identified as the 1st Dragoons if records created before 1861 are being described.

The correspondence and issuances of any regiment involved in Indian affairs can be expected to contain some information about the subject. For example, among the letters sent by the 4th Infantry are several reports relating to Indian problems in Washington Territory. These reports discuss past treaties with Indians; problems created by settlers, missionaries, and road construction crews; Russia's cooperation with the Army; and major errors in the Army's Indian policy. Among the orders received by the 4th Artillery are general orders relating to a court of inquiry assembled at Frederick, Md., in 1836 to report on the causes for the failure of the Florida campaigns and the delay in opening the campaign against the Creek Indians in Alabama and Georgia. The decision of the court was received by the 4th Artillery as a general order; it contains a history of the military operations against the Seminole and Creek Indians before 1837.

In addition to the correspondence and issuances, other regimental records may contain information relating to Indians. The muster rolls and monthly returns contain "records of events," listing the battles, scouting parties, or patrols in which troops of the regiment participated. The quarterly tabular statements of scouts and expeditions give the posts from which the parties were sent, the names of commanding officers, units and Indian tribes involved, the strength of the command, dates of departure and return, the route and distance traveled, and the results, including the number of Indians killed, wounded, or taken captive. Often there are histories and scrapbooks of the regiments, which usually list or describe the Indian battles, scouts, and expeditions in which the regiment was involved.

Besides the general regimental records, there are several special series of records created by specific battalions, companies, or detachments. Some of these contain information on field expeditions, scouts, or campaigns against Indians in which the units were involved. A brief description of some of these special series follows.

Records Relating to Indians In General

ARTILLERY

Among the records of the 2d Artillery is a series of orders received and letters sent by batteries stationed in Florida for the period 1834 to 1838 (1 vol.). By January 1835, seven companies of the 2d Artillery were stationed at Fort Brooke, Fort King, and St. Augustine to aid in the removal of the Seminole Indians, which was to begin January 1, 1836. The general and special orders received by the troops summarize the Army's Indian policy and the military preparations made to ensure their scheduled removal. The letters sent from Fort Brooke relate mainly to the Seminole attack of December 28, 1835, on a detachment led by Bvt. Maj. Francis Dade; only 3 of the 110 members of the detachment survived. There are also reports of other actions with the Indians, such as Gen. Duncan Clinch's battle on the Withlacoochee River, December 29, 1835.

CAVALRY

1ST DRAGOONS

After the Pawnee Expedition ended in September 1834, detachments of the 1st Dragoons were stationed at various posts throughout what is now Kansas, Nebraska, Iowa, Oklahoma, and Arkansas. During this time, the troops were engaged in exploring, scouting, and preserving peace between Indians and non-Indians and among Indians. The letters and orders issued by these detachments (3 vols.) contain much information on these activities. Although conflicts never reached the point of open warfare, the troops constantly faced such recurring problems as the smuggling of alcohol onto the reservations by settlers, swindling of Indians by white traders, encroaching on land held by Indians by settlers, and rustling cattle by Indians. Of special interest are the letters sent by a detachment of dragoons stationed at Fort Wayne, Indian Territory, in 1839. They contain information relating to the conflict between the Ross and Ridge factions of the Cherokee Nation. After Elias Boudinot, Major Ridge, and John Ridge were assassinated on June 22, 1839, the dragoons were actively involved in tracking down the murderers and preventing further bloodshed between the two factions.

1ST CAVALRY

Two series of letters sent and received and orders issued by a battalion of the 1st Cavalry under Maj. George B. Sanford (2 vols.) cover the battalion's involvement in the Nez Percé campaign of 1877 and the Bannock Indian campaign of 1878.

After the Battle of Wounded Knee on December 29, 1890, there were fears of further unrest among the Indians. To prevent such disturbances, Maj. Henry Carroll was ordered to patrol the Little Missouri Valley and intercept any Indians heading north from the Pine Ridge Agency. A series of letters, telegrams, and orders received by Carroll during December 1890 and January 1891 (3 in.) contain much information on affairs in the Dakotas immediately after the Battle of Wounded Knee.

4TH CAVALRY

Between 1871 and 1881 several field expeditions of the 4th Cavalry used the same record books, consisting of letters and endorsements sent, registers of letters and letters received, and orders and circulars issued (14 vols.). These records were used as follows:

July–Oct. 1871	Scouting expedition in Texas
June–Dec. 1872	Scouting expedition in Texas
Aug.–Nov. 1874	Southern column near Fort Griffin, Tex.
1876	Powder River expedition
1877–78	4th Cavalry in the field at Camp Robinson, Nebr.; Fort Hays, Kans.; Fort Sill, Indian Territory; and Pinto, Tex.
1881	Fort Garland column

Most useful are the letters sent, June–December 1872, which report results of battles, movements of Indians, and general observations relating to Indians in Texas.

6TH CAVALRY

A volume of letters sent by Troop M, 1881–83, contains several letters from Capt. W. A. Tupper, who was involved in an action with a large band of Warm Springs and Chiricahua Apache Indians on April 28, 1881. Tupper briefly describes the battle and recommends several enlisted men for certificates of merit.

7TH CAVALRY

A series of letters sent by the surgeon of a 7th Cavalry detachment in Kansas and Arizona in 1868 and under George A. Custer in 1870 (1 vol.) includes reports of those wounded or killed in Indian battles, descriptions of burial sites for soldiers killed by Indians, and reports of civilians supposedly killed by Indians.

8TH CAVALRY

A field detachment of the 8th Cavalry was stationed near the Cheyenne River Agency from autumn 1890 to spring 1891. The letters sent by this detachment provide a detailed, almost daily account of Indian affairs in South Dakota for that period. These records are especially useful for information relating to Big Foot and the events surrounding the Battle of Wounded Knee.

9TH CAVALRY

On September 21, 1881, a battalion of the 9th Cavalry commanded by Capt. Henry Carroll was ordered to Separ Station, New Mexico Territory, on the Southern Pacific Railroad, where the troops were to observe the country south and west of Separ for signs of Indians. The letters and telegrams sent and received and orders issued (3 vols.) contain reports of scouts and a battle with the Chiricahua Apache near Camp Grant. The letters sent also contain several references to Indian scouts who were employed by the battalion but were evidently in sympathy with the Apache.

10TH CAVALRY

There is a set of records created by a 10th Cavalry detachment stationed near Fort Hays, Kans., in May 1868; at Fort Wallace, Kans., in July 1868; near Fort Dodge, Kans., in September 1868 and April–May 1869; at Fort Lyon, Colorado Territory, in March 1869; and at Camp Supply, Indian Territory, in the summer of 1869. The four series of records include letters sent, May–August 1869; a register of letters received and endorsements sent, June 1868–April 1869; letters received, 1868–69; and general and special orders issued, May 1868–August 1869.

The letters sent and received contain information relating to the negotiations for the release of Indian prisoners at Fort Hays. The letters sent by Col. A. D. Nelson, commander of the detachment, mostly concern the Arapaho near Camp Supply. Several letters explain the system Nelson used to distribute daily rations to more than 1,200 Indians. Other letters, sent to the headquarters of the Department of the Missouri, request that the Arapaho not be sent to the area chosen for their new reservation. According to Nelson, the designated land was totally unfit for anything and force alone could convince the Indians to emigrate there. Nelson also reminded his superiors that the future conduct of tribes such as the Cheyenne would depend on the Army's treatment of the Arapaho.

INFANTRY

6TH INFANTRY

In the winter of 1858–59 a battalion of the 6th Infantry marched from Los Angeles and crossed the Colorado River at the 35th parallel. Their objective was to select a site for a post that would effectively control the Indian tribes living along the Colorado River. The letters sent by the battalion (1 vol.) contain reports of the expedition and its conflicts with the

Mohave Indians. The commander of the expedition, Col. William Hoffman, also made several recommendations on the strategy to be used against the Indians.

8TH INFANTRY

A volume of letters and endorsements sent by Company H of the 8th Infantry contains several letters relating to the company's involvement in the Nez Percé campaign in 1877 and the Bannock Indian war in 1878.

Company K, 8th Infantry, was variously located at Fort D. A. Russell, Wyoming Territory (Nov. 1872–Feb. 1874), a camp near the Spotted Tail Agency (Mar.–July 1874), and Camp Apache, Arizona Territory (Oct. 1874–May 1875). Particularly useful are the letters sent (1 vol.) from Camp Apache where Company K was stationed to contain the Verde Indians within their reservation. The letters contain reports of the efforts to disarm the Indians and of a resulting battle which broke out near San Carlos, Arizona Territory.

Records Relating to Indians As Soldiers

An act to increase and fix the military peace establishment of the United States was published by the War Department as General Order 56, August 1, 1866. Section 6 authorized the President "to enlist and employ in the Territories and Indian country a force of Indians, not to exceed one thousand, to act as scouts." The following records were created by these scouts.

Descriptive books for Companies A, B, C, and F, 1872–86

Descriptive book for a battalion consisting of Companies A, B, C, and D, 1882–84

Muster rolls, 1877–88

Letters sent by Company A, January 1891–October 1899

Register of letters received by Company A, January 1891–August 1899

Letters and telegrams sent by Company C, August 1878–December 1881

Descriptive rolls of Warm Springs and Chiricahua Apache Indian bands, 1884–85

Descriptive book for a detachment of Seminole Indian scouts, 1889–93. Although the records of Indian scouts do not extend beyond 1899, the scouts were an active force in the Regular Army well into the 20th century.

The descriptive books contain rolls and lists of noncommissioned officers, men discharged, and deaths. These and the muster rolls show each scout's name, age, physical description, and place of birth; the date and location of enlistment and the officer by whom he was enlisted; payroll information; and remarks, which usually indicate the date of discharge. The letters sent by Company A and the letters received that were registered were mainly sent and received by a detachment of Indian scouts at San Carlos and Fort Grant, Arizona Territory. The letters and telegrams from Company C were sent from Camp Supply, Indian Territory, and Fort

Bowie, Arizona Territory. These series of correspondence contain mainly transmittal letters and letters relating to routine clerical work. A few mention such problems as drunkenness among the scouts and civilians attacking or abusing individual Indians.

On March 9, 1891, War Department General Order 28 authorized the enlistment of one company of Indians for each of 26 regiments of white cavalry and infantry. The order specified that Troop L of each of the cavalry regiments, except the 9th and 10th, and Company I of each of the infantry regiments, except the 6th, 11th, 15th, 19th, 24th, and 25th, would be recruited by the enlistment of up to 55 Indians for each troop or company. The primary object of this experiment was to employ a considerable number of Indians from the warlike tribes and, in so doing, to aid them in adjusting to a new way of life. It was hoped "that the habits of obedience, cleanliness, and punctuality, as well as of steady labor in the performance of both military and industrial work inculcated by service in the Army, would have a good effect on those who might enlist, and also furnish an object lesson of some value and exert a healthy influence upon others of their tribes."

By 1894 it was concluded that the experiment was not successful enough to warrant its continuation. Illiteracy, lack of facility with the English language, restlessness and discontent, marriage, and demoralization when stationed near Indian reservations were cited as the main factors preventing the adjustment to military life. It was decided therefore to discontinue the enlistment of Indians except as scouts. The organizations were gradually eliminated as their troops became eligible for discharge. The last Indian unit, Troop L of the 7th Cavalry, was disbanded in 1895.

Record books for these Indian units consist of the following:

letters sent by Troop L, 3d Cavalry, 1891–94

letters sent by Company I, 12th Infantry, 1891–94

descriptive book, Troop L, 3d Cavalry, 1891–94

orders issued, 1891–94, and special orders received by Company I, 12th Infantry, 1891–93

register and letters received by Company I, 12th Infantry, 1891–94

register of letters received by Company I, 21st Infantry, September 1891–November 1892

The letters sent are especially interesting and reveal a great deal about the unique problems facing these particular units. Several letters sent from the 12th Infantry stationed at Mt. Vernon Barracks, Ala., concern a mixed-blood Sioux who had been kidnapped from his tribe by a French trapper. He had not lived among Indians since he was 5 and therefore knew nothing of Indian habits, customs, or language. Because of his background, he could neither get along with the other members of Company I nor transfer to another unit. Many letters relate to the problem of educating and training soldiers who could not understand commands spoken in English. One letter tells of an Indian corporal who asked to be reduced to the grade of private; he was considered an excellent soldier but could not learn English and therefore could not be used as a squad leader. The letters from the commander of Troop L, 3d Cavalry, contain repeated requests that the issue of Indian rations not be discontinued to members of his unit. When the Indians enlisted, they had been promised that their service in the Army would not interfere with the rights and privileges granted them by the Interior Department. The commander insisted that, by refusing to issue rations to the new recruits, the Government was only creating further distrust and hatred among the Indians.

RECORDS OF THE AMERICAN EXPEDITIONARY FORCES (WORLD WAR I), 1917–23 (RECORD GROUP 120)

Among the records of the Historical Section of the General Staff of the American Expeditionary Forces (AEF), the U.S. forces in Europe in World War I, is a series of records, 1917–19 (1 ft.), relating to American Indians serving with the AEF. It consists principally of replies to two sets of questionnaires sent in February 1919 by the Historical Section "to battalion-scout, company, and other officers, in whose units Indians are enrolled." The first questionnaire requested information concerning the merits of Indians as soldiers and more specifically as scouts. Do they stand the nervous strain? Do they prove natural leaders in the ranks? Do they associate readily with white men? Have they demonstrated fitness for any specific arm of service? To what degree have they shown courage, endurance, judgment, humor, dexterity? Have they demonstrated ability as nightworkers, runners, observers, verbal reporters?

The second questionnaire gives, for individual Indians, name, tribe, date and place of birth, education, occupation, grade, military unit, combat record, and "remarks." The questionnaires are arranged numerically by infantry division.

Preceding the questionnaires is a folder containing more general information about the combat records of Indians in the AEF, including a report on the use of Choctaw by Indians serving with the 36th Division to transmit messages at the front.

NAVAL RECORDS COLLECTION OF THE OFFICE OF NAVAL RECORDS AND LIBRARY (RECORD GROUP 45)

The origins of the Office of Naval Records and Library can be traced to General Order 292, March 23, 1882, which placed the Navy Department Library under the newly created Office of Naval Intelligence. An act of July 7,

1884 (23 Stat. 159, 185), provided for a small staff to collect, compile, and arrange Civil War naval records. The Office of the Library and Naval War Records, as it became known, was transferred to the Office of the Secretary of the Navy by an order of October 19, 1889, and was designated the Office of Naval Records and Library in 1915.

Many of the series in this record group were first assembled from records already in Navy Department custody for publication in what ultimately became the multivolume series *The War of the Rebellion, A Compilation of the Official Records of the Union and Confederate Navies* (Washington, D.C., 1894-1922). Other records were acquired from private sources, including the large collection of naval officers' journals, logs, diaries, and letter books. Artificial series, such as the subject and area files, eventually were created to accommodate loose papers or copies of papers received, and later materials were continually added to them. Other records were added to the Naval Records Collection during the 20th century.

Information pertaining to the Navy's involvement with Indians generally is widely dispersed and difficult to locate among the materials in Record Group 45. The Navy did participate in the Florida Seminole wars and from about 1855 to 1857 in the Indian disturbances around Puget Sound. It also became interested at various times in Indian tribes inhabiting areas in which it was conducting coastal operations—Alaska, for example. However, relevant documentation usually does not exist in consolidated files or other segregated entities but must instead be located item by item among different correspondence series. Since there is little subject indexing, research is greatly facilitated if the researcher knows both the names of individuals involved and their rank at the time in question.

Records of the Secretary of the Navy

CORRESPONDENCE

Among the Navy Department records, the major correspondence series were determined by the rank or station of the correspondents. The most significant of the correspondence series have been reproduced on microfilm, including M149, *Letters Sent by the Secretary of the Navy to Officers, 1798-1868;* M89, *Letters Received by the Secretary of the Navy From Commanding Officers of Squadrons ("Squadron Letters"), 1841-1886;* M125, *Letters Received by the Secretary of the Navy From Captains ("Captains' Letters"), 1805-1861, 1866-1885;* M147, *Letters Received by the Secretary of the Navy From Commanders ("Masters Commandant" Through 1837, Thereafter "Commanders Letters"), 1804-1886;* and M148, *Letters Received From Commissioned Officers Below the Rank of Commander and From Warrant Officers ("Officers' Letters"), 1802-1884.*

Many of the communications and directives from the Secretary of the Navy to officers involved in Indian affairs can be found among the Department's letters sent to officers ("Officers Ships of War"). An example of this correspondence is a letter from the Secretary of the Navy to Commodore William B. Shubrick, June 14, 1839, directing that he prevent communications between Indians and fishing boats or other craft from the Bahamas and Cuba. A similar letter to Comdr. Isaac Mayo, commanding an expedition in Florida for the suppression of Indian hostilities, specified that Lt. John T. McLaughlin was to proceed to a chosen point on the Florida coast, "giving every annoyance to the hostile Indians and cooperating with the military officers."

The series of letters received from commanding officers of squadrons ("Squadron Letters") reflects the geographical command system used by the Navy throughout much of the 19th century. Although the squadrons existed before 1841, the correspondence from commanding officers was not segregated until that date; for the earlier period it is usually found among the series of captains' letters. The squadron letters include correspondence of the squadron commander and subordinate officers with the Secretary of the Navy concerning affairs in the area in which the squadron operated.

Some of the letters of the Pacific Squadron pertain to its role in the Indian hostilities around Puget Sound, Washington Territory, from 1855 to 1857. There is, for example, a letter from the squadron commander, Commodore William Mervine, November 29, 1855, to Comdr. James Alden of the surveying steamer *Active,* ordering him, because of "the savage demonstration of the Indians in Washington Territory," to proceed to Puget Sound with his vessel and cooperate with military and naval forces in the area in protecting the inhabitants. Similarly, in a communication of January 13, 1856, Mervine ordered Comdr. Samuel Swartwout to proceed to Puget Sound with the steamer *Massachusetts* and to take command of naval forces there from Comdr. Guert Gansevoort of the sloop of war *Decatur.* There are also a number of communications received by Mervine from commanders of vessels in the Puget Sound area relating to Indian problems in which they were involved. Typical is a report of Comdr. Isaac Sterrett, then commanding the *Decatur,* November 4, 1855, which discusses the Indian situation and the problems of the settlers as well as Sterrett's assistance, including the issuance of arms and ammunition from the ship's stores.

There is some correspondence for 1856 relating to the Navy's involvement once again in Seminole Indian problems in Florida. On January 24, 1856, Commodore Hiram Paulding, commander of the Home Squadron, reported a rumor of a flare-up of Indian hostilities in the vicinity of Tampa Bay and Cape Florida and dispatched the U.S.S. *Fulton* to investigate.

The series of captains' letters includes a number of documents pertaining to the destruction by a joint Army-Navy-Indian force of the Negro Fort on the Apalachicola River in the summer of 1816. The fort, which housed some 300 Negroes and 20 Choctaw Indians, had long been a refuge for fugitive slaves and disaffected Indians. The documents include reports received and sent by Commodore Daniel F. Patterson, who commanded the U.S. naval forces in New Orleans. There are lists of articles captured at the fort by the Army and its Indian allies and a report by Sailing Master Jairus Loomis, who commanded the gunboat *No. 149* during the destruction of the fort. There also is an earlier letter from Maj. Gen. Edmund P. Gaines, commanding the Army forces in the area, concerning certain Indian outrages that precipitated the expedition to destroy the Negro Fort.

Also among the captains' letters are a number of reports to the Secretary of the Navy from Commodore Alexander J. Dallas and his successor, Commodore William B. Shubrick, pertaining to the activities of the West India Squadron during the second Seminole war. There also is correspondence to and from subordinate officers and State officials. In a report of October 2, 1836, typical of many others in this series, Dallas discussed a proposed expedition of marines and seamen to be dispatched from the U.S.S. *Vandalia* to Cape Florida and New River for the purpose of surprising and capturing Seminole Indians. In a similar report of March 29, 1837, Dallas discussed a proposed expedition from the U.S.S. *Constellation,* which was to cooperate with mounted Volunteer Army troops in apprehending Creek Indians alleged to have murdered whites.

The series of commanders' letters contains valuable information about the Navy's role in the Florida war and at Puget Sound. There are some 20 letters and reports from Comdr. Isaac Mayo of the steamer *Poinsett,* who commanded the 1839 expedition in Florida. Several of his reports relate to his reconnaissances in the area where the Battle of the Caloosahatchie, in which forces under the command of Col. William S. Harney were destroyed by the Indians. Mayo's expedition evidently was unsuccessful in locating the bodies of the men killed. The series contains reports from commanders of vessels involved in the Puget Sound Indian difficulties (Sterrett and Gansevoort of the *Decatur,* Swartwout of the *Massachusetts,* Alden of the *Active*), together with related correspondence. One of the more significant reports is Gansevoort's for January 31, 1856, in which he describes an Indian battle in which his men participated, supported by gunfire from the ship.

The letters received from lower ranking officers ("Officers Letters") include many communications for the period 1839 to 1842 from Lt. John T. McLaughlin, commanding the Florida expedition. The reports cover all aspects of military operations against the Indians, including many in which naval forces participated. In a typical report, one of May 22, 1840, McLaughlin related that the boats of the vessel *Otsego* had been fired upon by a party of Indians. A report of January 24, 1841, described a joint expedition into the Everglades of seamen under his own command and soldiers under the command of Col. William S. Harney. Pertaining to later difficulties with the Seminole is a report from Lt. Richard L. Tilghman, February 12,

1856. Tilghman, commanding the *Fulton,* gives an account of his expedition to Cape Florida and Tampa Bay to investigate an alleged Seminole uprising. Information on Navy involvement with the natives of Alaska may be found in several reports of 1883 and 1884 from Lt. George M. Stoney of the schooner *Ounalaska.* Several reports for July 1883 concern the distribution of arms and ammunition to the Chuckees of St. Lawrence Bay, and a report of June 22, 1884, concerns poverty in a native village on Nunivak Island.

There are other correspondence series that contain some information relating to Indians. In a volume of confidential letters sent ("Private Letters"), February 1813–March 1822 and January 1840, are several communications, indexed under "Indians," that contain references to Indian allies of Great Britain in the War of 1812. Among the letters from officers commanding expeditions are several volumes pertaining to the Wilkes Pacific exploring expedition, 1838–42. Among these is a report of June 1842 on the Oregon Territory, which makes brief references to the Indian tribes of the area. The report has been reproduced as part of M75, *Records of the United States Exploring Expedition Under the Command of Lieutenant Charles Wilkes, 1836–1842.*

RECORDS RELATING TO SERVICE OF THE NAVY AND MARINE CORPS ON THE COAST OF FLORIDA, 1835–42

This volume is a typescript of an 1853 Navy Department compilation prepared in response to a request by the Commissioner of Pensions for information about the service of the Navy and Marine Corps in the Florida Seminole war, 1835–42. The first part consists of copies and abstracts of instructions to U.S. Navy officers by the Secretary of the Navy. The second part consists of copies of and extracts from reports sent and received by U.S. Navy officers in Florida, including Commodore Alexander J. Dallas, Lt. John T. McLaughlin, and Comdr. Isaac Mayo. The third part contains extracts from the logs of vessels operating off the Florida coast and a list of vessels attached to the Home and Gulf Squadrons during the years 1836 to 1842, which were operating off the coast of Florida against the Indians. This compilation is a good source for beginning a study of the Navy's activities during the second Seminole war. The original reports and correspondence are in the pertinent correspondence series.

Records Partially or Wholly Acquired From Sources Outside the Navy Department

LETTER BOOKS OF OFFICERS OF THE UNITED STATES NAVY AT SEA, 1773–1908

This collection includes eight volumes of correspondence sent and received by Rear Adm. William Mervine, 1836–68. For 1847 there is correspondence related to Mervine's role in commanding military forces in California, and a few letters refer to Indian raids and depredations. Much of the correspondence for 1855–57 relates to Mervine's command of the Pacific Squadron during the Puget Sound Indian difficulties; it includes letters to and from subordinate vessel commanders, many of which are duplicated in the squadron letters and commanders' letters discussed above.

There is a volume of letters sent and received by Lt. Comdr. C. R. Perry Rodgers, commanding the U.S.S. *Phoenix* off the coast of Florida, August 1840–May 1842. Several letters, notably those of June 11 and 22, 1841, contain accounts of expeditions against Indians.

The two volumes of correspondence of Comdr. Guert Gansevoort, commanding the *Decatur,* Pacific Squadron, include information about the Puget Sound crisis, much of which also is available in the commanders' letters discussed above. Included are copies of Gansevoort's reports to the Secretary of the Navy, reports received from commanders of naval vessels in the Puget Sound area, and correspondence with local government officials and other civilians relating to Indians.

ARTIFICIALLY CREATED SERIES

The area file consists of both original documents and copies arranged by the geographical area to which they pertain. It can be used as a reference tool for locating further documentation and has been reproduced as M625, *Area File of the Naval Records Collection, 1775–1910.* The documents were first acquired in the course of preparing the *Official Records of the Union and Confederate Navies* and subsequently were arranged and augmented by later acquisitions. Filed under "Area 8" (the Atlantic Ocean off the southeast coast of the United States) are copies of reports written by Lt. John T. McLaughlin from 1840 to 1842 during the Seminole war. Filed under "Area 9" (the Pacific Ocean east of longitude 180°) are a number of documents relating to the Puget Sound crisis, including a communication from the Secretary of the Navy to Commodore William Mervine, April 15, 1855; a typescript copy of Comdr. Guert Gansevoort's report of January 31, 1856 (discussed above); a letter of November 18, 1856, from the Governor of Oregon to Commodore William Mervine relating to the progress of the Indian wars and requesting that the *Massachusetts* remain around Puget Sound to guard against warlike Indians; and a letter from the Secretary of the Navy to Comdr. Samuel Swartwout, January 23, 1857, concerning the latter's report of unsuccessful interviews with a party of northern Indians. Pertinent to conditions among Alaskan natives are reports from Comdr. Henry Glass of the U.S.S. *Jamestown,* October 11, 1880, and from Lt. Comdr. Charles H. Stockton, of the U.S.S. *Thetis,* November 11, 1889.

The subject file consists of original documents and copies arranged under general subject matter categories. Also a byproduct of the *Official Records* project, the file evidently was maintained and augmented subsequently as a ready reference device. The following files, listed chronologically, are pertinent to the Navy's involvement with Indians.

Typescript and photostatic copies of reports by Col. Duncan L. Clinch, June–October 1816, relating to the destruction of the Negro Fort on the Apalachicola River in Florida (files OJ and HJ). See also pages 356 and 357.

Typescript copies of a journal, March 13–April 13, 1841, and a report, June 11, 1841, concerning an expedition from the schooner *Wave* to the Mangrove Islands and Everglades (file OH).

Typescript copies of reports by Commodore William Mervine and Comdrs. James Alden, Guert Gansevoort, Isaac Sterrett, and Samuel Swartwout relating to the naval participation in the Puget Sound Indian hostilities, 1855–56 (file OJ).

The report of Lt. George M. Stoney, October 15, 1883, relating to the natives of Alaska, including information about their physical attributes, living conditions, hunting and fishing practices, marriage customs, tribal structures, clothing, housing, and general disposition (file OC).

The report of Lt. Alexander McCracken, June 11, 1887, concerning a trip over the Chilkoot Trail in Alaska. Accompanied by men from the U.S.S. *Pinta,* McCracken visited the Chilkoot Indian village and reported on conditions there. Enclosed with his report is a statement by Claanot, chief of the Chilkoot tribe, June 2, 1887, relating to intrusions by whites on the tribe's trail to the Yukon (file OH).

GENERAL RECORDS OF THE
DEPARTMENT OF THE NAVY, 1798–1947
(RECORD GROUP 80)

In the general photographic file, 1942–57, 20 photographs are indexed under the subject headings "Indian Tribes," "Indians," and "Eskimos," 1943–45 and 1954–56. They show Navy personnel of Indian blood; an American Indian exposition at Anadarko, Okla., in 1944; Aleuts being removed from the Pribilof Islands; whale hunters off Point Barrow, Alaska; and Indian pilots on the U.S.S. *Bear.*

RECORDS OF THE UNITED STATES SENATE
(RECORD GROUP 46)

The U.S. Senate and the U.S. House of Representatives, established by article 1, section 1, of the Constitution, were given coordinate legislative authority, with the exception of all legislation to raise revenue, which must originate in the House. The official records of the Congress in the National Archives are primarily records created and collected by congressional committees and documents of a general nature, such as original bills. The originals of laws passed by Congress are in General Records of the U.S. Government, Record Group 11. They have been published in the *United States Statutes at Large*. Many records of the Congress have been published in the serial set of congressional documents.

Among the committee papers series, the records of the Committee on Indian Affairs are, of course, the most relevant for American Indian history. This committee existed from 1819 until 1947, when it became a subcommittee of the Committee on Interior and Insular Affairs. The Indian Affairs Committee's files are often found in three series: correspondence and other papers that accompanied specific bills, committee papers proper, and petitions. The committee papers series comprises generally all committee records, such as general correspondence and committee reports, that are not included in the other two series.

Nineteenth-century correspondence in the accompanying papers and committee papers series consists mostly of incoming letters, much of it received either from the two Departments (War and Interior) that successively had jurisdiction over the Bureau of Indian Affairs or from attorneys or delegates representing Indians. As an example of the kinds of subjects documented, the records of the Indian Affairs Committee for the 45th Congress, 1877–79, concern topics such as the incursion of white fishermen into the Pyramid Lake Reservation in Nevada, Indian uprisings in Idaho, the disposition of stocks on behalf of the Prairie Band of Potawatomi, the U.S. Government payment of counsel in the suits concerning Osage land cessions, the removal of the Ponca Indians from Dakota to Indian Territory, and the possible extension of the Homestead Act to Indians.

Many records relating to claims, both for compensation for Indian depredations and for payments and allotments due Indians, are in the records of the Indian Affairs Committee and the Claims Committee. These records accompanied private relief bills introduced to pay claims.

Committee records generally are filed separately for each Congress; however, a separate subject file of the Indian Affairs Committee, amounting to 59 ft. and arranged by legislative topic, State, and tribe, exists for the period from 1928 through 1952. The earlier records in this series apparently date from a 1928 Senate resolution authorizing an intensive investigation of Indian conditions.

Other committee records relating to Indians and the Bureau of Indian Affairs might be found in papers of Senate committees, such as Military Affairs, Territories, and Appropriations. Another series of relevant Senate records consists of petitions and memorials submitted to the Senate, both by and about Indians. These documents, found under the Indian Affairs Committee and other committees, concern topics such as Indian removal, protection from Indian raids, claims, the opening of Oklahoma to settlement, and Indian appropriations.

Until 1871 the United States negotiated treaties with Indian tribes, and these treaties had to be approved by the Senate. The Indian treaties series (actually another series of records of the Indian Affairs Committee) usually includes a copy of each treaty, a Presidential message concerning it, and correspondence received from the Commissioner of Indian Affairs relating to the negotiation of the treaty. Other correspondence and the roll call vote on the treaty may also be in the file.

Other records created as a result of an exclusive Senate function are documents, usually letters of approval or denunciation, accumulated in connection with nominees to offices that required Senate approval. Although there are records for only a small number of nominees, files do exist for several Indian agents and Territorial Indian superintendents, including Christopher (Kit) Carson.

Additional papers are found among the so-called Senate Territorial papers, a separate file of records relating to specific Territories. These papers include bills, correspondence, and petitions relating to land claims, Indian agents, Indian depredations, and Indian removal.

Among the cartographic records are several published maps showing Indian tribes and routes of surveys in the Indian country. Of special interest is a large-scale map, six sheets of the "Hydrographical Basin of the Upper Mississippi River." Published by order of the Senate in 1842, the printed version includes references not shown on the manuscript, which is in Records of the Office of the Chief of Engineers, Record Group 77. There is also a map of Oregon and Upper California that shows the names of many Indian tribes and bands. This map was compiled from John C. Fremont's surveys and other authorities by order of the Senate in 1848. A published copy of a map of the military road from Fort Walla Walla to Fort Benton, prepared from Capt. John Mullan's field notes, shows names of Indian tribes along the route and indicates a few battles with Indians by symbols.

Among the manuscript and annotated maps is a finished copy of the J. Goldsborough Bruff map that shows the status of land occupied by Indian tribes and lands ceded to the United States. This map was compiled in 1839 by the Bureau of Topographical Engineers in compliance with a Senate resolution (a rough draft of this map in Record Group 77 includes a census of tribes not shown on the finished copy). Also among the records of the Senate is a manuscript map, "Cherokee Country and the Western Outlet," showing the boundaries of a reservation for the Arapaho and Cheyenne Indians according to the treaty of October 28, 1867, and part of the Creek country ceded to the United States by the treaty of June 14, 1866.

See Harold E. Hufford and Watson G. Caudill, comps., *Preliminary Inventory of the Records of the United States Senate*, PI 23 (1950).

RECORDS OF THE UNITED STATES
HOUSE OF REPRESENTATIVES
(RECORD GROUP 233)

All legislation to raise revenue must originate in the House of Representatives, and by custom all appropriation bills also originate in the House. The series and types of House records generally parallel Senate records. The House Indian Affairs Committee existed from 1821 until 1947, when it became a subcommittee of the House Committee on Interior and Insular Affairs. Committee records of the 45th Congress, 1877–79, illustrate the topics documented in the files. They relate to the Cherokee educational fund; Gen. J. P. C. Shanks, special commissioner for Indian Territory; Osage land cessions; lands allotted to the Mexican Potawatomi Indians; the proposed transfer of the Bureau of Indian Affairs back to the War Department; and other subjects.

Another series of House records exists for the 1865–1903 period, the so-called accompanying papers. These records are separate from the regular series of committee papers and relate primarily to individual private relief and claim bills. (Much Indian legislation, in fact, concerned specific tribes and individuals.) The file is arranged alphabetically by name, but records affecting tribes are filed under "Indians" and thereunder by tribe or subject. Records relating to Indian legislation may also be found in this series under the name of the State in which the Indians lived.

See Buford Rowland, Handy B. Fant, and Harold E. Hufford, comps., *Preliminary Inventory of the Records of the United States House of Representatives*, PI 113 (1959).

RECORDS OF THE UNITED STATES
GENERAL ACCOUNTING OFFICE
(RECORD GROUP 217)

The General Accounting Office was created by the Budget and Accounting Act of 1921 (42 Stat. 20) as an agency in the legislative branch. It performs an independent, Government-wide audit of the receipts and expenditures of public funds. It also settles fiscal accounts of responsible Federal officers and prescribes accounting standards for Federal agencies. The records of the General Accounting Office include those of the six Auditors and the Comptrollers of the Treasury Department, the officials responsible for settling U.S. Government accounts before 1921.

Most of the records concerning Indian affairs were for many years maintained by the Indian Tribal Claims Branch of the General Accounting Office. The Branch was established in 1925 to prepare reports for the Department of Justice for use in processing claims before the U.S. Court of Claims and, beginning in 1946, before the Indian Claims Commission (see pages 369–371 and 394 and 395). These reports often amount to histories of the financial relations between the United States and Indian tribes. In 1965 the Branch was transferred to the General Services Administration (GSA). After a number of administrative changes, its functions are now the responsibility of the Indian Trust Accounting Division of the GSA Office of Finance.

The records, 1792–1951 (17,916 ft.), consist primarily of the settled accounts of fiscal officers and claimants and ledgers, journals, registers, copies of warrants and requisitions, and other account books maintained by the Auditors and Comptrollers of the Treasury and, more recently, by the General Accounting Office.

Most of these fiscal records up to 1817 are account books originally maintained by the Office of the Accountant of the War Department, although there are a set of Treasury Department general appropriation ledgers dating from 1796 and records of the First and Fifth Auditors consisting of accounts of Indian fiscal officers, 1794–1815. Most of the early volumes relate to all of the activities of the War Department, not just Indian affairs.

The basic account books are the interrelated journals and ledgers. The same transactions are recorded in each, but in the journals the entries are arranged chronologically, while in the ledgers they are divided into accounts for various uses of funds and for individuals. There are also registers and copies of warrants and report books, which contain certificates for persons entitled to a specified amount of money. Among the more unusual items is a register of horses, supposed to have been stolen by Indians, that were delivered to the agent of the War Department in Tennessee, 1796–1801. There are also several volumes, including letter books as well as account books, relating to Indian annuities. These appear to have been maintained by the Office of Indian Trade and its predecessors. From 1811 to 1822 this Office was responsible for the purchase and transmittal of annuities and presents for Indians. These volumes may have accompanied unbound accounts of the Office submitted to the Treasury Department for settlement. For the main body of records of the Office of Indian Trade, see Records of the Bureau of Indian Affairs, Record Group 75, on pages 17–23.

The Treasury Department used essentially the same accounting procedures as the War Department, but over the years they became increasingly complicated. Separate ledgers, journals, and other account controls were started for disbursing officers, claims, trust funds of tribes and individuals, transportation, and supplies. The records include some letter books as well as account books. In time, most bound records concerning accounts of the Bureau of Indian Affairs were kept in separate volumes, but even for the 20th century these are volumes that include records for other bureaus and even for departments other than the Department of the Interior, to which the Bureau had been transferred in 1849.

Most useful to researchers, particularly those interested in other than strictly financial transactions, are the accounts of fiscal officers and claimants, which date to 1951 and 1923, respectively. Fiscal officers included superintendents of Indian affairs, Indian agents, treaty commissioners, land surveying and locating agents, special disbursing agents, school superintendents, missionaries, medical officers, irrigation engineers, and other officials authorized to disburse funds to Indians or to administer Indian affairs. Claimants were chiefly persons and firms who furnished provisions and implements for Indians, supplies and equipment for Indian Service employees, and a wide variety of services. They also included persons who claimed losses from Indian depredations or other losses and Indians with claims against the Government.

Accounts are usually identified by the name of the fiscal officer or claimant. Finding aids are available if the name of the agency or other administrative unit is known and available to some extent if the tribe is known.

Fiscal officers normally were expected to submit their accounts quarterly, but this was not always possible, especially for those in remote areas. The accounts consist of various statements, schedules, and abstracts and supporting vouchers and documents. During the 19th century the account current (or state of the account) and the abstract or schedule of disbursements were considered the basic documents. There are also property returns, certificates of issue, schedules of collections, payrolls, muster rolls, annuity and other per capita payment rolls, and correspondence. To support individual transactions listed on abstracts and schedules, there are vouchers, receipts, invoices, and bills of lading. The accounts were sent to the Bureau of Indian Affairs and then to the auditor where additional documents were created, including auditors reports and statements of differences.

Almost every kind of document can be found among the supporting records. In addition to payment rolls there are sometimes extensive sets of affidavits and other evidence submitted by Indians or others to establish entitlement to settlement. An 1836–37 diary for a party of Creek Indians emigrating from Alabama to Indian Territory is an example of such evidence.

The documents for claims are usually less voluminous than those for fiscal officers accounts. They include statements, affidavits, invoices, bills of lading, and correspondence. They went through the same process as accounts: to the Bureau of Indian Affairs and then to the Treasury Department, where other documents were created, including a certificate of settlement or statement certifying that the person was entitled to a certain sum of money.

Until 1907 accounts and claims were filed together and assigned settlement numbers, which were started over at erratic intervals. Thereafter, the claims are separate from the accounts.

Although basically records of financial transactions, these records provide information on almost every aspect of civilian Indian administration. To some extent they also document military activities in the earlier years.

Some subjects for which the records may be of particular value are delegations of Indians visiting Washington, Indian removal, activities of missionary groups, annuities, sales of Indian lands, depredation and spoliation claims, the operation of agencies and other field offices, and fiscal operations of tribal governments. The records also contain information concerning transportation, including ferry service across rivers and food and lodging available to travelers, and commerce, education, medicine, and other aspects of life in the United States during the 19th and 20th centuries.

Of the other records of the General Accounting Office relating to Indians, most relate to various claims made against the United States by States and individuals for services and supplies furnished in Indian wars. The Congress passed several acts appropriating money to compensate for these expenditures, and the parties concerned presented accounts and claims to the Treasury. These records were originally among the files of the Second, Third, and Fifth Auditors, but they were later collected and grouped by war and State. They include lists of items supplied; muster rolls and payrolls of the State troops involved; vouchers for supplies and equipment; correspondence with State offices, officers, and individuals submitting claims; and registers listing the claims and awards arising from the Indian campaigns. There are claims records for Indian wars in Montana, Oregon, Washington, Dakota Territory, and California; the Black Hawk war; the Seminole war in Florida; the Aroostook expedition in Maine; and the Minnesota Sioux Indian war.

The records of the Second Comptroller include a series of letters sent by the Indian Division, 1875–95, to auditors, other officials, and Indian agents. They relate primarily to settlement of accounts and claims. Some concern disputes over contracts for goods and services for Indians. There are also a series of Indian contracts, 1820–36, and a few volumes of registers of Indian contracts for various periods during the 19th century. The registers list the contractor, the Government agent, the items to be supplied, the delivery date, and the cost.

RECORDS OF THE GOVERNMENT PRINTING OFFICE (RECORD GROUP 149)

This record group includes the record set of publications of the Federal Government, 1790–1971, formerly maintained by the Public Documents Division of the Government Printing Office. It is a likely source for Government publications about Indians or Indian administration. Many of these publications, of course, are available in libraries throughout the country.

RECORDS OF THE SUPREME COURT OF THE UNITED STATES (RECORD GROUP 267)

The Supreme Court, provided for in article 3 of the Constitution, was established by the Judiciary Act of September 24, 1789 (1 Stat. 73). Membership originally consisted of a Chief Justice and five Associate Justices. The present number of eight Associate Justices was set by a law enacted in 1869. The Supreme Court has original jurisdiction in cases affecting ambassadors, ministers, and consuls and in cases in which a State is a party. The Court's appellate jurisdiction is defined by law, but the Court usually hears only cases involving the construction or constitutionality of legislation or other issues of general importance.

The Court's original and appellate case files, 1792-1970, are in the National Archives of the United States, and many of these files relate to Indian lawsuits. The Court decided cases concerning almost every aspect of Indian life, including the determination of a tribe's existence and an individual's membership in a tribe *(United States* v. *Holliday,* 1865; *Wallace* v. *Adams,* 1907); the political status of a tribe *(Cherokee Nation* v. *Georgia,* 1831, in which Chief Justice Marshall ruled that an Indian nation was not a foreign state); tribal property rights and the scope of Federal power over Indian affairs *(Cherokee Nation* v. *Hitchcock,* 1902); and jurisdiction over criminal acts on reservations *(United States* v. *Kagama,* 1886). It also heard many other cases involving treaties, property rights, claims, and other matters. Case files may include petitions for writs of error or certiorari; transcripts of records from lower courts; and exhibits, agreements of counsel, briefs, depositions, motions, orders, judgments, mandates to lower courts, correspondence, and other papers.

Many of the records of the Court are available as microfilm publications, including its minutes, 1790-1950, M215; dockets, 1791-1950, M216; index to appellate case files, 1792-1909, M408; and appellate case files, 1792-1831, M214.

See Marion Johnson, comp., *Preliminary Inventory of the Records of the Supreme Court of the United States,* PI 139 (revised 1973).

RECORDS OF DISTRICT COURTS
OF THE UNITED STATES
(RECORD GROUP 21)

The Judiciary Act of 1789 (1 Stat. 73) established the system of Federal district and circuit courts. Each had original jurisdiction in certain matters (sometimes concurrent), and the circuit courts had appellate jurisdiction over decisions of the district courts. In 1891 the appellate jurisdiction of the circuit courts was transferred to the newly created circuit courts of appeals. In 1911 the circuit courts were abolished, and their records and remaining jurisdiction were transferred to the district courts. Records of district and circuit courts, including some Territorial courts, are in Record Group 21; records of circuit courts of appeals are in Records of the U.S. Courts of Appeals, Record Group 276. Most Federal court records that are part of the

National Archives of the United States are in the several Federal archives and records centers.

Indians have been involved in almost every conceivable kind of legal dispute, both civil and criminal. Some of the more prominent subjects of the cases have been the legal force of treaties, the relationship between the tribes and the United States, trade and commercial relations, the control of tribal affairs, the scope of tribal self-government, tribal membership and enrollment, citizenship, voting, the eligibility of Indians for public office, taxes, tribal and individual lands, boundaries, the legal meaning of "incompetency" and "wardship," civil liberties, slaves and freedom, individual rights in tribal property, timber, fishing, grazing, health service, irrigation, liquor laws, and crimes in Indian country. Individual Indians were parties in the same kinds of cases as other persons, but, owing to their special relationship with the Federal Government, there are records for cases not ordinarily held in Federal courts, particularly cases concerning land, heirship, money accounts of individuals, and criminal matters.

Most cases involving Indians were tried in the areas where they lived, but cases could be held in any court. Many were tried in the District of Columbia as the seat of Government.

Records of cases involving Indians are rarely segregated, and often the names of the parties in the cases do not make it evident that Indians are involved. Usually, therefore, a researcher would not consult court records unless some reference to a particular case was found in some other source.

The various courts kept their records in different ways, but they all kept sets of files for different kinds of cases, sometimes with docket books and indexes as finding aids. Often they kept minutes as a chronological record of proceedings. The kinds of records in case files vary according to the nature of the case, but typically there are the bill of complaint, petition, indictment (in criminal cases), or other document stating the cause of action of the plaintiff; answers of defendants; pleadings; briefs; affidavits, depositions of witnesses, and other documents submitted as evidence; and orders, notices, subpenas, judgments, notices, and other documents created by the court. For cases removed from a State court or appealed from a district to a circuit court, there may be a transcript of the proceedings of the earlier trial.

Many of the earlier district and circuit court records have been reproduced as microfilm publications. See also Henry T. Ulasek and Marion M. Johnson, comps., *Preliminary Inventory of the Records of the United States District Court for the Southern District of New York,* PI 116 (1959); Marion M. Johnson, Mary Jo Grotenrath, and Henry T. Ulasek, comps., *Preliminary Inventory of the Records of the United States District Court for the Eastern District of Pennsylvania,* PI 124 (1960); and R. Michael McReynolds, comp., *List of Pre-1840 Federal District and Circuit Court Records,* Special List 31 (1972). For citations to many important cases, see

Felix S. Cohen's *Handbook of Federal Indian Law* (Washington, 1942) or the revision brought up to date through 1956 by the Department of the Interior, Office of the Solicitor, *Federal Indian Law* (Washington, 1958).

RECORDS OF THE UNITED STATES COURTS OF APPEALS (RECORD GROUP 276)

U.S. circuit courts of appeals, established by an act of March 3, 1891 (26 Stat. 826), assumed the appellate jurisdiction over decisions of district courts previously exercised by U.S. circuit courts (see page 367). Their records consist primarily of appellate case files. Cases concerning Indians cover the same wide variety of subjects as district court case files, but proportionately fewer (only 6 of 11 districts) of their records have been transferred to the National Archives of the United States. Of these, those that appear to have the most records about Indians are the records of the court for the 8th Circuit (St. Louis), 1891–1945 (in FARC Kansas City), and for the 10th Circuit (Denver), 1929–45 (in FARC Denver). The 8th Circuit includes Minnesota, Iowa, Missouri, Arkansas, Nebraska, and North and South Dakota. The 10th Circuit includes Colorado, Wyoming, Utah, Kansas, Oklahoma, and New Mexico.

RECORDS OF THE UNITED STATES COURT OF CLAIMS (RECORD GROUP 123)

The U.S. Court of Claims was established by an act of February 24, 1855 (10 Stat. 612), to provide a means of litigation of certain types of claims against the U.S. Government. The court originally had no power to award a judgment and could only report its findings to the Congress. Power to award final judgments, except for appeals to the Supreme Court, was given to the Court of Claims by acts of March 3, 1863 (12 Stat. 765), and March 17, 1866 (14 Stat. 9). Originally the court had three judges, but it now has seven, including a chief judge.

The court's general jurisdiction includes any claim against the United States based upon the Constitution, any act of Congress, any regulation of an executive department, and any expressed or implied contract with the United States. The Congress also has given the court certain special jurisdictions; either House may refer a bill granting a claim to it for a report. The court reports, but it makes an award only if the claim is one over which it has jurisdiction under other acts of Congress. These are known as congressional jurisdiction cases. Similarly, there are departmental jurisdiction cases referred by the head of an executive department for a report. Temporary jurisdiction was occasionally conferred upon the court for special types of cases, including depredation claims against Indians.

The National Archives has case files for general jurisdiction cases, 1855–1939; congressional jurisdiction cases, 1884–1933; and departmental jurisdiction cases, 1883–1943. There are files for approximately 200 Indian tribal cases under these three categories. Most, however, were general jurisdiction cases, involving the interpretation or fulfillment of treaties. Tribes sued the United States for land taken from them and losses from erroneous surveys; losses of hunting and fishing rights, timber, coal, minerals, and livestock; the Government's failure to provide stipulated goods, services, and money; the loss or improper handling of funds; depredations by white citizens and soldiers; and other losses. Some cases not strictly tribal in nature involved claims for fees for legal and other services furnished the Indians and disputes about eligibility for tribal enrollment and participation in tribal benefits. Since 1946 most Indian tribal cases have been presented to the Indian Claims Commission (see pages 394 and 395).

Case files include transcripts of testimony, petitions, pleadings, briefs, affidavits, depositions, findings of fact, conclusions of law, orders, and other documents customarily found in records of court cases. Often there is material submitted as evidence, which may include correspondence, General Accounting Office and other reports, financial records, maps, photographs, and reference material. Case files also contain many copies of documents among the records in the National Archives of the Bureau of Indian Affairs and other agencies. Occasionally agencies sent original documents, which are still in the case files. The records concerning many of these cases present a valuable compilation of information about relations between Indians and the United States. There are separate cartographic records consisting of maps, 1940–47, submitted as exhibits by both the plaintiff and the defendant in General Jurisdiction Case 45585, *Confederated Bands of the Ute Indians* v. *the United States,* which involved the value of land ceded by the Indians to the United States in trust but not yet sold.

There is a special aggregation of records involving three general jurisdiction cases filed as a result of Cherokee grievances over the treaties providing for their removal to the West. In 1905 the court rendered a judgment for more than $1 million for the Eastern Cherokee (those still living in the East at the time of the treaty of 1835 and their descendants) and appointed a special commissioner, Guion Miller, to compile a roll of persons eligible to receive a share of the award. Between 1906 and 1909, applications from more than 45,000 claimants were received, of whom 30,820 were enrolled as eligible. These applications contain detailed information on the claimants' family backgrounds and are frequently accompanied by correspondence and other papers. Other records concerning the enrollment include Miller's report, miscellaneous correspondence, transcripts of testimony taken while some of the applications were being investigated, and various earlier rolls of Cherokee membership. Other records concerning this enrollment are among the records of the Land Division of the Bureau of Indian Affairs (see page 94).

By an act of March 3, 1891 (26 Stat. 851), the Court of Claims was given authority to render judgment on all claims by U.S. citizens for property destroyed by Indians belonging to any tribe in amity with the United States. The depredations on which these claims were based occurred from the early 19th century through the 1890–91 Sioux uprising, although most of them resulted from hostilities during the period 1860 to 1880. The victims were usually isolated miners and ranchers, but sometimes stagecoaches and trains were attacked. More than 10,000 case files document these claims filed between 1891 and 1894. One extensive file (45388) records the claim of the famous Lincoln County rancher John Chisum for cattle stolen during a drive from Texas to New Mexico in the 1860's. These case records include petitions, answers, depositions, motions, briefs, findings of fact, and opinions of the court. They also contain material submitted as evidence, most of which was furnished by the Department of the Interior, to which claims had been submitted before 1891. This material consists of Bureau of Indian Affairs reports, lists of property destroyed, agreements of the Secretary of the Interior to recommendations for allowances of claims, letters, and contracts.

See Gaiselle Kerner, comp., *Preliminary Inventory of the Records of the United States Court of Claims,* PI 58 (1953).

RECORDS OF TEMPORARY COMMITTEES, COMMISSIONS, AND BOARDS (RECORD GROUP 220)

Records of the National Council on Indian Opportunity

The National Council on Indian Opportunity was established by Executive order in 1968 to encourage and coordinate Federal programs to benefit the Indian population, appraise the impact and progress of such programs, and suggest ways to improve them. The Vice President was chairman, and the Council included several members of the Cabinet, the Director of the Office of Economic Opportunity, and a number of Indian leaders appointed by the President.The Council elicited viewpoints of Indians and others by correspondence and consultation with tribes and organizations, public meetings, and hearings. It acted as a clearinghouse for projects, coordinated interagency activities, reviewed budgets, and issued a newsletter and other publications to advertise and promote its activities. The Council was particularly concerned with economic development, housing, education, Indian manpower, health, urban Indians, and the prevention of alcoholism. The Executive Director of the Council was the chief Government mediator during the Indian occupation of Alcatraz Island, 1969–71. The Council was discontinued in 1974.

Most of the records of the Council are in a series of general files arranged alphabetically by subject except for some oversize materials (48 ft.). The subjects include tribes, organizations, specific projects, agencies, individuals, companies, meetings and councils, and Indians of particular States. There are also headings for such matters as alcoholism, arts and crafts, budget, the Council, economic development, education, employment, health, housing, human resources, labor, lands, legislation, sports, suicide, technical assistance and consultation, and urban Indians. There is a large file on Alcatraz, which includes much correspondence with Indians and others and photographs, most taken by the Coast Guard.

Other records include publications and issuances of the Council, including transcripts of regional hearings on proposals of the President, proceedings of public meetings of the Council's Committee on Urban Indians, copies of the Council's newsletter, and reference files, consisting chiefly of 1974 issues of Indian newspapers.

RECORDS OF THE BUREAU OF THE BUDGET
(RECORD GROUP 51)

The Bureau of the Budget was created by the Budget and Accounting Act of 1921 (42 Stat. 20) as a part of the Treasury Department but under the immediate direction of the President. In 1939 the Bureau was transferred to the Executive Office of the President. Its functions were to assist the President in preparing the U.S. budget, to develop plans for improving management in Government service, to aid the President in clearing legislative proposals received from Federal agencies, and to keep the President informed of the activities of Federal agencies. On July 1, 1970, the Bureau was reorganized as the Office of Management and Budget.

A significant number of records about Indians are in the Bureau's general subject files concerning legislation, 1921-38. These records resulted from the Bureau's role in determining whether any bill introduced in Congress and sent to the appropriate Federal agency for comment conflicted with the President's program. There are records, therefore, for most bills related to Indians considered by the Congress in this period. Many of the bills were introduced to refer specific tribal claims to the Court of Claims. Others concerned the Indian Reorganization Act of 1934, reservations, schools, allotments and per capita payments, and the disposition of tribal funds. The records include correspondence with the White House, congressional committees, the Interior Department, and other agencies; interoffice memorandums of Bureau staff members; and copies of the bills under consideration.

RECORDS OF THE OFFICE OF GOVERNMENT REPORTS
(RECORD GROUP 44)

From 1933 to 1948 there was a succession of agencies to coordinate Federal emergency activities, first in Depression relief and recovery programs and later in homefront aspects of the defense and war efforts. The Office of Government Reports, created in 1939, and its predecessors provided a clearinghouse for Government information and served as a liaison between the Federal Government and State governments. Records concerning Indians are widely dispersed, but, especially among the records of the National Emergency Council, 1934–39, there is much information about programs for Indians, with particular reference to cooperation between the Bureau of Indian Affairs and the Civilian Conservation Corps and other agencies. Included are reports of proceedings of statewide coordinating meetings of Federal officials, in which representatives of the Bureau of Indian Affairs participated.

On the recording of the radio program "Civilian Conservation Corps," September 19, 1939, in the "Agency Series," Robert Fechner, Director, discusses the Corps objectives of providing employment for youth and to some extent for veterans and Indians.

See H. Stephen Helton, comp., *Records of the Office of Government Reports,* PI 35 (1951).

RECORDS OF THE NATIONAL RESOURCES PLANNING BOARD (RECORD GROUP 187)

There are only occasional, widely dispersed references to Indians among the records of the National Resources Planning Board. However, part X of the *Supplementary Report of the Land Planning Committee* is entitled "Indian Land Tenure, Economic Status, and Population Trends" (1935, 73 p.).

GENERAL RECORDS OF THE DEPARTMENT OF STATE (RECORD GROUP 59)

Some documents relating to Indian treaties are among the miscellaneous letters, 1789–1906, and domestic letters, 1784–1906, of the Department of State. These records consist, respectively, of letters received from and letters sent to persons other than U.S. and foreign diplomats. Most of them have been reproduced as M179, *Miscellaneous Letters of the Department of State, 1789–1906,* and M40, *Domestic Letters of the Department of State, 1789–1906.*

From 1789 to 1873 the Department of State supervised affairs in the Territories of the United States. It was responsible for handling the correspondence between the President and Territorial officials, the printing of Territorial laws, and other matters, including Indian affairs. Territorial governors often served ex officio as superintendents of Indian affairs. Most of their records in this capacity are in Records of the Bureau of Indian Affairs, Record Group 75, but there are records concerning Indian matters dispersed throughout the series known as the Territorial papers of the Department of State. They include letters and reports sent by the Governor or secretary of the Territory to the Department of State. The reports include copies of correspondence of the Executive Office, proclamations and messages of the Governor, and records of proceedings of the Executive Office and the legislative assembly. Copies of letters to Territorial officials are among the domestic letters. Some representative subjects are Indian hostilities, militia activities in Indian wars, solutions to the "Indian problem," disruptions of mail routes, depredations, the sale of liquor to Indians, Indian captives and slaves, the legality of enslaving Indians, and charges against Territorial officials concerned with Indian administration. The Governor of New Mexico in 1851 was concerned that Pueblo Indians should either pay taxes or give up their land. There are records for the following Territories: Alabama, 1818–19; Arizona, 1864–72; California, 1846–47; Colorado, 1859–74; Dakota, 1861–73; Florida, 1777–1828; Idaho, 1863–72; Illinois, 1809–18; Indian, 1869; Indiana, 1804–16; Kansas, 1854–61; Louisiana, 1796–1812; Michigan, 1802–36; Minnesota, 1858; Mississippi, 1797–1817; Missouri, 1812–20; Montana, 1864–72; Nebraska, 1854–67; Nevada, 1861–64; New Mexico, 1851–72; Northwest, 1787–1801; Oregon, 1792–1858; Orleans, 1764–1813; Southwest, 1775–96; Utah, 1853–73; Washington, 1854–72; and Wyoming, 1868–73. The records for many of these Territories are available as NARS microfilm publications. David W. Parker's *Calendar of Papers in Washington Archives Relating to the Territories (to 1873)* serves as a guide and register to these papers. In 1873 responsibility for Territorial administration was transferred to the Department of the Interior (see page 204).

State Department records of a diplomatic nature also include occasional references to Indians, particularly concerning raids and depredations along the United States-Mexican border. Such records are in the despatches from U.S. ministers and consuls in such places as Piedras Negras, Hermosillo, Guerrero, Chihuahua, Guaymas, and Nogales; in notes from the Mexican legation in the United States to the Department of State; and in reports of State Department bureau officers. Among the despatches from U.S. consuls in Guaymas, for example, is information concerning the death of Cochise and the surrender of Geronimo and his band of Apache to Gen. Nelson A. Miles. Many of these records have been reproduced as microfilm publications. The War of 1812 papers of the Department of State, 1789–1815 (reproduced as M588), includes intercepted correspondence of British military officers relating principally to Indian affairs on the U.S.-Canadian frontier.

The journal, 1763–68, kept by Charles Mason during the Mason and Dixon survey of the boundary between Pennsylvania and Maryland (reproduced as M86 and published as *The Journal of Charles Mason and Jeremiah Dixon* in Memoirs of the American Philosophical Society, vol. 76

(Philadelphia, 1969)) includes comments on Indians. Other records include correspondence concerning West Florida, 1813–18, which relates in part to Indian raids and the Spanish Governor's advice to Indians hostile to the United States.

Brussels World's Fair Commission motion pictures, 1958, include three short color films on costumes, churches, and houses showing Indian costumes and a Pueblo village and church.

See Daniel T. Goggin and H. Stephen Helton, comps., *Preliminary Inventory of the General Records of the Department of State,* PI 157 (1963).

RECORDS OF THE FOREIGN SERVICE POSTS
OF THE DEPARTMENT OF STATE
(RECORD GROUP 84)

To a considerable extent, the records maintained by diplomatic and consular posts of the Department of State duplicate records in the General Records of the Department of State, particularly the instructions received from the Department and the despatches sent to it. Sometimes, however, there are records that are not in the central office files.

See Mark G. Eckhoff and Alexander P. Mavro, comps., *List of Foreign Service Post Records in the National Archives,* Special List 9, revised by Mario Fenyo and John Highbarger (1967).

RECORDS OF BOUNDARY AND CLAIMS COMMISSIONS
AND ARBITRATIONS
(RECORD GROUP 76)

Records of Boundary Commissions

Commissioners to establish international boundaries and members of their parties sometimes were among the first American officials to visit particular areas. They were expected to report on a wide range of subjects relating to the country they visited, including the Indians there. Their encounters with Indians were not always friendly. Andrew Ellicott, a U.S. commissioner appointed under the treaty of October 17, 1795, to determine the boundary between the United States and the Spanish possessions of East and West Florida, for example, met active opposition from Indians; he entered into negotiations with them in conjunction with Superintendent of Indian Affairs Benjamin Hawkins. Ellicott's experiences are documented in a printed journal and among three volumes of letters received from him by the Department of State, 1796–1802.

William H. Emory, the U.S. member of the commission established under the Treaty of Guadalupe Hidalgo and the Gadsden Treaty to determine the boundary line between the United States and Mexico, was interested in Indians. His letters and reports, 1849–60, contain much information about the Apache, Pima, Papago, Maricopa, Yuma, and other tribes with discussions of such subjects as their land and crops, the use of Pima Indians as a defense against Apache Indians, and hostilities with and among Indian tribes. There is also an undated map of the area between San Diego and El Paso, which shows missions and Apache trails. Emory's final report was published in three volumes as *Report of the United States and Mexican Boundary Survey,* . . . House Executive Document 135, 35th Congress, 1st session.

Among the records concerning the commission established in 1856 to run the boundary between the United States and British Columbia are seven journals of exploring surveys, 1854–58, which include Indian alphabets and vocabularies, drawings, and information about Indian villages, burials, property, and other subjects. There also are other lists of Indian words and an undated report on northwest explorations and migrations, which includes information on such subjects as Blackfeet and Crow hunting grounds.

Records relating to the Alaska-Canada boundary include a map showing Indian villages in southeastern Alaska and 11 photographs taken by topographer E. C. Barnard in 1898 of Indians and their boats at Forts Selkirk and Yukon, the Holy Cross Mission, and an Indian fish trap. Documentary evidence submitted with the U.S. case to the Alaskan Boundary Tribunal of 1903 includes letters and certificates of Indians relating to the occupation of the Lynn Canal area, 1866–1903, and miscellaneous documents, 1867–1903, among which are letters to Indians in Alaska from U.S. agencies and a statement of William Duncan on the establishment of an Indian village at the head of the Lynn Canal.

Records of Claims Commissions

There have been several United States and Mexican commissions to adjudicate claims of their citizens against the Government of the other. Among the records of some of these commissions are files concerning depredations committed by Indians on both sides of the international boundary. A commission created under the claims convention of July 4, 1868, was established to settle claims that had arisen since the signing of the Treaty of Guadalupe Hidalgo in 1848. Submitted were 366 claims for depredations in Mexico committed by Indians from the United States between 1848 and the signing of the Gadsden Treaty in 1853. Comanche and Apache Indians were most frequently named when specific tribes were charged. The records of these claims include minutes, opinions and decisions, an exchange of correspondence between the U.S. commissioner and the Mexican commissioner, other correspondence, reports, memorials of the claimants, defense arguments of the agent for the United States, and dockets. These Mexican claims were rejected as a group. There were also a few claims submitted by citizens of the United States for depredations committed by Mexican Indians.

The U.S. Commission to Texas, established by a joint resolution of Congress of May 7, 1872 (17 Stat. 395), was to investigate depredations committed by Indians and Mexicans from Mexico upon the property and lives of citizens of Texas. This commission, which operated from July 4, 1872, to June 30, 1873, determined that there had been losses totaling more than $48 million. Its records include proceedings, reports, petitions and depositions filed with the Commission, and reference materials.

The General Claims Commission, United States and Mexico, was created under the claims convention of September 8, 1923, to settle claims arising after July 4, 1868. Presented to this commission were 462 claims, known as the Texas cattle claims, for depredations committed by Mexicans and Kickapoo and other Indians from Mexico. Included were the claims investigated by the Commission to Texas and other claims for losses up to about the year 1878. However, the General Claims Commission was unable to reach agreement on these as well as on most of the other claims presented to it. In 1941 the United States agreed to accept $40 million as full payment for all these claims, and the following year the Congress established the American-Mexican Claims Commission to adjudicate the individual claims. This commission existed until 1947. The records of the General Claims Commission concerning the Texas cattle claims include dockets, reports, case files, and other evidence. There are case files and some other records of the American-Mexican Claims Commission.

Case files, 1912–26, for claims adjudicated under the terms of a special agreement of August 18, 1910, between the United States and Great Britain, include some for claims based on events involving Cayuga Indians as early as 1789.

See George S. Ulibarri, comp., *Preliminary Inventory of the Records of United States and Mexican Claims Commissions,* PI 136 (1962); Daniel T. Goggin, comp., *Preliminary Inventory of the Records Relating to International Boundaries,* PI 170 (1968); and George S. Ulibarri, comp., *Preliminary Inventory of Records Relating to International Claims,* PI 177 (1974).

GENERAL RECORDS OF THE DEPARTMENT OF THE TREASURY (RECORD GROUP 56)

The Treasury Department was established by an act of September 2, 1789 (1 Stat. 65), to superintend and manage national finances. In 1921 its functions pertaining to auditing and settling accounts were transferred to the newly created General Accounting Office. This record group comprises records of the Office of the Secretary, primarily general correspondence and appointment records, and records of various research and statistical units. See Carmelita S. Ryan and Hope K. Holdcamper, comps., *Preliminary Inventory of the General Records of the Department of the Treasury,* PI 187 (1977).

Records relating to Indians include correspondence of the Secretary of the Treasury concerning trust funds of the Chickasaw Indians and other tribes in two series, 1834-72 and 1836-49. The correspondence was conducted with the President, Cabinet members, bankers, the Commissioner of Indian Affairs, the Treasurer of the United States, Indian agents, and others; it concerns the sale of ceded lands, investments made in stocks and bonds for the trust funds, and amounts of money on hand. The records are similar to those relating to trust funds in Records of the Treasurer of the United States, Record Group 50 (see page 379). The 1834-72 series has been reproduced as M749, *Correspondence of the Secretary of the Treasury Relating to the Administration of Trust Funds for the Chickasaw and Other Indian Tribes ("S" Series), 1834-1872.* There are also returns (monthly statements) from land office receivers, 1838-49, which show the amounts of money received from the sales of Chickasaw lands. The correspondence of the Secretary of the Treasury with the Secretary of the Interior, 1850-1910, also contains letters relating to trust fund bonds as well as to such matters as the settlement of accounts of Indian agents and estimates of funds needed for projects of the Bureau of Indian Affairs.

Portraits of Indians in Washington, D.C., 1875, consist of six photographs of Modoc Indians, including Toby Riddle and her son; one of Toby Riddle's Kentuckian husband; five of Chickasaw, Cherokee, Creek, and Seminole delegates; one of a member of the Klamath tribe; and one of a member of the Siletz tribe.

RECORDS OF THE BUREAU OF ACCOUNTS (TREASURY) (RECORD GROUP 39)

The Bureau of Accounts, established in the Treasury Department by a reorganization plan in 1940, was the bookkeeping agency of the Government until 1974, when its functions were transferred to the new Bureau of Government Financial Operations. It maintained accounts relating to receipts, appropriations, and expenditures of public money for all agencies of the Government and made all disbursements for most civilian agencies. Included in this record group are records of certain predecessors of the Bureau, such as the Division of Bookkeeping and Warrants and the Commissioner of Accounts and Deposits.

Records relating to Indians include Indian and Indian agent appropriation warrants (certificates by the Secretary of the Treasury that a specific law had appropriated a certain amount of money, which accordingly was to be entered on the Treasury books), appropriation ledgers, and various account books, letters, and registers dealing with deposits and expenditures on behalf of certain tribes, interest paid on bonds of Southern States held by Indian trust funds, and accounts of Indian agents. There are also surety bonds of Federal officials, including Indian agents, responsible for disbursing Government money. The bonds include information on the property value of the sureties; correspondence relating to the bonds also may be in the files. The bond series, arranged alphabetically by surname of official, runs from 1789 through 1925.

RECORDS OF THE TREASURER
OF THE UNITED STATES
(RECORD GROUP 50)

The office of Treasurer was created by the act of September 2, 1789 (1 Stat. 65), that created the Treasury Department. Until most of its duties were transferred to the new Bureau of Government Financial Operations in 1974, it was essentially the banker for the Federal Government, charged with receiving and disbursing public funds; procuring, issuing, and maintaining custody of U.S. paper currency and coin; furnishing checking account facilities for all Federal agencies; and paying principal and interest on the public debt.

By an act of June 10, 1876 (19 Stat. 58), physical custody of all stocks and bonds held in trust for Indian tribes was transferred from the Secretary of the Interior to the Treasurer. Stocks with a value of more than $6 million were accordingly transferred. Correspondence in this record group between the Treasurer and the Secretary of the Interior, State officials, and bankers concerns the Treasurer's efforts to secure payment of bonds, especially those of certain States and railroads that had defaulted. Other letters transmit information on the amounts of different bonds held in trust and make arrangements for exchanging maturing bonds for new ones. Also in this record group are account books for Indian trust funds.

RECORDS OF THE BUREAU OF THE PUBLIC DEBT
(RECORD GROUP 53)

This Bureau of the Treasury Department, responsible for conducting transactions in the public debt issues of the United States, has been known under its present name since 1940, when it assumed responsibilities held at various times by State commissioners of loans, the second Bank of the United States, the Treasury Department's Division of Loans and Currency, and the Commissioner of the Public Debt. Documents relating to Indians include records (a journal, ledger, and numerical register) of the loan authorized in 1861 to pay expenses incurred by Washington and Oregon Territories during the Indian hostilities of 1855-56. There are also some miscellaneous records relating to Indian bonds, 1837-43, and Indian treaties and claims, 1871-73.

RECORDS OF THE BUREAU OF THE MINT
(RECORD GROUP 104)

The Bureau of the Mint was established in the Treasury Department by an act of February 12, 1873 (17 Stat. 424), succeeding the Mint of the United States, which had been an independent agency founded at Philadelphia in 1792. After 1835 the Mint's coinage operations had been supervised by the Secretary of the Treasury. The Bureau has responsibilities for manufacturing and distributing domestic coins, producing national medals, and receiving, storing, and selling gold and silver bullion.

See Lyle J. Holverstott and Jean McNiece, comps., *Preliminary Inventory of the Records of the United States Mint at Philadelphia,* PI 40 (1952).

Records relating to Indians concern the manufacture of Indian peace medals by the Philadelphia Mint, beginning with the administration of Thomas Jefferson and extending through that of Benjamin Harrison. The United States presented these medals, bearing the image of the incumbent President, to Indian chiefs and warriors on important occasions, such as the signing of treaties or visits to Washington by Indian representatives, and the medals became an important tool in the conduct of Indian relations. The records consist primarily of letters between the Director of the Mint and officials in the War Department and the Bureau of Indian Affairs and usually concern the cost of the medals and other administrative details. Some of these letters are in a general correspondence series that contains both letters received and copies of letters sent, 1792–1899, arranged chronologically. Other series of letters sent cover the periods 1795–1804, 1824–35, and 1866–1900. Records relating to the medals also are in letters received by the Superintendent of the Mint from the Chief Coiner and in various medal account books, 1861–68, which have information on the number and cost of medals struck.

RECORDS OF THE UNITED STATES CUSTOMS SERVICE
(RECORD GROUP 36)

Among reports and letters from special agents of the Treasury Department is a report from W. P. Howland concerning an unsuccessful attempt to take several hundred head of cattle and horses that Geronimo and a band of Apache were driving from the Sierra Madres in Mexico to the San Carlos Indian Reservation in March 1884.

GENERAL RECORDS OF THE DEPARTMENT OF JUSTICE
(RECORD GROUP 60)

The Department of Justice was established by an act of June 22, 1870 (16 Stat. 164), and was given responsibility for the legal and administrative duties of the Attorney General's Office, which had been created by the

Judiciary Act of 1789 (1 Stat. 73). The Attorney General's original duties were to represent the United States in suits before the Supreme Court and provide opinions on legal matters when requested by the President and heads of departments. Other functions were added later, such as supervising U.S. attorneys and marshals, detecting and investigating violations of Federal laws, supervising Federal prisons, administering immigration and naturalization laws, and registering aliens in the United States.

The main series of letters received by the Attorney General before the Department of Justice was established is known as the Attorney General's papers and covers the period 1817 to 1870. The letters are arranged first by source (President, Cabinet members, foreign diplomats, Congress, and the States) and thereunder chronologically. Letters from States are mostly from U.S. attorneys and marshals, but letters from State officers can also be found. Most letters relating to Indian affairs are in the correspondence from the War and Interior Departments and from States where Indians lived. Subjects discussed in the letters include the 1849 hostilities in Florida; negotiations with the Comanche Indians for the release of white captives, 1845; lawsuits in New Mexico against encroachments on Pueblo lands and a judicial ruling that the Pueblo did not fall within the 1834 Intercourse Act's definition of Indians; alienation of Choctaw lands and the Treaty of Dancing Rabbit Creek, 1842–44; and the alleged embezzlement of $40,000 of Indian funds by the Governor of Idaho, 1866.

Letters received by the Attorney General continue as a separate series from the establishment of the Department in 1870 until 1904. Beginning in 1884 the arrangement is by a year-numerical case file scheme. Typical are letters relating to the trial of hostile Indians in Oregon; 1898 proceedings against the Indian agent at Ponca, Oklahoma Territory, for bribery; sales of liquor to Indians; and numerous suits involving land titles.

Various series of letters sent by the Attorney General span the periods before and after the creation of the Department and are, of course, closely related in content to the letters received series. The miscellaneous letters sent series comprises virtually all outgoing letters for the period 1813 to 1867. After 1867 several subseries begin. Letters to executive departments and Members of Congress and instructions to U.S. attorneys and marshals are the most useful for records related to Indians. Many of the letters to the Secretary of the Interior transmit reports from U.S. attorneys on cases or problems involving Indians. Most of the letters sent are available as NARS microfilm publications.

Beginning in 1904 incoming and outgoing letters were filed together with other papers on a case or topic, and each case was numbered in order and filed in sequence. After 1914 this straight numerical file gradually was replaced by a classified subject system for the Department's central files. More than 150 subject classification numbers have been assigned, each class generally including all papers arising out of the enforcement of a law or group of laws. Record card abstracts (on 3- by 5-inch slips) arranged by source and alphabetical indexes exist for both the numerical and classified files.

Class 90-2 of the classified file constitutes the subject area for Indian matters. There is correspondence with U.S. attorneys and the Bureau of Indian Affairs over such matters as a former Indian school employee's complaint that Bureau agents were violating the law in regard to food purchases and an Indian's claim for damages to property on his allotment caused by construction blasting across a highway. A large number of letters relate to suits over land allotment titles and to cases arising from criminal charges against Indians.

RECORDS OF THE COURT OF CLAIMS SECTION (JUSTICE) (RECORD GROUP 205)

The act of 1855 (10 Stat. 612) that created the Court of Claims also provided for a solicitor to represent the United States before the court. This office was abolished in 1868, and its functions were transferred to the Attorney General. Since then, claims have been handled by a unit, first in the Attorney General's Office and later in the Department of Justice, directed by an Assistant Attorney General. This claims unit has been known by various titles, with a Claims Division being formally established in 1934 and a Court of Claims Section within it in 1937.

See Gaiselle Kerner and Ira N. Kellogg, Jr., comps., *Preliminary Inventory of the Records of the Court of Claims Section of the Department of Justice,* PI 47 (1952).

The records of the Court of Claims Section include case files for substantially the same cases as the records of the Court of Claims (see pages 369–371), including the Indian tribal cases among the general (1855–1945), congressional (1884–1944), and departmental (1883–1943) cases and the Indian depredation case records (1891–94). They do not usually contain as many legal documents as the Court of Claims records, but they include correspondence, memorandums, and other records concerning the preparation of the case. For the depredation cases, there is correspondence, 1891–1915, of the Assistant Attorney General in charge of the cases with U.S. attorneys and other Government officials and claimants' attorneys concerning such matters as the taking of depositions, the Government's investigation of claims, and the status of cases before the court. The general correspondence of the Assistant Attorney General also includes letters relating to tribal cases and depredation cases.

RECORDS OF THE SOLICITOR OF THE TREASURY
(RECORD GROUP 206)

Although this record group probably contains fewer documents relating to Indians than other legal or judicial records, certain series may be valuable. The Solicitor's Office was established in the Treasury Department in 1830 and assumed functions previously performed by the Agent of the Treasury under an act of 1820. The principal duty of the Solicitor was handling the legal proceedings involved in collecting debts owed the United States by individuals. To carry out this duty the Solicitor had authority over U.S. attorneys and marshals in the judicial districts. The Solicitor also had charge of lands acquired by the United States for debts and was authorized to dispose of surplus property. The Solicitor's Office was transferred to the Department of Justice in 1870, and many of its functions were gradually absorbed by units of the Department. The Office was finally abolished in 1934.

See George S. Ulibarri, comp., *Preliminary Inventory of the Records of the Solicitor of the Treasury,* PI 171 (1968).

Letters received by the Solicitor from executive departments before 1896 are filed chronologically under the name of the department and agency; after that date, all incoming letters are grouped in numerical case files. Letters sent are mainly in one chronological series, 1820–1934. Much of the correspondence relating to Indian matters was conducted with the Auditor of the War Department, U.S. attorneys, and the Commissioner of Indian Affairs and concerns suits against Indian agents who had defaulted on payments of Government money. Extensive correspondence with the U.S. Attorney for the District of Missouri and other officials relates to suits against Pierre Chouteau, Jr., and Company (western affiliate of the American Fur Company), 1846–49, for allegedly introducing liquor into Indian country. Also among the records of the Solicitor is a series known as closed cases, or miscellaneous case files of letters, reports, and briefs relating to special topics or lawsuits, which apparently were separated from other series. Numerous papers in this file relate to closing out the Office of Indian Trade after 1822, to the question of paying certain troops in the Seminole war in Florida, and to unlawful timber cutting on public lands and reservations.

RECORDS OF UNITED STATES ATTORNEYS AND MARSHALS
(RECORD GROUP 118)

U.S. attorneys investigate violations of Federal criminal laws, present evidence to grand juries, prosecute Federal criminal cases, and serve as the Government's attorney in civil litigation in which the United States is involved or has an interest. U.S. marshals execute and serve writs, processes, and orders and notify the Department of Justice of defiances of Federal authority. Their records relate to many of the same cases and other matters as those of Federal district courts (see pages 367–369). Most of their records that are part of the National Archives are in the Federal archives and records centers.

Most of the records concerning Indians are dispersed among other records, but the correspondence of the U.S. Attorney for the District of Arizona, 1903–12, relates in part to the sale of liquor to Indians, and there is correspondence of the marshal for the same district concerning Indian cases, 1917–23 (in FARC Los Angeles). There are case files, correspondence, and Indian genealogies, 1910–23, of the U.S. Attorney for the District of Minnesota, relating to an investigation of alleged land allotment frauds perpetrated against the Chippewa Indians of the White Earth Reservation (in FARC Kansas City). There is correspondence of the U.S. Attorney for the Western District of Wisconsin concerning Indian matters, 1894–1908 (in FARC Chicago).

RECORDS OF THE POST OFFICE DEPARTMENT (RECORD GROUP 28)

The records of the Post Office Department contain a considerable amount of information concerning the establishment and discontinuance of post offices at Indian agencies or in Indian country, appointments of postmasters, mail routes, and related subjects, but there are only widely dispersed references to Indians. In the chronologically arranged letters sent (few of the letters received have survived) are occasional letters, chiefly to the Secretaries of War and the Interior, about such subjects as Indian attacks on mail stages, military protection for the mail, and the frequency and quality of mail service to Indian agencies.

See Arthur Hecht, Frank J. Nivert, Fred W. Warriner, Jr., and Charlotte M. Ashby, comps., *Preliminary Inventory of the Records of the Post Office Department,* PI 168, revised by Forrest R. Holdcamper (1967).

RECORDS OF THE COAST AND GEODETIC SURVEY (RECORD GROUP 23)

The correspondence among the records of the Coast and Geodetic Survey for the period 1844 to 1900 (the 20th-century records are relatively few and fragmentary and are largely concerned with routine administrative matters) consists of some 500 volumes and document the work of surveying and charting coasts and related activities. Research in these records is time-consuming, because there is no overall index to the material; locating specific documents requires a page-by-page examination of a great many volumes. If such a search is undertaken, however, scattered references can be found to Indians as they affected the surveys being made in the western States and Territories. For example, a letter in an 1851 volume from Lt. Comdr. J.

Alden, USN, Assistant in the Coast Survey, to Prof. A. D. Bache, Superintendent, relating to Humboldt Harbor and Trinidad Bay, Calif., mentions "the depradations of the Indians" there that were "a serious drawback to the farming operations" forcing the settlers into town for protection. In an 1855 volume the following was found:

> The savage demonstrations of the Indians in Washington Territory, in murdering many of the settlers; the concert of action between the different tribes, together with their attacks upon the Regular troops, seem to indicate a general Indian War, the declared object of which is the termination of all the white population. This alarming state of affairs calls for all the available Naval Force which can be spared from other duties. ... The U.S. Surveying Steamer "Active" is to proceed to Puget Sound to join the Sloop of War "Decatur" to aid and protect the Inhabitants residing on the Sound.

NARS microfilm publications of Coast and Geodetic Survey records include M642, *Correspondence of A. D. Bache, Superintendent of the Coast and Geodetic Survey, 1843–1865*. See Nathan Reingold, comp., *Preliminary Inventory of the Records of the Coast and Geodetic Survey*, PI 105 (1958).

RECORDS OF THE BUREAU OF THE CENSUS
(RECORD GROUP 29)

The first decennial census that enumerated Indians as a separate race was the one taken in 1860. For this and the following census, however, only Indians living with the general population were counted. In 1880 an attempt was made to enumerate nontaxed Indians, which meant those living on reservations. A special schedule was prepared, but it was used only for a few reservations near military installations. There are schedules in the National Archives of the United States for those Indians in Washington Territory under the Yakima Agency near Fort Simcoe and the Tulalip Agency; the Hunkpapa, Miniconjou, and Oglala Sioux of the Standing Rock Agency near Fort Yates, Dakota Territory; and the various tribes of the Round Valley Reservation, Calif. The census was to include all Indians living on October 1, 1880. Members of families who died after that date were included, but children born later were omitted. The schedule called for the name of the tribe, reservation, agency, and nearest post office; the number in the household and a description of the dwelling; and the Indian name (with an English translation) of each person in the family, his relationship to the head of the family, marital and tribal status, description, and information about occupation, health, education, ownership of property, and source of subsistence. Often the enumerator was unable to furnish all the data required, but in some cases information was added about tribal customs or living conditions.

Most of the census schedules for 1890 were destroyed by fire, but the Census Bureau used a special schedule for Indians to prepare the *Report on Indians Taxed and Non-Taxed in the United States Except Alaska* (1894). Other special reports on Indians were published from information gathered in the 1910, 1930, 1950, and 1960 censuses. There is also information about Indians in the general population schedules for 1900 and later years, but only those for 1900 are open for research. The population schedules through 1890 are available as microfilm publications.

Cartographic records of the Bureau of the Census include enumeration district "Office Copy" maps and enumeration district descriptions, 1880–1950. The maps do not show population figures. The census enumeration description volumes for 1900, 1910, and 1920 give population figures for Indian reservations from records of the Bureau of the Census. Volumes for 1930 and 1940 give Indian population figures that apparently were furnished by the Bureau of Indian Affairs. "Supervisor omit—Indian Bureau takes this district" is stamped under the name and description of many districts constituting all or part of an Indian reservation. The 1950 volumes give Bureau of the Census population figures; however, notes sometimes state "the Indians in this E.D. were included in special Indian Tabulation."

Among the published records of the Bureau of the Census is an outline map of the State of New York showing the reservations of the Six Nations and giving in tabular form the acreage and population of each reservation for the 11th census, 1890. There are also separate maps on a larger scale of the Onondaga, Tonawanda, Cattaraugus, Tuscarora, and St. Regis Reservations, showing population figures for 1890 (the Allegany Reservation map is missing).

Audiovisual records include 60 photographs of the Navajo Indian enumeration, 1930. Twenty-four of these photographs show the Indians and their homes and activities, and the remainder show the enumerator and the terrain.

See Katherine H. Davidson and Charlotte M. Ashby, comps., *Preliminary Inventory of the Records of the Bureau of the Census,* PI 161 (1964).

RECORDS OF THE UNITED STATES COAST GUARD (RECORD GROUP 26)

In peacetime, the Coast Guard was a unit of the Department of the Treasury from its creation by an act of January 28, 1915 (38 Stat. 800), until it was transferred to the Department of Transportation in 1967. The documents relating to Indians in this record group are actually records of other Treasury Department agencies that became units of the Coast Guard: the Lighthouse Service (called the Lighthouse Board from 1852 to 1910 and the Bureau of Lighthouses from 1910 to 1939) and the Revenue-Cutter Service. Letters from the collector of customs (who was also Superintendent of

Lights) at Key West, Fla., to the Fifth Auditor of the Treasury, who had jurisdiction over the Lighthouse Service, describe events during the second Seminole war, 1835-42, when Indians attacked and destroyed the Cape Florida Lighthouse at Key Biscayne. Related records of the Revenue-Cutter Service include logbooks of vessels that were ordered to Florida to assist the Army and Navy and the correspondence ("X" series) between officers of these cutters and the Secretary of the Treasury about events of the war.

The Revenue-Cutter Service had special duties in Alaska, notably the enforcement of regulations prohibiting the sale of liquor or firearms to natives and the unauthorized killing of fur-bearing animals and the protection of fishing grounds. In the Alaska file of the Service, 1867-1914, reproduced as M641, are records concerning Eskimos; Indians; Sheldon Jackson, General Agent for Education in Alaska; reindeer; and other related subjects.

In the general photographic subject file, 1886-1947, under "Alaska" are approximately 100 photographs of Eskimos in Alaska and the Aleutian Islands, ca. 1946. They show handicrafts, boats, egg and walrus hunts, homes, and graveyards. There are another 25 photographs, ca. 1890. Other photographs in these sets show Siberia and Siberian natives, and both sets may have been taken in connection with the annual importation of reindeer from Siberia. Three motion picture films, 1922 and 1938, show Alaskan natives; one of the two 1938 films shows the commander of the *Bear* marrying an Eskimo couple aboard the cutter.

RECORDS OF THE BUREAU OF PUBLIC ROADS (RECORD GROUP 30)

A decimal subject classification (487) for roads on Indian reservations is part of the general correspondence and related records of the Bureau of Public Roads, 1912-50. Under this classification are filed 10 inches of correspondence, reports, memorandums, procedural issuances, applications for emergency relief funds in 1935, tables, and other records. These documents relate mostly to general programs and relations between the Bureau of Public Roads (whose main function was the administration of the Federal-aid highway program) and the Bureau of Indian Affairs, but they also concern individual construction projects. Many cross-references to records in other subject classifications also are included. Roads on reservations, access roads, and roads through reservations were involved.

The cartographic records of the Bureau include State and county transportation maps. Among photographs illustrating the history of transportation, 1896-1952, under the subject "Indians," are 75 photographs or photographic copies of artworks, many copied from books. Included are works by Frederick Remington, Charles Schrevogel, and George Catlin. There are four photographs of Cherokee Indians along the Blue Ridge Parkway, June 1939.

See Truman R. Strobridge, comp., *Preliminary Inventory of the Records of the Bureau of Public Roads*, PI 134 (1962).

GENERAL RECORDS OF THE DEPARTMENT OF HEALTH, EDUCATION, AND WELFARE (RECORD GROUP 235)

The general records of the Department of Health, Education, and Welfare, formerly known as the Federal Security Agency, are arranged according to a decimal classification scheme. Information relating to Indians can be found in file 370.3, which concerns conferences, conventions, and congresses, and in file 600, which relates to public assistance. File 370.3 includes correspondence relating to U.S. participation in the First and Second Inter-American Conferences on Indian Life, held in April 1940 and October 1948. File 600 includes correspondence, memorandums, and reports, 1948–49, concerning racial discrimination against Indians through the denial of public assistance provided for under the Social Security Act.

See Jerry N. Hess, comp., *Preliminary Inventory of the Records of the Department of Health, Education, and Welfare*, PI 181 (1975).

RECORDS OF THE OFFICE OF EDUCATION (RECORD GROUP 12)

The Alaska Division of the Office of Education conducted education, medical, and other programs for Alaska natives from 1885 until 1931, when it was transferred to the Bureau of Indian Affairs. Most records concerning Alaskan activities also were transferred (see pages 112–114), but some are still among the records of the Office of Education, particularly the letters sent, 1870–1909. Most of these letters have been reproduced as M635. Most of the corresponding letters received apparently no longer exist.

See Carmen Delle Donne, comp., *Preliminary Inventory of the Records of the Office of Education*, PI 178 (1974).

RECORDS OF THE PUBLIC HEALTH SERVICE (RECORD GROUP 90)

The Public Health Service has administered Indian health programs since 1955 and before then it cooperated with the Bureau of Indian Affairs. There are only a few records, however, concerning such matters among the records of the Public Health Service now in the National Archives. They include reports and correspondence on the incidence of diseases on Indian reservations and the investigation of diseases among Indians, principally during the period 1900 to 1920. Most records concerning Indian health activities are in Records of the Bureau of Indian Affairs, Record Group 75, especially those of the Health Division (see pages 109–111).

RECORDS OF THE CHILDREN'S BUREAU
(RECORD GROUP 102)

The Children's Bureau was established in 1912 to investigate and report on all matters relating to childhood and subsequently was given various administrative responsibilities. Records relating to Indian children are in the central files of the Bureau, 1912-40, under the classifications 9-3-7-3, 1912-20; 0-2-8-4, 1921-28; and 0-2-9-4, 1929-40. They relate especially to health, education, and economic conditions.

See Carmen R. Delle Donne, comp., *Preliminary Inventory of the Records of the Children's Bureau,* PI 184 (1976).

RECORDS OF THE OFFICE
OF THE SECRETARY OF AGRICULTURE
(RECORD GROUP 16)

The general correspondence of the Office of the Secretary of Agriculture, 1906-69, is arranged by year and thereunder in part by subject. It relates more to general policies and departmental procedures than to individual programs, which are documented in detail among the records of individual bureaus. For most years through 1963, there are records under the heading "Indians," although for the most part these are cross-reference sheets. The records concern such subjects as land, forestry, employment, soil conservation, water, farm credit, the distribution of food to needy Indians, agricultural extension, and legislation. Sometimes there are records about some matter in which the Secretary took a personal interest.

In the general photographic subject file under "Indians," there are 25 photographs relating to Indian life, 1920-32, 1935-39, and 1943-45. These photographs are from the Soil Conservation Service, Extension Service, Agricultural Adjustment Agency, and Information Division of the Department.

See Helen Finneran Ulibarri, comp., *Preliminary Inventory of the Records of the Office of the Secretary of Agriculture,* PI 191 (1979).

RECORDS OF THE FOREST SERVICE
(RECORD GROUP 95)

The Bureau of Forestry had been operating for 4 years within the Department of Agriculture when it took the designation Forest Service in 1905 and received jurisdiction over the national forest reserves previously controlled by the Department of the Interior. The Congress had authorized the establishment of forest reserves from the public domain in 1891. Managing Indian timberlands has been the direct responsibility of the Bureau of Indian Affairs except during 1908-9 when the Forest Service undertook this task. Otherwise the Service's involvement with Indian timberlands has been restricted to such matters as fire control and Indian ownership of lands within national forest areas. For these reasons and because of the organizational structure of the Forest Service, only a small quantity of materials relating to Indian timberlands is segregated from the rest of its records.

The correspondence of the Office of Federal Cooperation in the Branch of Silviculture, 1908–11 (6 ft.), documents the management of Indian timberlands by the Forest Service under the short-lived agreement with the Bureau of Indian Affairs. In 1909 it was estimated that Indian lands contained about 12 million acres of timber. Besides logging and timber sales, the Forest Service was concerned with improving yield and extinguishing fires as well as with the Indian labor needed to carry out its programs. Some of the correspondence specifically concerns defining the cooperative agreement between the two agencies, but most of it pertains to general timber operations and related work. Information about work plans, expenditures, contracts, trespasses, the disposition of dead timber, and the condition of the forests is also included in this correspondence.

Filed with the records of the Division of Cooperative Forest Protection are annual fire reports for individual Indian reservations, 1934–47 (1 ft.). The type of information given varies somewhat depending on the year, but each report, when applicable, shows the number and causes of fires, the number of acres burned, and the cost arising from the damage. The reports were prepared to further the cooperative fire protection programs authorized by the Clarke-McNary Act of 1924 (43 Stat. 653).

Among the records of the Division of Recreation and Land Uses is some correspondence between the Forest Service and the General Land Office concerning allotment applications of Skagit Indians to lands within the boundaries of the Washington National Forest. This correspondence, 1915–21, contains recommendations of the Forest Service as to whether the applications should be approved or rejected.

Some Indian-related reports, 1933–36, are filed with the central files of the Forest Research Divisions under "R Cooperation, Indian."

Cartographic records include maps of Indian reservations showing forest classifications, 1903–20, and published maps of the United States and of Forest Service regions, which show Indian reservations.

In a general photographic negative file, 1897–1930, are several hundred photographs relating to Indians. Subject headings include Indians, artifacts, arts and handicrafts, and ruins and totem poles.

See Harold T. Pinkett, comp., *Preliminary Inventory of the Records of the Forest Service,* PI 18, revised by Terry W. Good (1969), and Charlotte M. Ashby, comp., *Preliminary Inventory of the Cartographic Records of the Forest Service,* PI 167 (1967).

RECORDS OF THE FEDERAL EXTENSION SERVICE
(RECORD GROUP 33)

The Federal Extension Service (now Extension Service) is the educational agency of the Department of Agriculture, working in cooperation with other Federal and State agencies. Extension programs for Indians are for the most part conducted by the Bureau of Indian Affairs (see pages 111 and 112); they have included classes, demonstrations, work supervision, and experiments. The general correspondence of the Federal Extension Service, 1907–46, is arranged by year and thereunder by different categories, including Federal bureaus, until 1943, when a subject-numeric scheme was adopted. There are records concerning Indians under headings for the Department of the Interior and Indian affairs. In 1955 extension activities for Indians in some States were transferred from the Bureau of Indian Affairs to the State extension services. The annual narrative and statistical reports of extension workers from then through 1960 include reports from workers assigned to Indian agencies.

Five Department of Agriculture motion picture films have sequences relating to Indians. These include Flathead dances in Montana, 1921; a Paiute chief presenting a war dance, 1926; Dakota Indians in the Nebraska National Forest, 1929; a Sauk war dance in Iowa, 1932; and Chinese air cadets watching a New Mexico Indian dance festival, 1944.

See Virgil E. Baugh, comp., *Preliminary Inventory of the Records of the Extension Service,* PI 83 (1955).

RECORDS OF THE BUREAU OF ENTOMOLOGY
AND PLANT QUARANTINE
(RECORD GROUP 7)

Some records, mainly concerning insect pests such as grasshoppers, beetles, and bollworms, are among the general correspondence of the Bureau of Entomology, 1925–34, under the heading "Special Folders-Indian Affairs," and of the Bureau of Entomology and Plant Quarantine, 1934–51, under the heading "Interior-Indian Affairs."

See Harold T. Pinkett, comp., *Preliminary Inventory of the Records of the Bureau of Entomology and Plant Quarantine,* PI 94 (1956).

RECORDS OF THE BUREAU OF AGRICULTURAL ECONOMICS
(RECORD GROUP 83)

Among the project files of the Bureau, which conducted and coordinated economic and statistical research for the Department of Agriculture, are some records concerning farming prospects on the Colorado River Indian Reservation, 1951, and among the general correspondence of the Public Finance Section are some records concerning Indian land policy, 1934.

In the photographic subject file of the Office of Farm Management, under "Addenda-Indians," are 50 photographs showing Indians and their living conditions mainly in Arizona and New Mexico, 1900–1905. Three photographs were made in the State of Washington in 1915, and there are an additional 20 photographs under "Addenda-Indians-Prehistoric," showing ruins and sites mainly in Arizona and New Mexico in 1903. Two of the items are of an Indian shell mound near Coden, Ala., 1911, and one is an undated view of a mound near Miamisburg, Ohio.

See Vivian Wiser, comp., *Preliminary Inventory of the Records of the Bureau of Agricultural Economics,* PI 104 (1958).

RECORDS OF THE SOIL CONSERVATION SERVICE (RECORD GROUP 114)

The creation of the Soil Conservation Service in the Department of Agriculture in 1935 and the subsequent expansion of its duties were the result of attempts to consolidate efforts of several Government agencies to prevent soil erosion. By an agreement between the Agriculture and Interior Departments, a unit called Technical Cooperation-Bureau of Indian Affairs (TC-BIA) was established in the Service in December 1935. From surveys of land conditions, use, tenure, and dependency on resources of Indian reservations, plans and programs were to be developed to control erosion and use and manage Indian lands properly. By 1939 much of the unit's work had been taken over by the Service's regular organization, and the remaining staff concerned itself with cooperative relations with the Bureau of Indian Affairs. There are general records of the Soil Conservation Service pertinent to Indian reservation work, but records of the separate TC-BIA unit are more useful.

Files of the Director of TC-BIA, 1937–39 (4 ft.), relate to the administration of the headquarters office of that unit and to its relationships with the main offices of the Soil Conservation Service, the Bureau of Indian Affairs, and other cooperative agencies. The coordination of work on Indian reservations is the major subject of these records.

General operations of the TC-BIA unit are documented in the unit's subject classified files, 1935–39 (7 ft.). The main headings used for filing are: Administration and Organization, Cooperation, Education-Information, Fiscal and Accounts, Legislation, Personnel, Procurement and Purchase, Property, Reports, Research-Compilation, Social Economic Studies, and Technical Surveys. Each heading is further divided into subject subheadings, with Technical Surveys having the most extensive amount of materials; there are major subheadings for Agronomy, Conservation Surveys, Engineering, Erosion Surveys, Reconnaissance Reports, Forestry, Geology-Hydrology, Range Management, and Wildlife.

There are TC-BIA project records for about 90 individual Indian agencies or reservations, 1936–39 (15 ft.). They are arranged alphabetically by name of unit and thereunder by subject subheadings.

Many records relating to work on Indian reservations were accumulated in regional offices of the Soil Conservation Service after its regular field organization absorbed TC-BIA functions. For example, such materials (7 ft.) are with the Rapid City Regional Office records; other types of field units created Indian-related records as well.

There are also records concerning demonstration Indian land projects carried out in cooperation with the Bureau of Indian Affairs as part of a program to purchase and convert submarginal land. This program was conducted successively by the Federal Emergency Relief Administration, Resettlement Administration, Bureau of Agricultural Economics, and Soil Conservation Service. The Indian projects were transferred to the Bureau of Indian Affairs when the land had been acquired. There are both general records and records concerning individual projects. Project files for Indian lands are interfiled with those for other projects, but they can be identified from project description books.

Cartographic records consist of aerial photographs and photo indexes of selected areas in the United States, 1933–39, including specific projects on 11 western reservations, and manuscript and published maps of the United States, its regions, and the States, compiled by the Soil Conservation Service and its predecessors; these include maps that were prepared for TC-BIA reports. The maps show land classification, soils, erosion, alkalinity, agronomy, ground water levels, forage types, woodlands, and engineering facilities for individual reservations.

Audiovisual records include about 500 photographs illustrating the lives and activities of Navajo, Pima, Papago, Hopi, Havasupai, Zuñi , Pueblo and other Indians in Arizona and New Mexico, 1935–37.

RECORDS OF THE FARMERS HOME ADMINISTRATION (RECORD GROUP 96)

Records of the Farmers Home Administration and its predecessors, the Resettlement Administration, 1935–37, and Farm Security Administration, 1937–46, include some information about the participation of Indians in Depression emergency programs, such as rural rehabilitation, land utilization, and resettlement. Most of the pertinent records are in the 071 Cooperation with Federal Agencies decimal classifications of central and regional office general correspondence. There are also some maps of California showing boundaries of Indian reservations, with a table for each reservation indicating the manner of land acquisition, land ownership, agricultural values, grazing values, and commercial timber values.

See Stanley W. Brown and Virgil E. Baugh, comps., *Preliminary Inventory of the Records of the Farmers Home Administration, PI 118* (1959).

RECORDS OF THE INDIAN CLAIMS COMMISSION
(RECORD GROUP 279)

When the Indian Claims Commission was created by an act of August 13, 1946 (60 Stat. 1049), it was granted power to hear and determine claims against the United States on behalf of any identifiable group of American Indians residing within the United States or Alaska. Interested parties were to be given the opportunity to present evidence in hearings conducted by the Commission before any final determination was made upon a claim. The Commission could require by subpena the attendance and testimony of witnesses and the production of all necessary evidence; it could also require the taking of written depositions before any individual competent to administer oaths. In taking testimony, allowance was to be made for cross-examination.

Originally it was intended that the Commission should receive claims for a period of 5 years only and that its work would be terminated after another 5 years. Later acts extended the life of the Commission several times. Until it was abolished in 1978, it consisted of five members, with three necessary to provide a quorum for a decision. Before the establishment of the Commission, tribal claims against the United States were heard by the U.S. Court of Claims (see pages 370 and 371).

Most of the claims are based on inadequate compensation for lands ceded by the tribes. The adjudication involves establishing Indian title to the land, determining the value of the land at time of the cession, and determining the amounts of payments made by the United States and of counterclaims, or offsets, by the Government against the Indians.

The records of the Indian Claims Commission now in the National Archives consist of 197 feet of files for closed cases, 1947-67. A case file usually pertains to one tribe or related or allied tribes or bands. Records of consolidated case files are often placed together, but occasionally parts of them are maintained under the original docket numbers. The original papers in a case file might include correspondence, petitions, motions, briefs, findings, objections, memorandums, reports, transcripts of proceedings, orders, opinions, final judgments, and appeals. There also may be extensive materials submitted as evidence by plaintiffs and defendants. Exhibits include copies of documents from other record groups in the National Archives and from other depositories, cartographic and photographic materials, constitutions and charters of Indian groups, ethnological and anthropological reports, appraisals of Indian lands, mineral appraisals, General Accounting Office financial reports (see pages 363 and 364), published works, and excerpts from them. These case files not only document matters at issue in the claims proceedings, but they are also a valuable source for compiled information about the tribes and their relations with the United States.

The overall arrangement of the records is by docket number (except where there is a consolidation) and thereunder by kind of document. Plaintiff's and defendant's exhibits within a case file are separately arranged according to numbers stamped on the backs of the individual items.

RECORDS OF THE VETERANS ADMINISTRATION (RECORD GROUP 15)

Although the first national pension act of the United States was passed as early as August 26, 1776, responsibility for the administration of the pension system was divided among the President; the Congress; the Departments of War, Navy, and Treasury; and the States until 1833. In that year, the Congress authorized the appointment of a Commissioner of Pensions to administer the military pension system under the direction of the Secretary of War (4 Stat. 619, 622). An act of 1840 (5 Stat. 369) transferred responsibility for Navy pensions to the Commissioner of Pensions, and an act of 1843 (5 Stat. 597) gave the Commissioner responsibility for military bounty land warrants. In 1849 the Commissioner of Pensions was transferred to the new Department of the Interior, and in 1930 the Commissioner's Office (known as the Bureau of Pensions), the U. S. Veterans' Bureau, the National Home for Disabled Volunteer Soldiers, and the functions of the Office of the Surgeon General concerning the provision of artificial limbs and other appliances were consolidated to form the Veterans Administration, an independent executive agency.

Pension and Bounty Land Warrant Application Files

Included in this voluminous body of records are approximately 54,000 pension application files and also several thousand bounty land warrant applications based on the service of Indian scouts, Indian soldiers, and other soldiers in Indian wars throughout the 19th century. There are also applications for pensions and bounty land warrants by Indians who served in other wars of the United States.

A pension or bounty land warrant application file may contain one or more applications of a veteran or his dependents or heirs; documents supporting the identity, service, or character of the claimant; and evidence of the action taken on the claim. A veteran's application was a sworn statement submitted on a printed form that might include information on the act under which he applied; date of application; name, address, age, birthplace, and date of birth of the veteran; date and place of enlistment and discharge; rank, company, and commanding officer; physical description; occupation; date and circumstances of any disability resulting from his service and the medical treatment received; other enlistments or military service of the veteran; date, number, and amount of any other pensions and bounty land warrants received; names and date and place of marriage of the veteran's parents; date and place of marriage and divorce; names and dates of birth of his children; his addresses since leaving the service; his signature or mark; and sometimes date and place of death. The applications of Indians generally are brief. The greater command of the English language by other soldiers sometimes resulted in extensive narrative accounts, verging on the autobiographical, of experiences in battles or campaigns.

Claimants often submitted documentary evidence to support their applications, such as marriage certificates, wills, commissions, discharges, affidavits of other veterans or knowledgeable persons, and miscellaneous correspondence. An especially interesting example is a four-page letter from Patrick Henry to George Rogers Clark in the Revolutionary War pension application of William Meriwether, containing instructions on the handling of Indians on the Northwest frontier.

Other Records

The records of the Veterans Administration also include many series of pension payment and control registers that could be used to locate records pertaining to Indians. Registers maintained by pension agencies in the States, for instance, contain lists of the names and service histories of veterans paid by those agencies. One such compilation has been reproduced as M123, *Eleventh Census of the United States, 1890: Schedules Enumerating Union Veterans and Widows of Union Veterans of the Civil War.* Among the records of the Special Examination Division of the Bureau of Pensions are correspondence and memorandums, 1917–30 (1 ft.), concerning verification of Indian scouts' military service and alleged violations of pension laws.

RECORDS OF THE SMITHSONIAN INSTITUTION (RECORD GROUP 106)

Cartographic Records

There are copies of two maps compiled by Charles C. Royce in 1884 and published in the *Fifth Annual Report of the Bureau of Ethnology*. One shows the former territorial limits of the Cherokee Nation and has a chronological schedule of Cherokee cessions. The other shows the territory west of the Mississippi River originally assigned to the Cherokee and the areas occupied by them in 1884. There is also a published map prepared by John Wesley Powell for the seventh annual report of the Bureau, showing the distribution of American Indian linguistic stocks in Greenland and North America, excluding Mexico.

Audiovisual Records

There are 160 oversize glass negatives of photographs of American Indians, 1870-1907, from the Bureau of American Ethnology. They show individuals, groups, delegations in Washington, D. C., and views of Indian homes, pueblos, and activities. The Smithsonian Institution has retained most of the Bureau's photographs. A portfolio of 21 watercolor sketches by Matilda Coxe Stevenson, 1882, are of Acoma, Cochiti, and Laguna Pueblos and of ruins and landscapes in the vicinity with copies of ancient pottery pieces. An album of photographs by F. A. Ames, 1887-89, includes views of Hopi Indians, their homes and activities, reservation headquarters, and Navajo neighbors.

Bureau of American Ethnology sound recordings, 1915-41, include 110 recordings made by John P. Harrington of songs of the Mission Indians of California sung by Jose Orivas Albanas, 1930-41; a series of 12 discs recording the voices of Aleuts Agripina Merkulieva, Anna Sepatin, and Irskiy Sepatin telling stories and giving linguistic and cultural information in their native tongue, with English translations by Irskiy Sepatin; and four Cherokee recordings and an address of Woodrow Wilson to the Indians, 1915. Recordings of six episodes of the radio program "The World is Yours," 1936-39, relate to Indian life and history. The subjects are American Indians, mound builders, arrowheads, John Smith and the Virginia Indians, Eskimos, and Indians of the Great Plains. The recording of the radio program "Racial Equality," May 24, 1937, in the "Let Freedom Ring" series dramatizes racial prejudice through history and racial discrimination against Indians, Orientals, and Negroes in America.

Motion picture films, 1903-49, include three reels dealing with Indian sign language demonstrations at Fort Browning, Mont., 1931; two dealing with archeological work at ruins in Arizona and New Mexico, 1932; and one showing Charles Lindbergh and his wife posing with Eskimos in Nome, Alaska, 1931.

RECORDS OF THE PUBLIC WORKS ADMINISTRATION
(RECORD GROUP 135)

The Federal Emergency Administration of Public Works was established in 1933, renamed the Public Works Administration (PWA) in 1939, and abolished in 1943. It administered a program of Federal and non-Federal public works by means of loans and grants. The Bureau of Indian Affairs sponsored many PWA projects. Unfortunately, most of the records of the PWA were destroyed; and records of the Bureau of Indian Affairs (Record Group 75), particularly those of the Construction Division, are the main source for information about these projects. Among the surviving PWA records, however, are several series of records of the Projects Control Division with identifiable records concerning Bureau of Indian Affairs projects. These include correspondence relating to Federal projects, with two folders relating chiefly to the employment of Indians on projects; records of transfers of funds and changes in projects; records relating to the justification of projects, including letters from Members of Congress, and local officials and others, approvals by the President, and photographs; and lists of projects recommended for allotments of funds.

See L. Evans Walker, comp., *Preliminary Inventory of the Records of the Public Works Administration*, PI 125 (1960).

RECORDS OF THE WORK PROJECTS ADMINISTRATION
(RECORD GROUP 69)

The Works Progress Administration was established by Executive Order 7034 on May 6, 1935, to operate the work relief program as a whole. Its chief function was to provide jobs for needy persons through the establishment of useful projects. On July 1, 1939, the Works Progress Administration was incorporated into the Federal Works Agency and renamed the Work Projects Administration; operations were terminated in 1943. Of the funds that had been expended under the program by 1942, about 75 percent went to construction and engineering projects, while the remaining 25 percent was used for public service projects employing white collar workers.

The central correspondence files of the Work Projects Administration include a small file (001) relating to Indian relief in 1935. Most of the documents concern the need and eligibility of Indians for relief assistance. It also contains a list of projects sponsored by the Bureau of Indian Affairs, Indian agencies, and Indian reservations. Among the records of the Information Division are two folders containing records relating to Indians benefited by the Work Projects Administration (982–A and 982–B). Serial reports of Federal Project No. 4, the Survey of Federal Archives, are useful for information on the location, use, and content of the Bureau of Indian Affairs records in the field during the late 1930's. Also pertinent are records of the arts projects under Federal Project No. 1—music, theater, writers', and art—each of which conducted programs dealing with Indian culture. Copies of some of the publications resulting from research projects concerning Indians are maintained with the Records and Research Library of the Work Projects Administration.

There are microfilm copies of files for individual projects, chiefly from State and local offices. They are mostly administrative, however, and it is frequently difficult to locate records for a particular project. Records of the Rehabilitation Division of the Bureau of Indian Affairs (see pages 127 and 128) usually are a better source.

In the central office photographic subject file, 1936–42, under "Sociological—Indians" are 25 photographs showing activities on the Tonawanda Reservation, N.Y., in 1936; homes built on the L'Anse Reservation, Mich.; an Osage family in Oklahoma; and the dedication of a fish screen in Yakima County, Wash., May 6, 1939. There are also 75 photographs, filed under "Historical Projects–Archeological Restoration," showing the identification, excavation, and restoration of Indian mounds and sites in Alabama,

Arizona, Georgia, New Jersey, Ohio, and Texas, 1936–39. A motion picture film, "A Better Minnesota," made by Pathe News in 1937 shows Sioux and Chippewa Indians weaving, embroidering, and making beads.

RECORDS OF THE CIVILIAN CONSERVATION CORPS
(RECORD GROUP 35)

The Civilian Conservation Corps (CCC), 1937–43, and its predecessor, Emergency Conservation Work, 1933–37, were intended primarily to provide employment and training for youths through conservation and natural resources development work. Indians of any age, however, were eligible. There are some records concerning CCC Indian activities in its general correspondence, correspondence of the Division of Planning and Public Relations, and correspondence of the Division of Selection with Federal and private agencies. The main source for information about the Civilian Conservation Corps program for Indians, however, is among the records of the Civilian Conservation Corps—Indian Division of the Bureau of Indian Affairs (see pages 126 and 127).

In the central office photographic subject file, 1940–42, under "Indian Service" are 15 photographs showing Indian CCC activities on the Santa Clara Indian Reservation, N. Mex., stabilization of the ruins of Pecos Mission and Pueblo Bonito, and the Chippewa burial ground at Tamarac Lake, Minn. There are also 24 photographs that show Tlingit Indian CCC enrollees restoring the totems in the Tongass National Forest, Alaska.

See Harold T. Pinkett, comp., *Preliminary Inventory of the Records of the Civilian Conservation Corps,* PI 11 (1948).

RECORDS OF THE NATIONAL YOUTH ADMINISTRATION
(RECORD GROUP 119)

The National Youth Administration (NYA) conducted programs for needy young people from 1935 to 1944. Records of the NYA concerning Indians are widely dispersed and difficult to locate, but a file of printed and processed materials includes two handbooks for Indian counselors prepared in New York. There is also a color motion picture film, 1942, showing Apache Indians presenting the matachina dance.

RECORDS OF THE SELECTIVE SERVICE SYSTEM, 1940–
(RECORD GROUP 147)

The Selective Service System was established in 1940 to provide a method of obtaining men for military and naval service. Among the central files of the System are folders marked "Indians" or "Indian Reservations" for the years 1940 to 1944. They include correspondence, memorandums, circulars, tables, maps, and other records concerning such subjects as procedures for registering Indians, the liability of Indians for compulsory military service, and the refusal of certain Indians to register. There are also cross-references to other subject headings.

See Richard G. Wood, comp., *Preliminary Inventory of the Records of the Selective Service System, 1940–47,* PI 27 (1951).

RECORDS OF THE COMMITTEE ON
FAIR EMPLOYMENT PRACTICE
(RECORD GROUP 228)

The first Committee on Fair Employment Practice was established in 1941. It was replaced in 1943 by a second Committee, in the Office for Emergency Management, which operated until 1946. The Committee formulated and interpreted policies to combat racial and religious discrimination in employment; received, investigated, and adjusted complaints of such discrimination; and assisted Government agencies, employers, and labor unions with problems of discrimination. The Committee was concerned primarily with the employment of blacks, but there are a few files for cases involving complaints by Indians.

See Charles Zaid, comp., *Preliminary Inventory of the Records of the Committee on Fair Employment Practice,* PI 147 (1962).

RECORDS OF THE WAR RELOCATION AUTHORITY
(RECORD GROUP 210)

The War Relocation Authority (WRA) was established within the Office for Emergency Management by Executive Order 9102 of March 18, 1942, to assist persons of Japanese ancestry who had been evacuated from the West Coast by military order for national security. The WRA enlisted the cooperation of a number of Federal and State agencies in selecting sites for relocation centers to house evacuees. Centers were established at Poston, Ariz., on the Colorado River Indian Reservation (the Colorado River Relocation Center); and at Sacaton, Ariz., on the Pima Indian Reservation (the Gila River Relocation Center). The Leupp Indian School on the Navajo Reservation was turned over to the WRA for use as a camp for malcontents from relocation centers.

Documentation of the establishment of the centers is among the WRA's headquarters subject-classified general files that relate to administration and to relocation centers. File 11.122, "Memos and Agreements With Other Agencies," includes correspondence and copies of agreements pertaining to the Leupp Indian School and to the Colorado River location. There also is material concerning a controversy between the WRA and the Bureau of Indian Affairs over the water supply at Gila River. File 41.020 consists of agreements, memorandums, correspondence, and other records concerning the Gila River Center, 1942–46. There are similar materials for the Colorado River Center, 1942–46, under 41.050.

There are also subject-classified files maintained at the centers, but a document-by-document search would be required to locate any relevant records. Guides to the files of the Colorado River and Gila River Relocation Centers are available for use in the National Archives Building.

See Estelle Rebec and Martin Rogin, comps., *Prelimimary Inventory of the Records of the War Relocation Authority*, PI 77 (1955).

RECORDS OF THE OFFICE OF WAR INFORMATION (RECORD GROUP 208)

The Office of War Information coordinated the Government's World War II information programs, both foreign and domestic. In the photographic subject file of the Pictures Division of the Overseas Operations Branch, 1942–45, are seven photographs filed under "Indians (American) in the U.S. Armed Forces," 1943–44. The card index refers to 15 other photographs filed under other subjects. These include an Indian receiving the Congressional Medal of Honor and others serving in New Britain and in the women's auxiliaries. Among photographs used to illustrate feature stories, 1942–45, are 20 photographs relating to Indian culture, the Gilcrease Museum in Tulsa, Okla., and a rally in Denver, Colo. (files 1313, 1825, 1843, 1858, and 2052). In photographs depicting "Life in the United States" are 10 photographs concerning Indian crafts and religion; those concerning the latter relate to the 1948 ordination of John J. Brown, the first Blackfoot Indian to be a Roman Catholic priest. The photographic subject file of the Magazine Branch includes 75 photographs under "American Indian" showing Indian activities, handicrafts, artworks, and homes, 1938–44. Motion picture films include a reel of United News Films showing Navajo Indian women making gifts for Red Cross packages, 1943.

RECORDS OF THE UNITED STATES INFORMATION AGENCY (RECORD GROUP 306)

The U.S. Information Agency carries out international information activities. In its general photographic subject files, 1948–65, there are about 120 photographs filed under "Indians (American)" showing Indians and their activities in the United States. The subject index on 3- by 5-inch cards refers to approximately 50 other photographs filed under other subjects.

Among photographs of the Paris Bureau of the *New York Times*, 1932–40 and 1944–50, are approximately 50 photographs of American Indians filed under "Peaux Rouges," 1928–39 and 1947–50. They show Indians in their home areas and also in New York City, London, and Paris and with President Franklin Roosevelt. Additional photographic negatives for which there are no prints may be located by consulting the card index under the same subject heading.

RECORDS OF AGENCIES FOR ECONOMIC OPPORTUNITY AND LEGAL SERVICES (RECORD GROUP 381)

The Office of Economic Opportunity (OEO) was established in the Executive Office of the President by the Economic Opportunity Act of August 20, 1964 (78 Stat. 508). The Office directed a number of programs to combat poverty and coordinated programs of other agencies. There were special programs for Indians, most under the direction of the Community Action Program Office. They varied according to the needs of the tribes, but included education (including adult education and the Head Start program for young children), job training, economic development, reservation development, housing, homemaking, day care, community health, emergency food care, community organization, and cultural enrichment. In 1969 direction of Indian programs was taken over by the Office of Operations of OEO. In 1975 the Office of Economic Opportunity was replaced by the Community Services Administration, but by this time the Indian programs had been transferred to the Department of Health, Education, and Welfare. Among the records of the Office of Operations are records concerning Indian programs in the States, 1965–72 (5 ft.), programs conducted by Arizona State University to provide training and technical assistance for Indians on reservations, a college and university consortium for Indian community activity programs, and public relations. There are also 1973 tabulations, prepared from the 1970 decennial census, concerning low income neighborhoods in large cities and giving some statistics for Indians, particularly for those living in cities in California. Among motion pictures of the Office of Economic Opportunity, 1965–72, are some that show conditions of poverty among Indians.

See Debra Newman, comp., *Preliminary Inventory of the Records of the Office of Economic Opportunity*, PI 188 (1977).

NON-FEDERAL RECORDS

WAR DEPARTMENT COLLECTION OF CONFEDERATE RECORDS (RECORD GROUP 109)

The present War Department Collection of Confederate Records was transferred to the National Archives from the Adjutant General's Office in 1938. The collection had first come into Federal custody when the U.S. Army seized the records during its occupation of Richmond at the end of the Civil War. By that time, however, many records already had been destroyed by fire, and those that came into War Department custody consisted largely of records of the Confederate Congress and the Departments of War, Treasury, and Post Office. Some records were subsequently acquired by the War Department by purchase and donation and were added to the original collection.

An act of February 21, 1861, gave the Confederate War Department jurisdiction over Indian affairs, and a subsequent act of March 15, 1861, established a Bureau of Indian Affairs in the Department. No central office records of this Bureau are known to have survived, but there are a few records of field offices among the records of the U.S. Bureau of Indian Affairs (see page 144).

See Elizabeth Bethel, comp., *Preliminary Inventory of the War Department Collection of Confederate Records,* PI 101 (1957). Further information about Confederate records, including those pertaining to Indians, is in Henry P. Beers, *Guide to the Archives of the Government of the Confederate States of America* (1968). Many of the surviving Confederate records relating to Indians have been published in the multivolume War Department publication *The War of the Rebellion: A Compilation of the Official Records of the Union and Confederate Armies* (Washington, 1880–1901). Chapter and volume citations given below are to this work.

General Records

RECORDS RELATING TO INDIAN TREATIES

Compilations of Treaties Negotiated by the Confederate Provisional Government with Indian Tribes in 1861, chapter VII, volume 36, and chapter VIII, volume 297, contain identical printed compilations of treaties negotiated by Albert Pike, the Confederate commissioner to the Indian nations west of Arkansas. The treaties were printed as part of *The Statutes at Large of the Provisional Government of the Confederate States of America . . . And the Treaties Concluded by the Confederate States With Indian Tribes* (Richmond, 1864). Included are treaties with the Choctaw and Chickasaw, Seminole, Wichita and affiliated tribes, Osage, Quapaw, and Cherokee.

There is also an incomplete manuscript of Albert Pike's report to President Jefferson Davis on the result of his mission to the Indian nations west of Arkansas during the spring and summer of 1861. Pike summarizes his meetings and dealings with the various tribes and gives his overall impressions. The Confederate commissioner also recommends general and specific policies to be pursued by the Confederate Government in dealing with the Indians.

MISCELLANEOUS CORRESPONDENCE

In a series of miscellaneous papers and correspondence, 1862–64 (2 ft.), are several letters of Brig. Gen. Albert Pike relating to Indian affairs; a copy of Pike's address to the Cherokee, Creek, Seminole, Chickasaw, and Choctaw on the occasion of relinquishing his command over Indian Territory, July 31, 1862; and a statement by Creek and Cherokee Indians given in March 1868, relating to the exodus of Creek Indians under Hopthleyoholo from the Creek and Cherokee country following the battles fought in the winter of 1861–62.

War Department

CENTRAL OFFICE CORRESPONDENCE

The letters sent and received by the Confederate Secretary of War and Adjutant and Inspector General contain correspondence with Commissioners of Indian Affairs, military officers in the field who were involved in Indian battles or Indian administration, and prominent Indians. The most pertinent series and their accompanying finding aids are available as NARS microfilm publications, including M522, *Letters Sent by the Confederate Secretary of War, 1861–1865;* M523, *Letters Sent by the Confederate Secretary of War to the President, 1861–1865;* M437, *Letters Received by the Confederate Secretary of War, 1861–1865;* M474, *Letters Received by the Confederate Adjutant and Inspector General, 1861–1865;* M409, *Index to Letters Received by the Confederate Secretary of War, 1861–1865;* and M410, *Index to Letters Received by the Confederate Adjutant and Inspector General and the Confederate Quartermaster General, 1861–1865.* Many of the pertinent letters received, however, are no longer in their original file locations, having been used in compiling the *Official Records* and thereafter placed in a new publication file.

MILITARY COMMAND RECORDS

TRANS-MISSISSIPPI DEPARTMENT

A Trans-Mississippi District, embracing parts of Louisiana, Indian Territory, Arkansas, and Missouri, was established on January 9, 1862. On May 26, 1862, it was joined with the Department of Texas to form the Trans-Mississippi Department. During the later years of the war, this Department was the highest level Territorial command having jurisdiction over those Western tribes under Confederate control. The records date from 1863, when Lt. Gen. Edmund Kirby Smith assumed command.

Four volumes of letters and telegrams sent and circulars issued, 1863–65, chapter II, volumes 70–72 and 73½, contain copies of correspondence with successive Confederate commanders of the District of Indian Territory and with commanders of Indian troops in the field. Letters relate primarily to military operations and troops in Indian Territory. Several 1865 letters pertain to a proposed Indian council on the False Washita in May of that year.

The letters and telegrams received, 1863–65 (8 in.), also contain correspondence with Confederate commanders and officials in Indian Territory. Included are copies of letters from Col. Stand Watie to the principal chief of the Creek Nation and to the governor of the Choctaw and Chickasaw Nation, August 9, 1863, and to the commander of the 2d Choctaw Regiment, December 10, 1863. There is a copy of written remarks addressed by Watie to an unidentified "Grand Council" of tribes, November 12, 1863. The documents are concerned primarily with the Indian military situation and the need for Indian unity and self-reliance. Otherwise, Indians would be "enslaved by an inferior race and trodden under the feet of an ignorant and insolent foe. . . ." Also among the letters and telegrams received is a 33-page report, August 20, 1864, by Col. R. W. Lee, assistant superintendent of Indian affairs, Arkansas and Red River Superintendency, concerning Indian affairs there.

DISTRICT OF INDIAN TERRITORY

Most Confederate Indian operations centered in western Arkansas and Indian Territory. The Indian country west of Arkansas and south of Kansas was the Department of Indian Territory, created in 1861. Merged into the Trans-Mississippi Department in May 1862, it became a separate district under that command in July 1864. Those command records that exist as separate entities and contain significant information on Indians are described below.

The letters transcribed in the four volumes of letters sent, 1863–65, chapter II, volumes 258, 267, 268, and 270, were written to military officers in the field, including commanders of Indian troops, Indian agents, Indian leaders, and officials in the Confederate War Department. The correspondence relates to a variety of subjects, including the raising and administering of Indian regiments, military campaigns, depredations committed upon Indians by whites, destitution among Indians and efforts made by Confederate authorities to cope with this problem, councils and meetings of various groups of tribes, and attitudes of Indians and Confederate authorities toward each other.

A letter from Brig. Gen. William Steele to his superior in the Trans-Mississippi Department in March 1863 illustrates typical problems encountered by both Indians and Confederates. "I hold the Indians firm in their allegiance. A decided and strenuous effort must be made to relieve them of the cruel and relentless oppression to which they are now subjected. There is scarcely a day that I am not in receipt of some sad tale of murder and outrage, this in connection to their starving condition has been quite sufficient to drive them to the enemy. I wonder at their firmness and loyalty under circumstances so truly discouraging." On the Indians as troops, however, Steele confided in 1863, "They are of very little value as soldiers, but they are better as friends than enemies."

Letters received, mostly 1864–65 (1 in.), are from Brig. Gen. D. H. Cooper and other Confederate commanders, Indian chiefs, and Federal officers. The correspondence relates to prisoners, Federal raids, the disposition of Indian slaves, military forces in the district, the collapse of Confederate authority over the Indian Territory, and the resumption of Federal control. This series also includes copies of the proceedings of a grand council of the Confederate Indian tribes at Cherokee Town on the Washita River, August 8, 1864; a compact between Confederate and prairie tribes made at Camp Napoleon, Washita River, May 26, 1865; and a treaty between Texas authorities and various tribes including the Kiowa, Arapaho, Lipan, and Cheyenne, May 27, 1865.

The letters sent by the Inspector General's Office, 1864–65, chapter II, volumes 259 and 260, many of which were written to the commander of the District of Indian Territory and other military officers in the field, relate primarily to administrative and organizational matters connected with the various troops, both Indian and white, who served under the command. The letters deal with such problems as appointments, courts-martial, military discipline, the general condition of the troops, and the keeping of muster rolls, returns, and other records. In addition to the letters, several inspection reports have been transcribed, including a report of an inspection of Brig. Gen. Douglas H. Cooper's Division in July 1864. Regarding the condition of troops of the 1st Indian Brigade under Col. Stand Watie, Col. E. E. Portlock, the inspecting officer, noted their lack of arms, clothing, other supplies, and pay for a year. He praised their continued adherence to the Confederate cause despite such hardships, stating that "the habits of obedience which the Indian displays controlled by a strong will is capable of being molded in any form by those whom they know and respect among themselves."

Letters received, 1864–65 (½ in.), are mostly from the Inspector General of the Trans-Mississippi Department. They relate to inspections of posts and troops, the keeping of records and the filing of reports, and various procedural and administrative matters.

GEN. THEOPHILUS HOLMES

Holmes commanded successively the Trans-Mississippi Department and the District of Arkansas and sometimes became involved in Indian matters. Several letters in his private correspondence, 1861–64, chapter II, volume 358, relate to Indians, including one of November 11, 1862, in which Holmes alleged conditions of drunkenness among Cooper's command of Indians and Texans, and one to the Secretary of War, November 15, 1862, expressing disapproval of a proclamation to the Indians issued by Brig. Gen. Albert Pike. On May 25, 1863, reporting on conditions in general among the Indians, Holmes noted that the "Indian country to the west of Arkansas is in a starving condition . . . Notwithstanding this the Indians are perfectly loyal and set examples many in Arkansas might follow to advantage."

Records Relating to Military Service

There are muster rolls (1 ft.) for various Indian organizations raised by the Confederate Government, in addition to other rolls for white organizations that served in the Indian Territory. Most of the relevant information, however, was abstracted onto cards during the late 19th century by the Adjutant General's Office, which had custody of the records. The information is currently available in compiled military service records, which include a file for each individual who served in an organization. There are also caption and record-of-events cards, which contain information about the activities of the unit as a whole. The caption cards are available as M861, *Compiled Records Showing Service of Military Units in Confederate Organizations;* information about the Indian organizations is on roll 74. Pertinent compiled military service records reproduced by the National Archives and Records Service include M258, *Compiled Service Records of Confederate Soldiers Who Served in Organizations Raised Directly by the Confederate Government,* and M331, *Compiled Service Records of Confederate General and Staff Officers and Nonregimental Enlisted Men.* The former includes records of the Cherokee, Chickasaw, Choctaw, Creek, Osage, and Seminole organizations (rolls 77–91), and the latter, files for such staff officers as Brig. Gens. Stand Watie, Douglas H. Cooper, and Albert Pike. Individual files in both collections include original papers in addition to abstracts on cards. Most of the documents pertain to the administrative aspects of an officer's career, including appointments, resignations, and recommendations for promotion. In some instances, these papers have substantive value. In Pike's file, for example, is a letter of December 9,

1861, relating to Indian enlistments and treaties and subsequent documents pertaining to ordnance supplies that he requisitioned for the Indian Territory. Watie's staff officer's file (roll 261) includes a copy of a letter of March 31, 1863, from the Secretary of War to the Adjutant General authorizing Watie to raise an Indian brigade.

Other Records

RETURNS OF COMMANDS AND POSTS

This series includes several returns for 1862–63 showing military forces employed in Indian Territory and the various forts or agencies at which they were stationed. There is also a return of medical officers, dated March 1865, for the entire war, and there are various rosters of staff officers serving in Indian Territory. There are post returns showing officers stationed at Fort Washita, dated April 7, 1865; Boggy Depot, dated February 22, 1865; and Doaksville, dated March 31, 1865, all in the Cherokee Nation.

CASUALTY LISTS AND BATTLE REPORTS

Most of these documents, particularly the battle reports, were printed in the *Official Records*. The casualty lists have been reproduced as M836, *Confederate States Army Casualties: Lists and Narrative Reports, 1861–1865,* and the documents pertaining to battles in Indian Territory appear on roll 7. There are reports for the engagements at Round Mountain, November 19, 1861; Chusto-Talasah, or Bird's Creek, December 9, 1861; Chustenahlah, December 16, 1861; Old Fort Wayne, October 22, 1862; and Cabin Creek, September 19, 1864. There also are battle reports for Round Mountain, Bird's Creek, and Chustenahlah.

RECORDS OF FORMER RUSSIAN AGENCIES
(RECORD GROUP 261)

With the purchase of Alaska in 1867, the United States acquired some of the records of the Russian-American Company, which had been established in 1799. The company was granted a monopoly of trade in Russia's North American possessions. The company engaged in trade, principally in furs, with the natives and employed them. Principal operations were in Alaska, but the company had outposts as far south as northern California. The records, 1802 and 1817–67 (92 vols.), are almost entirely in Russian. They consist principally of communications received and sent by the Governors-General of the company. There are also logs of vessels and journals of exploring expeditions. Records concerning Indians and other natives are dispersed throughout the records. These records have been reproduced as M11; the accompanying pamphlet includes a calendar to the first six volumes of communications received, which gives a good idea of the subject content of the records, including such matters as marriages with native women, churches, the sale of liquor and other illegal trade, and troubles with natives.

NATIONAL ARCHIVES GIFT COLLECTION
(RECORD GROUP 200)

This record group includes gifts of personal papers, historical manuscripts, and cartographic and audiovisual materials donated to the National Archives and Records Service.

Records of the Indian Superintendency at St. Louis

On six rolls of microfilm are copies of records in the Kansas State Historical Society, Topeka, of the successive Missouri, St. Louis, and Central Superintendencies, 1812–55. William Clark was superintendent until his death in 1838, and some of his personal records and records of the Missouri Fur Company, of which he was president of the board of directors, are included. The records include correspondence, field notes and plats of surveys, copies of treaties, council proceedings, claims records, licenses to trade, and many accounting records. See also the records of the Central Superintendency among the records of the Bureau of Indian Affairs (pages 131–133).

Sir Henry S. Wellcome Papers

Sir Henry S. Wellcome was an advocate for William Duncan, a lay minister for the Anglican Church Missionary Society who founded a settlement for the Metlakahtla Indians at Fort Simpson, British Columbia. He moved the settlement to Annette Island, Alaska, in 1887. In time controversies developed between Duncan and the U.S. Government arising from Duncan's domination of Metlakahtlan affairs and from his resistance to the establishment of a secular Government school. Duncan and later the trustees of his estate pressed claims against the Government for losses of industries and business and the seizure of buildings and other property. Wellcome collected materials to support the Metlakahtla case before the Department of the Interior and the Congress. The papers (105 ft. in FARC Seattle), originals and copies, came from the records of the Office of the Secretary of the Interior, Bureau of Indian Affairs, Office of Education, Alaska Board of Education, and Alaska Territorial Governor's Office; papers of Duncan and others; letters from persons with whom Duncan had dealings; and the records of the office that Wellcome opened in Washington, D.C.

The main series, ca. 1856–1936, is identified as "A Metlakahtla History" and is commonly called the A–L file because it is arranged by an alphabetical subject classification system as follows:

A. Government documents
B. Duplicate of "A" file
C. Council records
D. Excerpts from Government documents
E. Selected letters of Mr. Duncan
F. Duncan-Strong correspondence [T. N. Strong, an attorney in Portland, Oreg.]
G. Newspapers, periodicals, etc.
H. Minthorn correspondence [Dr. and Mrs. H. J. Minthorn, assistants to Duncan and his successors]
I. Native documents
J. Miscellaneous documents [for sources other than those listed above]
J. Special [groups of documents relating to special events, for which the date seems of prime importance]
K. Excerpts from books pertaining to Duncan and Metlakahtla
K-1. Excerpts from books not pertaining to Duncan and Metlakahtla
L. Alphabetically arranged documents for which the subject seems of prime importance.

The A–L file consists entirely of reproductions. There are also originals of some of the documents, ca. 1864–1930, which relate to Duncan, the Metlakahtla Indians, social and economic activities at the settlement, the controversies between Duncan and the Government, and more general matters. There are detailed subject indexes to both the reproductions and the original records.

Other records relate to the administration of the Metlakahtla case, principally the planning and promotional stages. There are records labeled "confidential" concerning the supervision of the settlement and its affairs, ca. 1926–36; a file of F. A. Ronan, an agent for Wellcome, ca. 1856–1933; legal records, ca. 1891–1927; and indexes. There are also photographs, chiefly depicting the inhabitants of the Metlakahtla settlements and the activities there, and maps, plats, plans, and drawings concerning Alaska and the development of the Metlakahtla colony.

See Elmer W. Lindgard, comp., *Preliminary Inventory of the Sir Henry S. Wellcome Papers in the Federal Records Center, Seattle, Washington,* PI 150 (1963).

Ethan Allen Hitchcock Papers

Papers of Ethan Allen Hitchcock, 1880–1909, include both personal and official papers for his period of service, 1898–1907, as Secretary of the Interior. Among papers arranged by subject are records concerning the Five

Civilized Tribes, the Flathead Reservation, miscellaneous Indian affairs, the Siletz Reservation (under "Oregon land frauds"), cattle grazing on the Osage Reservation, and various officials. There are also newspaper clippings about Indians, affairs in Indian Territory, and Hitchcock's trip through Oklahoma and Indian Territories in 1903. There is also published material about Indian affairs.

Herbert James Hagerman Papers

Papers of Herbert J. Hagerman (5 ft.) relate primarily to his period of service, 1923-32, as special commissioner to the Navajo Indians. He also served on the Pueblo Lands Board, and the papers include some records as early as 1891, presumably acquired from other officials, relating to Pueblo Indian matters.

Records of the Social Science Research Council

Among records of the Committee on Public Administration of the Social Science Research Council concerning a study of the Federal work relief program are a few records, 1935-36, about Bureau of Indian Affairs participation in emergency activities.

Cartographic Records

Maps, 1865-1927, given to the National Archives by Gen. W. C. Brown, include maps showing routes followed by Army units during Indian campaigns and plans of Indian battlefields.

Audiovisual Records

Still pictures include 29 photographs of Nez Percé and Coeur d'Alène Indians in northern Idaho, 1880-1915.

In the Ford collection of motion picture films, 1914-56, is footage showing Indians at a religious camp meeting, 1920; Indian activities in South Dakota, 1921; Blackfeet Indians performing at Waterton-International and Glacier National Parks, 1936 and 1939; Sioux Indians at Mandan, N. Dak., 1931; Seminole Indians in Florida, 1921; Hopi Indians in Arizona, 1937; Pueblo Indians, 1916, 1920, and 1941; and Navajo Indian activities, including sand painting, 1934, 1937, and 1941. See Mayfield Bray, *Guide to the Ford Film Collection in the National Archives* (1970).

The Harmon collection of motion picture films, 1930-51, includes four reels taken at the Santa Fe Indian School showing general activities and the teaching of silver craft, painting, and weaving; two reels in color showing how the Navajo painter Quincy Tahoma depicts the life of his people; and 10 reels on Indian contributions to modern civilization, arts and crafts, employment, and other topics.

Among Paramount News films, 1940-57, are 11 newsreels with scenes of Indians, 1942-44, 1946-47, and 1950-52. They show Indians collecting scrap, giving food and gifts to soldiers, making clothing and insignia for airmen, participating in a parade, presenting a war bonnet to General Vanaman, and being watched by Presidential candidate Eisenhower as they dance at Gallup, N. Mex.; Chief Swimming Eel claiming that Manhattan Island belongs to the Indians; and Ute Indians arriving at Fort Duchesne to collect payment from the United States for their lands. Another newsreel shows an Eskimo gathering for an Easter celebration on Baffin Island in 1955.

Universal Newsreel films, 1929–1967 (edited and unedited footage), include numerous sequences showing Indians. Many of them relate to such ceremonial activities as dances, parades, games and contests, rodeos, dedications, reenactments of historical events, visits with prominent persons, and participation in political conventions; others show fishing, logging, health care, archeology, and Civilian Conservation Corps and wartime activities.

"Our Own United States" films, 1935, have scenes showing a Seminole catching an alligator, a Blackfoot dance, and a Seminole carving wooden dolls. "See America First" films, 1934–35, have scenes of a Pueblo village in New Mexico and Seminole ruins in Florida. A Movietone News film shows scenes of the meeting of Indians in the Florida Everglades to form the United American Indian Republic, 1959. Eastman Teaching Films include a film on Glacier National Park showing Indians at their daily activities and a dance, 1930. A National Tuberculosis Association film tells the story of a young Navajo with tuberculosis, emphasizing the danger of refusing the aid of modern medicine, 1941. There are also three rolls of film taken by Herbert F. Robinson, a Bureau of Indian Affairs irrigation engineer, of Hopi and Pueblo Indians, 1920–25, and a film, ca. 1939, about a "lost city" submerged by Lake Mead.

INDEX

413

E

N

Pvt. Abraham Little Beaver, Winnebago of Nebraska;
Corp. Adam Bearcup, Sioux of Montana; Sgt. Delray B.
Echo-Hawk, Pawnee of Oklahoma, twice-decorated war
hero; and Corp. David Box, Sioux of Colorado; aviation
mechanics in training at Sheppard Field, Tex. World War
II. From Records of the Bureau of Indian Affairs, Record
Group 75. 75-N-MISC-115